Insect Colonization
and Mass Production

Insect Colonization and Mass Production

Edited by **CARROLL N. SMITH**

Entomology Research Division
Agricultural Research Service
U. S. Department of Agriculture
Gainesville, Florida

ACADEMIC PRESS
NEW YORK and LONDON 1966

ACADEMIC PRESS INC.
111 Fifth Avenue, New York, New York 10003

United Kingdom Edition published by
ACADEMIC PRESS INC. (LONDON) LTD.
Berkeley Square House, London W.1

LIBRARY OF CONGRESS CATALOG CARD NUMBER: 66-26274

PRINTED IN THE UNITED STATES OF AMERICA

List of Contributors

Numbers in parentheses indicate the pages on which the authors' contributions begin.

J. RALPH AUDY, *The George Williams Hooper Foundation, University of California Medical Center,* San Francisco, California (25)

ALFRED M. BAUMHOVER, *Entomology Research Division, U. S. Department of Agriculture,* Oxford, North Carolina (533)

H. P. BOLES,[1] *Stored-Product Insects Research and Development Laboratory, U. S. Department of Agriculture,* Savannah, Georgia (259)

G. T. BOTTGER, *Entomology Research Division, Agricultural Research Service, U. S. Department of Agriculture,* Tucson, Arizona (425)

G. S. BURDEN, *Entomology Research Division, Agricultural Research Service, U. S. Department of Agriculture,* Gainesville, Florida (175)

EDGAR W. CLARK, *U. S. Forest Service, Forestry Sciences Laboratory,* Durham, North Carolina (305)

M. M. COLE, *Entomology Research Division, Agricultural Research Service, U. S. Department of Agriculture,* Gainesville, Florida (15)

FRANK T. COWAN, *Entomology Research Division, Agricultural Research Service, U. S. Department of Agriculture,* Bozeman, Montana (311)

T. B. DAVICH, *Boll Weevil Research Laboratory, Entomology Research Division, Agricultural Research Service, U. S. Department of Agriculture,* State College, Mississippi (405)

BOTHA DE MEILLON,[2] *WHO Filariasis Research Unit, Burma Medical Research Institute,* Rangoon, Burma (101)

---

[1] Present address: Mid-West Grain Insects Investigations, Stored-Products Insects Branch, Marked Quality Research Division, Agricultural Research Service, Manhattan, Kansas.

[2] Present address: Army Mosquito Project, Smithsonian Institute, U. S. National Museum, Washington, D. C.

CARL W. FATZINGER, *Southeastern Forest Experiment Station, Forest Service, U. S. Department of Agriculture,* Olustee, Florida (451)

JAMES B. GAHAN, *Entomology Research Division, Agricultural Research Service, U. S. Department of Agriculture,* Gainesville, Florida (85)

R. T. GAST, *Boll Weevil Research Laboratory, Entomology Research Division, Agricultural Research Service, U. S. Department of Agriculture,* State College, Mississippi (405)

B. W. GEORGE, *Northern Grain Insects Research Laboratory, Entomology Research Division, Agricultural Research Service, U. S. Department of Agriculture,* Brookings, South Dakota (367)

ANDREW J. GRAHAM, *Animal Health Division, U. S. Department of Agriculture,* Mission, Texas (533)

J. D. GREGSON, *Research Station, Canada Department of Agriculture,* Kamloops, British Columbia, Canada (49)

D. W. HAMILTON,[3] *Entomology Research Division, Agricultural Research Service, U. S. Department of Agriculture,* Vincennes, Indiana (339)

PHILLIP K. HAREIN,[4] *Stored-Product Insects Research and Development Laboratory, U. S. Department of Agriculture,* Savannah, Georgia (241)

F. H. HARRIES,[5] *Entomology Research Division, Agricultural Research Service, U. S. Department of Agriculture, and Washington State University,* Pullman, Washington (429)

D. O. HATHAWAY, *Entomology Research Division, Agricultural Research Service, U. S. Department of Agriculture,* Yakima, Washington (339)

---

[3] Present address: Japanese Beetle Investigations, Entomology Research Division, Agricultural Research Service, U. S. Department of Agriculture, Moorestown, New Jersey.

[4] Present address: Department of Entomology, Fisheries, and Wildlife, University of Minnesota, St. Paul, Minnesota.

[5] Present address: Tree Fruit Research Center, Wenatchee, Washington.

T. J. HENNEBERRY, *Entomology Research Division, Agricultural Research Service, U. S. Department of Agriculture*, Riverside, California (461)

J. DAVID HOFFMAN, *Entomology Research Division, Agricultural Research Service, U. S. Department of Agriculture*, Oxford, North Carolina (479)

W. L. HOWE, *Northern Grain Insects Laboratory, Entomology Research Division, Agricultural Research Service, U. S. Department of Agriculture*, Brookings, South Dakota (367)

CHESTER N. HUSMAN, *Administrative Services, U. S. Department of Agriculture*, Beltsville, Maryland (533)

CARLO M. IGNOFFO, *International Minerals and Chemical Corporation, Bioferm Division*, Wasco, California (501)

STANLEY W. JACKLIN, *Entomology Research Division, Agricultural Research Service, U. S. Department of Agriculture*, Beltsville, Maryland (445)

CALVIN M. JONES,[6] *Entomology Research Division, Agricultural Research Service, U. S. Department of Agriculture*, Lincoln, Nebraska (145)

ROBERT HENRY JONES, *Entomology Research Division, Agricultural Research Service, U. S. Department of Agriculture*, Denver, Colorado (115)

A. N. KISHABA, *Entomology Research Division, Agricultural Research Service, U. S. Department of Agriculture*, Riverside, California (461)

E. F. KNIPLING, *Entomology Research Division, Agricultural Research Service, U. S. Department of Agriculture*, Beltsville, Maryland (1)

B. S. KRISHNAMURTHY, *National Institute of Communicable Diseases*, Delhi, India (73)

---

[6] Present address: Insectary, University of Nebraska, Lincoln, Nebraska.

M. M. J. LAVOIPIERRE, *The George Williams Hooper Foundation, University of California Medical Center*, San Francisco, California (25)

F. R. LAWSON,[7] *Entomology Research Division, Agricultural Research Service, U. S. Department of Agriculture*, Raleigh, North Carolina (479

W. H. R. LUMSDEN, *Trypanosomiasis Research Unit, Royal (Dick) School of Veterinary Studies, University of Edinburgh*, Easter Bush, Roslin, Midlothian, Scotland (153)

DIAL F. MARTIN, *Cotton Insect Research Branch, Entomology Research Division, Agricultural Research Service, U. S. Department of Agriculture*, Beltsville, Maryland (355)

F. O. MARZKE, *Stored-Product Insects Research and Development Laboratory, U. S. Department of Agriculture*, Savannah, Georgia (259)

JOHN W. MATTESON,[8] *Northern Grain Insects Laboratory, Entomology Research Division, Agricultural Research Service, U. S. Department of Agriculture*, Brookings, South Dakota (385)

EDWARD P. MERKEL, *Southeastern Forest Experiment Station, Forest Service, U. S. Department of Agriculture*, Olustee, Florida (451)

SHIZUKO MITCHELL, *Entomology Research Division, Agricultural Research Service, U. S. Department of Agriculture*, Honolulu, Hawaii (555)

HARVEY B. MORLAN, *Aedes aegypti Eradication Branch, Communicable Disease Center, Public Health Service, U. S. Department of Health, Education, and Welfare*, Atlanta, Georgia (585)

R. C. MUIRHEAD-THOMSON, *Division of Communicable Diseases, World Health Organization*, Geneva, Switzerland (127)

EBEN A. OSGOOD, JR., *Department of Entomology, University of Maine*, Orono, Maine (305)

---

[7] Present address: Entomology Research Division, Agricultural Research Service, U. S. Department of Agriculture, Columbia, Missouri.

[8] Present address: Monsanto Company, Agricultural Division, Insecticide Chemicals Development Department, St. Louis, Missouri.

EARLE S. RAUN, *Corn Borer Laboratory, Agricultural Research Service, U. S. Department of Agriculture*, Ankeny, Iowa (323)

ALBERT E. RYCKMAN, *Department of Microbiology, Loma Linda University*, Loma Linda, California (183)

RAYMOND E. RYCKMAN, *Department of Microbiology, School of Medicine, and Biology Department, Graduate School, Loma Linda University*, Loma Linda, California (183)

D. S. SAUNDERS, *Department of Zoology, University of Edinburgh*, Edinburgh, Scotland (153)

F. J. SIMMONDS, *Commonwealth Institute of Biological Control, Gordon Street, Curepe*, Trinidad, West Indies (489)

EDWARD H. SMITH, *Department of Entomology, North Carolina State University*, Raleigh, North Carolina (397)

FLOYD F. SMITH, *Entomology Research Division, Agricultural Research Service, U. S. Department of Agriculture*, Beltsville, Maryland (445)

BURRELL J. SMITTLE, *Entomology Research Division, Agricultural Research Service, U. S. Department of Agriculture*, Gainesville, Florida (227)

EDWIN L. SODERSTROM, *Stored-Products Insects Research and Development Laboratory, U. S. Department of Agriculture*, Savannah, Georgia (241)

D. SPILLER, *Plant Diseases Division, Department of Scientific and Industrial Research*, Auckland, New Zealand (203)

LOREN F. STEINER, *Entomology Research Division, Agricultural Research Service, U. S. Department of Agriculture*, Honolulu, Hawaii (555)

VIJAYAMMA THOMAS, *College of Agriculture, Serdang-Selangor*, Sungei Besi, P. O. Malaysia (101)

ERMA S. VANDERZANT, *Entomology Research Division, Agricultural*

Research Service, U. S. Department of Agriculture, Texas A & M University, College Station, Texas (273)

LEW E. WALLACE, *Wheat Stem Sawfly Investigations, Agricultural Research Service, U. S. Department of Agriculture,* Bozeman, Montana (419)

ROBERT YAMAMOTO, *Department of Entomology, North Carolina State University,* Raleigh, North Carolina (479)

Preface

Recent developments in entomological research have augmented the importance of insect colonies to basic research and practical control. Students in such fields as insect physiology, behavior, and genetics need plentiful supplies of specimens of standard quality, such as can be obtained only by rearing strains of known ancestry under controlled regimens of nutrition, temperature, and photoperiod. Control methods now in use, or foreseen for the future, such as the release of sterile males, the extensive distribution of insect pathogens, the practical use of pheromones, and the genetic manipulation of natural populations, will require the production of millions of insects per week for the control of certain economically important species.

Within recent years great strides have been made in the culture of some of the more important species, whereas other equally important groups cannot yet be maintained in even small self-perpetuating laboratory colonies. In this book we have tried to bring together the most recent information on methods of rearing representative species with emphasis on the general principles of nutrition and management that can be applied to the colonization of other species as well. We have selected for inclusion some of the outstanding successes in mass production and some examples of groups in which the difficulties inherent in laboratory rearing have not yet been overcome.

Each chapter is largely self-contained. Some are concerned with only a single species, selected to stand as an example of its taxonomic group, and to a lesser extent of other insects with similar nutritional and environmental requirements. Other chapters discuss rearing methods for entire groups of species that share common requirements. Although each chapter contains some historical background, as well as a description of the most efficient recent methods of production, the bibliographical listings are not intended to provide citations to all available articles on colonization.

CARROLL N. SMITH

Gainesville, Florida
September, 1966

Contents

16. Coleoptera Infesting Stored Products
PHILLIP K. HAREIN AND EDWIN L. SODERSTROM

17. Lepidoptera Infesting Stored Products
H. P. BOLES AND F. O. MARZKE

Section C. Phytophagous Insects and Mites

18. Defined Diets for Phytophagous Insects
ERMA S. VANDERZANT

Section D. Insect Parasites, Predators, and Pathogens

Section E. Insects by the Million

39. Yellow Fever Mosquitoes
  HARVEY B. MORLAN

Chapter 1

Introduction

E. F. KNIPLING

Entomology Research Division,
Agricultural Research Service,
U. S. Department of Agriculture,
Beltsville, Maryland

The ability to rear insects under controlled conditions has long been regarded as desirable or necessary to facilitate research on many aspects of entomology. Major research efforts to achieve this capability were slow to develop among entomologists, but great advances in this field have been made during the past two decades. As research delves into more fundamental aspects of entomology and as various new approaches to insect control emerge, scientists are beginning to realize that successful insect colonization is a basic necessity for efficient and productive research on virtually every aspect of entomology.

Fortunately, the establishment and maintenance of colonies of certain insects is not difficult and relatively little space, equipment, and know-how are required to maintain thriving and productive colonies. As any housewife knows, negligence in storage of fresh fruits or vegtables in the home can give rise to a thriving colony of fruit flies (*Drosophila* spp.). The ease with which these insects can be reared, plus the short period of time required for completion of a generation, are no doubt among the main reasons why fruit flies

1

became the principal organism for use in research on the funda-
mentals of genetics. We can hardly estimate what this rather simple
achievement in insect colonization has meant to the advancement of
science and to the welfare of man. As we learn more about colonization of different kinds of insects and how different insects may be
used as organisms for basic studies in various life processes, we can
expect further direct and indirect contributions to science attributable
to the ability to colonize specific insects. We must not overlook the
fact also that man's ability to colonize the silkworm gave rise to one of
the world's great industries and that colonization of the honey bee has
increased the efficiency of our agriculture through better pollinization
of many crops and also has provided an important food product.

However, for this scientific treatise, we are interested primarily
in the contributions to the science of entomology per se that have
been and can be made by knowing how to rear the insects with which
we are concerned. The ability to colonize insects can be important
to entomology whether it involves the production of only a few
hundred insects per generation or the production of insects by
the millions.

Why is insect colonization so important to the science of entomology? The reader can get the best answer to this question as it
relates to specific insects by referring to the material presented by
the many contributors to this publication. The purpose of this introduction to the subject of insect colonization and mass production is
to (1) indicate how research on many aspects of entomology can be
advanced by having available insect colonies, and (2) to discuss the
important role that mass rearing of insects may have in contributing
directly to insect control.

I. USE OF INSECT COLONIES TO FACILITATE
RESEARCH IN ENTOMOLOGY

Research on insects can be facilitated in many ways if the insect
species under study can be colonized and produced in the quantity
needed for both basic and applied investigations. We shall consider
and discuss some of the lines of research that are greatly facilitated
by having the means to maintain thriving insect colonies.

Basic information on the life history and behavior of insects has
always served as a guide to the development and efficient application
of certain types of control measures. Much has been accomplished
by observing the development and behavior of insects under field

conditions. However, detailed information on the development of various stages of an insect under a wide range of field conditions is often difficult and impractical. The ability to colonize an insect makes it possible to obtain information about the biology of an insect more precisely and with less effort.

Scientists are becoming more and more interested in the details of the development and behavior of insects in their efforts to devise new ways to control them or to utilize them if they are beneficial. It may be of vital importance, for example, to have precise information on the period from the time an insect emerges as an adult until it mates or until the first eggs are deposited. In controlling tropical fruit flies, such as the Mediterranean fruit fly (*Ceratitis capitata* Wied.) a bait spray has been developed. This method of control is successful in large measure because of the approximately 10-day interval between emergence of the insect and oviposition. This long preoviposition period provides greater opportunity for the insects to find and be destroyed by the bait spray droplets than would be the case for an insect that had a preoviposition period of only a day or two.

The time of mating of an insect after emergence and the frequency of mating may be significant factors in the application of the sterile insect release technique. The behavior of insects in relation to mating stimuli, attractants in food, and other attractants is a subject of increasing interest to entomologists. Close observations and appropriate experimental procedures under laboratory conditions may be the only way to obtain the information desired.

We might add a note of caution in the study of insect biology and behavior. As valuable as laboratory observations may be to obtain such information, appropriate investigations should be undertaken on field populations as well.

A thorough understanding of the physiology of insects is regarded by many scientists as our best hope to keep ahead of insect problems. We cannot expect to conduct the precise and complex research involved in studies of the various physiological processes in insects unless the insects under study can be colonized and investigated in the laboratory. Field-collected insects are too variable in age, nutritional condition, and general health to be employed for critical physiological studies.

The greatest deterrents to the continued successful use of insecticides is the capacity of insects to develop resistance to them. Much research has been conducted to obtain basic information on the mechanisms of resistance in insects and on the genetics of the resistance factors. Obviously, such investigations cannot be undertaken with field-collected insects. So long as we must rely on insecticides as our chief weapon for insect control, we will need to continue and perhaps intensify research on the insecticide resistance problem. The ability to colonize our major pest species will become of increasing importance to facilitate research on insecticide resistance mechanisms and how they might be overcome.

The relationship of insects as vectors of plant and animal diseases is another area of study that is of vital importance. Investigators in the past made progress in this area by utilizing field-collected material, but many vital questions regarding vector-host relationships can only be answered through carefully controlled laboratory studies with insects grown under controlled conditions.

Basic studies on the nutritional requirements of insects are of vital and increasing importance to entomology. Here again thriving laboratory colonies are essential for the conduct of research of this nature.

Finally, I should like to mention the importance of the ability to rear insects of many species and diversified types in support of basic studies in the field of insect taxonomy and classification. Insect taxonomists have done a remarkable job, but they have been toiling under great handicaps for centuries because, for the most part, they have had to rely on field-collected and preserved specimens in their research on the classification of insects. This procedure will continue to be necessary and productive. However, in order to make real progress in obtaining answers to critical questions in the field of species relationships, scientists in this field must also have the facilities and the means to study living material. As applied research progresses into methods of insect control based on the behavior of insects, the need will be increasingly great for the most reliable information possible on speciation, varieties, and strains of important species complexes. Insects from different ecological areas may show marked differences in responses to different hosts, to natural biotic agents, to each other, or to their environment in general. Until critical studies are undertaken with living material to supplement conventional taxonomic investigations, the scientists attempting to develop some of the newer approaches to insect control may encounter many serious obstacles. The ability to colonize insects of many kinds will be a necessity in order to obtain the type of information that applied entomologists will expect from taxonomists in the future.

II. USE OF COLONIZED INSECTS TO DEVELOP METHODS OF CONTROL

The outstanding progress in the development of new insecticides, fumigants, repellents, and other insect control chemicals during the past two decades is due in large measure to the advances that have been made in our ability to colonize insects and to the parallel development of techniques for evaluating candidate insect control chemicals in the laboratory.

It would be difficult to estimate the importance of the role that one of our worst insect enemies, the house fly, *Musca domestica* L., has played in the discovery of new insecticides. The ability to maintain thriving colonies of this insect at low cost has made it possible for many research workers to make contributions to the development of new insecticide formulations. Fortunately, high biological activity against the house fly by a candidate insecticide generally indicated that a high level of activity could be expected for the compound against a wide range of insects of medical or agricultural importance.

Perhaps the human body louse, *Pediculus humanus humanus* L., will serve as one of the best examples of the value of an insect colony in developing control methods for a specific insect. At the time of our entry in World War II, the armed forces had no practical way to protect military personnel from infestations of this important vector of typhus, especially under conditions of mobile warfare. Typhus, one of the most devastating diseases of man, had always been a major threat to military personnel and civilians alike during periods of war.

Although body lice had been reared in small numbers under controlled conditions, a technique for rearing the insect in large numbers had not been developed. The incidence of natural body-louse infestations in man is very low in this country. Even if adequate numbers of louse-infested subjects had been available, there would still remain the many variable factors that limit the ability to conduct meaningful tests with a variety of candidate insecticides on natural infestations. The problem of hazards in the testing of new materials on man was also a major obstacle. Accordingly, when the special research program, conducted by the Department of Agriculture for the Department of Defense, was developed at Orlando, Florida, in 1942, the highest priority was given to the development of methods for colonizing the body louse before beginning a concerted research program to develop new and effective ways to protect troops and civilians from attack by the insect. Details of the procedures that were developed for colonizing the insect will be discussed by M. M. Cole in another section of this report. However, the availability of unlimited test insects together with the development of excellent and rapid techniques for evaluating insecticide louse powders under laboratory conditions made it possible to develop a new highly effective and desirable louse control measure for the military within the remarkably short period of six months after initiating the research program.

The value of colonization methods for the body louse to facilitate the development of control measures is just one of many examples that could be cited to show the remarkable progress made during the past few decades in connection with the control of specific arthropods affecting man, animals, agricultural crops, and the household.

Research on the development of crop varieties resistant to insect attack is another line of work that can be made more efficient and productive by employing reared insects. This approach to insect control is one of the most desirable methods for meeting insect problems. There has been increased interest in this desirable approach to insect control.

Progress has been and can be made in the development of crop varieties resistant to insect attack by making all evaluations under conditions of natural attack by the insect species involved. However, the ability to colonize the insects and have them available in unlimited numbers when needed will result in more valid data and will often permit the evaluation of several generations of plants in a year. Under natural field conditions, evaluations are generally limited to only one generation of a plant per year.

Final observations on the performance of candidate resistant varieties need to be made under field conditions, but this in no way detracts from the important role that colonized insects can play in advancing the varietal resistance approach to insect control.

The introduction of parasites and predators to help control destructive insects is another important area of entomological investigations that is greatly facilitated by knowing how to rear the insects involved. In this case the rearing problems involve not only the parasite or the predator but also the host insects. Inability to rear the hosts or the parasites or predators that are to be introduced does not preclude the possibility of collecting sufficient numbers of the beneficial insects under field conditions for introduction and successful establishment. Entomologists, for more than a century, have introduced many parasites and predators by making such field collections. However, research in this area can be made more productive in many cases if both the host insects and the insect prey can be colonized in sufficient number to increase the chances of successful establishment. There is more and more interest in the use of parasites and predators to control or help control insects. International exchange of parasites and predators, one of the great opportunities for advancing biological control of insects, is greatly facilitated by knowledge of ways to colonize them.

Another field of biological control that is of increasing importance is the introduction and establishment of insects for the biological control of weeds. In this case it is necessary to determine in advance if the insect considered for introduction is likely to feed or develop on desirable plant species. It is almost essential to know how to colonize the insect so that the extensive studies required can be carried out before the insect is released for establishment.

Insect microbiology is emerging as one of the most promising means of insect control. Insect pathologists have identified a wide range of organisms that are known to be pathogenic to insects. Research in this area to identify new organisms, determine the degree of pathogenicity of the organisms, study the manner of introduction and spread, and many other aspects of insect microbiology is almost wholly contingent on studies with insects under controlled laboratory conditions. Although field-collected insects can be used for certain studies, there is no assurance that insects collected in the field do not carry other organisms which could confuse the investigator and interfere with valid interpretations of results.

III. MASS REARING OF INSECTS FOR USE IN CONTROL

One of the most exciting new developments in entomology is the role that insects themselves or products derived from insects may play in the future for the control of insects. The full development of these potentials may mean that in the years ahead the mass production of insects will become an important industry in support of insect control. Several ways are discussed below in which insects themselves or products derived from them may be employed to control insects directly.

A. MASS PRODUCTION OF INSECT PARASITES AND PREDATORS

In earlier discussions it was pointed out that methods of rearing insect parasites and predators were vitally important in studies of the parasites and predators and in providing enough of them for introduction and establishment. We are concerned here with mass production methods for parasites and predators in sufficient quantity to exert a direct effect on the destructive host, largely independent of any natural production in the environment. The employment of insect parasites and predators for this purpose is not a new development, since limited use has been made of beneficial organisms in this manner in the past. However, more interest in this approach for the control of some of our important pests is being generated among entomologists. Important progress is being made in the mass production of insects at low cost. More and more precise information is being obtained on the density of insect populations and their population dynamics. There is every reason to believe that it will be feasible to rear many kinds of insect parasites or predators at levels of thousands or even tens of thousands per crop acre to be released as needed for insect control. The use of parasites and predators in this manner may become competitive in cost with chemical control in certain cases. Much research remains to be done to determine what kind and what numbers of selected parasites or predators would be required to exert enough direct effect to prevent population build-up to economic levels of such insects as the corn earworm, *Heliothis zea* (Boddie); tobacco budworm, *Heliothis virescens* (Fabr.); tobacco hornworm, *Protoparce sexta* (Johann.); various aphids; plant mites or other destructive pests that conceivably might be controlled by the mass and sustained liberation of parasites or predators. Rearing the host insect would be feasible in many cases at reasonable cost on which to rear such parasites. The screwworm, *Cochliomyia hominivorax* (Coq.), can be mass produced at cost levels of about $.50 per 1000. Tropical fruit flies can be mass produced at a cost of less than $.10 per 1000. No doubt lepidopterous insects, such as cabbage looper, *Trichoplusia ni* (Hübner), or tobacco budworm, can eventually be mass reared at levels of about $1.00 per 1000 if the occasion required the production of such species in numbers of hundreds of millions. As research progresses, scientists may find that because of the phenomena of imprinting the effective use of parasites or predators may require that they be reared on the same insect that is to be controlled.

B. Mass Production of Insects for the Production of Insect Microbial Agents

Insect pathogens, as pointed out earlier, offer promising means for controlling a wide range of insect pests. One of the major obstacles to the practical use of insect pathogens has been finding a satisfactory and economical means for the production of the pathogenic organism. The most advanced insect pathogen for practical control, currently, is *Bacillus thuringiensis.* This organism can be produced on artificial media. However, there is no assurance that artificial media will provide the means for the production of most of the promising insect pathogens now known that could conceivably be used for effective insect control. The milky spore disease of the Japanese beetle, *Popillia japonica* Newman, may serve as an example of the difficulties that may be involved in the mass production of the pathogen on noninsect media. The Department of Agriculture is devoting a great deal of research effort to the mass production of the milky spore disease, but thus far the effort has not met with success. A similar effort might be justified in developing economical mass production methods for the Japanese beetle and thus produce the spore disease organisms at low cost.

Many of the insect viruses affecting insects are highly virulent and generally highly specific. Virus material from ten to one hundred larvae is regarded as sufficient material to treat one acre of host plants for protection from attack by the larvae. The chapter in this publication by Carlo M. Ignoffo on the subject of mass production of viruses in insects, including the *Heliothis* spp. and the cabbage looper, indicates the progress and potential for employing the host insects themselves as a practical means for producing insect pathogenic organisms.

Considering the cost potential for the mass production of insects in relation to the amount of virus material needed for insect control, there is every reason to regard the mass production of such pathogenic organisms in insects themselves as feasible and practical, even though there would also be every justification for research to develop insect tissue culture methods that eventually might provide more economical ways to mass produce such organisms.

C. Mass Production of Insects for Use of Attractants

Recent research on insect attractants has provided information that suggests the use of insects themselves or products derived from insects for detection and control of a wide variety of species.

It has been known for many years that virgin females of certain insects, especially among the Lepidoptera, produce a chemical substance that is highly attractive to the males. The Department of Agriculture and cooperating states have for many years used extracts of virgin female gypsy moths, *Porthetria dispar* L., as a survey tool in support of control operations. The identification of the chemical structure of the gypsy moth attractant and subsequent synthesis of

(Hübner); corn earworm; gypsy moth; and tsetse flies (*Glossina* spp.). The writer feels that in time the release of sterile insects will provide an important aid to the control or complete elimination of populations of at least some of the insects named and perhaps also for a wide range of other insects. The sterile insect release method should prove practicable or advantageous for use against a number of the more important insect pests in various parts of the world under one or more of the following circumstances: (1) To eliminate incipient infestations or to prevent establishment of major insects in critical areas subject to frequent accidental introductions; (2) to prevent the spread of insects by establishing a barrier of sterile insect releases between the main population and the area to be protected; (3) for the elimination of natural and well-established populations of major insects that are subject to extremes in population density; and (4) for use as an adjunct to other methods of control for eliminating well-established insect populations.

Regardless of the manner in which sterile insects might be employed to control or eliminate insect populations, it will be necessary or highly advantageous to develop ways to rear the insect in large numbers and at the lowest cost possible. The extent to which the sterile insect release method will be practicable for any species and the number of kinds of insects against which the technique will be useful will depend largely on the ability to mass produce large numbers of vigorous insects at the lowest possible cost.

IV. CONCLUSIONS

The ability to colonize insects can represent direct and indirect contributions to many aspects of entomology. The many lines of research in entomology that are facilitated by the availability of thriving insect colonies have been discussed in this introductory chapter. The possibility of controlling insects directly by utilizing the insects themselves or by utilizing products derived from insects may be of equal value to the science of entomology. Insects in large numbers may be needed in the future to control insects by releasing sterile insects, by using caged insects to attract and destroy their own kind, for the production and use of attractants, for the production and use of insect pathogens, insect parasites, and predators, or for producing growth-regulating substances for insect control.

Section A

Animal Parasites and
Haematophagous Arthropods

Chapter 2

Body Lice

M. M. COLE

Entomology Research Division,
Agricultural Research Service,
U. S. Department of Agriculture,
Gainesville, Florida

I. INTRODUCTION

An excellent account of the biology of the human body louse, *Pediculus humanus humanus* Deg., was given by Buxton (1946). Colonization and rearing of this species, once considered to be a difficult task, has now evolved into several rather simple procedures. Many workers have established and maintained laboratory colonies successfully by using various procedures (Culpepper, 1944, 1946, 1948; Davis and Hansens, 1945; Smith and Eddy, 1954; and Haddon, 1956a, b). Each one in succession made important contributions toward better methods. Rearing procedures usually differ mainly in the method of feeding. This is perhaps the most difficult and certainly the most time-consuming part of the operation. The source and use to be made of the lice will determine to a great extent the method of feeding. For instance, to start a new colony from an established one, it would be advisable to continue feeding in the same manner for one or more generations. Then, if a change is desirable, it

15

should be made gradually. It is necessary to feed new colonies of wild-caught lice on humans for a certain length of time, usually several generations.

II. GENERAL CONDITIONS OF MAINTENANCE

A. TYPE OF CLOTH

Methods for holding lice, as in many other rearing procedures, will depend upon the size of the colony and the use to be made of the lice. They are usually kept on some sort of cloth where they may rest and lay their eggs. Loosely woven woolen suiting has been used (Culpepper, 1944, 1946, 1948), and was cut approximately 1½ inches square. It was dyed black because lice and eggs would be more visible against a dark background. Other types of cloth, such as black cotton corduroy, have been found to be quite satisfactory. Care must be used in order to be certain that the cloth has not been treated or contaminated with toxic chemicals during manufacture or processing. If it has been so treated it must be completely decontaminated before use in rearing lice.

Lice may be left on the same cloth throughout the life cycle or changed according to certain needs. One such instance would be during egg-laying when cloth should be changed every day or two to obtain eggs near the same age. Another would be when it is desired to expose the lice to cloth treated with insecticide for resistance studies. The manner of changing patches will be discussed under feeding of lice since that is the most convenient time to change.

B. CONTAINERS

Some sort of container must be used for holding the patches of cloth. Small colonies need only small containers, such as pill boxes or Petri dishes. However, for large colonies various kinds of dishes may be used. Stainless steel or porcelain containers are more suitable than glass since they are unbreakable. They should have a smooth surface and straight sides to prevent lice from crawling out. Large numbers of lice in a single container will make frequent cleaning advisable. Although lice do not seem to suffer any ill effects from an accumulation of filth, clean containers and cloth make handling and study easier.

C. TEMPERATURE AND HUMIDITY

It is advisable to keep colonies in incubators where temperature and humidity can be controlled. Although lice will do well at a wide range of conditions, the temperature should be between 80° and 90°F and the relative humidity between 50 and 75%. The author has found a constant temperature of 88°F and a relative humidity of 60% to be about ideal. Temperatures over 90°F for a few hours will kill many lice. Relative humidity over 90% will be detrimental.

III. METHODS OF FEEDING

A. FEEDING ON HUMANS

Small colonies may be fed satisfactorily on humans. Early workers fed their colonies on themselves or volunteers. A pill-box method has been used by British workers (Buxton, 1946). It is useful for small colonies or for maintaining lice in transit while transporting them over periods of time in excess of 1 or 2 days. It has been found to be very useful in maintaining wild lice before they are fully adapted to laboratory conditions or animals. Lice are kept in cardboard or metal pill boxes fitted with coarse-meshed cloth windows through which lice may feed without escaping. The original material used for the windows was bolting silk, but many synthetic materials such as nylon do equally well. The cells may be worn next to the skin beneath underwear or socks or held in place with elastic or adhesive tape.

A very large colony was maintained at Orlando, Florida, from 1942 through 1945 by feeding on human volunteers (Culpepper, 1944, 1946). The process consisted of systematically placing cloth patches containing the lice on the bare back of the subject. It is a characteristic of lice under these conditions to migrate to the skin of the host and begin feeding. They were left on the subjects 30–45 minutes. After the lice finished feeding, most of them would cling to the patches when they were removed. As many as 30,000 to 40,000 were fed on the back of one subject at the same time. In early days the lice were fed twice each day, early in the morning and late in the afternoon, at about 12-hour intervals. Later, it was found that one feeding per day was sufficient (Culpepper, 1946). Some subjects were sensitive to louse feeding and developed severe skin rash and itching, which subsided in 7–10 days. Others showed little or no reaction. Usually a subject was required to feed lice only about once a week.

B. FEEDING ON RABBITS

In large-scale production of lice, it has been found to be more satisfactory to feed them on domestic rabbits. The large colony maintained at Orlando, Florida, was later adapted to, and maintained on, rabbits (Culpepper, 1948; Smith and Eddy, 1954). Many of the details

M. M. COLE

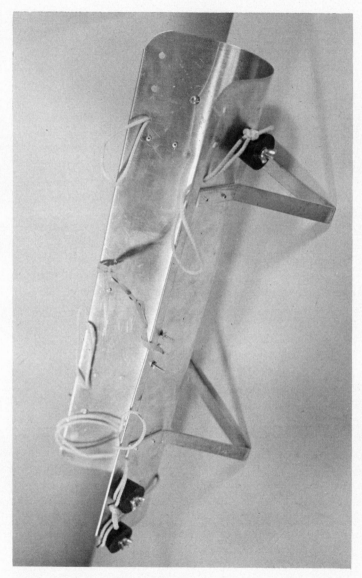

FIG. 1. Aluminum (0.040 gauge) stanchion for restraining rabbit. The four small nylon cord loops are placed around the rabbit's legs and tightened by turning the rubber stoppers (as shown in Fig. 2). The large nylon loop (at left end) goes across (not around) the rabbit's throat. Wing nuts are adjusted so that the rubber stoppers can be turned by hand and will remain in position.

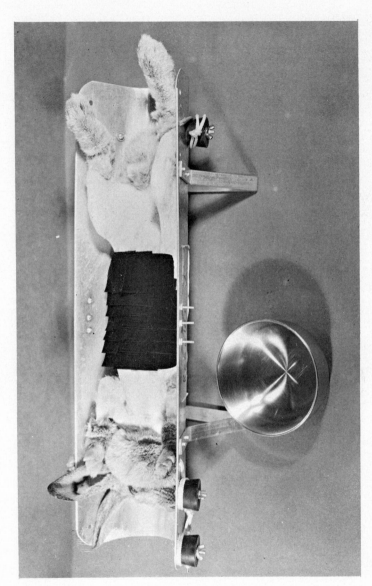

FIG. 2. Rabbit restrained in stanchion. Cloth patches containing lice laid shingle fashion on rabbit's abdomen. Stainless steel dish in which patches with lice are kept between feedings.

M. M. COLE

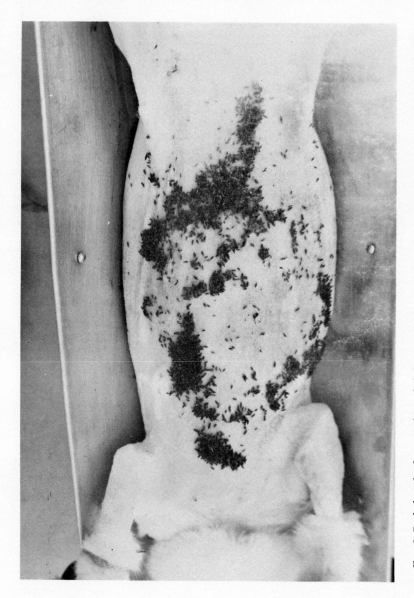

FIG. 3. Body lice feeding on clipped abdomen of rabbit. Patches shown in Fig. 2 have been removed carefully so that lice remain on the rabbit. (Reduced to approximately one-half natural size.)

FIG. 4. Body lice feeding on clipped abdomen of rabbit. (Approximately 3 times natural size.)

of that procedure have been followed (with a few modifications) by the author and co-workers.

The present procedure at the Gainesville, Florida, Laboratory of the Entomology Research Division, U. S. Department of Agriculture, still utilizes domestic rabbits. Occasionally some rabbits seem to be unfavorable hosts (Culpepper, 1948; Smith and Eddy, 1954). On these rabbits, lice fed poorly and their development was slower. On other occasions, certain rabbits, which at one time were satisfactory, suddenly became unfavorable. In these cases, the lice appeared to be bloated within a few minutes after feeding and many of them died within 24 hours. A peculiar fact about such rabbits was that they could be rested for a few weeks and again prove to be good hosts. The reason or reasons for this unfavorability has never been determined; but, in some way, it appears to have been associated with the physical condition of the rabbit. Healthy rabbits are essential. It is now standard procedure to use rabbits for about a month and rest them for about a month. They are also rested when they show signs of poor physical condition or of becoming unfavorable hosts.

A rabbit is prepared for louse feeding by restraining it on its back in a special stanchion (Figs. 1 and 2). The fur is then closely clipped with electric clippers. Special clippers are necessary for the fine fur. The Oster small animal clipper, Model A2 with blade ANG-RA A2, is an excellent choice. The area clipped is on the ventral side extending from front to hind legs and well down on each side. Clipped fur is easily removed with vacuum cleaners. It may also be wiped away with a handful of absorbent cotton.

Patches of cloth containing lice are then spread on the abdomen of the rabbit in lateral rows with edges overlapping (Fig. 2). Usually 20–30 patches measuring about 2 inches square are about all that can be conveniently placed on an average rabbit at one time. This will determine the maximum number of patches that should be kept in a dish. However, several hundred lice are kept on this number of patches and fed at one time on a rabbit. Individual lice will engorge in 15 minutes or less, but in the case of large numbers being fed at one time, they are left on the rabbit for 30 minutes. This is necessary to enable all the lice to crawl from the patches down to the skin of the rabbit and feed completely (Figs. 3 and 4). The lice are fed once a day.

After feeding is completed, the cloth patches are moved gently back and forth by hand on the rabbit before being removed to dishes. This disturbs any lice still remaining on the rabbit and causes them to cling to the cloth. A few that may remain are either picked by hand or cleaned from the rabbit with a vacuum cleaner. Several dishes of lice may be fed on each rabbit daily without apparent ill effects to the rabbit. Ordinarily the different dishes of lice are fed in order of their age, starting with young newly hatched nymphs.

If different strains of lice are being maintained, extreme care must be taken to prevent mixing. At one time at Orlando, Florida, thirteen separate colonies of several thousand lice each were maintained. Individual rearing facilities down to the smallest item are necessary for each colony. This particularly applies to incubator, rabbits, rabbit stanchions, and cages. In the case of using insecticides for selection in resistance studies, special precautions are taken to prevent accidental exposure of other colonies.

C. FEEDING THROUGH MEMBRANES

For certain biological and disease transmission studies, artificial feeding methods may be necessary. Lice have been fed by injection of defibrinated blood into the anus (Buxton, 1946). Many workers have fed them on blood through different membranes, such as human cadaver skin (Pshenichnov, 1943), mouse skin (Buxton, 1946), chick skin (Fuller *et al.*, 1949), and gutta percha (Haddon, 1956a, b). Undoubtedly there are many more that could be used. Fresh skins from hamsters, rats, and rabbits, and two commercial membranes have been used with other bloodsucking arthropods (Tarshis, 1958). Citrated blood is widely used today for feeding colonies of bloodsucking insects and arthropods.

IV. STARTING COLONIES FROM WILD LICE

Wild lice, obtained from naturally infested people, are usually difficult to colonize when first collected. The main reason for this is that the lice are forced to adapt to several unnatural conditions at once, not the least of which is the time of feeding. Of course, a change of host may be a deterrent to feeding. It is not known how often an individual louse feeds in nature or how much blood it consumes in its lifetime. A female weighing 3 mg will take approximately 1 mg of blood after fasting for 6–12 hours (Buxton, 1946). It is generally believed by most observers that lice take several light meals of blood over a 24-hour period. On the other hand, lice from laboratory colonies that are given one blood meal a day will engorge completely each time. Wild lice thrive best for the first few days after capture if they are kept almost constantly next to the human body where they may feed at will. They may be maintained for an indefinite time by feeding on humans. If there is a possibility that the lice are infected with typhus or other disease organisms, immunization of the human feeder is urgently indicated.

As mentioned before, lice should be fed as they have been accustomed for some time after colonization. When and if it is desirable, the change from humans to laboratory animals or artificial feeding should be made gradually. Feeding alternately on humans and then on laboratory animals may be used.

Fully fed lice are necessary for good colony production. Colonies have been known to barely subsist under unfavorable conditions and gradually die out almost unnoticed. There may simply be less egg production each succeeding generation.

Although the louse is an adaptable animal, it must be realized that an individual from a laboratory colony is no longer the same ecologically or perhaps even physically. Its reactions and responses to stimuli, e.g., insecticides, may be more or less different than they would be in the wild state. This principle applies to all species. Still, dependable studies are possible with laboratory colonies; indeed, they are vitally necessary to modern research.

REFERENCES

Buxton, P. A. (1946). "The Louse," 2nd ed., 164 pp. Williams & Wilkins, Baltimore, Maryland; Butler and Tanner Ltd., London.

Culpepper, G. H. (1944). The rearing and maintenance of a laboratory colony of the body louse. *Am. J. Trop. Med.* **24**(5), 327–329.

Culpepper, G. H. (1946). Factors influencing the rearing and maintenance of a laboratory colony of the body louse. *J. Econ. Entomol.* **39**(4), 472–474.

Culpepper, G. H. (1948). Rearing and maintaining a laboratory colony of body lice on rabbits. *Am. J. Trop. Med.* **28**(3), 499–504.

Davis, W. A., and Hansens, E. J. (1945). Bionomics of *Pediculosis* [Pediculus] *capititis*. *Am. J. Hyg.* **41**, 1–4.

Fuller, H. S., Murray, E. S., and Snyder, J. C. (1949). Studies of human body lice, *Pediculus humanus corporis*. *Public Health Repts.* **64**(41), 1287–1292.

Haddon, W., Jr. (1956a). An artificial membrane and apparatus for the feeding of the human body louse *Pediculus humanus corporis*. *Am. J. Trop. Med. Hyg.* **5**(2), 315–325.

Haddon, W., Jr. (1956b). The maintenance of the human body louse *Pediculus humanus corporis* through complete cycles of growth by serial feeding through artificial membranes. *Am. J. Trop. Med. Hyg.* **5**(2), 326–330.

Pshenichnov, A. V. (1943). A universal method for studying infections transmitted to man by blood-sucking insects and a new vaccine against spotted typhus. (In Russian.) *Zhur. Mikrobiol., Epidemiol., Immunobiol.* (*Moscow*) **1–2**, 43–48.

Smith, C. N., and Eddy, G. W. (1954). Techniques for rearing and handling body lice, oriental rat fleas, and cat fleas. *Bull. World Health Organ.* **10**: 127–137.

Tarshis, I. B. (1958). Feeding techniques for bloodsucking arthropods. *Proc. Intern. Congr. Entomol. Montreal* **3**, 767–784.

Chapter 3

Parasitic Mites

J. Ralph Audy and M. M. J. Lavoipierre

*The George Williams Hooper Foundation,
University of California Medical Center,
San Francisco, California*

This chapter is restricted to acarines other than ticks parasitic on warm-blooded vertebrates. The culturing of mites has not progressed nearly so far as the culturing of ticks. Since every species has its own special requirements, and since every culture method is capable of much more refinement, it is most important to set down basic principles which have emerged from the experiences of many entomologists. The authors have published elsewhere a general review of culturing acarines and a more detailed review with an annotated bibliography is in preparation (Audy and Lavoipierre, 1964; to be published). This chapter attempts to summarize the general principles as briefly as possible and then to deal systematically with individual species.

I. BASIC PRINCIPLES

We are concerned with three problems in this field: the establishment of a colony of a parasitic mite which has hitherto never been reared through successive generations in the laboratory; the improvement of existing colonization techniques; and the establishment of mass colonization when large numbers of mites are required. The purposes of colonization are to determine life histories and life requirements with a view to influencing the mites in nature, working out vector potentials and mechanisms of transmission, and, sometimes, the preparation of vaccines.

Methods have on the whole been empirical and, as indicated by Audy and Lavoipierre (1964), there has been a tendency to neglect for each species the following potentially important features: behavioral characteristics in nature; the chemical quality of the ambient air and the substrate; the physiological state of the host; circadian rhythmic fluctuations in activity and physiological requirements; the influence of exposure to light of different colors at particular critical times; and improving the media and methods of artificial and semiautomatic or small closed-system feeding.

A number of careful physiological and behavioral studies have been made, e.g., Cross and Wharton (1964), Wharton and Kanungo (1962), Camin (1963, 1964), Furman (1959). Sasa (1961) has reviewed the trombiculids. These papers should be consulted.

An attempt should always be made to get into the little private universe or *Umwelt* of the mite, with the approach suggested by von Uexküll (1957). This is made easier by recognizing an ecological grouping of parasites into host-, nest-, field-, and food-dwelling following Audy (1948, 1958). Camin (1963, 1964) independently developed an almost identical classification (his groups I to III), starting from a very different viewpoint, and he applied this to the culturing of acarina. In brief, parasites of the host-dwelling group I spend their entire life cycle on the host, feed frequently or almost continuously, tend to have strict requirements, and often show some degree of physiological host-specificity. They tend to parasitize gregarious hosts because cross-infestation is by close contact. Examples are the scabies and mange mites. Mites of the nest-dwelling or nidicolous group II tend to live in the nest substrate, to feed by taking larger meals at less frequent intervals, and to show ecological specificity related to the nest conditions rather than physiological host-specificity. They usually parasitize hosts with well-developed nests or burrows. Examples are the ectoparasitic Mesostigmata generally, some of which show signs of evolution toward the more intimate relations of group I. Mites of the field-dwelling (campestral, agricolous) group III tend to show the greatest independence of their hosts, take even larger feeds at even longer intervals, remain on the host only for a single feed, are the most resistant to starvation, and have a broader range of hosts in nature than the others. They frequently feed on several different individuals during the course of a lifetime, sometimes (e.g., many ixodids) on individuals of more than one species. The characteristics of these three groups greatly influence the selection of culture technique, from the choice of host animal to the type of chamber.

Further insight into the *Umwelten* of parasitic acarines is gained by inquiry into their behavior in orientation, questing, selection of feeding site on the host, decision to feed, and exact manner of feeding. It is common to find presumably hungry acarines failing to feed on an evidently suitable host, because some essential factor is lacking in the chain of stimuli and of requirements to be satisfied. Similarly, a chain of requirements is involved in mating. Camin (1964) discussed Lees's (1948) observation that three phases of behavior lead to successful feeding: (1) "taking up position," (2) active questing and transfer to the host, and (3) attachment and feeding. Each of these phases may involve a succession of stimuli. For example, phase (1) is important to group III parasites but not to those of group II. It is remarkable how mouth parts, manner of feeding, and sensory and locomotor apparatus are all adapted to the specific modes of life. Therefore, one may infer much by careful study of the living mites under the microscope, preferably using a Rousselet's compressorium,* water immersion mount, or similar restraining device. Sometimes it is practicable to allow an acarine to satisfy some prior requirement in order to get it to a state in which it may be transferred to an experimentally more convenient situation. For example, as Gregson (Chapter 4) has noted, ticks may be allowed to start a feed on an accustomed host in the normal way, thereby facilitating their transfer either to an artificial arrangement or to a laboratory animal which otherwise would often be rejected.

The *precise manner of feeding* also demands attention: [for some of the earlier works on feeding mechanisms of parasitic acarines, including one of the first on any arthropod parasite, refer to Gudden (1871), Hughes (1949), and Gorirossi (1950)]. A parasite's effectiveness as a vector can be correlated to a large extent with its ability to puncture the intact skin of its host. The exact method of penetrating the skin and the tissue level that may be reached are important in determining the types of pathogens transmissible. The parasite may be a surface or follicular-secretion feeder (*Demodex*), a tissue-juice feeder (trombiculids, some other immature acarines), a tissue burrower (*Sarcoptes*), a vessel feeder (females of *Chiropto-*

---

* Obtainable from Flatters and Garnett, Ltd., 309 Oxford Road, Manchester 13, England.

nyssus robustipes (Ewing), reduviid bugs), a tissue pool feeder (protonymphs of *Chiroptonyssus robustipes*), or a surface pool feeder (taking blood exuding from a wound; most individuals of *Haemogamasus liponyssoides* Ewing, at least when feeding on a laboratory host). Vessel feeders typically have slender flexible mouthparts, take blood from the lumen of a small vessel, and engorge rapidly (3–5 minutes for mosquitoes and 15–20 minutes for some species of triatomines). Pool feeders, such as ticks, horse flies, and stable flies, often possess coarse mouth parts with an inflexible biting fascicle. Feeding usually is prolonged; argasid ticks, for example, may take more than 1 hour to engorge. Feeding by pool or vessel feeders may be enhanced by using thin-skinned experimental hosts, such as weanling or suckling mice, and either brushing the skin to cause dilation of the superficial vessels or lightly scarifying the skin. The food source on a single host may differ in the same species at different stages in its life cycle or even during the same instar. Beck and Lavoipierre (in press) have found that, while females of *Chiroptonyssus robustipes* are vessel feeders, the protonymphs are pool feeders, and this difference probably is due to the shorter mouth parts of the latter. The protonymphs feed on the bat's wing by excavating craters, first imbibing exudate and later blood. Wharton (1954, 1960) has described a method for detection of tissue fluid-feeding by injection of Evans blue into the host.

The *chemical quality of the ambient air* in breeding chambers has been sadly neglected except by some workers on plant-parasitic acarines. The success of using a substrate of charcoal and plaster of Paris (1:9) in culture chambers is presumably partly due to its adsorbent qualities as well as to its ability to conserve moisture without permitting free condensation. The exhalations of host animals, and particularly the fouling of the air by the host's feces and urine, may be deleterious to mites in culture. Suitable ventilation must be contrived. Nidicoles of group II will live in nature in close relationship with their host, perhaps in a burrow, so that they may demand at least some of the host's emanations. In such cases it would be advisable to sample the air from the parts of the burrows where parasites are found, both before the host returns to the nest and before it leaves for foraging. Group III acarines in particular may, however, be disturbed by excessive exhalations. For example, Sasa (1961) has found it helpful and sometimes necessary to remove excess CO_2 from chambers in which trombiculids are being fed on animals: the larvae are activated by CO_2 and a continued concentration or an excess upsets their physiology.

The *physiological state of the host* is undoubtedly important. Some of the changes in the same host from time to time may be very subtle, so that every attempt should be made when rearing unknown or difficult species to anticipate natural conditions. The physiological state of any animal is not the same at night as during the day. It is also different if the animal is stressed. It is different, for humoral and immunological reasons, if the host has had previous experience of the parasite, to such an extent that for many species the same individual host can hardly be used more than once (see Chapter 4 by Gregson). The mites themselves will be subject to fluctuating physiological states and therefore varying requirements and behavior patterns, and they will usually attach on their own initiative to the host at the optimum time. For example, mites which normally feed at night will continue to do so in the laboratory. It should be assumed that the host itself will be in the optimum physiological state at night. It may therefore be prudent to present the host to the mites in the evening rather than the morning. Also, care should be taken that artificial lighting schedules do not set mites and hosts on different dark/light regimes prior to feeding.

Some further aspects of the physiological optima of the host concern nutritional state, pregnancy, age, possibly sex, and stress. Too little is known of the effects of these, but it is certain that they merit careful attention for culturing the more fastidious species. Not only the adequacy of diet but the kind of diet may be important: some items in the artificial diet of the laboratory animal may be lacking or may render the host relatively less attractive to the mite. The effect of green vegetables on complement in the blood of guinea pigs is a measurable example, although this may not affect the feeding of mites. Pregnancy has been found important in one parasite, and more examples are sure to be found where the presence of some hormone of pregnancy is necessary for oviposition in the parasite. Mead-Briggs (1964) has found that the rabbit flea requires a blood feed from a pregnant rabbit before it will successfully oviposit. Nothing is known to us about the importance of sex as such in the feeding of mites in the laboratory, but age may certainly be important: some mites feeding readily on very young animals rather than on adults; others may prefer adults. Irwin (1937) maintained that demodectic mange could be transmitted only among puppies.

In spite of so much evidence that stress affects the degree of parasitic multiplication on or in a host, relatively little attention has been paid to increasing the suitability of a host by stressing it. In some cases, the stressed host may be more heavily infested in nature or in the laboratory simply because it does not groom itself. When this is so, the same effect might be gained by restraining the host (by collars, hobbles, etc.) rather than troubling to stress it, (see Bell *et al.*, 1962, and Bell and Clifford, 1964, for basic work concerning lice on the laboratory mouse). In part, the stressed host may simply be less active generally, which may encourage the parasites. If so, the same effect might be obtained by anesthetizing or tranquilizing the host. However, an anesthetic may affect the future development of some species of mites. In addition to lack of grooming and feeding on parasites wandering on the substrate and to generally lowered activity, other attributes of stressed animals may encourage or discourage the successful feeding of a parasite. Successful feeding means more than engorgement and detachment; it also means ovipositing or molting successfully thereafter. Although there is yet no satisfactory experimental proof that laboratory confinement of a wild animal may be responsible for "blowing up" a relatively inapparent infestation by ectoparasites, sufficient evidence exists that this is likely to occur. Most workers who have looked for mange in the wild find this a disappointing pursuit, yet clinically obvious cases of mange are found in zoos or laboratory animal houses where originally healthy animals are kept in confinement, and this can also obtain in overcrowded populations in the field. The laboratory mouse, rat, or guinea pig is not normally stressed by usual laboratory procedures. Therefore it may be worthwhile deliberately to stress these hosts before and during the period of feeding of mites in culture. Physical confinement of a mouse in a tube or wire-mesh jacket is very stressful, but overcrowding will usually suffice.

Fortunately the range of animal species used experimentally is rapidly increasing, and this opens up new fields for the entomologist. The successful culturing of *Rattus natalensis* (Smith) in South Africa has enabled workers in Johannesburg to establish cultures of *Psorergates oettlei* Till, responsible for remarkable skin lesions. The establishment of colonies of the house shrew, *Suncus murinus* (L.), in Singapore has enabled Dr. Lavoipierre to establish cultures of a new Malaysian species of *Notoedres* recovered from a shrew of the genus *Crocidura*. In addition to exploration of new experimental hosts, new techniques may be devised by the ingenious investigator, such as feeding acarines on the everted cheek pouches of hamsters.

Circadian physiological and behavioral rhythms (see Wolf, 1962; Cloudsley-Thompson, 1961; Harker, 1961, 1964) have hardly been studied in acarines, but they are certain to exist in every species. Trombiculid larvae in Malaya tend to leave their host at night rather than during the day (Harrison, 1957), but this could be related more to the behavior of the host than to anything inherent in the mites. George (1964) has demonstrated a marked peak in drop-off of *Haemaphysalia leporis-palustris* (Packard) from its rabbit host and has described a turntable to record this. This phenomenon has long been known to workers at the Rocky Mountain Laboratory, Hamilton, Montana. Although bees and ants show feeding rhythms monitored by the time(s) of previous feeds, the provision of food does not even act as a weak phase-setting factor in cockroaches (Harker, 1955, 1964). Although acarines, like all living creatures, are more or less adaptable, optimum conditions occur when the acarine is not called upon to adapt or to act contrary to the persuasions of its biological clock. In principle, one may therefore prescribe adhering as closely as possible to the timing adopted in nature, checking the synchrony of dark/light regimes in both acarine and host prior to feeding, attempting strict regularity in all procedures, by the clock, and avoiding possible phase-setting by unscheduled exposures to light, especially bright light, during the dark period. Also, there may be disadvantages in pursuing the usual goal of having all controllable conditions (light, temperature, humidity) rigidly constant; for a given acarine may in fact thrive better if subjected to fluctuating conditions that correspond more closely to the fluctuations in its natural environment to which it will be genetically conditioned.

That arthropods generally are greatly affected by light tends to be overlooked. There is evidence that bright light is almost always disturbing, that even brief exposures to light during a dark-adaptation phase may reset circadian phases, and that light of different wavelengths has various effects, sometimes remarkable, upon both arthropod and vertebrate. The importance of these effects in the culturing of arthropods generally is unknown, although their importance to some species is known; but attention surely must be paid to lighting, at least for the more fastidious species. Deep red light seems to have the least effect on both arthropods and hosts; therefore a red light during the dark phase may allow many maneuvers to be carried out without turning on full lighting and stressing the mites. Also, the structuring of the culture chambers may allow for lights to be left on in the laboratory while the mites themselves seek their optimum light conditions in appropriate sanctuaries. It must be possible for them to find almost complete darkness.

II. BASIC METHODS

Radinovsky and Krantz (1961), Woodring (1963), and Solomon and Cunnington (1964) have reviewed a variety of rearing cells. We distinguish capsules as being simple containers for acarines, while chambers are more elaborate, larger containers that may hold a capsule or capsules, with or without the host. Special precautions must be taken to prevent mites from escaping, thereby contaminating other cultures or becoming a hazard. Such precautions are taken with capsules by careful sealing; with chambers by standing them in a moat of mineral oil. Mites may, however, readily be airborne and care must be taken to prevent this by enclosing chambers in special hoods, and also by proofing the room in the manner described by Kohls (1937) and Gregson (Chapter 4). The atmosphere of the room should be as close as possible to the optimum physical conditions of the acarines being cultured, and certainly not well below the tolerable limit of dryness, to obviate the risk of stressing mites when capsules or chambers are opened.

Feeding capsules for attachment to the host are described by Gregson (Chapter 4). The capsules usually must be firmly cemented to the skin, and in some cases even stitched and cemented, e.g., with snakes and *Ophionyssus* (Camin, 1950). The host must usually be restrained by Elizabethan collars or harness or hobbles. The growth of hair after shaving may be troublesome; Downing (1936) had to move his capsules every 3 or 4 days for this reason. Lavoipierre has obtained good results with a depilatory cream (Nair) applied for no more than 5 minutes and then thoroughly washed off with a jet.

Special chambers are described in the following text under specific groups.

Artificial feeding has been successful mostly with lappers in group II, but some success has been achieved with feeding on heparinized blood through artificial membranes, and it is necessary to persevere. Cross (1954) used bolting silk, Macdonald and Scott (1952) used membranes, and Tarshis (1958a,b) has reviewed and tested different membranes. Animal membranes are better than synthetic ones, apparently because they become soft and readily penetrable in contact with blood.

III. SPECIFIC EXAMPLES WITH BIONOMIC DATA

The following is a list of parasitic mites which have been partly or completely reared in the laboratory, together with the major reference(s), summary of the life cycle with durations of stages in days (unless otherwise stated), and miscellaneous data in parentheses. There follows the recorded and presumably optimum temperature and relative humidity (RH), and the duration of the total life cycle with comments on the life span of various stages; then the preferred experimental host(s), and any special comments on the conditions of culturing or pertinent observations by other authors. An account of culture methods is given at the beginning of each major section (see also Figs. 1 to 5).

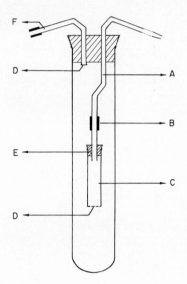

FIG. 1. Aspiration tube for collecting parasitic Mesostigmatid mites. (A) Glass tubing. (B) Rubber connecting tube. (C) Storage or collecting tube. (D) Bolting silk. (E) Rubber stopper. (F) Glass tubing leading to aspirator. (After Wisseman and Sulkin, 1947.)

A. MESOSTIGMATA

The parasitic mites most often cultured are Mesostigmata (Dermanyssidae, Macronyssidae, Haemogamasinae, and Laelapinae) and the Trombiculidae. Apart from papers referred to in the text, reference should be made to the excellent works of Bregetova (1956) and Bregetova *et al.* (1955), the first on gamasoid Mesostigmata and the second on all acarines associated with rodents. Most Mesostigmata are nidicoles of group II. Among the many devices adopted for these and similar acarines, the two primary vessels are (*a*) feeding capsules applied to the host, based on the capsules of Jellison and

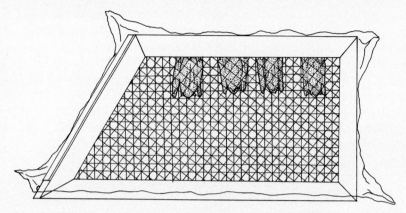

Fig. 2. Cage (side view) for rearing Mesostigmata parasitic on bats. The rodent cage which houses the bats is set in a moat of mineral oil. The cage is kept constantly covered with white flannel in which the mites take refuge when they are not feeding on the host. (Beck and Lavoipierre, 1966).

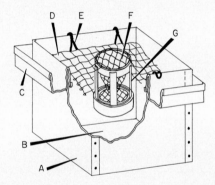

Fig. 3. Galvanized iron tank for rearing rat mites. (A) Galvanized iron tank. (B) Bottom of tank, covered with a sheet of hardware cloth (overlying wood shavings). (C) Oil moat. (D) Cover of hardware cloth, ½ inch wire mesh. (E) Wire slings for the cover. (F) Food container. (G) Feeding basket. (After Scott, Allen, Stembridge, and Sisley, 1947.)

Philip (1933), and (b) chambers simulating a nest and designed to hold the host without fouling the substrate with urine and feces. Downing (1936) and Camin (1950, 1953) are among those who have used capsules attached to the host for feeding mites. The most elaborate chamber for nidicoles such as *Dermanyssus gallinae* (De Geer), *Ornithonyssus bacoti* (Hirst), and *Ophionyssus natricis* (Gervais) is a wire-mesh cage for the host within a chamber for the simulated nest material (Scott *et al.*, 1947; Camin and Ehrlich, 1960). The inner cage has a removable top, and the bottom, including a plastic cup for dejecta, can be removed from within the cage. Camin, in correspondence, points out that this type of chamber is less successful for *Ornithonyssus sylviarum* (Canestrini and Fanzago) (intermediate between groups I and II) and *Echinolaelaps echidninus* (Berlese). For these Camin prefers placing the mechanically immobilized host in a jar half-buried in wood shavings, then placing the mites on the host. Suvorova and Sidorov (1962) described a wood and cardboard substrate for the mites held with the host in a glass jar. Radovsky (1964) and Lavoipierre (unpublished), in feeding dermanyssids on caged bats, found a cloth over the cage served as a suitable substrate for the mites (Fig. 2).

1. Dermanyssidae

Dermanyssus gallinae (De Geer, 1778), Chicken mite: Brown (1953), Cross and Wharton (1954), Sikes and Chamberlain (1954), Wisseman and Sulkin (1947). *Life cycle:* egg 2–3; larva 1–2 (no feed); protonymph 2; deutonymph 2. At 27°C (*ca.* 80°F), complete in 7, average 12. Oviposition 1 day after each meal, *ca.* 40 per female in batches of 1–8. Adults may resist starvation 4–5 months. *Hosts:* chickens, pigeons, sparrows; not mammals. Cross (1954) fed this mite on heparinized blood.

Allodermanyssus sanguineus (Hirst, 1914), House mouse mite: Fuller (1954), Nichols, Rindge, and Russell (1953). *Life cycle:* egg 4–5; larva 3 (no feed); protonymph 4.5 (engorge within 1 hour); deutonymph 6–10. At 23°–25°C (73°–77°F), RH 80%, complete in about 3 weeks. Female observed to live 9 weeks; unfed females 7 weeks. *Hosts:* mice; adults fed singly on 6- to 8-day-old suckling mouse in cotton-stoppered vial. This important species has not yet been satisfactorily colonized.

2. Macronyssidae

Ornithonyssus bacoti (Hirst, 1913), Tropical rat mite: Bertram, Unsworth, and Gordon (1946), Cross (1954), Ohmori (1935, as *Liponyssus nagayoi* Yamata, synonym), Skaliy and Hayes (1949). *Life cycle:* egg 1–4 (unfertilized eggs develop into fertile males); larva 1 (no feed); protonymph 5–14 (requires at least one feed); deutonymph 1–2 (no feed). Oviposition for 2–10 days after each feed; several batches of 1–20 eggs in lifetime; average total eggs 99, perhaps 120. At 27°–29°C (80°–85°F) complete in 13 (over 70% of mites). Female life span 61 (Ohmori: 28). *Hosts:* mice, rats; or heparinized rat blood. Olson and Dahms (1946) discuss this mite as a pest of laboratory animals.

Ornithonyssus bursa (Berlese, 1888), Tropical fowl mite: Sikes and Chamberlain (1954). *Life cycle:* egg 1.5–2 (when off the host); larva 17 hours (no feed); protonymph 2.5–4 (at least 2 feeds); deutonymph 1 (no feed). Oviposition in 3. At 27°–35°C (80°–95°F), RH 90–100%, complete in 5–7. *Hosts:* chickens, sparrows; not mammals.

Ornithonyssus sylviarum (Canestrini and Fanzago, 1877), Northern fowl mite: Sikes and Chamberlain (1954). *Life cycle:* egg 1; larva 9 hours (no feed); protonymph 2–4 (at least 2 feeds); deutonymph 3–4 (no feed). Oviposition mostly on the host, 2 days after engorgement. At 38°–40°C (100°–104°F), RH 90–100%, ideally complete in 5–7. Adults may live 2.3 weeks without food. *Hosts:* chicks; not mammals. Cross (1954) fed this and the similar species *bursa* on heparinized blood. Cross and Wharton (1954) described attachment and feeding.

Chiroptonyssus robustipes (Ewing, 1925): Beck and Lavoipierre (1966). The feeding behavior of protonymphs and adult females is known in detail and is discussed earlier in this chapter (Section I). Major features of the life history are similar to *Ornithonyssus bacoti* and particulars are described by Radovsky (in press). *Hosts: Tadarida brasiliensis* (Geoffroy), the guano bat.

3. *Laelapidae—Laelapinae*

Echinolaelaps echidninus (Berlese 1887), Spiny rat mite: Owen (1956). *Life cycle:* larviparous; larva 1 (no feed); protonymph 4–8 (1 feed); deutonymph 4–8 (1 feed); oviposition (parthenogenetically or otherwise) 5 days after feed, probably laying every few days. At room temperature and humidity, cycle complete in perhaps 2–3 weeks. Fed artificially on blood through silk screen (after Cross, 1954). The mites lap readily. The female readily cannibalizes the young.

Haemolaelaps glasgowi (Ewing, 1925): Furman (1959). This species is a general feeder satisfactorily feeding on suckling mice in small plastic boxes with grass substrate and moistened cotton-wool balls (cf. Radovsky, 1960). No life cycle details available.

4. *Laelapidae—Haemogamasinae*

Haemogamasus liponyssoides (Ewing, 1925): Radovsky (1960). *Life cycle:* egg 4; larva 1 (no feed); protonymph 2 (no feed); deutonymph 7 (requires 3 or more feeds); adult (daily feeds). Oviposition up to 2 eggs a day. At 20 (18°–28°C) (64°–82°F), RH 98–100%, complete in less than 3 weeks. Females live to 105, males 75, on heparinized blood; deutonymphs and adults up to or over a month without feeding. *Hosts:* suckling mice; *Microtus californicus; Reithrodon-tomys magalotis.* Mass cultures in plastic boxes with grass and moistened cotton-wool balls, fed on suckling mice placed in boxes. Reared on fresh heparinized blood with less success.

Haemogamasus ambulans (Thorell, 1872): Furman (1959). *Life cycle:* larviparous; larva 0.5 (no feed); protonymph 1.5; deutonymph 6 (daily feeds); adult daily feeds. Oviposition, 1 egg every 2 days. At 20°C (68°F), RH 92%, birth to adult averaged 6.7 days for males and 7.5 days for females. Under the same conditions, maximum survival was 214 for a female; unfed mites lived up to 51, 43, and 50 for female, male, and deutonymph, respectively. *Hosts:* reared on heparinized blood. Although it is a vector of a blood protozoon (*Hepatozoon*) of squirrels, this species is a facultative parasite, feeding opportunistically at wounds or abrasions, but able to subsist on dried blood, flea feces, or small arthropods.

Brevisterna utahensis (Ewing, 1933): Allred (1957), Allred and Marchette (1957). *Life cycle:* egg less than 1; larva less than 1 (no feed); protonymph 1-2 (no feed); deutonymph estimated as 90 days, prolonged under conditions of observation (frequent feeds). At 22°C (72°F), RH 81%, fed females up to 396 and deutonymphs up to 192; starved females as long as 90. *Hosts:* fed on stored blood.

5. *Rhinonyssidae, Halarachnidae*

No data, but perhaps these parasites of the respiratory tract could be cultured in millipore filters (see *Demodex*).

6. *Spinturnicidae*

Reviewed by Rudnick (1960). Not yet colonized. Egg and larva develop in female which "lays" protonymphs; they molt to produce deutonymphs that may be morphologically distinguishable as male and female. Nymphs and adults will require feeding on wing membranes of bats unless artificial membrane-feeding techniques can be devised. *Paraspinturnix* and *Ancystropus* are exceptional, the first feeding within the anal orifice, the second on the eyelids and canthus of bats.

B. TROMBIDIFORMES

1. *Trombiculidae (Chiggers)*

Only the six-legged larvae (chiggers) are parasitic, normally feeding only once on a vertebrate host. Engorged larvae may be obtained by suspending infested hosts in cages over water. The detached larvae will float and a screen below the cage will prevent pollution of the water by excreta of the host. Similarly, dead animals may be suspended over dishes of water. The animals may be infested naturally in the field or laboratory animals may be set out as bait or infested with laboratory-reared chiggers.

Rats (especially newborn rats, less active and producing less excreta), rabbits, and guinea pigs make better bait animals than mice. Questing larvae may also be obtained by examination of plastic sheets laid out in the field, preferably in the early morning. In areas where they are abundant, large groups of unfed larvae may be seen with the naked eye (e.g., among rock crevices) and can be swept into vials with a brush.

The larvae usually can be induced to feed by placing them on a preferred host, which may have to be restrained in a wire-mesh cylinder or by Nembutal anesthesia, at least until the mites settle and start feeding. Different species have different favored sites of attachment on their hosts (Audy, 1956). Some species are somewhat host-specific; e.g., most will prefer rats to mice, but many accept a wide range of hosts, especially those species causing scrub itch in man which will accept reptiles, birds, and mammals. The larval feed takes from 1–2 days to over a month: data on feeding times for a number of Malayan species are given by Harrison (1957). After feeding, the larvae require some microshelter and a film of moisture until they become akinetic. At this stage they may grip the substrate, so that their exuviae adhere to it after the nymph has emerged. Therefore, when rearing single nymphs to be correlated with the larval exuviae for identification, the akinetic larvae should be detached gently, or the engorged larvae may be floated in water. In the latter case the emergent nymph will sink while the larval skin floats, but there is risk of drowning the nymph. Nymphs may be reared for taxonomic purposes while in the field by the method described by Audy and Nadchatram (1954).

Eight-legged nymphs emerge from the first pupa or nymphophane, later to molt again (teleiophane) to become adults. These two pupalike stages may each take 1–2 weeks. The postlarval stages are not parasitic but predatory (some species may be scavengers). They present a troublesome aspect of culturing chiggers, requiring to be fed on eggs of various other arthropods in the case of the less delicate and more voracious species, and on crushed eggs or bodies in the case of the more delicate species. Postlarval stages will cannibalize each other readily. Some [e.g., *Leptotrombidium akamushi* (Brumpt), *L. deliense* (Walch)] will feed on mosquito eggs [*Culex*

fatigans (Wiedeman), *Culex pipiens* L., *Aedes aegypti* (L.)] and
a variety of other eggs. Others will feed only on collembolan eggs;
some species have so far refused all food offered to them, even
crushed eggs or bodies. Mosquito eggs require troublesome hand-
feeding. The standard culture method that gives least trouble is to
keep cultures of the collembolan *Sinella curviseta* Brook in plaster-
charcoal-lined pots with brewer's yeast as food. The collembolan
eggs (in some cases the collembolans, whole or crushed) are fed to
the trombiculids. Ito *et al.* (1957) had outstanding success with
eggs of dragon flies in Japan: these eggs normally overwinter and
may therefore be collected in large numbers and preserved indefinitely en masse at $-3°C$ in saline until needed. Kumada (personal
communication) has used eggs of *Musca domestica vicina* Macquart,
which had to be rationed because the mites tended to overeat, become grossly distended, and then burst. This may also happen when
mosquito eggs are used. An artificial medium would give a great
impetus to rearing chiggers.

For the postlarval stages two types of cell may be used: (1) A
simple pot, preferably with snap-fitting lid, is partly filled with
charcoal-plaster (1:9), reaching up the sides of the pot. Small pots
minimize foraging by the postlarval stages, and it may be advantageous to make small sanctuaries by indenting the surface of the
plaster with a narrow blunt glass rod. The pot may be glass or plastic,
but some plastics have the advantage that the mites cannot crawl
up the sides. For species such as *L. scutellaris* (Nagayo *et al.*), sand
is spread over the plaster of Paris because these trombiculids are
better maintained in comparatively arid conditions. To maintain
an appropriate humidity level within the jar while suppressing
mold, merthiolate solution (1:10,000) should be used (Sasa, 1956).
(2) Cockings (Nadchatram *et al.*, to be published) first devised a
cell consisting of a porous flat-bottomed earthenware pot about 6
cm in diameter and 4 mm thick, with a flat-ground rim. Metal strips
are fixed over water in a large tray. Each strip has a series of slots,
a tongue of filter paper dipping into the water through the slot
while its upper end lies on the strip. Each pot is placed in contact with the paper. By varying the water table and the proportion of
pot lying on the wet paper, a variety of humidities may be maintained, using the same layout for a variety of species. A pinch of
coarse sterile soil is placed within the pot, to provide a sanctuary
for the mites, and food for them is regularly placed on the edge of
this pinch. The lid is a square of optical glass usually kept covered
with black paper. The contents can be examined with great ease.

Unengorged larvae may be driven from the underface of the plate by means of bright light, if necessary. Immediately upon lifting the lid, the rim should be flooded with water to form a barrier. Larvae may be transferred from cells or pots either by placing the immobilized host on the open pot on a wire-mesh square, or by picking up larvae with small balls of wool which are transferred to the host, or after collection by aspiration.

While many species have been reared, the following summaries will provide representative examples with similar species grouped together.

Leptotrombidium akamushi (Brumpt, 1910), and *Leptotrombidium deliense* (Walch, 1922), two major vectors of scrub-typhus: Sasa and Miura (1953), Audy and Nadchatram, unpub. *Life cycle:* egg 2–3 weeks; larva 1–3 (⅔ recovered within 24 hours; followed by presettling period, 1–10 days, which is shortened by presence of free water film); nymphophane 10; nymph nonparasitic, 20–30 (take 1–5 *Culex fatigans* eggs every 3 days to total 25–35 during this instar, take 2 minutes to consume each egg); teliophane 10; adult nonparasitic, about twice as many eggs per feed as nymph. Oviposition for many months. At 32°C (90°F), RH near 100%, complete in 2 months. Adult life span may exceed 8 months. Similar course follows feeding on eggs of *Sinella*, etc. *Hosts:* laboratory mice for larvae; arthropod eggs or fly larvae for postlarval stages.

Eutrombicula splendens (Ewing, 1913), *Eutrombicula alfreddugesi* (Oudemans, 1910), and *Eutrombicula batatus* (Linneaus, 1758): Michener (1946), Jenkins (1947, 1948), Hyland (1951). *Life cycle:* egg, 5–6; deutovum, 7; larva, feeding time dependent on host, 1–3 on rodents and up to 65 on reptiles; postfeeding larva, 1–2; nymphophane 5–7; nymph nonparasitic, 6; teliophane, 5–7; adult nonparasitic; average of 30 mosquito eggs per day consumed by 1 ovipositing female; oviposition after 7, and average of 7 eggs per female per day. At 28°–32°C (82°–90°F), RH 86–100%, complete in minimum of 50–71. *Hosts:* for larvae, hamsters and other rodents, chickens, lizards, snakes, turtles; for postlarval stages, mosquito, collembolan, and other arthropod eggs.

Eutrombicula wichmanni (Oudemans, 1905), common scrub-itch mite: Audy and Nadchatram, unpublished. *Life cycle:* egg plus deutovum, 21–25; larva fed for 3; postfeeding larva, 5; nymphophane, 7; nymph nonparasitic, 12–14; teliophane 10–12; adult nonparasitic; eggs laid in 15–20. Life cycle complete in 73–86. Average number of mosquito eggs taken by single adult, 5 per day; oviposition for 7 months. Adult life span approximately 10 months. *Hosts:* laboratory mice for larvae; culicine eggs for postlarval stages.

Neotrombicula autumnalis (Shaw, 1790), European harvest mite: Jones (1951). *Life cycle:* egg, incubation period unknown; larva, fed for 2–4; engorged larva, 12–20; nymphophane, 11; nymph nonparasitic, 6–8 hours to become fully engorged, alive 21 days at room temperature; teliophane, 28 (at 25°C); adult nonparasitic. Temperature, 30°C (86°F), RH 100%. *Hosts:* young mice (8 days old) for larvae; mixture of yeast, molasses, and agar, or mosquito eggs for postlarval stages.

Blankaartia acuscutellaris (Walch, 1922), marsh and ricefield chigger: Audy and Nadchatram (unpublished). *Life cycle:* egg 12–13; larvae feed for 3, pupate in 3 more; nymphophane 6–8; nymphs nonparasitic 6–8; teleiophane 10–12; adults nonparasitic, life span 16 months; oviposit in 15–20, continuing for about one year. *Hosts:* white rat; culicine eggs for postlarval stages (avid feeders: average 8 eggs a day).

Babiangia parmifera (Womersley, 1952): Audy and Nadchatram (to be published). *Life cycle:* egg 5; larva 4 or longer; nymphophane 9; nymph nonparasitic 30; teleiophane 11; adults nonparasitic, oviposition in 60. *Hosts:* skink (*Mabuya*); culicine eggs for postlarval stages.

Vatacarus ipoides Southcott, 1957, lung-chigger of seasnakes: Audy and Nadchatram (unpublished). *Life cycle:* egg 16; larva, parasitic in air-sacs of seasnakes of genus *Laticauda*, feed for unknown periods probably of months, between intervals of egg-laying by the snake; nymph bypassed, does not emerge, preadult stage 5; adult nonparasitic, emerges directly from larval-nymphal envelopes as only active postlarval stage; eggs produced in 12. Successful laboratory feeding of hatched larvae not yet accomplished.

Fonsecia celesteae Audy, 1957, snake mite: Domrow (1960), Audy and Nadchatram (unpublished). *Life cycle:* egg 25–27; larva, duration of feed on snake unknown; nymphophane 12; nymph 88 to teleiophane; teleiophane 23; eggs laid by adult in 120. *Hosts:* snake; culicine eggs for postlarval stages. The duration of feed of larvae feeding on coldblooded animals is greatly influenced by the ambient temperature.

Ascoschoengastia (Laurentella) tafia Nadchatram and Domrow, 1964, intranasal chigger of Malaysian forest rat: Audy and Nadchatram (unpublished). *Life cycle:* egg 9–12; larva engorges 1–7 but then remains in nasal cavity for an indefinite period; nymphophane 6–10; teleiophane 6; adult nonparasitic, life span 3–4 months in laboratory, oviposition commencing in 15–18, lasting about 30. *Hosts:* Malaysian forest rats; culicine eggs for postlarval stages.

Walchiella oudemansi (Walch, 1922), a common white chigger of forest rats: Audy and Nadchatram (unpublished). *Life cycle:* egg 20; larva feeds varying times, may pupate in 3; nymphophane 6–7; nymph nonparasitic 22; teleiophane 9; adult nonparasitic, life span about a year; eggs produced in 30. *Hosts:* white mouse; culicine eggs for postlarval stages.

Gahrliepia (G.) fletcheri Gater, 1932: Audy and Nadchatram (unpublished). *Life cycle* (not completed): engorged larva to nymphophane 8; nymphophane 8; nymph nonparasitic 11; teleiophane 14; adults nonparasitic, not fed satisfactorily. *Hosts:* white mouse, rat; *Sinella* eggs for postlarval stages.

Hannemania hegeneri (Hyland, 1956), Frog mite: Hyland (1961). *Life cycle:* egg 6; larva, fed for 14–21 but parasitic phase may last for 6 months or more; nymphophane 3; nymph nonparasitic 13; teleiophane 17; adult nonparasitic, may oviposit in 29. Nymph kept alive without food for one year; adult lived 233 days, with food. *Hosts:* Frogs, *Rana pipiens* and *R. palustris; Sinella* eggs for postlarval stages.

2. *Myobiidae, Psorergatidae*

None of these parasitic cheyletoid mites (group I) has been successfully colonized *in vitro.* Of the myobiid fur mites, the life history of *Myobia musculi* (Schrank) has been studied in greatest detail (Grant, 1942; Wharton, 1954, 1960), by examination of mites or laboratory mice and holding individuals in different stages until the molt. Wharton's studies (1954, 1960) demonstrated ingestion of interstitial fluid by the mites. Murray (1961) similarly worked out the life cycle of *Psorergates ovis* Womersley on sheep.

3. *Demodicidae*

Demodex folliculorum (Simon, 1842), and *D. muscardini* (Hirst, 1919), follicle mites: Nutting and Rauch (1961), Nutting (1961, 1964). These are group I mites not yet successfully colonized, though they have been kept alive on egg white for 51 days. The most promising method of culturing these and other endoparasitic mites is by encapsulating them in millipore filter tubes and implanting these in the skin (or elsewhere). Nutting (1964) reports recovery of *Demodex* from such tubes more than 3 months after implantation. Porosity of the filter was about 7 μ, and the ends of the tubes were plugged with Carter's glue.

C. SARCOPTIFORMES

1. *Sarcoptidae and Psoroptidae*

Most attempts at culture of scabies and mange mites have been unsuccessful (see Heilesen, 1946), the greatest success being by Sweatman (1957, 1958), who cultured *Chorioptes bovis* (Gerlach) for 3–8 months and *Otodectes cynotis* (Hering) for 2 months (Figs. 4 and 5). The mites were presented with epidermal debris and hair in 5 cm-high vials closed with bolting silk and held in sets of 10 in a block of paraffin wax covered with sulfuric acid solution to maintain RH 80%. Such mites can be restrained by a surface capsule. In con-

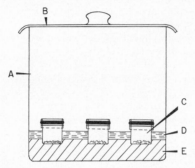

FIG. 4. Rearing chamber and vials for nonburrowing mange mites. (A) Glass jar. (B) Lid with petroleum jelly seal (C) Vial containing skin scrapings and mites. (D) Sulfuric acid solution. (E) Paraffin wax. (After Sweatman, 1957.)

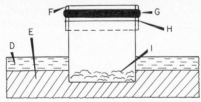

FIG. 5. Enlargement of C in Fig 4. (F) Bolting silk. (G) Head ring to hold bolting silk in place and to weigh down the vial. (H) Rubber band. (I) Skin scrapings and mites. (After Sweatman, 1957.)

trast, *Sarcoptes* and *Notoedres* are burrowing mites forming tunnels in the epidermis. The life cycle of these may nevertheless be studied by staining the skin: Gordon *et al.* (1943) used carbol fuchsin successfully in their studies of *Notoedres muris* (Meghin). Stressing the hosts is likely to be an important method of increasing the multiplication of the mites. A real challenge would be presented by audycoptids which inhabit the sinus hairs of the oral region of primates (Lavoipierre, 1964).

2. Analgesidae, Listrophoridae

No data are available, but skin capsules should provide suitable isolation of small colonies. Stressing the host is likely to be profitable.

REFERENCES

Allred, D. M. (1957). Notes on the life history and bionomics of the wood rat mite, *Brevisterna utahensis* (Acarina). *Trans. Am. Microscop. Soc.* **76**, 72–78.

Allred, D. M., and Marchette, N. J. (1957). Experimental feeding of the mite *Brevisterna utahensis* (Acarina: Haemogamasidae). *J. Parasitol.* **43**, 51–54.

Audy, J. R. (1948). Natural history and scrub typhus. *Malayan Nature J.* **3**, 114–129.

Audy, J. R. (1956). Malayan trombiculid mites. 2. Naked-eye observations on attached chiggers, with a simple checklist of Malayan species and details of preferred hosts. *Bull. Raffles Museum 28*, 86–101.

Audy, J. R. (1958). The localization of disease with special reference to the zoonoses. *Trans. Roy. Soc. Trop. Med. Hyg.* **52**, 308–334.

Audy, J. R., and Lavoipierre, M. M. J. (1964). The laboratory rearing of parasitic acarina. A general review. *Bull. World Health Organ.* **31**, 583–586.

Audy, J. R., and Lavoipierre, M. M. J. Practical methods for Acarina in field and laboratory. *J. Med. Entomol.* To be published.

Audy, J. R., and Nadchatram, M. (1954). A method of rearing individual trombiculid mites in the field. *Nature* **174**, 1021–1022.

Beck, A. J., and Lavoipierre, M. M. J. (1966). The feeding mechanisms of *Chiroptonyssus robustipes*. In press.

Bell, J. F., and Clifford, C. (1964). Effects of limb disability on lousiness in mice. II. Intersex grooming relationships. *Exptl. Parasitol.* **15**, 340–349.

Bell, J. F., Jellison, W. L., and Owen, C. R. (1962). Effects of limb disability on lousiness in mice. I. Preliminary studies. *Exptl. Parasitol.* **12**, 176–183.

Bertram, D. S., Unsworth, K., and Gordon, R. M. (1946). The biology and maintenance of *Lyponyssus bacoti* Hirst, 1913, and an investigation into its role as a vector of *Litomosoides carinii* to cotton rats and white rats, together with some observations on the infection in the white rats. *Ann. Trop. Med. Parasitol.* **40**, 228–254.

Bregetova, N. G. (1956). ["The Gamasid Mites, Gamasoidea"]. 246 pp. Acad. Sci. USSR, Moscow.

Bregetova, N. G., Bilanova-Zachvatkina, E. M., Volgin, V. I., Dubinin, V. B., Zachvatkin, A. A., Zemskaya, A. A., Lange, A. B., Pavlovsky, E. N., Serdukova, G. V., and Schluger, E. G. (1955). ["Acarina of the Rodents of the Fauna of the USSR"], 459 pp. Acad. Sci. USSR, Moscow.

Brown, J. H. (1953). Chicken mite infestation in a hospital. *J. Econ. Entomol.* **46**, 900.

Camin, J. H. (1950). An isolation chamber for the study of individual ectoparasites on their hosts. *J. Parasitol.* **36**, 41–44.

Camin, J. H. (1953). Observations on the life history and sensory behaviour of the snake mite, *Ophionyssus natricis* (Gervais) (Acarina: Macronyssidae. *Chicago Acad. Sci. Publ. No.* **10**, 1–75.

Camin, J. H. (1963). Relations between host-finding behavior and life histories in ectoparasitic acarina. *In* "Advances in Acarology" (J. A. Naegele, ed.), Vol. I, pp. 411–424. Comstock, Ithaca, New York.

Camin, J. H. (1964). Application of behavioral data to problems of laboratory rearing of parasitic acarines. *Proc. 1st Intern. Congr. Acarology, Fort Collins, Colorado, September 2-7, 1963. Acarologia* **6** (Suppl.), 350–356.

Camin, J. H., and Ehrlich, P. R. (1960). A cage for maintaining stock colonies of parasitic mites and their hosts. *J. Parasitol.* **46**, 109–111.

Cloudsley-Thompson, J. L. (1961). "Rhythmic Activity in Animal Physiology and Behavior," 236 pp. Academic Press, New York.

Cross, H. F. (1954). Feeding tests with blood sucking mites on heparinized blood. *J. Econ. Entomol.* **47**, 1154–55.

Cross, H. F., and Wharton, G. W. (1954). Techniques for testing the attachment and feeding rates of mites on living hosts. *J. Econ. Entomol.* **47**, 1153–1154.

Cross, H. F., and Wharton, G. W. (1964). A comparison of the number of tropical rat mites and tropical fowl mites that fed under varying conditions of humidity. *J. Econ. Entomol.* **57**, 443–445.

Domrow, R. (1960). Malaysian parasites. XLI. Nymphs of *Vercammenia* and *Fonsecia* (Acarina, Trombiculidae). *Studies Inst. Med. Res., Malaya* **29**, 172–176.

Downing, W. (1936). The life-history of *Psoroptes communis* var. *ovis* with particular reference to latent or suppressed scab. *J. Comp. Pathol. Therap.* **49**, 163–180; 183–209.

Fuller, H. S. (1954). Studies of rickettsial pox. III. Life cycle of the mite vector *Allodermanyssus sanguineus*. *Am. J. Hyg.* **59**, 236–239.

Furman, D. P. (1959). Feeding habits of symbiotic mesostigmatid mites of mammals in relation to pathogen-vector potentials. *Am. J. Trop. Med. Hyg.* **8**, 5–12.

George, J. E. (1964). The circadian rhythm of "drop-off" of engorged *Haemaphysalis leporispalustris* from rabbits. *Proc. 1st Intern. Congr. Acarology, Fort Collins, Colorado, September 2-7, 1963. Acarologia* **6** (Suppl.), 343–349.

Gordon, R. M., Unsworth, K., and Seaton, D. R. (1943). The development and transmission of scabies as studied in rodent infections. *Ann. Trop. Med. Parasitol.* **37**, 174–194.

Gorirossi, F. E. (1950). The mouthparts of the adult female tropical rat mite, *Bdellonyssus bacoti* (Hirst, 1913) Fonseca, 1941 [= *Liponissus bacoti* (Hirst)] with observations on the feeding mechanism. *J. Parasitol.* **36**, 301–318.

Grant, C. D. (1942). Observations on *Myobia musculi* (Schrank) (Arachnida: Acarina: Cheyletidae). *Microentomology* **7**, 64–76.

Gudden, B. (1871). Über eine Invasion von *Leptus autumnalis*. *Arch. Pathol. Anat. Physiol.* **52**, 255–259.

Harker, J. E. (1955). Control of diurnal rhythms of activity in *Periplaneta americana*. *Nature* **175**, 733.

Harker, J. E. (1961). Diurnal rhythms. *Ann. Rev. Entomol.* **6**, 131–146.

Harker, J. E. (1964). "The Physiology of Diurnal Rhythms." Cambridge Univ. Press, London and New York.

Harrison, J. L. (1957). Malaysian parasites. XXX. Additional feeding times of trombiculid larvae. *Studies Inst. Med. Res., Malaya* **28**, 383–393.

Heilesen, B. (1946). Studies on *Acarus scabei* and scabies. *Acta Dermato-Venereol.* **26** (Suppl.), 14.

Hughes, T. E. (1949). The functional morphology of the mouthparts of *Lyponyssus bacoti*. *Ann. Trop. Med. Parasitol.* **43**, 349–360.

Hyland, K. E., Jr. (1951). Observations on the chigger mite *Trombicula* (*Eutrombicula splendens* Ewing (Acarina: Trombiculidae). *Ann. Entomol. Soc. Am.* **44**, 297–301.

Hyland, K. E. (1961). Parasitic phase of chigger mite, *Hannemania hegeneri*, on experimentally infested amphibians. *Exptl. Parasitol.* 11, 212–225.

Irwin, I. (1937). Demodectic mange in dogs. *Vet. Med.* 32, 318–319.

Ito, T., Obata, Y., and Oono, M. (1957). Eggs of dragon fly as new food for trombiculid mites. *Acta Med. Biol.* 5, 169–199.

Jellison, W. L., and Philip, C. B. (1933). Techniques for routine and experimental feeding of certain Ixodid ticks on guinea pigs and rabbits. *Public Health Repts.* 48, 1081–1082.

Jenkins, D. W. (1947). The ecology and laboratory rearing of chiggers affecting man in the United States (Acarina, Trombiculidae). *Abstr. Doctoral Dissertations, Ohio State Univ. Press* 56, 75–80.

Jenkins, D. W. (1948). Trombiculid mites affecting man. I. Bionomics with reference to epidemiology in the United States. *Am. J. Hyg.* 48, 22–35.

Jones, B. M. (1951). The growth of the harvest mite, *Trombicula autumnalis* Shaw. *Parasitology* 41, 229–248.

Kohls, G. M. (1937). Tick rearing methods with special reference to the Rocky Mountain wood tick, *Dermacentor andersoni* Stiles. Family Ixodidae. *In* "Culture Methods for Invertebrate Animals" (J. G. Needham *et al.*, eds.), pp. 246–257. Comstock, New York. Reprinted 1959, Dover Publications, Inc., New York.

Lavoipierre, M. M. J. (1964). A new family of acarines belonging to the suborder Sarcoptiformes parasitic in the hair follicles of primates. *Ann. Natal Museum* 16, 191–208.

Lees, A. D. (1948). The sensory physiology of the sheep tick *Ixodes ricinus* L. *J. Exptl. Biol.* 25, 145–207.

Macdonald, E. M., and Scott, J. A. (1952). Methods for feeding tropical rat mites on blood and other fluids through a membrane. *Exptl. Parasitol.* 1, 283–290.

Mead-Briggs, A. R. (1964). The reproductive biology of the rabbit flea *Spilopsyllus cuniculi* (Dale) and dependence of this species upon breeding of its host. *J. Exptl. Biol.* 41, 371–402.

Michener, C. D. (1946). Observations on the habits and life history of a chigger mite, *Eutrombicula batatas* (Acarina: Trombiculinae). *Ann. Entomol. Soc. Am.* 39, 101–118.

Murray, M. D. (1961). The life cycle of *Psorergates ovis* Womersley, the itch mite of sheep. *Australian J. Agr. Res.* 12, 965–973.

Nadchatram, M., Audy, J. R., and Cockings, K. L. To be published.

Needham, J. G., Galtsoff, P. S., Lutz, F. E., and Welch, P. S., eds. (1937). "Culture Methods for Invertebrate Animals." Comstock, New York. Reprinted 1959, Dover Publications, Inc., New York.

Nichols, E., Rindge, M. E., and Russell, G. G. (1953). The relationship of the habits of the house mouse and the mouse mite (*Allodermanyssus sanguineus*) to the spread of rickettsialpox. *Ann. Internal Med.* 39, 92–102.

Nutting, W. B. (1961). *Demodex aurati* sp. nov. and *Demodex criceti*, ectoparasites of the golden hamster (*Mesocricetus auratus*). *Parasitology* 51, 515–522.

Nutting, W. B. (1964). Demodicidae: status and prognosis. *Proc. 1st Intern. Congr. Acarology, Fort Collins, Colorado, September 2–7, 1963. Acarologia* 6 (Suppl.), 280.

Nutting, W. B., and Rauch, H. (1961). The effect of biotin deficiency in *Mesocricetus auratus* on parasites of the genus *Demodex*. *J. Parasitol.* 4–7 319–322.

Ohmori, H. (1935). [On the life history of *Liponyssus nagayoi* Yamada.] *Tokyo Iji Shinshi* 2960, 3250.

Olson, T. A., and Dahms, R. G. (1946). Observations on the tropical rat mite *Liponyssus bacoti* as an ectoparasite of laboratory animals and suggestions for its control. *J. Parasitol.* **32,** 56–60.

Owen, B. L. (1956). Life history of the spiny rat mite under artificial conditions. *J. Econ. Entomol.* **49,** 702–703.

Radinovsky, S., and Krantz, G. W. (1961). The biology and ecology of granary mites of the Pacific Northwest. II. Techniques for laboratory observation and rearing. *Ann. Entomol. Soc. Am.* **54,** 512–518.

Radovsky, F. J. (1960). Biological studies on *Haemogamasus liponyssoides* (Ewing) (Acarina: Haemogamasidae). *J. Parasitol.* **46,** 410–417.

Radovsky, F. J. (1964). "The Macronyssidae and Laelapidae (Acarina: Mesostigmata) Parasitic on Bats," Vols. I and II. (Unpublished Ph.D. thesis, Univ. Calif., Berkeley.)

Radovsky, F. J. The Macronyssidae and Laelapidae (Acarina: Mesostigmata) parasitic on bats. *Univ. Calif. (Berkeley) Publ. Entomol.* In press.

Rudnick, A. (1960). A revision of the mites of the family Spinturnicidae (Acarina). *Univ. Calif. (Berkeley) Publ. Entomol.* **17,** 157–284.

Sasa, M. (1956). "Tsutsugamushi and Tsutsugamushi Disease," 497 pp. Igakushoin, Tokyo.

Sasa, M. (1961). Biology of chiggers. *Ann. Rev. Entomol.* **6,** 221–244.

Sasa, M., and Miura, A. (1953). Studies on the life-history of tsutsugamushi (trombiculid mites) of Japan in the laboratory (Studies on Tsutsugamushi, Part 34). *Japan J. Exptl. Med.* **23,** 171–185.

Scott, J. A., Allen, J., Stembridge, V. A., and Sisley, N. M. (1947). A method for providing a constant supply of tropical rat mites, *Liponyssus bacoti*, infected with the cotton-rat filaria, *Litomosoides carinii. J. Parasitol.* **33,** 138–141.

Sikes, R. K., and Chamberlain, R. W. (1954). Laboratory observations on three species of bird mites. *J. Parasitol.* **40,** 691–697.

Skaliy, P., and Hayes, W. J. (1949). The biology of *Liponyssus bacoti* (Hirst, 1913) (Acarina, Liponyssidae). *Am. J. Trop. Med.* **29,** 759–772.

Solomon, M. E., and Cunnington, A. M. (1964). Rearing acarid mites. *Proc. 1st Intern. Congr. Acarology, Fort Collins, Colorado, September 2–7, 1963. Acarologia* **6** (Suppl.), 399.

Suvorova, L. G., and Sidorov, V. E. (1962). [A method of rearing gamasid-mites.] *Zool. Zhur.* **41,** 1421–1422.

Sweatman, G. K. (1957). Life history, non-specificity, and revision of the genus *Chorioptes,* a parasitic mite of herbivores. *Can. J. Zool.* **35,** 641–689.

Sweatman, G. K. (1958). Biology of *Otodectes cynotis,* the ear canker mite of carnivores. *Can. J. Zool.* **36,** 849–862.

Tarshis, I. B. (1958a). A preliminary study on feeding *Ornithodorus savignyi* (Audouin) on human blood through animal-derived membranes. (Acarina: Argasidae). *Ann. Entomol. Soc. Am.* **51,** 294–299.

Tarshis, I. B. (1958b). Feeding techniques for blood-sucking arthropods. *Proc. 10th Intern. Congr. Entomol., Montreal, Aug. 17–25, 1956* **3,** 767–784.

von Uexküll, J. (1957). A stroll through the worlds of animals and men, Part I. *In* "Instinctive Behavior. The Development of a Modern Concept." (C. H. Schiller, ed.), pp. 5–80. Intern. Univ. Press, New York.

Wharton, G. W. (1954). Life cycle and feeding habits of *Myobia musculi. J. Parasitol.* **40** (Sect. 2), 29.

Wharton, G. W. (1960). Host-parasite relationships between *Myobia musculi* (Schrank,

1781) and *Mus musculus* Linnaeus, 1758. *In* "Homenaje al Doctor Eduardo Caballero y Caballero," pp. 571–575. Mexico, D. F.

Wharton, G. W., and Kanungo, K. (1962). Some effects of temperature and relative humidity on water-balance in females of the spiny rat mite, *Echinolaelaps echidninus* (Acarina: Laelaptidae). *Ann. Entomol. Soc. Am.* **55**, 483–492.

Wisseman, C. L., Jr., and Sulkin, S. E. (1947). Observations on the laboratory care, life cycle, and hosts of the chicken mite, *Dermanyssus gallinae. Am. J. Trop. Med.* **27**, 463–469.

Wolf, W. (Conference Editor) (1962). Rhythmic functions in the living system. *Ann. N. Y. Acad. Sci.* **98**, 753–1326.

Woodring, J. (1963). The nutrition and biology of saprophytic sarcoptiformes. *In* "Advances in Acarology" (J. A. Naegele, ed.), Vol. I, pp. 89–111. Comstock, Ithaca, New York.

Chapter 4

Ticks

J. D. GREGSON

Research Station,
Canada Department of Agriculture,
Kamloops, British Columbia, Canada

I. INTRODUCTION

The importance of ticks to students and workers in the fields of natural history, public health, and veterinary medicine has long been realized (Arthur, 1961). As Philip (1963) notes, the ticks, along with mites, have through the course of time become the most versatile vectors of animal disease agents. They rank second only to mosquitoes in their present importance as transmitters of human disease, their role in spreading protozoan and rickettsial infections to livestock is world-wide, and North American species are now being shown to be involved in Eurasian-like arbovirus reservoirs in wildlife. Ticks also cause several forms of toxicosis in man and animals (Neitz, 1962).

As a result of efforts to control tick-borne diseases, or to reduce their hazard to man and animals, several projects involving the mass culture of the vectors have been undertaken. Chief of these have been the rearing of *Dermacentor andersoni* Stiles (Kohls, 1937) and *Amblyomma cajennense* (Fabricius) (Travassos and Vallejo-Freire, 1944–1945) for the production of vaccines against rickettsial diseases, and of *Boophilus microplus* (Canestrini) (Hitchcock, 1955a,b) for life history and toxicological studies.

These large-scale operations have enabled routine procedures to be established for the raising of immense numbers of the tick species concerned. However, the methods are specific in design and are not entirely adaptable for smaller cultures of other species. Indeed, the life histories of different species of ticks contain so many peculiarities that, although the basic design is similar, rearing procedures must usually be fitted to the species under study. These differences, together with the many subtleties that appear when the parasite meets the host, render tick rearing a challenging and interesting endeavor. It was well reviewed by Enigk and Grittner in 1953. Many of the procedures and conditions that are common to both tick and mite rearing are also listed by Audy and Lavoipierre (1966).

II. REARING ROOM

The degree to which labor and materials are invested in tick rearing will depend on the purpose of the project. Large-scale operations involving disease studies will demand costly facilities. At the other extreme, Schuhardt (1940) maintained a colony of *Ornithodoros turicata* Dugès in a "ticktorium" in his office for several years.

In general, the longevity of ticks necessitates scrupulous care in procedures so that escapes and stray infections can be kept at a minimum. Where disease is involved, rearing rooms should be of concrete and plaster, crevices should be absent, and tanglefoot barriers provided around all openings. Kohls (1937) recommends a daily flushing with near boiling water under pressure and the provision of changing rooms, lockers, mirrors, and "deticking" facilities for workers.

Bailey (1960) describes a suitable room for small-scale rearings of ticks. He cites its main requirements as being free from drafts, sunshine, and extremes of temperature (range of 17°–22°C), and stresses the importance of avoiding the use of any insecticides or fly sprays in it. The room should be provided with a white-topped table for examination of cages, an incubator for storage of rearing containers, and facilities for holding cages of infested animals. A nearby steam chest and an incinerator are desirable so that stray ticks on cages, animal cadavers, and discarded food can be destroyed.

III. SOURCE OF TICK MATERIAL

The object of the pursuit will determine the tick species to be used. If the selection of the material is obligatory and little is known about it, considerable experimentation must precede the establishment of satisfactory rearing methods. If a free choice is possible, then much can be gained from the experience of others. Of the two main groups of ticks, the argasids (soft ticks) are the easier to colonize because of their shorter and less complex life cycle. *Argas* species feed mainly on birds and *Ornithodoros* on mammals. The ixodids, or hard ticks, as a rule require longer blood meals and as a result demand more care during feeding. If diseases are incorporated in the study, freshly collected stock from infected hosts may be desired; otherwise, for the safety and convenience of the operator, disease-free specimens are preferable and should be so proved or verified at source.

The collection of ticks in nature is described by Pavlovsky (1930) and Hooker *et al.* (1912). Infested hosts serve as one source; live hosts, if small, may be kept in a cage in a bag or over water until the engorging ticks fall off. Dead hosts should be bagged immediately after death and later searched for fallen and attached specimens. Ticks with long mouthparts should never be pulled from such hosts; preferably they should be removed with a portion of skin and allowed to detach at will. Dampness aids disintegration of the skin. If they are partially fed they may be induced to attach to a new host, particularly if they are adpressed to shaved skin by a padded capsule.

Collections of tick species that quest off the ground, such as certain species and stages of *Dermacentor* and *Ixodes*, can be made by dragging a square yard of flannel on a stick over infested vegetation (Kohls, 1937). The ticks are dropped into vials and should be kept on ice in a thermos to prevent undue activity before being stored.

Other sources of ticks in nature include the nests and burrows of hosts.

IV. SELECTION OF HOSTS

The selection and care of hosts forms an integral part of a tick-rearing program. Wherever possible animals should be chosen which are both favorable to the tick species being cultured and convenient for maintaining, handling, and infesting. They should be housed suitably and cleaned and fed regularly (Harvey, 1947).

Host specificity is common among tick species. Enigk and Grittner (1953) mention several examples of stages and species of ticks which restrict their feeding to certain birds and mammals. Others will feed, but will not mature if the host is of the wrong species. *Hyalomma rufipes* Koch females will engorge on dogs and rabbits but give rise to viable larvae only if fed on ruminants. *Boophilus calcaratus* (Birula) larvae will feed on dogs, but the nymphs and adults do poorly; on rabbits, the larvae of the following generation become debilitated. Similarly, the early instars of *Ornithodoros lahorensis* Neumann, a parasite of ruminants, die as they mature on rabbits. Anthony (1964) states that *Dermacentor* (=*Otocentor*) *nitens* Neumann, normally a one-host tick of Equidae, can be reared on rabbits provided the freshly molted adults are transferred to new animals, in which case about 10% of the females complete development and lay viable eggs. The possibility that ticks can be adapted to new hosts is offered by Delpy and Gouchey (1939), who reared *Hyalomma dromedarii* Koch on rabbits and calves. Other species of ticks are less host-specific; *Argas reflexus* (Fabricius), normally a bird tick, will develop when fed on rodents and even attack humans. *Ornithodoros parkeri* Cooley will likewise feed on both mammalian and avian hosts.

Ticks may be induced to feed on an unfavorable host by allowing them to commence on a normal host. Feldman-Muhsam (1964) observed that adult *Rhipicephalus* which were transferred from a host in nature attached readily to laboratory animals on which they were, otherwise, reluctant to feed.

The grooming habits of the host are important. White mice and rats rid themselves of ticks more readily than do wild *Microtus* spp. (Hadani *et al.*, 1961; Smith *et al.*, 1946).

While continued use of the same species of host contributes to a uniformity of maintenance and infesting procedures, attention must be paid to the formation of immunity in individuals from repeated infestations or from age. Hays (1964), on the other hand, finds that *Amblyomma americanum* (L.) and *Rhipicephalus sanguineus* (Latreille) do better if the host species is changed every five to six generations. He alternates rabbits with dogs.

V. MAINTENANCE OF PARASITIC STAGES

All ticks feed on blood at various times in their lives. As a rule a meal is required after egg hatching and after each subsequent molt.

However, the larvae of *Ornithodoros braziliensis* Aragão, the first nymphs of *Ornithodoros coriaceus* Koch and the adults of *Otobius megnini* (Dugès) are among certain exceptions. The majority of ticks drop from their hosts after feeding and so have to seek the same, or new ones, for the next meal. Some, such as *Dermacentor albipictus* (Packard), *Boophilus* spp., and *Ornithodoros lahorensis*, remain on the same animals throughout their feedings.

It is thus apparent that infesting procedures will occupy the major portion of any tick-rearing labors. It need hardly be said that a great many devices and methods have evolved from this phase of the work. The main objectives are to encourage ticks to feed on the chosen hosts, to afford them maximum protection from the host, and to cause the host a minimum of discomfort during the process. The preferred site, if any, of the tick on the host is worth noting. Ixodid larvae which prefer avian hosts, such as *Ixodes signatus* Birula, *Haemaphysalis chordeilis* (Packard), and *Ixodes auritulus* Neumann, are best fed on the head; argasids do better under the wings. *Haemaphysalis leporis-palustris* (Packard) usually feeds on the ears of rabbits; *O. megnini*, in the ears of ungulates.

A. INFESTING APPLIANCES

The simplest infesting procedure, and the most natural, is to place the host with the ticks, or to sprinkle the ticks on the host. However, this method is likely to lead to some loss of parasites from scratching, shaking, biting or pecking. This can be prevented by temporarily anesthetizing the animal with sodium nembutal (about 0.5 ml/lb body wt) if the ticks are fast-feeding, or by restraining its movements by means of close-fitting cages, hobbles, or tethers for longer periods. The yield of ticks from cattle may be increased by preventing the animals from licking themselves (Snowball, 1956). Glass "slippers," made from cut-down vials and cemented over the feet of rodents with plaster of paris, have also been used by the author to protect ixodid ticks from injury. Loomis (1961) describes a useful rack for the temporary immobilization of rabbits. It consists of a V-shaped trough, with sides 2 feet long by 7 inches wide set at an angle of 80°. Transverse boards fit into slots to keep the legs extended and ticks are fed under a Petri dish held against the belly by a leather strap.

Alternatively, the ticks may be shielded by collars, garments, bags or capsules (Hooker *et al.*, 1912). Gregson (1956) describes "Elizabethan" collars to protect *D. andersoni* adults on mice. A 2½-inch diameter disc is cut from a thin rubber glove and reinforced at the center with a bicycle tire patch ¾ inch wide. A ⅜-inch diameter hole is then cut out of the center of the disc. The collar is placed over the head of the mouse by slipping it off a 1-inch vial. Larger collars may be used for bigger rodents. Garments, in the form of leather "waistcoats" for dogs, or breeches, bonnets, and hoods also serve to protect either ticks or their containers.

Rabbits' ears furnish convenient infesting areas, particularly if they are enclosed in cloth bags which tie around the bases. The bags must be protected from the animal's scratching by hobbling its hind legs or, as Bailey (1960) recommends, placing around its neck a collar of ¼-inch leather, which is taped from the base under the forelegs and over the back of the rabbit, and from the sides around the belly. Travassos and Vallejo-Freire (1944–1945) enclose the bags in 15-cm leather cylinders, fastened by straps around the rabbits' necks. Enigk and Grittner (1953) fasten rabbit ear bags with adhesive, having first degreased the ear base with ether. They describe similar methods for horses and cattle; also a sleeve which may be taped at each end on the clipped portion of the tail and be protected from soiling by an outer bag or by tying the end of the tail to the belly band. Woke (1951) describes a conical celluloid ear cage, aerated by cloth at the top, with front screen inserts; Harris (1959) used a flanged cylinder rolled from plastic and covered with cloth at the top.

A great variety of infesting capsules have been used. The most familiar is that described by Kohls (1937) (Fig. 1a). It consists of a tin capsule made from the threaded end ring and top of a cardboard mailing-tube. The base of the ring may be soldered to a collar, and this is secured to the clipped body of the host by a girdle of adhesive tape. Screen inserted in the lid prevents condensation during use. If sheep are used, dome-shaped capsules of 20 gauge brass screen, dipped in solder and rimmed with adhesive tape for reinforcement, may be glued or sewn onto the hide (Gregson, 1956) (Fig. 1b). As Sapre (1943) notes, a cloth placed over the ticks under the capsule will aid attachment. This is particularly true if reattachment is desired of partially fed ticks. Capsules should be inspected daily so that edema, dermatitis, and, more particularly, capsule damage can be avoided. The site of the capsule on sheep should be washed with warm water and soap, then rinsed, to remove grease. Sheep should be kept in a cool place to reduce subsequent sweating. Their enclosure should be free of projections against which they may rub.

Capsules for use on large animals are described by Sapre (1943). These are of either metal or wood rings, 2–3 inches in diameter, ¼ inch deep, with a ¼-inch rim or wall. Screen or holes provide aeration. Johnson (1964) uses a similar but smaller ring-type container and

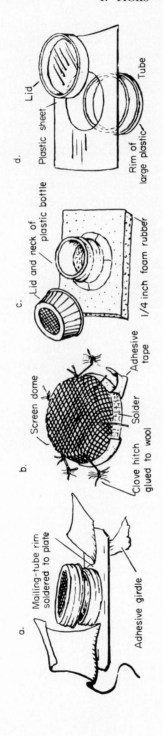

FIG. 1. Types of capsules used for infesting ticks. (a) Mailing-tube type used by Kohls (1937); (b) screen-dome type, suitable for placing on sheep (Gregson, 1956); (c) polyethylene type, used by Kaiser (1964); (d) plastic type, used by Johnson (1964)

fashions it from rings cut from two close-fitting plastic tubes (Fig. 1d).
A collar of plastic sheeting fits against the lower glued rim and serves
for taping the appliance to the host; the loose-fitting lid is covered
with a disc of plastic or screen. For the observed feeding of *Ornithodoros* Streissle (1961) devised a capsule of inner and outer rings between which a cloth bottom was clamped, and at the top of which a
Plexiglas cap was screwed. The container was strapped to chicks
with an elastic belt.

Various types of flanged capsules have been devised from modern containers. Anthony (1964) makes capsules from the tops and
shoulders of wide-mouth screw-top polyethylene centrifuge bottles
and attaches them to the sides of rabbits and calves with adhesive
tape. Kaiser (1964) tapes the capsules over pads of polyurethane
foam (Fig. 1c). Hays (1964) opens the bottom of a "salve tin" to form
a star-shaped flange which he first covers with tape to protect the host,
then glues and tapes against the animal. When infesting wild musk-
rats with *Ixodes banksi* Bishopp he bound the shaved belly with a
2-inch-wide strip of adhesive tape in which there was a 1-inch
aperture, then confined the ticks within the hole by taping a cloth
cover down on all edges.

Řeháček (1957) infested suckling mice by means of "small hats"
made of gauze-capped Pertinax tubing. The capsules, which were
cemented on with 4% collodion, were well suited for disease study
and collection of tick feces.

Rau (1963, 1965) describes a similar method, attaching bottomless
"pill boxes" to a clipped area on rabbits' rumps and ears by gluing the
surrounding hair to them with Durofix. Cloth-covered lids confined
the ticks. Varma (1964) used cloth feeding sleeves and duraluminum
capsules. Stone (1962) fastened bottomless cardboard ointment boxes
to the clipped skin of cattle with a hot glue made from a 4:1 mixture
of resin and beeswax. Sacktor *et al.* (1948) cemented pillboxes to
discs of chamois cloth, which were in turn cemented to rabbits.
Kaiser (1964) recommends an adhesive paste, developed by Neitz,
made up of gelatine (20 gm), glycerine (25 ml), zinc oxide (15 gm),
which is dissolved in this order in 40 ml of hot water.

Racks and cages for infested rabbits are illustrated by Kohls (1937).
The cages are constructed of ¼-inch wire mesh, are 10 × 10 × 14
inches in size, and are supported in 15 × 17 × 18-inch frames made of
¼-inch welded rods (Fig. 2). It is important that the cages contain no
crevices which will harbor fallen and engorged ticks and that the outer
frames bear no projections which will tear the surrounding tick-
collecting bags.

Small wild rodents (*Neotoma, Citellus, Marmota,* etc.) are best infested in a cylinder of "expanded metal," closed at either end with a removable cap (Fig. 2). The size of the cage will depend on the species of host. Such a cage may be suspended in the above-type frame and recovery bag. Cylinders of 15 × 15-mm mesh netting, as used by Hadani *et al.* (1961) for *Microtus,* have also been used by

FIG. 2. Cage and cylinders used at the Kamloops laboratory for infesting larvae, nymphs, and adults of *D. andersoni* on rabbits and marmots.

the author for the feeding of *Ixodes kingi* Bishopp on white mice. An outer sleeve of copper wire screening is advisable if the assembly is wrapped in cloth (Smith *et al.,* 1946). Apple or carrot provides sufficient food and water for the host during infestation.

Allred and Roscoe (1956) reared *Dermacentor parumapertus* Neumann larvae and nymphs on kangaroo rats over sand in mesh-covered jars, but obtained better attachment by first confining the host in a ¼-inch mesh sleeve and placing this and the ticks in a gauze-capped mailing tube.

In all cases where there is danger of ticks escaping during infesting procedures, or where collecting is so facilitated, the hosts may be placed in wire cages over a tray of water. The engorged ticks will sink as they fall off. Enigk and Grittner (1953) state that the larvae of *Dermacentor, Ixodes,* and *Haemaphysalis* will live under water for 3 days; the adults for 3 weeks. They should be dried for a day on blotting paper before being stored. Although the adults of some argasids can exist under water for 1 week, the larvae drown after 2 hours or so and should be collected in a bag when dropping com-

mences. Wilkinson's (1964) chalk barrier might be a useful alternative for such tick isolations.

The nymphs and adults of argasids usually feed for only ½ to 2
hours and can be fed on a clipped guinea pig or bird tied onto a board
or anesthetized in a smooth-walled enamel dish. However, the larvae
frequently feed for several days and must be infested accordingly.
It has been noted that while the early stages of most ticks are relatively robust, those of *Ornithodoros moubata* (Murray) and *O. lahorensis* are particularly easy to crush.

One-host ticks of large animals must be applied as larvae. During
mass rearing the hosts are usually kept on wooden racks on a moated
concrete floor (Hitchcock, 1955a). When the engorged females fall
they are collected by washing and flotation.

B. NUMBER OF TICKS PER HOST

The number of ticks that are placed on a host will depend on the
magnitude of the rearing, the species and stage of the tick, and the
tolerance of the host. Hadani *et al.* (1961) reared up to 5000 larvae or
100 nymphs of *Rhipicephalus secundus* Feldman-Muhsam on an
average-sized *Microtus;* Smith *et al.* (1946), up to 2644 larvae of
Dermacentor variabilis (Say). Kohls (1937) fed up to 30,000 larvae,
1200 nymphs, or 40 pairs of adults of *D. andersoni* per rabbit and
then sacrificed the animals. Travassos and Vallejo-Freire (1944–1945)
placed 14,000 larvae (2 egg masses) of *O. cajennense* in each ear of
each rabbit, and 250 and 75–100 adults, respectively, on rabbits and
guinea pigs. Enigk and Grittner (1953) suggest 1000 larvae and 400
nymphs of three-host ticks and 200 larvae of two-host species per
rabbit and 12 pairs of adults of *Amblyomma*, 16 of *Dermacentor,* or 30
of *Rhipicephalus* per dog. Large animals will tolerate vast numbers
of one-host ticks. Wharton (1964) states that cattle are infested with
20–100 thousand larvae (from 1–5 gm of eggs) of *B. microplus.* Rare
species on uncommon hosts will be used sparingly, but, considering
the possibilities of an immunity build-up, it is better to aim at a
large and healthy initial infestation than to reinfest and encounter
resistance.

As a rule, equal numbers of males and females are applied if
fertilized females are required for subsequent egg laying, particularly in the case of those which mate during feeding.

A few species, noteably *Haemaphysalis bispinosa* Neumann
(Bremner, 1959) and *Amblyomma rotundatum* Koch (Nuttall *et al.*,
1926) reproduce by parthenogenesis.

C. Feeding Periods of Ticks

The feeding period of female ticks of some species is regularly influenced by their mating habits. Females of *D. andersoni* need to feed for 1 day, the males for 5 days, before mating takes place. In the absence of mating, the females remain attached for another week or more (Gregson, 1947). Srivastava and Varma (1964) note the same for *R. sanguineus*. *Ixodes dentatus* Neumann females mate successfully only after having fed for 4 days; they may remain waiting for males for as long as 40 days (Smith, 1945).

The handling of the active, immature instars of ticks requires skill and practice; it is preferable to apportion the preceding egg or fed stages before they hatch or molt (Allred and Roscoe, 1956; Srivastava and Varma, 1964). Sacktor *et al.* (1948) immobilize the ticks with CO_2. A certain period of hardening-off is required after emergence, during which time small pellets of waste are excreted. Enigk and Grittner (1953) state that larvae and nymphs of *Dermacentor marginatus* (Sulz.) and *Dermacentor pictus* (Herm.) mature quickly and are ready to feed 7–14 days after hatching; if kept at 26°C, batches should be fed within 3 to 5 weeks from first emergence. Larvae of *A. reflexus*, *Ornithodoros rostratus* Aragão, and *O. coriaceus* will feed 6 days after hatching.

The feeding periods of larvae of argasid ticks vary greatly. Enigk and Grittner (1953) cite 15 min for *Ornithodoros hermsi* Wheeler, Herms and Meyer, 20 min–3 hr for *Ornithodoros venezuelensis* (=*rudis* (Karsch)), 12–48 hr for *O. rostratus*, 4 days for *Ornithodoros talaje* (Guérin-Méneville), 5–10 days for *Argas persicus* (Oken) and *A. reflexus*, and 6–8 days for *Ornithodoros delanoei* Roubaud and Colas-Belcour and *O. coriaceus*. Johnson (1964) found that larvae of *Ornithodoros kelleyi* Cooley and Kohls take as long as 2 months to feed on bats.

The number of nymphal stages, and the number of feedings of each, also vary within species. Smith (1944) noted that *O. coriaceus* may have from 3 to 7 nymphs, that those of the first stage ordinarily did not feed; but a few in each of the other stages fed several times, and about one third refused to feed at any time and died before molting. Davis and Walker (1940) and Enigk and Grittner (1953) remark that *O. hermsi* and *O. rostratus* may also feed several times during one instar. The ambient temperature during tick infestation may be of importance. Saito (1960), observed that *Haemaphysalis flava* Neumann refused to attach if it was 30°C, but behaved well if the host was subjected to 15°C surroundings. The room temperature also affected the length of the larval engorging periods, but apparently only if they were fed on the ears (Saito, 1962).

Adults of ticks from temperate zones present a problem in that often a natural annual rhythm must be broken before they will engorge. Smith and Cole (1941) observed that lengthening artificial photoperiods aided the feeding of larval and nymphal *D. variabilis*, but had no apparent effect on the adults. Lancaster (1955) attributes decreasing day length as the factor responsible for the cessation of nymphal and adult activity in *A. americanum*. Belozerov (1964) concludes that the diapause of both unfed and fed *D. marginatus* females is broken only after 4 months of cold treatment (5°C).

Loew (1964) surmises that the metamorphosis of *Ixodes ricinus* (L.) is dependent on exogenous (environmental) factors and shows that reared nymphs need a photoperiod of 14-hr light (of 5 lux) to develop.

The falling-off of engorged ticks is primarily induced by their attainment of repletion. However, it is also affected by light, and this must be considered during the transfer of infested animals from their cages. Balashov (1954) has noted that the dropping of *Ixodes persulcatus* Schulze females from cattle occurs more readily when the animals turned out to pasture, thereby subjecting the ticks to new conditions of light, temperature, and humidity. Hitchcock (1955a) observed a similar peak in the dropping of *Boophilus microplus;* Nuttall *et al.* (1911) also, in *B. decoloratus* (Koch). Enigk and Grittner (1953) state that *A. reflexus* larvae fall off mostly at night. Nymphs of *I. dentatus* fall more in the daytime, the larvae more at night (Smith, 1945). Kitaoka (1962) suggests that a diurnal rhythm controls feeding and predisposes dropping. George (1964) demonstrated that a circadian rhythm, influenced by a 24-hour light cycle, exists for *H. leporispalustris*.

D. HOST INJURY AND REACTIONS

It is outside the scope of this review to touch on diseases that may be contracted by hosts through tick-transmitted organisms. However, noninfected ticks can readily induce conditions that are detrimental to the quantity and quality of reared specimens. The protracted sucking periods of the ixodid ticks are particularly conducive to a variety of host skin responses varying from edema to hemorrhage, necrosis, pyemia, and sepsis. According to Enigk and Grittner (1953), when purulence occurs at sites of attachment the blood supply becomes walled off and the ticks obtain only pus. Such ticks perish during diapause after molting. Larvae and nymphs of *Hyalomma detritum*

Schulze are stated to fall in this category and may cause the deaths of dog and rabbit hosts through sepsis. Riek (1962) observed both acquired and innate resistances in cattle to *B. microplus.* Feldman-Muhsam (1964) is of the opinion that during multiple feedings on a host, the first infestation sensitizes the animal, enabling the second infestation of ticks to feed better, and that subsequently the host becomes immunized. Brumpt and Chabaud (1947) found that "almost absolute immunity" was induced in guinea pigs by larvae of *R. sanguineus.* Gregson (1942a) has observed a similar reaction in fitches from infestations of *Ixodes texanus* Banks larvae. Enigk and Grittner (1953) cite an instance of immunity in sheep which deferred engorgement of *Amblyomma hebraeum* Koch adults for over 4 months and refer to the production of cross-immunities within, but not between, genera of ticks. Trager (1939) observed that single infestations of guinea pigs with *D. variabilis* induced immunity within 2 weeks that lasted 3 months, and that a cross-immunity could develop from infestations of *Dermacentor* and *Haemaphysalis* larvae. It has been the author's experience that it is unwise to rely on individual sheep or rabbits for satisfactory repeated infestation of *D. andersoni* adults, nymphs, and larvae, During mass feedings of ticks workers should be prepared to observe this precaution.

Tick toxins liberated into the host's blood stream during feeding cause a variety of toxicoses, among which are sweating sickness and tick paralysis (Neitz, 1962). In North America, dogs, sheep, guinea pigs, and marmots may be killed while feeding female *D. andersoni* on them (Gregson, 1962). Enigk and Grittner (1953) refer to guinea pigs dying within a few hours of the feeding of *O. moubata* adults; of horse and cattle fatalities by *O. megnini* and of sheep by *O. lahorensis.* Gregson (1942b) notes that guinea pigs may be killed by the larvae and nymphs of *Ixodes californicus* (= *pacificus* Cooley and Kohls). Saito (1962) similarly observes that individual mice will not tolerate more than 700 larvae or 10 nymphs of *Ixodes japonensis* Neumann or *I. persulcatus.* Excessive numbers of *D. andersoni* nymphs on rabbits may also cause death by exsanguination, as observed by Jellison and Kohls (1938). When host mortality thus interferes with the production of engorged ticks, the size of the infestations must be decreased.

VI. MAINTENANCE OF FREE-LIVING STAGES

Different species of ticks vary widely in their resistance to dessication because of differences in their "critical temperatures" (Lees, 1947). Most species require a relative humidity (RH) ranging between 70 and 90% and many workers have kept their material over damp

sand or in glass cylinders set in soil. However, for the sake of reference and uniformity it is desirable to maintain all free-living stages
of ticks in closed containers over saturated salt solutions of known
vapor pressure at constant temperatures (selected humidities given
by O'Brien, 1948).

Containers for individual lots of ticks should be of clean, straight-
walled glassware and plugged with cotton or cloth-covered hollow
stoppers. Saito (1960) placed considerable stress on the inhibition of
molds in containers and recommended a lining of 6 parts gypsum and
4 parts charcoal, but later (1962) advocated moist inserts of Stylone
sponge in its place. Srivastava and Varma (1964) inhibited fungal
growth with a 1:10,000 merthiolate solution.

A. DEVELOPING TICKS

1. *Molting*

During their metamorphosis from fed larvae and nymphs to successive flat stages, ticks undergo metabolic changes that require more
heat than is needed for mere quiescent survival. *Ixodes scapularis* Say
larvae molt best at 100% RH and 80°F (even 90°F); the duration of
molting decreases as the humidity is raised from 90% and as the
temperature is raised from 70° to 80°F; nymphs molt better at 90%
RH and 80°F (Harris, 1959).

Low temperatures will retard molting, and can be used to advantage in manipulating rearing procedures. Feldman-Muhsam (1964)
states that nymphal quiescence in *Hyalomma excavatum* Koch varies
from 20–30 days at 32°C up to 450–500 days at 17.5°C. In nature,
winter may delay the molting of both engorged larvae and nymphs
of *I. dentatus* for over 300 days (Smith, 1945).

The molting period of stored, fed nymphs may depend on the sex
of the ensuing adult, whose emergence time in nature appears to be
designed for optimum mating conditions.

Nymphs of *I. dentatus* and *D. variabilis* molt evenly, produce
more females than males, and, as adults, mate on the host. With *Ixodes
muris* Bishopp and Smith, the females are fewer, hatch later, and
mate on the ground (Smith, 1945). Males of *D. andersoni* appear first
in nature, and this species mates on the host.

2. *Oviposition*

In ixodids, egg laying commences a week or two after feeding and
extends over a period of several weeks until the tick wastes away and
dies. Argasid ticks usually lay a relatively small number of eggs after
each of several blood meals.

The preoviposition period may vary within species. Walker and Parsons (1964) observed a difference of 76 days in two specimens of *Amblyomma sparsum* Neumann that were kept under identical conditions.

According to Belozorov (1963), the preoviposition period of *D. marginatus* is conditioned in the female before laying by the day length to which it was exposed. Those raised under long-day conditions (18 hr of light per day) began to lay only after an average of 7 months, whereas those under short-day conditions (9 hr of light per day) began mostly within 12–30 days and always within 3.5 months.

Harris (1959) found that 90% RH and 70°F was the optimum combination of humidity and temperature for the oviposition of *I. scapularis*. Hitchcock (1955b) showed 75°F to be optimum for *B. microplus* regardless of relative humidities ranging between 45 and 99%.

3. *Hatching*

The fertility of eggs from mated ixodid ticks is usually high. However percentage hatch under different conditions of relative humidity varies greatly with different species. Harris (1959) found that a drop of only 10% from the apparent optimum of 90% caused a marked decrease in the hatching of *I. scapularis*. Temperature changes from the optimum of 70°F were not as critical. Hitchcock (1955b) showed that maximum hatch of *B. microplus* eggs occurred between 85° and 95°F and at relative humidities above 95%; no hatch occurred at 70% or lower. A graph of the rate of egg development in relation to temperature formed a sigmoid curve. Robinson (1942) obtained full fertility at a relative humidity of only 50% for *O. moubata*, but found that repeated matings a day or two before each feeding were necessary for maximum egg production.

B. UNFED TICKS

Low temperatures, along with high humidities, are most favorable to the survival of unfed ticks. Feldman-Muhsam (1951) showed 17.5°C to be preferable to 30° and 37° for *Hyalomma savignyi* (Gervais) imagines, but did not try lower temperatures. Studies in progress at the Kamloops laboratory suggest that for the survival of *D. andersoni* adults 15°C (over a saturated solution of KNO_3) is preferable to 6–10°C (over water). Harris (1959) found that larvae and nymphs of *I. scapularis* lived longer when maintained at 90% RH and 60°F than when at 80% or 70°F.

Given suitable conditions, the life cycle of ticks can be extended greatly. Juvenile stages of most ixodids may be maintained for at least 4–5 months. Enigk and Grittner (1953) cite 10–13 months for

Haemaphysalis leachii (Audouin) and *Rhipicephalus bursa* Canestrini and Fanzago; *I. ricinus* and *D. pictus*, if kept at 4°C, may reach an age of 2 years. Longevity of adult ixodids is stated to vary from 2 years for *H. rufipes* and *H. savignyi* to nearly 3 years for *Rhipicephalus appendiculatus* Neumann and *I. ricinus*.

Gregson (1949) demonstrated that larvae, nymphs, and adults of *I. texanus* are capable of living for at least 96, 103, and 101 months, respectively. Argasids are even longer lived, and extreme records extend up to 9 years for imagines of *O. turicata* (Francis, 1938) and 11 years for the life cycle of *O. hermsi* (Pavlovsky and Skrynnik, 1960). However, too much faith should not be placed on longevity, and it is advisable to safeguard against extinction of strains through age by maintaining a secondary advance colony.

VII. ARTIFICIAL FEEDING

Artificial feeding of the slow-feeding ixodid ticks for rearing purposes has not yet been practicable. However, mass feeding of *Ornithodoros papillipes* Birula, as reviewed by Pavlovsky (1930), may be accomplished by placing the ticks on an artificial membrane over defibrinated blood at 37°C; although this technique does not appear to have been pursued, it seems possible that other species of argasids could be fed in this fashion. The membrane best suited for penetration by larval and nymphal *O. turicata* and *O. moubata* was of gutta-percha material (Haddon, 1956).

VIII. SELECTED EXAMPLES OF REARING

The literature contains too many references to rearing of ticks to cite here. The following selections will serve as guides and enable workers to contact sources where more information is available.

Ornithodoros coriaceus Koch. Reared by Smith (1944) on guinea pigs and rabbits. Larvae fed for an average period of 9.2 days; nymphs of each of the three to seven stages (except the first, which molts without feeding) for 5 to 60 minutes; the adults, likewise. The total time spent in each of the nymphal stages which fed and molted ranged from 39 to 480 days. A fed but unmated nymph lived up to 1911 days, unfed adults lived only 9 months; fed females up to 5 years. Loomis (1961) describes infesting methods for which he obtained a minimum life cycle of 8 months at 32°C.

Ornithodoros hermsi Wheeler, Herms, and Meyer. Reared by Wheeler (1943). At 75°F, 90% RH, the life cycle could be completed in 4½ months; females lived up to an age of 7 years. All feedings were made on white mice.

Ornithodoros kelleyi Cooley and Kohls. Sonenshine and Anastos (1960) showed the minimum and maximum life-cycle lengths to be 54 and 258 days when kept at 30°C, 77% RH. The first-stage nymph did not feed. Larvae fed on bats and rats; the nymphs and adults only on bats. In contrast, Johnson (1964) could feed larvae only on bats, but found that other stages would feed on guinea pigs.

Ornithodoros moubata (Murray). The rapid development of a 2.5-month life cycle for this species was obtained by Loomis (1961) by maintaining all stages at 32°C, 51–61% RH. The larvae do not feed; the nymphs and adults were fed on the shaved abdomens of rabbits. Pierquin and Niemegeers (1953) suggest a life cycle of 62 days for the male and 73 for the female.

Argas arboreus Kaiser, Hoogstraal, Kohls. Standardized rearing methods, applicable to the rearing of this and other argasid ticks have been described in detail by Kaiser and will be published shortly in *Ann. Entomol. Soc. Am.* Besides containing much data on the rearing and biology of this species, the paper contains notes on diapause, host resistance, and tick paralysis.

Argas persicus (Oken). Micks (1951) maintained a small colony with a minimum of effort by confining a chicken with them at intervals of several hours in a screen-topped can. Pads of cellulose fiber served as tick refuges. When kept at 25°–28°C, 70–80% RH, larvae lived for 2 months without feeding, fed in 5 days, and molted in 1 week. The two nymphal stages fed in 15 min to 2 hr and molted in 12–14 days. Adults fed every 25–28 days and laid about 100 eggs after each meal. A similar method was used by Loomis (1961), who obtained a life cycle of 8 weeks. Sapre (1943) fed adults overnight on hooded fowls.

Ornithodoros turicata (Dugès). Fed in all stages on narcotized rats or mice (Sonenshine, 1964). Specimens were stored over saturated ammonium chloride at 85°F. Davis (1941) records engorging and mating times from 100 observations.

Otobius megnini (Dugès). The immature stages of this tick are entirely parasitic; the adults do not feed. If fed in the ears of their normal domestic hosts (sheep and cattle), cages must be applied over long periods of time. Loomis (1961) successfully fed larvae and nymphs under a zippered girdle taped on the shaved belly of a rabbit. The nymphs engorged for 2–4 months.

Amblyomma americanum (L.). Reared by Loomis (1961) in a manner similar to that described by Kohls (1937), by Lancaster (1955) on chickens and cattle, during which he obtained a minimum life cycle of 95 days, and by Sacktor *et al.* (1948) on rabbits.

Amblyomma cajennense (Fabricius). The early stages of this species were reared in large numbers by Travassos and Vallejo-

Freire (1944–1945) in the ears of rabbits. The adults, which normally parasitize horses and mules, were fed on guinea pigs and rabbits. Yields and developmental periods are given.

Amblyomma geoemydae (Cantor). A tortoise tick which was found to be fairly specific to its natural host, *Testudo emys.* The box tortoise *Cuora amboinensis* was a fair substitute; guinea pigs were unsatisfactory. The life cycle was completed in 185–271 days (Nadchatram, 1960).

Amblyomma sparsum Neumann. Collected from tortoises and reared by Walker and Parsons (1964) on rabbits to adults which, in one strain, fed well on a ram's scrotum. Female engorging times on sheep and tortoises were 3–5 weeks and 9 weeks, respectively.

Boophilus microplus (Canestrini). Reared in large numbers on cattle in Australia; feeding time, from attachment of larvae to fall-off of females was 18.9–35.5 days; period from preoviposition to mature larvae, 21–229 days (Hitchcock, 1955a,b). When larvae were infested on unrestrained European-bred cattle about 9% were recovered as engorged females.

Dermacentor andersoni Stiles. Kohls' (1937) outline of rearing methods for this species has been followed at the Kamloops laboratory for many years with but slight modifications. Larvae are infested on domestic rabbits by either emptying the progeny of one to four egg masses into the two ears and taping them together, or scattering them onto one or more animals that are immediately enclosed in a 12 × 18-inch sack of unbleached cotton. The animal is placed in a cage, which in turn is placed in a frame that is covered with a loosely fitting nylon bag. At the end of the first day the tape on the ears, or the sack around the rabbit, is removed and the mouth of the outside bag is tightly tied. The animal is fed carrots daily. Engorged ticks commence to drop from the host about the fifth day.

The engorged larvae are collected by means of a sieve and funnel. Under optimum conditions Kohls (1937) was able to collect up to 5600 larvae per rabbit. Molting to nymphs takes place in about 4 to 5 weeks if they are kept at 22°C and 50% RH. A similar procedure is followed in feeding the nymphs except that only about 1000 ticks are placed on each rabbit. Engorgement takes about 8 days and normally yields about 400 nymphs. Molting of nymphs to adults takes place in about 21 days at 22°C, 40–80% RH; it is accelerated by a lower RH and retarded by higher. Kohls recommends sifting, washing, and drying the engorged larvae and nymphs to remove soluble wastes and detritus. Conditioning methods for breaking the diapause, frequently encountered in reared adults of this species, have yet to be perfected. Wild-caught adults feed well on rabbits, guinea pigs, or sheep. Engorgement is completed in 7 to 10 days; the fed ticks are stored in shell vials at 22°C, 80% RH; oviposition is completed in about 21 days and hatching in another 3 weeks.

Dermacentor (=Otocentor) nitens Neumann. This one-host parasite of Equidae has been reared through three generations on rabbits (Anthony, 1964). Adult engorgement was poor.

Dermacentor parumapertus Neumann. Kangaroo rats (*Dipodomys* sp.) are convenient laboratory hosts for larvae and nymphs which feed in 4–13 days and 26–36 days, respectively (Allred and Roscoe, 1956). Storage was at 20°C, 95% RH. Adults feed on *Lepus* sp.

Dermacentor variabilis (Say). Smith *et al.* (1946) record normal preoviposition periods ranging from 6–58 days; incubation, from 27–57 days; larval longevity without food, up to 540 days; larval engorgement, 3–13 days; larval molting, 6–247 days; nymphal longevity, up to 584 days; nymphal engorgement, 3–11 days; nymphal molting, 20–291 days; adult longevity, up to 1032 days; adult engorgement, average 10.5 days. Temperatures ranged from 80°F to cooler outdoor conditions. Sonenshine (1964) fed all stages on albino rats.

Haemaphysalis flava Neumann. Fed well in all stages on angora rabbits; less so on hens. Its minimum life cycle at 20°–30°C was 4 months. The male needed a 10-day blood meal before mating (Saito, 1960). *Haemaphysalis bispinosa* Neumann was also reared but required a winter resting period.

Hyalomma marginatum isaacii Sharif. The small and large mammal hosts of this species were substituted by guinea pigs and rabbits, respectively. Rau (1963) obtained high yields of all stages and a life cycle of 60 days at 81°–94°F, 80–90% RH.

Ixodes dentatus Neumann. Smith (1945) fed all stages on cottontail rabbits. The average feeding times for larvae, nymphs, and adults were 6.3, 5.7, and 21.5 days, respectively. Adults lived for 2 years and still fed and laid viable eggs.

Ixodes granulatus Supino. This species was reared on white rats by Nadchatram (1960). At 75°–84°F the life cycle was completed in 174–272 days.

Ixodes persulcatus persulcatus Schulze and *Ixodes japonensis* Neumann. Reared by Saito (1960) on mice and rabbits. Minimum life cycle periods at 20°–30°C were 4.5 and 5 months, respectively.

Ixodes ricinus (Linn.). Reared by Nosek (1964) on mice and kept at 24°C for development, had a life cycle of 171–215 days. Unfed ticks were kept moist at 4°C.

Ixodes scapularis Say. Reared by Harris (1959) on rabbits. Life cycle under optimum conditions, 132 days.

Ixodes texanus Banks. A hardy and easily reared tick that can be maintained on mustelid hosts. Adults will also feed on sheep or dogs (Gregson, 1942c, 1949).

Rhipicephalus appendiculatus Neumann. Bailey (1960) describes a simple procedure for maintaining a small colony of this species on rabbits.

Rhipicephalus sanguineus (Latreille). Srivastava and Varma (1964), who remark on the ease with which this species can be maintained, obtained prefeeding periods as short as 7 and 4 days and life cycles of 86–123 days at 25°C and 65–90 days at 29°C.

Rhipicephalus secundus (Feldman-Muhsam). Larvae and nymphs were reared on *Microtus* by Hadani *et al.* (1961). Egg to adult took 52–91 days at 17°C–20°C, 75–80% RH. Larvae 12–15 days old and nymphs 7–25 (even 40–50) days old fed well.

Other notes on the biology of species of Argasids and of *Boophilus*, *Dermacentor*, *Ixodes*, *Rhipicephalus*, *Amblyomma Aponomma*, *Haemaphysalis*, *Hyalomma*, and *Margaropus* are contained within the works of Nuttall *et al.* (1908, 1911, 1915, 1926), Hooker *et al.* (1912), and Hoogstraal (1956).

REFERENCES

Allred, D. M., and Roscoe, E. J. (1956). Life history of the tick *Dermacentor parumapertus* in Utah. *J. Parasitol.* **42**, 516–522.

Anthony, D. W. (1964). U. S. Dept. Agr. Entomology Res., Beltsville, Maryland. Personal communication.

Arthur, D. R. (1961). "Ticks and Disease" 445 pp. Pergamon Press, Oxford.

Audy, J. R., and Lavoipierre, M. J. (1966). The laboratory rearing of parasitic *Acarina*. Hooper Foundation Working Paper HFI/63 (to be published in *J. Med. Entomol*).

Bailey, K. P. (1960). Notes on the rearing of *Rhipicephalus appendiculatus* and their infection with *Theileria parva* for experimental transmission. *Bull. Epizool. Diseases Africa* **8**, 33–43.

Balashov, Y. S. (1954). Peculiarities of the daily rhythm of dropping of engorged female *Ixodes persulcatus* from cattle. *Dokl. Akad. Nauk SSSR* **98**, 317–319.

Belozorov, V. N. (1963). Day length as a factor determining the delay of egg laying of females of *Dermacentor marginatus* (Sulz.). *Med. Parazitol. i Parazitarn. Bolezni* **32**, 521–526.

Belozorov, V. N. (1964). The diapause and conditions of reactivation in female *Dermacentor marginatus*. *Vestn. Leningr. Univ.*, *Ser. Biol.* **21**, No. 4, 5–11.

Bremner, K. C. (1959). Observations on the biology of *Haemaphysalis bispinosa* Neumann with particular reference to its mode of reproduction by parthenogenesis. *Australian J. Zool.* **7**, 7–12.

Brumpt, E., and Chabaud, A. G. (1947). L'infestation par des Ixodines provoque-t-elle une immunite chez l'hote? *Ann. Parasitol. Humaine Comparee* **22**, 348–356.

Davis, G. E. (1941). *Ornithodoros turicata*: The male; feeding and copulation habits, fertility, span of life, and transmission of relapsing fever spirochaetes. **56**, 1799–1802.

Davis, G. E., and Walker, M. E. (1940). *Ornithodoros hermsi*—feeding and molting

habits in relation to the acquisition and transmission of relapsing fever spiro-
chetes. *Public Health Rept.* (*U. S.*) **55**, 492–504.

Delpy, L., and Gouchey, S. H. (1939). Biologie de *Hyalomma dromedarii* (Koch).
Arch. Inst. Hessarak **1**, 184–196.

Enigk, K., and Grittner, I. (1953). Zur Zucht und Biologie der Zechen. *Z. Parastenk.*
16, 56–83.

Feldman-Muhsam, B. (1951). On the longevity of fasting ticks, *Hyalomma savignyi*
Gerv. *Parasitology* **41**, 63–65.

Feldman-Muhsam, B. (1964). Laboratory colonies of Rhipicephalus. Symposium on
culture procedures for arthropod vectors and their biological control agents. *Bull.
World Health Organ.* **31**, 587–589.

Francis, E. (1938). Longevity of the tick *Ornithodoros turicata* and of *Spirochaeta
recurrentis* within this tick. *Public Health Rept.* (*U. S.*) **53**, 2220–2241.

George, J. E. (1964). The circadian rhythm of "drop-off" of engorged *Haemaphysalis
leporispalustris* from rabbits. *Proc. 1st Intern. Congr. Acarology, Fort Collins,
Colorado, 1963* pp. 343–349.

Gregson, J. D. (1942a). Host immunity to ticks. *Proc. Entomol. Soc. Brit. Columbia*
38, 12–13.

Gregson, J. D. (1942b). Host poisoning by *Ixodes californicus* Banks. *Proc. Entomol.
Soc. Brit. Columbia* **38**, 5–6.

Gregson, J. D. (1942c). Notes on the laboratory rearing of some Canadian ticks. *Proc.
Entomol. Soc. Brit. Columbia* **39**, 32–35.

Gregson, J. D. (1947). Feeding periods prerequisite to the mating of *Dermacentor
andersoni* Stiles. *Proc. Entomol. Soc. Brit. Columbia* **43**, 3–6.

Gregson, J. D. (1949). Note on the longevity of certain ticks. *Proc. Entomol. Soc. Brit.
Columbia* **45**, 14.

Gregson, J. D. (1956). The Ixodoidea of Canada. *Can. Dept. Agr., Bull.* **930**, 49.

Gregson, J. D. (1962). The enigma of tick paralysis in North America. *Proc. 11th Intern.
Congr. Entomol., Vienna, 1960* Vol. III, pp. 97–101. Druck: Christoph, Reiners
Söhne, Vienna.

Hadani, A., Mer, G. G., and Cwilich, R. (1961). The rearing of *Rhipicephalus secundus*
on the Levant vole (*Microtus guentheri*, D. & A.) and its use as an experimental
animal for testing acaracides and tick repellents. *Refuah Vet.* **18**, 1–7.

Haddon, W. (1956). An artificial membrane and apparatus for the feeding of the human
body louse *Pedeculus humanis corporis. Am. J. Trop. Med. Hyg.* **5**, 315–325.

Harris, R. L. (1959). The biology of the black-legged tick. *J. Kansas Entomol. Soc.* **32**,
61–68.

Harvey, A. E. C. (1947). The care and maintenance of laboratory animals and arthropod
vectors of disease. *E. African Med. J.* **24**, 58–71.

Hays, K. L. (1964). Dept. Zool., Auburn Univ., Auburn, Alabama. Personal communication.

Hitchcock, L. F. (1955a). Studies on the parasitic stages of the cattle tick *Boophilus
microplus* (Canestrini). *Australian J. Zool.* **3**, 145–155.

Hitchcock, L. F. (1955b). Studies of the non-parasitic stages on the cattle tick *Boophilus
microplus* (Canestrini). *Australian J. Zool.* **3**, 295–311.

Hoogstraal, H. (1956). "African Ixodoidea" Research Rept. NM 005 050.29.07, 1101 pp.
U. S. Naval Med. Res. Unit No. 3, Cairo, Egypt.

Hooker, W. A., Bishopp, F. C., and Wood, H. P. (1912). The life history and bionomics of
some North American ticks. *U. S. Dept. Agr., Tech. Bull* **106**, 1–239.

Jellison, W. L., and Kohls, G. M. (1938). Tick host anaemia. *J. Parasitol.* **24**, 143–154.

Johnson, D. E. (1964). Univ. of Utah, Dugway, Utah. Personal communication.

Kaiser, M. (1964). Med. Zool. Dept., U. S. Naval Med. Res. Unit No. 3, Cairo, Egypt. Personal communication.

Kaiser, M. N. The subgenus Persicargas (Ixodoidea, Argasidae *Argas*). 3. The life cycle of *A. (P.) arboreus* Kaiser, Hoogstraal and Kohls and a standardized rearing method for argasid ticks. *Ann. Entomol. Soc. Am.* (in press).

Kitaoka, S. (1962). Physiological and ecological studies on some ticks. Part VIII. *Natl. Inst. Animal Health Quart.* **2,** 106–111.

Kohls, G. M. (1937). Tick rearing methods with special reference to the Rocky Mountain wood tick, *Dermacentor andersoni* Stiles. "Culture Methods for Invertebrate Animals." Cornell Univ. Press (Comstock), Ithaca, New York.

Lancaster, J. L., Jr. (1955). Biology and seasonal history of the Lone Star tick in Northwest Arkansas. *J. Econ. Entomol.* **48,** 295–297.

Lees, A. D. (1947). Transpiration and the structure of the epicuticle in ticks. *J. Exptl. Biol.* **23,** 379–410.

Loew, J. L. (1964). Über den Einfluss der Photoperiode auf die Metamorphose von *Ixodes ricinus*. *Angew. Parasitol.* **5,** 3–13.

Loomis, E. C. (1961). Life histories of ticks under laboratory conditions. *J. Parasitol.* **47,** 91–99.

Micks, D. W. (1951). The laboratory rearing of the common fowl tick, *Argas persicus* (Oken). *J. Parasitol.* **37,** 2–4.

Nadchatram, M. (1960). Notes on rearing Malayan ixodid ticks (Acarina, Ixodidae) with special reference to *Ixodes granulatus* Supino and *Amblyomma geoemydae* (Cantor). *Studies Inst. Med. Res., Malaya* **29,** 217–224.

Neitz, W. O. (1962). The different forms of tick toxicosis: A review. *2nd Meeting FAO/ OIE Expert Panel Tick-Borne Diseases Livestock, Cairo, UAR.* pp. 6–8.

Nosek, J. (1964). Inst. Virology, Czech. Acad. Sci., Bratislava, Czechoslovakia. Personal communication.

Nuttall, G. H. F., Warburton, C., Cooper, W. F., and Robinson, L. E. (1908). "Ticks, a Monograph of the Ixodoidea," Part I. Cambridge Univ. Press, London and New York.

Nuttall, G. H. F., Warburton, C., Cooper, W. F., and Robinson, L. E. (1911). "Ticks, a Monograph of the Ixodoidea," Part II, p. 296. Cambridge Univ. Press, London and New York.

Nuttall, G. H. F., Warburton, C., Cooper, W. F., and Robinson, L. E. (1915). "Ticks, a Monograph of the Ixodoidea," Part III. Cambridge Univ. Press, London and New York.

Nuttall, G. H. F., Warburton, C., Cooper, W. F., and Robinson, L. E. (1926). "Ticks, a Monograph of the Ixodoidea," Part IV, p. 300. Cambridge Univ. Press, London and New York.

O'Brien, F. E. M. (1948). The control of humidity by saturated salt solutions. *J. Sci. Instr.* **25,** 73–76.

Pavlovsky, E. N. (1930). Sammeln, Züchtung und Untersuchung von Zecken. *Abderh. Handb. Biol. Arbetismethoden* **9,** 11–96.

Pavlovsky, E. N., and Skrynnik, A. N. (1960). Laboratoriumbeobachtungen and der Zecke. *O. hermsi* Wheeler, 1935. *Acarologia* **2,** 62–65.

Philip, C. B. (1963). Ticks as purveyors of animal ailments: A review of pertinent data and of recent contributions. *In* "Recent Advances in Acarology" (J. A. Naegele, ed.), Vol. I, Part V, pp. 285–325. Cornell Univ. Press (Comstock), Ithaca, New York.

Pierquin, L., and Niemegeers, C. (1953). Notes sur l'elevage de *Ornithodoros moubata* (Murray). *Inst. Roy. Sci. Nat. Belg., Bull.* **29**, 1–6.

Rau, K. R. U. (1963). Observations on the maintenance of a laboratory strain of *Hyalomma marginatum isaacii. U. S. Armed Forces Med. J.* **19**, 40–46.

Rau, K. R. U. (1965). Some observations on the feeding of ticks on experimental animals with special reference to the pill box method. *J. Med. Entomol.* **2**, 58–60.

Řeháček, J. (1957). Contribution to the laboratory method of tick-feeding on mice in laboratories. *Biologia* **12**, 140–143.

Riek, F. R. (1962). Studies of the reactions of animals to infestations with ticks. VI. Resistance of cattle to infestation with the tick *Boophilus microplus. Australian J. Agr. Res.* **13**, 532–550.

Robinson, G. G. (1942). Fertility in the argasid tick, *Ornithodoros moubata*, Murray. *Parasitology* **34**, 308–314.

Sacktor, B., Hutchinson, M., and Granett, P. (1948). Biology of the Lone Star tick in the laboratory. *J. Econ. Entomol.* **41**, 296–301.

Saito, Y. (1960). Studies on ixodid ticks. II. On the rearing and life history of three tick species (*Haemaphysalis flava, Ixodes japonensis*, and *Ixodes persulcatus persulcatus*) in Japan. *Acta Med. Biol.* (*Niigata*) **7**, 303–321.

Saito, Y. (1962). Studies on ixodid ticks. VI. Additional report of tick raising, with a presentation of a new tick container. *Acta Med. Biol.* (*Niigata*) **10**: 127–146.

Sapre, S. N. (1943). Some methods of feeding ticks. *Indian J. Vet. Sci.* **13**, 175–177.

Schuhardt, V. T. (1940). A ticktorium for the propagation of a colony of infected *Ornithodoros turicata. J. Parasitol.* **26**, 201–206.

Smith, C. N. (1944). The life history of the tick *Ornithodoros coriaceus* Koch. *Ann. Entomol. Soc. Am.* **37**, 325–355.

Smith, C. N. (1945). Biology of *Ixodes dentatus* Neumann. *Ann. Entomol. Soc. Am.* **38**, 223–233.

Smith, C. N., and Cole, M. M. (1941). Effect of length of day on the activity and hibernation of the American dog tick, *Dermacentor variabilis* (Say). *Ann. Entomol. Soc. Am.* **34**, 426–431.

Smith, C. N., Cole, M. M., and Gouck, H. K. (1946). Biology and control of the American dog tick. *U. S. Dept. Agr., Tech. Bull.* **905**, pp. 1–54.

Snowball, G. J. (1956). The effect of self-licking by cattle on infestations of cattle tick, *Boophilus microplus* (Canestrini). *Australian J. Res.* **7**, 227–232.

Sonenshine, D. E. (1964). Old Dominion College, Dept. Biol., Norfolk, Virginia. Personal communication.

Sonenshine, D. E., and Anastos, G. (1960). Observations on the life history of the bat tick *Ornithodoros kelleyi. J. Parasitol.* **46**, 449–454.

Stone, B. F. (1962). The inheritance of DDT-resistance in the cattle tick, *Boophilus microplus. Australian J. Agr. Res.* **13**, 984–1007.

Srivastava, S. C., and Varma, M. G. R. (1964). The culture of the tick *Rhipicephalus sanguineus* in the laboratory. *J. Med. Entomol.* **1**, 154–157.

Streissle, G. (1961). Versucke zur Übertragung des Virus der Frühsommer-Meningoencephalitis durch Lederzecken. *Zentr. Bakteriol., Parasitenk., Abt. I. Orig.* **182**, 159–169.

Trager, W. (1939). Acquired immunity to ticks. *J. Parasitol.* **25**, 57–81.

Travassos, J., and Vallejo-Freire, A. (1944–1945). Criação artificial de *Amblyomma cajennense* para o preparo da vacina contra a febre maculosa. *Mem. Inst. Butantan.* (*Sao Paulo*) **18**, 145–235.

Varma, M. G. R. (1964). A metal capsule for experimental feeding of ixodid ticks on animals. *Trans. Roy. Soc. Trop. Med. Hyg.* **58**, 5.

Walker, J. B., and Parsons, B. T. (1964). The laboratory rearing of *Amblyomma sparsum* Neumann 1899. *Parasitology* **54**, 173–175.

Wharton, R. H. (1964). Vet. Parasitol. Lab., Yeerongpilly, Brisbane, Australia. Personal communication.

Wheeler, C. M. (1943). A contribution to the biology of *Ornithodoros hermsi* Wheeler, Herms, and Meyer. *J. Parasitol.* **29**, 33–41.

Wilkinson, P. R. (1964). A barrier for ticks and crawling organisms. *J. Econ. Entomol.* **47**, 414.

Woke, P. A. (1951). A rabbit-ear cage for bloodsucking arthropods. *Public Health Rept. (U. S.)* **66**, 464–471.

Chapter 5

Rat Fleas

B. S. KRISHNAMURTHY

National Institute of Communicable Diseases,
Delhi, India

I. LABORATORY REARING OF FLEAS

A. THE NEED FOR COLONIZATION AND EARLY EXPERIENCE IN REARING RAT FLEAS

Rearing of insects in the laboratory is recognized as the first essential step to study the biology and toxicology of insect pests. The rapid strides in the field of biological control of insect vectors of diseases have necessitated studies of techniques for the mass rearing of insects. Techniques for such mass production have been evolved for some insects and successfully used in the field. An outstanding example of such mass production was that of the American screwworm, *Cochliomyia hominivorax*, (Coquerel), (Knipling, 1960) for use of sterile males in the program for the eradication of the species. Ramakrishnan *et al.* (1962) and Krishnamurthy *et al.* (1962) used mass rearing of *Culex fatigans* Wied. for sterilization of the males by irradiation and mass release in the field to determine its effect on the mosquito population. Trials on similar mass rearing and use of sterile *Aedes aegypti* (L.) males in an attempt to eradicate this species were reported by Morlan *et al.* (1962, 1963) and Fay *et al.* (1963).

The oriental rat flea, *Xenopsylla cheopis* (Rothschild), the well-known vector of human plague, is well suited for mass rearing. Before a simple technique suitable for this purpose is described, the experience of a number of investigators who raised flea cultures in the past will be reviewed briefly. The first recorded attempt to breed fleas in the laboratory was in 1683 by Leeuwenhoek. Ever since his day, scientists have been attempting breeding of fleas in the laboratory. Sikes (1930) has briefly discussed the efforts of these naturalists.

Bacot (1912, 1914) has given detailed account of the studies he carried out regarding breeding of rat fleas and their bionomics. He raised colonies of *X. cheopis* in Poona, India, during the period 1909 to 1912, when he studied the biology of this species with special reference to factors such as temperature and humidity conditions influencing rate of reproduction, length of life, variation in their rate of growth, and pupation. Leeson (1932) has described techniques of rearing and maintaining large stocks of fleas for experimental purposes. Hollenbeck (1946) and Kilpatrick and Fay (1952) described methods by which large numbers of *X. cheopis* could be raised in the laboratory for test purposes. Smith and Eddy (1954), while describing mass rearing techniques of insects of public health importance, have given a lucid account of the simple technique adopted by them for rearing fleas. Stark and Kartman (1957) have described techniques of rearing *X. cheopis* and *Xenopsylla vexabilis hawaiiensis* Jordan. Roy and Brown (1954), Seal and Bhattacharji (1961), and Krishnamurthy *et al.* (1963) have also described the techniques adopted by them for rearing fleas.

B. STANDARDIZATION OF TECHNIQUE AND ITS IMPORTANCE

The supply of biological material is generally subsidiary to the main purpose of experimental studies on toxicology or on disease transmission. Therefore, the technique should ensure the maintenance of continuous stock of material. It is also necessary that the technique should be so devised as to achieve maximum mass production with minimum of effort and with the least expenditure in time and money. In other words, this preparatory work of the flea cultures should be as nearly automatic and self-sustaining as possible. The investigators mentioned earlier used techniques which are basically

the same but different in detail. Therefore, it is necessary to standardize the technique for mass culture, using simple material available in
most of the places. It has been the experience of many workers in the
past that lack of attention to factors such as inadvertent contamination
of the colonies, or inadequate attention to temperature or humidity
conditions, has made all the difference between success and failure
in establishing or perpetuating these cultures. This emphasizes the
need to study carefully, initially, the behavior of the insects before
the cultures are started or before they are put on production line
with special reference to temperature, humidity, food, and rearing
conditions.

II. MATERIALS AND METHODS
FOR REARING FLEAS

A. Breeding Cages and Medium

Mass rearing of fleas requires materials which are readily available and inexpensive. The materials generally used for breeding
cages have been of glassware, where the risk of breakage was great,
necessitating very careful handling. Smith and Eddy (1954) and
Kilpatrick and Fay (1952) have, therefore, used enamel or galvanized ironware. The experience at the National Institute of Communicable Diseases (NICD), Delhi, has shown that galvanized iron
is the material of choice for preparing breeding cages. These cages
(Fig. 1) prepared by the local tinsmith have been found to be suitable
for maintaining self-supporting mass cultures of *X. cheopis*.

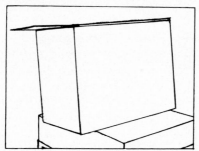

FIG. 1. Flea breeding cage with sliding lid.

Breeding cages are rectangular boxes measuring 45 cm long, 30 cm
wide, and 40 cm deep (18 × 12 × 16 inches), made of galvanized iron
sheet of 22-gauge thickness and open at the top. They are provided
with a sliding lid and painted white inside and outside. The lid is

comprised of fine iron mesh screen fitted to an iron frame which slides in grooves provided in the cage for this purpose. The fine mesh screen of the lid is painted with aluminum paint, whereas the box is painted with white lead paint. The flea rearing cage is then kept on wooden supports in a galvanized iron tray 60 cm long, 40 cm wide, and 15 cm deep (24 × 16 × 6 inches) which is also painted white and filled with water to a depth of about 10 cm (4 inches). This tray is supported on a frame 60 cm high (2 ft) made of angle iron (Fig. 2).

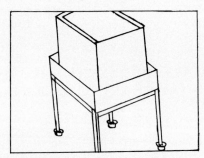

FIG. 2. Galvanized iron tray with angle iron stand in which flea breeding cage is kept.

The bottom of the breeding cage is lined with sterile sand (the sand is heated to a temperature of 200°C for 1 hour and cooled before introducing it into the breeding cage) to a depth of 1.5 cm (about 0.5 inch). Rat pellets (feces) are autoclaved, finely ground, and mixed with the sterile sand (substratum) as food for the larvae.* Sterile wood shavings or paper strips are introduced as shelter for the adult fleas.

B. COLLECTION OF EGGS

For seeding a flea culture, gravid female fleas can either be obtained from an established colony or collected from live trapped rats. When the fleas are from a known culture they are directly introduced into the breeding cage in order to obtain eggs. The gravid female rat fleas, if obtained from the field, are isolated, one in each test tube in which a small quantity of moist, sterile sand is introduced; these tubes are covered with fine nylon netting and kept in a dark, cool place in the insectarium where the temperature ranges between 24° and 28°C (75°–82°F) with a humidity of 65 to 75%. The species of the wild caught fleas from which eggs have been obtained have to be

* Initially powdered blood had to be used as efforts to start the colony only on rat feces did not prove successful; once the colony was established the use of dry blood was discontinued.

determined by clearing in 10% potassium hydroxide, examined under a stereoscopic microscope, and identified. Only eggs from female fleas identified as *X. cheopis* are retained; the others are destroyed to avoid contamination. The eggs deposited on the moist sterile sand in the tube can easily be removed. However, those eggs sticking to the sides of the test tubes should be left undisturbed, as attempts to remove them even with a soft brush often result in damage to a certain proportion of them. The eggs are kept in the dark and examined daily for the appearance of larvae.* The larvae which hatch out are transferred to the breeding medium. The first molt usually occurs after 4 to 7 days. Subsequently, further moltings occur and cocoons are formed between the fifteenth and twentieth day. However, depending upon the temperature and humidity, there are likely to be variations in the period required from egg to cocoon stages. Variations in the developmental stages of the flea have been noticed; active larvae and cocoons could be found at the same time although all eggs belonged to the same batch. However, this feature is likely to be seen more during the initial stages of standardization than later. It is probably due to differences in the amount of food intake by the larvae rather than to temperature and humidity variations. It is not certain whether this could also be ascribed to genetically controlled unspecified factors.

C. COCOONS

When the larvae are full-grown they spin cocoons to enclose themselves and pupate. Most of the larvae incorporate sand particles or debris such as bits of paper with the silk of the cocoons. Occasionally, naked pupae are also encountered. Generally the cocoons are indistinguishable from the substrate; because of the sand particles or debris sticking to the silk, the pupae are visible inside the cocoon only when it is dissected. When pupation is complete the substratum of the breeding cage is passed through a set of sieves which consists of 8- and 16-mesh screens fixed in wooden frames with a handle (Fig. 3). The 8-mesh sieve is superimposed on the 16-mesh sieve, as seen in Fig. 3B, and the substratum with the flea larvae and the cocoons is put into the 8-mesh sieve and vigorously shaken. The debris is retained on the 8-mesh sieve and the cocoons on the 16-mesh sieve; the flea larvae, along with the breeding medium, pass into the enamel basin placed below and are later returned to the breeding

---

* It takes an average time of 48 hours in summer to 120 hours in winter at Delhi for the larvae to appear.

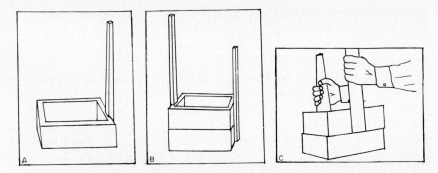

FIG. 3. A. Sieve in a wooden frame with handle for separating cocoons; B. 8-mesh sieve superimposed over 16-mesh sieve; C. set of sieves being shaken.

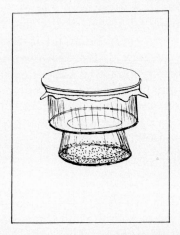

FIG. 4. A unit for emergence of adult fleas.

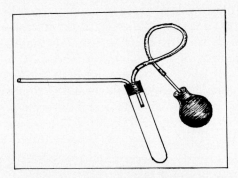

FIG. 5. Aspirator for collecting rat fleas.

cage. The cocoons thus collected are kept in an adult emergence unit (Fig. 4).

The fleas can be collected from the emergence unit by using an aspirator (Fig. 5). The aspirator consists of two pieces of glass tubing (5.0-mm inside diameter) bent at different angles, and passed through a rubber cork. The rubber bung is of the size that can be fitted into an ordinary test tube, into which the fleas are collected with the aspirator. A plastic tube with a small rubber bulb (4.5-cm diameter) is connected to one of the tubes. It is very convenient to aspirate the required number of adults directly into a test tube with this kit. The test tube can be replaced with another when the necessary number of fleas have been aspirated into it. This method of aspirating the adults is recommended by the World Health Organization (1963) for general use in susceptibility test techniques for rat fleas.

D. FEEDING OF ADULT FLEAS

Freshly hatched young adult fleas are provided with blood by introducing an albino rat into the breeding cage. The rat is confined in a wire mesh cage (20 × 17.5 × 7.5 cm) (Fig. 6), which is kept in a small galvanized iron tray (20 × 17.5 × 1.25 cm), and lined with filter paper, which should be renewed two or three times a week. The paper absorbs the rat urine and thus helps in keeping the breeding cages clean. Rats can be provided with food and water in the cage itself. Rat food consists of wheat bran pellets* or grains; water is provided from a flat bottle placed on the lid with a small bent tube connected to it and projecting into the cage (Fig. 6). Periodically the water is replenished. The female fleas leave the rat to oviposit, and lay their eggs in the sand.

The rat is kept in the breeding cage as long as necessary for the fleas to complete oviposition, usually about 3 or 4 weeks, but it may be replaced after 1 or 2 weeks. To remove the fleas remaining on its body the rat is put into an enamel basin 20.0 cm deep (Fig. 7). The rat is immobilized by grasping it about the neck with an artery forceps 22.5 cm long, and air is blown on its fur with a large rubber bulb. The

* The following formula is used at NICD for food given to albino rats and mice:

Whole wheat flour	70 parts
Skim milk powder	16 parts
Peanut (kernel)	8 parts
Dried brewer's yeast	2 parts
Shark liver oil	2 parts
Calcium carbonate	1 part
Table salt	1 part

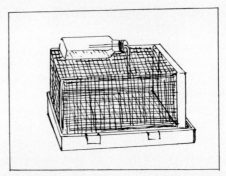

FIG. 6. Rat cage with tray to hold filter paper.

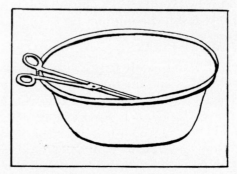

FIG. 7. Enamel basin for defleaing rats.

fleas are thus dislodged and drop into the enamel basin, and are collected with the aspirator. Rats can also be deflead by using soft nylon brushes, but this method is likely to injure the fleas.

III. FACTORS AFFECTING PRODUCTION OF FLEAS

A. TEMPERATURE AND HUMIDITY

Temperature and humidity conditions are of the utmost importance in the rearing of rat fleas. These factors influence almost all aspects of the life cycle of the fleas, such as egg laying, hatching, larval development, larval survival, molting, and pupation. They are also important in adult emergence and longevity. Bacot (1914) has recorded details of breeding experiments with several species of fleas including *X. cheopis*. He bred large numbers of fleas at fluctuating temperatures and humidity and demonstrated that *X. cheopis* can develop over a wide range of temperature, though not below 16°C.

Low humidities were fatal to larvae. Similar effects were observed by Sikes (1931), Mellanby (1933), and Edney (1945, 1948). Stark and Kartman (1957) observed specific difference in the temperature and humidity requirements between *X. cheopis* and *X. vexabilis hawaiiensis*.

The experiences of Bacot (1914), Leeson (1932), Kilpatrick and Fay (1952), Smith and Eddy (1954), and other workers have shown that the temperature in the insectarium where flea rearing is in progress should range from 23°–27°C and the relative humidity should be 70–78%.* These conditions are considered optimum for both the development and the longevity of the fleas.

B. LIGHT

Leeson (1932) showed that rat fleas are photophobic; taking advantage of this factor; he developed a method of collecting adult fleas. Bacot (1912) also demonstrated the need for darkness for egg laying by gravid females. The absence of light is an important factor in the life history of these insects. With this in mind the breeding cage was designed so as to minimize the entry of direct light.

C. SEASONAL VARIATIONS

Seasonal variations in the production of fleas deserves due consideration. Bacot (1912) has shown that despite the control of temperature and humidity there still was a regular seasonal fluctuation in the output from his colony. He also pointed out that this coincides with the seasonal fluctuations in transmission of plague to humans.

IV. NEED FOR VIGILANCE AGAINST CONTAMINATION OF CULTURES

It is needless to emphasize that constant vigilance in rearing fleas is necessary to avoid inadvertent contamination with arthropod parasites, predators, fungal or bacterial infection. Contamination usually occurs through (*a*) the breeding medium; (*b*) wood shavings; (*c*) mice or rats used for feeding adult fleas; and (*d*) the food given to these rodents.

The breeding medium, sand, and rat feces should be well sterilized before introduction into the breeding cage. Eggs of parasites

---

* The humidity in the insectarium was maintained at NICD, Delhi, with an electrically operated humidifier; the temperature was maintained by using two window-type air coolers in summer and an electric room heater in winter.

usually come through this source and infest the colony if they are not well sterilized. Similarly, wood shavings or paper strips, if not sterilized, are likely to introduce fungal infection or pathogenic bacteria as well as cockroaches and other pests.

Mites and other ectoparasites destructive to fleas are introduced through mice. Nonbloodsucking mites belonging to the Tyrogly-phidae are introduced commonly through the unsterilized food. Such inadvertent contamination has been the experience of most of the investigators.* Some of them had to completely abandon the colonies more than once and begin again. Proper care in sterilizing the material prior to introduction into the flea colonies would eliminate such contamination.

REFERENCES

Bacot, A. N. (1912). Observations on flea breeding in Poona. *J. Hyg.* **12**, Suppl. 1, 322–619.

Bacot, A. N. (1914). A study of bionomics of common rat fleas. *J. Hyg.* **14**, Suppl. 3, 447–634.

Edney, E. B. (1945). Laboratory studies on the bionomics of rat fleas. *Bull. Entomol. Res.* **35**, 399.

Edney, E. B. (1948). Laboratory studies on the bionomics of rat fleas. *Bull. Entomol. Res.* **38**, 263.

Fay, R. W., McCray, E. M., Jr., and Kilpatrick, J. W. (1963). Mass production of sterilized male *Aedes aegypti. Mosquito News* **23**, 211.

Hollenbeck, A. H. (1946). A practical method for mass production and transfer of *X. cheopis. J. Parasitol.* **32**, 463.

Kilpatrick, J. W., and Fay, R. W. (1952). DDT resistance studies with the oriental rat fleas. *J. Econ. Entomol.* **45**, 284–288.

Knipling, E. F. (1960). The eradication of the screwworm fly. *Sci. Am.* **203**, 54–61.

Krishnamurthy, B. S., Ray, S. N., and Joshi, G. C. (1962). A note on preliminary field studies of the use of irradiated males for reduction of *C. fatigans* Wied. populations. *Indian J. Malariol.* **16**, 365–373.

Krishnamurthy, B. S., Ray, S. N., and Joshi, G. C. (1963). Note on technique used in rearing and maintaining a colony of the oriental rat flea (*X. cheopis*) at the Malaria Institute of India. EBL/Working Paper No. 19/63. *World Health Organ.* (Mimeograph series).

Leeson, H. S. (1932). Methods of rearing and maintaining large stocks of fleas and mosquitoes for experimental purposes. *Bull. Entomol. Res.* **23**, 25.

Mellanby, K. (1933). The influence of temperature and humidity on populations of *X. cheopis. Bull. Entomol. Res.* **24**, 197.

Morlan, H. B., McCray, E. M., Jr., and Kilpatrick, J. W. (1962). Field tests with sexually sterile males for control of *Aedes aegypti. Mosquito News* **22**, 295–300.

Morlan, H. B., Hayes, R. O., and Schoof, H. F. (1963). Methods of mass rearing of *Aedes aegypti. Public Health Rept.* (*U. S.*) **78**, 719.

* Such inadvertent infestation of *X. cheopis* colony at NICD by tyroglyphid mites occurred in 1962, necessitating complete destruction of the colony.

Ramakrishnan, S. P., Krishnamurthy, B. S., and Ray, S. N. (1962). Laboratory studies on the use of irradiated sterile males to reduce *C. fatigans* Wied. populations. *India J. Malariol.* **16,** 357–364.

Roy, D. N., and Brown, A. W. A. (1954). "Entomology (Medical and Veternary)." Excelsior Press, Calcutta.

Seal, S. C., and Bhattacharji, L. M. (1961). Epidemiological studies on Plague in Calcutta. Part I. Bionomics of two species of rat fleas and distribution densities, and resistance of rodents in relation to the epidemiology of plague in Calcutta. *Indian J. Med. Res.* **49,** 976.

Sikes, E. K. (1930). Larvae of *Ceratophylus wickami* and other species of fleas. *Parasitology* **22,** 242–259.

Sikes, E. K. (1931). Note on breeding of fleas with reference to humidity and feeding. *Parasitology* **23,** 243.

Smith, C. N., and Eddy, G. W. (1954). Technique for rearing and handling bodylice, oriental rat fleas and cat fleas. *Bull. World Health Organ.* **10,** 127–137.

Stark, H. E., and Kartman, L. (1957). The Laboratory culture of *X. vexabilis hawaiiensis J. Am. J. Trop. Med. Hyg.* **6,** 707.

World Health Organization. (1963). 13th Expert Committee on Insecticides, Tech. Rept. Sr. No. 265.

Chapter 6

Anopheles quadrimaculatus Say

JAMES B. GAHAN

Entomology Research Division,
Agricultural Research Service,
U. S. Department of Agriculture,
Gainesville, Florida

I. INTRODUCTION

Under field conditions larvae of *Anopheles quadrimaculatus* Say usually breed in fresh-water ponds, swamps, rice fields, bayous, and borrow pits where sunshine and vegetation are plentiful and the water is slightly alkaline. They do not select the food they ingest but apparently subsist principally on naturally occurring plankton, such as algae, flagellates, and diatoms that dwell in the water.

The adults normally rest inside buildings or hollow trees during the daytime where they have ready access to the animals they use for a blood meal. They are general feeders and will consume the blood of domestic animals such as horses and cattle as readily or more readily than that of human beings. They are also known to feed on sheep, goats, dogs, pigs, rabbits, guinea pigs, rats, mice, and chickens. The adults do most of their feeding at night, although on dark, cool days they readily bite in their daytime resting places or in the woods. They are most active at dusk or dawn, and most of their feeding and egg laying is done at this time.

Because of the potential importance of this species as a disease carrier and its close relationship to other species of *Anopheles* that are still important disseminators of malaria it has been used extensively by investigators engaged in scientific studies. Ward and Kitzmiller (1963) list twelve institutions or laboratories that currently are maintaining colonies of *A. quadrimaculatus.* The species serves well to illustrate the general methods used and problems encountered in rearing mosquitoes of the genus *Anopheles*.

Availability of a laboratory colony can greatly facilitate studies on this insect, since it is rarely prevalent in a locality throughout the entire year and its density varies with the weather conditions encountered even during the more favorable seasons. Furthermore, much of the entomological information needed is extremely difficult to collect under field conditions because of the many variables that cannot be controlled. To insure a continuing supply of mosquitoes with a known history it is cheaper and more reliable to raise a colony under controlled laboratory conditions.

II. SOURCE OF INSECTS

Getting a colony of *A. quadrimaculatus* started can be a frustrating experience as the species does not adapt readily to laboratory culture. The difficulties can be minimized by obtaining the first insects from a colony that has already been established in another laboratory. Transfers of this type are usually made by sending eggs. The eggs can be placed on damp toweling or filter paper inside a pill box or plastic container and shipped by air express. It is advisable to place the eggs inside a mailing tube to minimize the likelihood of damage enroute. Such strains have already become adapted to living under laboratory conditions and usually adjust to another locality quite readily.

If it becomes necessary to start a strain from field-collected insects, as when attempts are being made to study insecticide resistance, the mosquitoes can be collected either as larvae or adults. The collection of larvae takes considerable effort for they are thinly scattered over a breeding area and must be gathered a few at a time. They are usually collected by skimming the top surface of the water with a white-enameled dipper, a sieve, or a pan. Since the larvae congregate near vegetation or algae on the top surface of the water, chief emphasis should be placed on these areas. The insects may be drawn into the collection container by submerging one edge slightly and allowing the surface water to enter rapidly.

Larvae captured in this manner can be transferred with a spoon or pipette to a smaller amount of water, transported to the rearing room, and fed daily. This method of starting a colony is time-consuming and has the further disadvantage of producing only one adult for each insect collected.

A more practical way of getting the insects needed is to collect the adult females inside buildings housing animals or from hollow trees. Particular attention should be paid to those that have already fed on blood, since most of them will have already been inseminated. Freshly fed mosquitoes are easy to catch in an aspirator as they are sluggish and do not fly readily. When placed in cages 1 ft³ or larger in size they usually lay fertile eggs. The time spent in collecting will produce many more adults in the F_1 generation than the larval-collecting method. Adults that have to be transported long distances should be maintained in a cool container. Such conditions can be supplied by confining the mosquitoes in a jar covered with a cloth or screen wire cap that is placed inside of a Styrofoam box partially filled with ice. To prevent the interior from getting too wet the ice can be put in a polyethylene bag.

One of the most difficult problems involved in starting a strain of field-collected Anopheles in the laboratory is getting the F_1 generation of adults to mate and lay fertile eggs. Frequent failures can be expected. Only a minute proportion of the A. quadrimaculatus in a natural population will adapt to living under laboratory conditions. Field collections must be continued until a few specimens whose progeny will mate in captivity are obtained. If progeny of these few individuals can be reared for several generations, a strain that will live under laboratory conditions eventually may be selected.

When difficulty is encountered in getting field-collected adults to mate, induced copulation may be of assistance in establishing the colony. McDaniel and Horsefall (1957) developed this method for use in studies with Aedes spp. Other workers, including Baker et al. (1962) and Ow Yang et al. (1963), modified the original technique slightly and used it successfully with Anopheles spp. At the Gainesville, Florida, Laboratory of the Entomology Research Division, U.S. Department of Agriculture, we have also employed this method to get the F_1 progeny of field-collected A. quadrimaculatus to mate in captivity. The technique developed by Ow Yang et al. (1963) appears to be one of the simplest devised so far. They recommend that the

males and females be allowed to emerge separately in 1-ft³ cages.
They estimate the sexes can be separated with at least 95% accuracy
by placing the large pupae in one cage and the small ones in another.
The larger pupae are usually females. The adults are fed 5% glucose
solution. Between the third and sixth days after emergence the males
are caught in a pipette attached to a suction device. Without anesthesia, the mesothorax of each is pierced laterally with a minute pin
attached to the end of a wooden stick, and the head and legs are removed. Blood-fed females are anesthetized in ether and then placed
on their backs. A pinned male is held near one of the females, venter
to venter, so that the tips of the two abdomens are close together. A
responsive male will clasp the female genitalia. At this time both
sexes can be transferred together to a holding cage. The copulation
process requires about 1 to 2 minutes after which the male releases
the female. If one male is not responsive another should be substituted for it. Ow Yang *et al.* (1963) found that the technique caused
fertility in about 85% of the pairings tried. Baker *et al.* (1962) have
found the males functional for periods up to an hour and capable of
inseminating at least 2 or 3 females. Since the mosquitoes remained
joined for only 5 to 20 seconds they sometimes transferred only the
females to the holding cage and used the males again.

III. REARING ROOM

Although *A. quadrimaculatus* exists in the field under a wide
range of conditions, much better success will be obtained in the
laboratory if considerable attention is paid to furnishing conditions
that are favorable for the development of large numbers of healthy
insects. The room used can be of any size or shape, but must be free
of insecticide contamination. It is not advisable to do the rearing in a
room that is close to another in which insecticide studies are being
conducted unless there is no interchange of air between the two, as
some of the currently used insecticides have sufficient vapor toxicity
to cause mortality.

The temperature and humidity in the room must be kept within
reasonable ranges if a colony is to remain alive and active. Temperatures that are too low prevent larval development, whereas those that
are too high cause mortality of both the larvae and adults. Muirhead-
Thomson (1940) found temperatures of 40°–45°C (104°–113°F) could
kill fourth-instar larvae of several species of *Anopheles*. Work by
Huffaker (1944) showed the optimum temperature for *A. quadrimaculatus* was about 31°C (88°F) and the threshold of development about

7°C (45°F). There is general agreement among research workers that the temperature should be maintained between 24° and 32°C (75° and 90°F), but some laboratories prefer the upper part of the range and others the lower part.

The problems connected with the maintenance of satisfactory temperatures will vary with the region in which the insects are reared. In temperate climates a source of heat is essential if the colony is needed during the winter, whereas in the tropics cooling is the prime requirement. Any type of heater that does not inject toxic gases into the air should prove satisfactory. Similarly, the air conditioner used for cooling can be as simple as a small window unit or as elaborate as the circulating-water units used to cool large laboratories. Some type of thermostatic control is desirable to eliminate the necessity of making frequent adjustments.

If adult mosquitoes are to be kept alive more than a few days some humidity control is essential. Even in climates as damp as that of Florida the installation of humidifiers has helped considerably to prolong the life of these insects. High humidities, however, can be as disastrous as low humidity, because the wings of the insects become so wet they stick to the sides of the cage, and a heavy coating of mold develops on the walls and ceiling of the rearing room. A humidity somewhere between 50 and 80% appears to be the most desirable.

The humidifier can be simple or complex. If funds are limited adequate humidity control can be obtained by draping wet cloths over the cages in which insects are being maintained. If larger areas need to be controlled an electric fan can be placed to blow on cloths that have one end inserted in a pan of water. The cloth serves as a wick. The cloth has to be dampened occasionally as the capillary attraction is seldom sufficiently good to keep it continuously wet. Pans of water placed on heaters will also raise the humidity in a room. More accurate control is desirable and available through the use of commercial automatic humidifiers equipped with a humidistat.

The importance of accurate control of light conditions in the rearing room is somewhat controversial. Because the adults normally mate and lay eggs at dusk or after dark, some investigators contend that the rearing room should be kept dark except while technicians are working with the colony. However, the Gainesville Laboratory of the Entomology Research Division, U.S. Department of Agriculture, has successfully maintained a colony of A. *quadrimaculatus* for more than 20 years in rooms with unshaded windows. Under field conditions larvae of this species thrive in fields that are subjected to sunlight throughout the daylight hours, and the adults often bite during the daytime in animal barns. The author believes accurate light control is not one of the primary requirements for maintaining *A. quadrimaculatus*. The lighting conditions that normally occur in rooms not lighted continuously throughout the entire day are adequate.

In addition to these regulating devices all rearing rooms should have a series of shelves or racks to store the larval containers as well as several tables on which the cages of adult mosquitoes can be kept and the routine phases of the rearing process can be carried out. Preferably these furnishings should not be in contact with the wall and their legs should be placed in containers partially filled with water, oil, or one of the dust diluents, such as pyrophyllite, to prevent ants from destroying or seriously damaging the colony. A supply of containers for rearing the larvae, adult cages, a refrigerator for storing perishable supplies, miscellaneous pieces of glassware, and a source of water will also be needed. Good screening is needed to prevent the escape of any adult mosquitoes that get loose in the room.

IV. CARE OF THE ADULTS

There are numerous sizes and shapes of cages that are suitable for confining the adult mosquitoes. Most of them are satisfactory as long as they are tight enough to prevent the mosquitoes from escaping and large enough to allow unrestricted mating. Strains that will mate in large cages also can be expected to mate in cages with no more than 1 ft³ capacity. Since a large variety of cages is available, the type employed will depend on one's personal choice. The frame is usually wood or metal. The latter material is preferable because it is easier to wash. At least three sides of the cage should be covered with wire screen having at least 18 mesh to the inch or with mosquito netting. The top and bottom may also be covered with these materials, but some laboratories use ¼-inch plywood on these surfaces. Since an opening must be furnished to gain access to the cage, one side usually is covered with a glass slide, a door, or a cloth sleeve. The cloth sleeve has a distinct advantage in that the size of the opening can be adjusted to permit insertion of an arm without giving the mosquitoes space to escape. Recently there has been a trend toward covering the entire frame with tubular gauze and tying the two ends with string to complete the enclosure. This covering is disposable and reduces the labor involved in cleaning the cage.

The number of adult mosquitoes maintained per cage will vary with the size of the enclosure. The population should be high enough that the males and females can easily find each other when they are ready to mate, but low enough that individual mosquitoes moving from one spot to another do not disturb other mosquitoes sufficiently to keep them continuously in flight. The Ross Institute in London (Anonymous, 1963) maintains approximately 250 males and 250 females in cages with 1 ft³ capacity, and at our laboratory we keep several thousand in a cage 30 inches square by 25 inches high. New mosquitoes can be added to the same cage or other cages can be started periodically to maintain the breeding stock.

It is necessary that each cage be supplied with a source of food and water as well as a surface on which the females can lay eggs. Most investigators supply sugar, honey, or fruit juices as the males die within a few days if furnished only water. A piece of absorbant cotton, filter paper, or paper toweling dipped in a 10–50% solution of one of these materials in water can be placed in a small dish or suspended from the top of the cage. A screen wire cover over the dish will prevent the mosquitoes from getting stuck in the food. More elaborate apparatus that maintains the food level constant can also be used. Coluzzi (1964) has used a trough that consists of a tank and a side cup. The liquid in the cup maintains its level and keeps a piece of filter paper continuously wet until the supply in the tank is exhausted. Water must be supplied or the adults soon die. Later in this article methods of collecting eggs will be discussed. Since water is needed for this purpose no other source of moisture is required to keep the adults from dehydrating. With proper care adults live 1 to 3 weeks.

Females need a blood meal for ovarian development. Small mammals, such as rabbits, guinea pigs, rats, mice, or chickens are used for this purpose. A plentiful supply of such animals is needed so no one animal is used more often than once every 2 or 3 weeks. The animals can be placed inside the cage or against the outside of the covering where the mosquitoes can feed through the opening in the screen or cloth. The mosquitoes feed more readily on animals that are quiet than on those that are moving. For this reason animals that are introduced into the rearing cage should be fastened to a stanchion or confined in a small hardware cloth cage that is just large enough to hold them. When a stanchion is used the animal is sometimes laid on its back in a V-shaped frame and its legs are fastened to posts at the corners. In others a stock attached to the end of a wooden platform is fastened around the neck to immobilize the head. Animals that are used while outside of the cage or that are not otherwise restricted inside of the cage should be anesthetized with Nembutal administered intraperitoneally [1 ml for each 5 lb (2.3 kg) of body weight]. In every case the side of the animal that is most readily accessible to the mosquitoes should be denuded of hair with electric clippers or scissors to allow the mosquitoes to feed readily. Some type of covering is desirable over the head of the host to prevent the mosquitoes from attacking the eyes, nose, and mouth. A 15 to 120-minute feeding period each day will be sufficient.

If other types of animals are unavailable the females will feed on the arm of a man. Care should be taken in selecting individuals for this purpose as some people get severe reactions if bitten frequently by *Anopheles* mosquitoes.

V. COLLECTION OF EGGS

Under field conditions *A. quadrimaculatus* normally lays its eggs on the surface of the breeding water. In the laboratory a pan or bowl of water placed in the adult cage will serve as the egg-collecting medium. Greenwald *et al.* (1948) reported that initial stocking of a breeding cage with about 5,000 mosquitoes and subsequent replenishment at weekly intervals with 2,000 adults gave an average daily egg production of 15,000 to 20,000 eggs. They also found that the first eggs were laid the day after the initial stocking and feeding of the females on a blood meal. Full production was reached by the end of the first week. The black, boat-shaped eggs, pointed at each end, are laid singly on the surface of the water. The eggs have a pair of floats which keep them from sinking. Some investigators line the pans or bowls with paper to prevent the eggs from becoming stranded on the sides and drying out. Unlike *Aedes* eggs, those of *A. quadrimaculatus* cannot withstand dessication so the oviposition surface must be kept continuously wet. Coluzzi (1964) recommends that damp filter paper be used for a deposition surface rather than a pan or bowl of water. Eggs are usually laid at night. Within 24 hours these containers should be replaced with others as the eggs hatch within 30 to 40 hours. The eggs can be left in the original container until they hatch or be transferred to filter paper or other pans immediately. If it is desirable to concentrate them, the excess water can be siphoned off, leaving the eggs stranded on the bottoms and sides of the container. A wash bottle or pipette is then used to wash the eggs into a beaker. Whenever a surplus of eggs is obtained, the excess supply may be wrapped in damp filter paper or toweling and stored in a refrigerator. The eggs will remain viable for approximately 10 days to 2 weeks for use on days when egg production is insufficient to meet the needs.

VI. CARE OF THE LARVAE

There is also considerable variation in the type of containers that have been used for larval rearing. The only requirements are that the container be clean and hold water. White enamelware and polyethylene pans 12 inches in diameter, photographic developing trays, or battery jars are suitable containers, but other types will work equally well. A light background is preferable to a dark one as it facilitates observation of the larvae. Since A. *quadrimaculatus* spends most of its time at the surface and the food often sinks to the bottom, feeding can be facilitated by keeping the water shallow in the rearing container. Enough water should be supplied to permit the mosquitoes to move about freely and still have easy access to the food on the bottom of the container. A water depth of approximately 1 inch has been found quite satisfactory.

Considerable attention should be paid to selection of the rearing water as this factor can play an important part in the health of the colony. If tap water is only lightly chlorinated it serves as a satisfactory medium. High concentrations of chlorine, however, can be so toxic that many larvae are killed. Under such conditions, rain, well, spring, lake, or distilled water can be used. Boiling the tap water and cooling it to room temperature before using may also remove the excess chlorine. While not an absolute necessity it is suggested that all water be held in the laboratory for at least 24 hours to enable it to reach room temperature, since the use of cold water may delay the egg hatch and maturation of the larvae. Unless a cover is used fresh water will be needed in all rearing pans each day to replace the liquid that evaporates.

The mosquitoes can be introduced into the rearing containers as eggs or larvae. Eggs sometimes become stranded on the sides of the rearing container and fail to hatch. This difficulty can be avoided by surrounding the eggs with a floating paper ring that has a hole in its center. There is no universal agreement on the exact number of eggs to use, but Fay (1963) recommended 400 to 700, Greenwald *et al.* (1948) suggested 1000, and the author prefers 100 to 250 eggs or larvae to a pan 12-inches in diameter. If too many are used the larvae, pupae, and adults produced are small and unhealthy and the mortality rate is high; cannibalism also occurs and the time required for larval growth is extended. If an insufficient number is used the larvae do not consume the food fast enough to prevent excessive decomposition and scum formation on the surface of the water. The only accurate method of determining the exact number of eggs introduced into the rearing pan is to count them. However, where large colonies are involved this task becomes time-consuming. In such cases the number used is usually estimated. Fay (1963) has suggested a few aids that will avoid the estimate becoming merely a guess. One method is to remove the eggs from the surface in a water film retained by a ⅜-inch diameter loop of 0.02-inch wire and transfer them to the rearing pan. The eggs may also be removed with an elliptical loop of 0.02-inch wire from the surface of 125 ml of water in a 4-inch diameter finger bowl that is rotating rapidly on a turntable; as the loop is raised slowly it fills completely with a single layer of eggs. A loop with axes of 3 and 11 mm will hold approximately 250 eggs.

In some laboratories all eggs are hatched in a single container of water and aliquots of the water and larvae are transferred to the rearing containers. Fay (1963) suggests that the water in the original container be stirred slowly with a mechanical mixer to distribute the insects evenly and that the number of larvae in a series of 1-ml samples be counted before measured aliquots are transferred to the rearing containers. When the eggs are allowed to hatch in the oviposition pan or bowl the water may need to be screened to eliminate dead adults and touched with a paper towel to remove unhatched eggs before the larval transfers are made.

Much of the information needed to evaluate the nutritional requirements of A. *quadrimaculatus* accurately has never been worked out. At the present time, most of the established A. *quadrimaculatus* colonies are being fed on balanced diets that contain carbohydrates, fats, minerals, and proteins. Since Crowell (1940) discovered that ground dog biscuits were a better larval diet than hay infusion, these biscuits have been used extensively. In some laboratories rabbit, mouse, or baby food is substituted for the dog food. Yeast is often included at concentrations of 10 or 20% as a supplement. Fay (1963) also recommends a preparation containing 60% whole wheat flour, 25% powdered yeast, 10% blood meal, and 5% nonfat dried milk. The ingredients are ground into a fine powder and kept dry until added to the breeding containers. If ground sufficiently fine the small particles will remain on the surface of the water for several hours where they are easily accessible to the larvae.

The author believes no specific instructions can be given to help others determine the quantity of food that should be supplied on any particular occasion, primarily because there is a variation in the rate of growth of different batches of larvae. Personnel doing the rearing must learn from experience how to regulate food amounts. Some laboratories provide no food on the first day; others lightly dust the water as soon as larvae become visible. It is apparent, however, that only small amounts of food are needed during the first instar and the daily requirements gradually increase as the larvae mature. Frequent observations must be made to ascertain that the food being added is consumed and that a sufficient amount is furnished to prevent stunting. Fay (1963) and Trembley (1955) have attempted to estimate the daily food requirements. Fay suggests the following quantities be used once a day in enamelware pans 10 to 12 inches in diameter that contain 500 larvae in 1 liter of water: 1st day, none; 2nd day, 20 mg; 3rd day, 60 mg; 4th day, 120 mg; 5th day, 80 mg; 6th day, 240 mg; 7th day, 360 mg; 8th day, 420 mg; 9th day, 480 mg; 10th day, 540 mg; 11th day, 420 mg; 12th day, 120 mg; 13th day, discontinue feeding. When Trembley used 300 larvae in $16 \times 19.5 \times 2$ inch trays with about 0.5 inch of distilled water, she sprinkled "on the water a pinch (25 mg) of powdered dry brewer's yeast and one pinch of Bacto-Brain Heart infusion" the night before hatching was expected. As soon as the larvae became visible, she added approximately 100 mg of a 1:1 mixture of powdered yeast and powdered dog food. The next day she started the following daily schedule of the yeast-dog food mixture: 1st day, 50 mg; 2nd and 3rd days, 100 mg; 4th to 14th days, 150 mg; unless there was an excess of food. Dividing the food into two or more applications a day will produce healthier larvae than a single feeding.

Although hay infusion has been used extensively in the past as larval food it is rarely used today. However, plant material is still employed in some laboratories and is reported to have a beneficial effect on the mosquitoes. The Ross Institute (Anonymous, 1963) has employed 4-inch ^{2} (25 cm²) pieces of grass turf in each larval container. They consider that this grass and its associated sod provide microorganisms for the very young larvae. Trembley (1955) reported that other investigators also have found that vegetation such as floating plants, algae, and grass promoted the development of larvae of *Anopheles maculipennis* Meigen. The author has watched larvae of *A. quadrimaculatus* feed on algae. Since plants form an important part of the natural breeding habitat of these mosquitoes it is likely they perform some function in the nutrition of larvae as well as furnishing protection.

Scum formation on the breeding medium is one of the principal problems encountered in rearing this species. Unless it is controlled a colony cannot be maintained successfully. It is one of the primary reasons care must be taken to prevent overfeeding for an excess of food usually results in sufficient scum collecting on the surface of the water to prevent the larvae from getting the oxygen they need. It must be removed with a spoon or at least broken up by bubbling air through the water. Care must be taken to avoid too violent aeration as larvae also will drown when the water is so rough that they cannot surface to obtain air. Asahina (1964) suggested that adding plant infusion or some absorbent material such as sand, loam, charcoal, or blotting paper to the bottom of the rearing container may be helpful in preventing scum formation. Whenever the scum becomes heavy the larvae should be carefully poured onto a fine-mesh screen and transferred to clean water.

Even though a colony is given the best attention some larval mortality can be expected. Proper evaluation of the importance of this kill varies with the number of mosquitoes needed. If a colony is being reared to obtain specimens for demonstration purposes or to conduct only occasional tests, a larval mortality rate of 25 to 50% may be unimportant, since enough survivors will remain to fill the needs. If, however, an extremely large number of adults is needed, as when sterile males are being released in a large-scale control program, loss of even 10 to 25% of the production could be a serious matter.

The time required to complete larval development will vary with the conditions furnished and the problems encountered. It can be as short as 7 or 8 days and as long as 22 to 23 days, but usually takes slightly more than 1 week if highly favorable conditions prevail.

Until more is learned about the factors that control the appetite and development of A. quadrimaculatus the successful rearing of larvae will depend partially on the skill and industry of the personnel who do the rearing.

VII. CARE OF THE PUPAE

After the larvae complete their development they pupate in the rearing containers. Usually several days to a week or longer pass between the time the first and last insects in a rearing container make the change. Because this stage lasts less than 2 days, all pupae should be removed from the rearing container at least once each day and placed in another pan or bowl of water. Unless this transfer is made regularly the adults will emerge and escape into the room.

Separation can be accomplished by pouring the contents of the rearing pans through the pupae separator described by Fay and Morlan (1959). This apparatus traps the pupae and allows the larvae to pass as the insect culture is poured between two plates of glass that are more constricted at one end than the other. The pupae of this species are so delicate that this treatment frequently injures many of them and they die without reaching the adult stage. Where the need for mosquitoes is small or moderate the number raised can sometimes be increased to compensate for this loss.

If the colony is small or the technician is not pressed for time the pupae can be transferred one at a time with a large medicine dropper or with a small, spoon-shaped sieve that is made by covering a small metal loop with wire screening or mosquito netting. This procedure is too laborious to use with very large colonies for it can take more time than all of the other rearing activities combined. An experienced worker can transfer about 1500 pupae per hour without injuring them.

Weathersby (1963) developed a separation method employing ice water that shows promise of being superior to any of the other methods. The contents of the rearing container are poured into netting or a sieve that will allow passage of the water but hold the larvae and pupae. The filtered culture water can be saved. The netting or sieve is then inverted into another basin or a funnel that contains ice water at a temperature of 38°–40°F (3.3°–4.4°C). The insects are immediately immobilized; the pupae float on the surface of the water and the larvae sink to the bottom. If a basin is used the top layer of ice water can then be poured carefully through the sieve, after which the sieve is inverted and touched to the top surface of water in another container to remove the pupae. The bottom layer is handled the same way to re-collect the larvae. Hazard (1964) modified the method of Weathersby by putting the ice water in a glass funnel that had a glass pet cock attached to the stem with a section of rubber tubing. With this arrangement the layers of water containing the larvae and pupae can be separated more easily by allowing them to flow through the pet cock onto a sieve. The larvae are usually returned to their original culture. Occasionally a few pupae are found with the larvae; they can be removed with the medicine dropper or small spoon-shaped sieve. If there is too much detritus in the original culture water, a fresh supply that has reached room temperature can be used. This method of separation is as fast as the pupae separator and causes less injury to the insects. There is no evidence so far that the cold water shock even extends the time for larvae to complete their cycle. Weathersby estimated that the time required for experienced personnel to harvest 1000 pupae from 1000 fourth instar larvae averages 52 minutes using a medicine dropper and 3.5 minutes with cold water. All pupae removed from the rearing container should be placed in another container of water. Greenwald et al. (1948) estimated that a 5-inch crystallization dish held about 100 pupae.

The container of pupae in water is sometimes put into the adult holding cage. Because *Anopheles* mosquitoes will lay on any water surface available, this container is generally covered with a screen cone that has an opening approximately 1 inch in diameter at the constricted end. This opening permits the emerging adults to escape into the larger cage, but prevents the fertile females from laying eggs on the water in the pupal container. The cones are not needed when the pupae are placed in empty cages because emergence is completed before egg laying starts.

VIII. DISCUSSION

It must be realized that *A. quadrimaculatus* from laboratory colonies may not react in every situation the same as those in natural habitats. The small proportion of individuals present in a natural population that will adapt to living under laboratory conditions shows that a colony may be composed of abnormal insects. When the actions of two colonies were studied in a box in which the light intensity could be controlled, mosquitoes from a colony reared in the laboratory for many years were active when a light intensity equal to that at dusk was programed. They were seen mating in the air, but swarming was not a preliminary to copulation. Sometimes coition was completed in flight, but at other times both mosquitoes fell to the bottom of the cage and completed the act. When the F_1 generation from field-collected adults was exposed to the same light intensity, they either spent their time trying to escape or sat quietly on the sides of the box. When disturbed they made no attempt to mate and flew a distance of only 1 or 2 ft before landing again. For this reason care must be exercised in using the results obtained with laboratory-reared mosquitoes to predict results that will be obtained with natural populations.

It is becoming increasingly difficult to establish colonies from field-collected mosquitoes that have acquired no resistance to insecticides. In areas where control programs have been conducted regularly most of the important species have developed some tolerance to one or more insecticides. Other strains breeding close to large farming areas where no mosquito-control operations were being attempted have been subjected to some selection because of the adults contacting plants that had been treated to kill leaf-feeding insects. Even colonies that have been raised for many years in the laboratory without intentional exposure to insecticides may develop some tolerance because the grains used in preparing the dog-food biscuits that are fed to the larvae sometimes contain residual deposits of insecticides. The Orlando strain of A. *quadrimaculatus,* which has been reared in captivity for more than 20 years, became 100 times as resistant to dieldrin in the late 1950's than it was during the early part of the 1940's.

There is a tendency in a large entomological laboratory to consider insect rearing a routine job that can be entrusted to low-salaried personnel; those engaged in this type of endeavor often feel they are a service organization that merely relieves others of a routine task. Actually, those engaged in insect rearing are doing one of the most essential tasks and have assumed one of the prime responsibilities of the organization, for without an ample supply of insects other members of the staff cannot conduct their studies. If salaries were based on the importance of the functions performed, the individual directing the colony work could justifiably be one of the highest paid individuals on the staff. At least the members of the group deserve a vote of thanks for doing a job that is often difficult and is seldom appreciated adequately.

REFERENCES

Anonymous (1963). "Practical Entomology in Malaria Eradication," Part I, MHO/PA/ 62.63, pp. 118–130. W.H.O. Division of Malaria Eradication, Geneva, Switzerland.

Asahina, S. (1964). Food material and feeding procedures for mosquito larvae. *Bull. World Health Organ.* **31,** 465–466.

Baker, R. H., French, W. L., and Kitzmiller, J. B. (1962). Induced copulation in *Anopheles* mosquitoes. *Mosquito News* **22,** 16–17.

Coluzzi, M. (1964). Maintenance of laboratory colonies of *Anopheles* mosquitoes. *Bull. World Health Organ.* **31,** 441–443.

Crowell, R. L. (1940). Insectory rearing of *Anopheles quadrimaculatus. Am. J. Hyg.* **C32,** 12–20.

Fay, R. W. (1963). Personal communication.

Fay, R. W., and Morlan, H. B. (1959). A mechanical device for separating the developmental stages, sexes and species of mosquitoes. *Mosquito News* **19,** 144–147.

Greenwald, M., Cochran, J. H., and Scharff, D. L. (1948). Large-scale rearing of *Anopheles quadrimaculatus* Say at Orlando, Florida. *Mosquito News* **8,** 50–56.

Hazard, E. I. (1964). Unpublished data.

Huffaker, C. B. (1944). The temperature relations of the immature stages of the malarial mosquito *Anopheles quadrimaculatus* Say with a comparison of the developmental power of constant and variable temperatures in insect metabolism. *Ann. Entomol. Soc. Am.* **37,** 1–27.

McDaniel, I. N., and Horsefall, W. R. (1957). Induced copulation of Aedine mosquitoes. *Science* **125,** 745.

Muirhead-Thomson, R. C. (1940). Studies on behavior of *Anopheles minimus*—Pt III. The influence of water temperatures on the choice and suitability of the breeding-place. *J. Malaria Inst. India* **3,** 323–348.

Ow Yang, C. K., Sta Maria, F. L., and Wharton, R. H. (1963). Maintenance of a laboratory colony of *Anopheles maculatus* Theobald by artificial mating. *Mosquito News* **23**, 34–35.

Trembley, H. L. (1955). Mosquito culture techniques and experimental procedures. *Am. Mosquito Control Assoc., Bull.* **3**, 14–20.

Ward, R. A., and Kitzmiller, J. B. (1963). A list of laboratory colonies of Anopheline mosquitoes. *Mosquito News* **23**, 291–297.

Weathersby, A. B. (1963). Harvesting mosquito pupae with cold water. *Mosquito News* **23**, 249–251.

Chapter 7

Culex pipiens fatigans Wied.

Botha de Meillon* and Vijayamma Thomas

WHO Filariasis Research Unit,
Burma Medical Research Institute,
Rangoon, Burma, and
College of Agriculture,
Serdang-Selangor,
Sungei Besi P.O. Malaysia

I. INTRODUCTION

Culex pipiens fatigans Wied. is a hardy mosquito distributed throughout most of the tropical and subtropical regions of the world. It finds the best conditions for proliferation when associated with man and so has become the major transmitter of Bancroft's filariasis in many parts of the world. In the cities and towns of many countries in which it was formerly rare or absent, and where rapid urbanization has outstripped sanitation, it is now a common and often the most abundant mosquito (Mattingly, 1962).

In nature it breeds prolifically in stagnant water in any type of man-made larval habitat such as drains, above or underground, ground pools, cesspools, septic tanks, pit latrines, and a host of other

Present address: Army Mosquito Project, Smithsonian Institute, U. S. National Museum, Washington, D. C.

places provided there is a sufficient degree of organic pollution. The adults are domestic and may be found resting in moist places, in cupboards or any relatively dark spot, on dark clothing, household articles, on hangings, and walls. They also occur in large numbers in some countries, at least, on vegetation, in unoccupied shelters such as lavatories, and empty buildings, abandoned motor cars, old drums, sheds, and so on, provided there is shelter from wind and sun.

The variety of resting site favored by the adult assists them in avoiding contact insecticides sprayed on walls. In addition *C. fatigans* possesses great genetic and physiological plasticity to resist insecticides. All these factors contribute to make it one of the most formidable and successful urban mosquitoes.

In the tropics, provided suitable breeding places are available, the species is prevalent throughout the year and all stages can easily be collected from natural breeding or resting places. All stages are easily adapted to a great range of artificial laboratory-rearing conditions so that the insect is readily colonized and maintained. Standardization of the various factors and techniques are a matter of personal preference; however, it is advisable to do the rearing under a set of standardized conditions to get uniform and comparable results. In addition, the method of obtaining materials for a colony and its maintenance should depend upon the purpose for which the mosquitoes are required.

II. COLONIES FOR GENERAL PURPOSES

Colonies for general purposes can be established from any stage collected from the natural breeding or resting places. It is, however, easier to establish them from egg rafts or adults.

A. EGG RAFTS

Egg rafts collected from natural breeding grounds or obtained from gravid females caught in resting places are kept for hatching in enamel or glass bowls which contain distilled or tap water. The interval between oviposition and hatching of eggs varies depending upon the temperature. Around $29° \pm 1°C$ temperature, the egg rafts collected from the field hatch within 20 to 28 hours (mean, 24 hours). The mean time between actual oviposition and hatching is about 36 hours at the above temperature.

Usually a high percentage of the field-collected egg rafts hatch completely, but a certain proportion hatch only partially because of the presence of unfertilized eggs or eggs containing dead embryos.

A small percentage of rafts do not hatch at all and this has been shown to be the result of nonfertilization (de Meillon and Sebastian, 1965).

B. LARVAE

Newly hatched larvae are small but sturdy. They can be grown in distilled, rain, or tap water, provided adequate food is supplied, in any type of shallow container.

1. *Rearing Dishes*

Rearing dishes can be either of glass, porcelain, or enamelware which are either rectangular or round in shape. Enamelware is preferable to other types as it is unbreakable, light, and easily handled and cleaned. The size of the rearing dishes depends upon the number of larvae reared. It is advisable to have different sizes of rearing dishes for different purposes. A suitable container for rearing 500–1000 larvae to the adult stage is a photographic dish measuring 25×35 cm. Such a dish filled with 2500 ml of water will allow 2.5 to 5 ml/larva and 0.9 to 1.8 cm^2 of surface area per larva. This is adequate to allow the production of large and vigorous adults.

2. *Larval Food and Other Rearing Conditions*

Larvae are omnivorous and thrive well on a variety of food and under a wide range of temperature and light intensities. Larvae can even develop perfectly in complete darkness (Jobling, 1937). The rate of growth, however, depends upon temperature, quantity, and quality of food supply and density of larvae per unit surface area as well as the unit volume of water. Good results are obtained when the temperature is around 29°C with about 2.5 to 5 ml of water per larva or less than 3 larvae per cm^2 of water surface.

The question of larval food is often determined by what is locally available and personal idiosyncrasy. In fact, the larval food in the form of rabbit dung, dog biscuit, grass or alfalfa infusion, yeast, and so on, serve largely as media for the growth of bacteria and yeasts on which the larvae actually feed. The scum which forms on breeding dishes after the addition of larval food is really the sign of a rich and adequate medium for larval growth. Larvae may be seen feeding on this by turning their heads to the surface and spinning round their siphons which form an anchor, and neglecting the debris on the bottom of the dish. Some mortality may arise when the scum is left undisturbed and becomes too dense. In the latter case simple stirring with a glass spatula will serve to break up the surface. Aerating, removal of scum with filter paper, and changing the water are not necessary except in very special circumstances. As a matter of fact the larvae themselves soon remove the surface scum and growth is retarded thereby unless it is induced to form again by adding more larval food. The great dangers ascribed to the presence of scum by Asahina (1964) do not seem to apply to *C. fatigans.* Since the scum is the result of contamination, largely by airborne organisms, its composition will no doubt vary not only from place to place but also from season to season. It is therefore likely that some scums will prove to be more lethal than others.

Insufficient food and overcrowding retard growth, prolong larval life, and give rise to small adults which are often not uniform in size. There is a complete linear correlation between food supply, overcrowding, and size of adult which is directly related to fecundity (Ikeshoji, 1965a).

3. A Simple Routine for Obtaining Large, Robust Adults

About 750 first-stage larvae from several egg rafts are counted into an enamel photographic dish measuring 25 × 35 cm and holding 2500 ml of water. One gram of a good dog biscuit such as finely ground Spratt's Bonio* is added at the same time or the day before and the water is stirred. One gram of this food is added each day until day 4 or 5, and each day the water is stirred a few times. No further attention is needed. In a dry climate the breeding water may evaporate too much but it is a simple matter to keep it up to the 2500-ml mark by the addition of tap water. Pupation will commence, at 29°C ± 1°C, on day 5; by day 7 80% or more of the larvae will have pupated. Adults from these larvae will have a wing length of 3.87 ± 0.18 mm.

Pupae are pipetted off as they arise, transferred to an adult cage, and supplied with a weak solution of sugar water. Such adults when fed on chicken will deposit rafts of from 228 to 280 eggs.

Trays such as these set up at daily intervals will ensure a steady supply of standard adults for experimental purposes.

If the number of available larvae is small and limited then special care has to be taken. The water may be changed and scum removed with filter paper so as to avoid accidental deaths.

In an insectarium where a number of adult colonies are maintained there is always the possibility of escaped stray adults contaminating larval cultures by oviposition. This is prevented by covering

---

* According to the makers the percentage composition of Bonio is as follows: protein 13, carbohydrate 69, oil 1.18, fiber 0.57, ash 3.97, phosphorus 0.48, calcium 0.85, salt 0.41. According to Dr. Tin Tin Oo of the Burma Medical Research Institute, who kindly carried out a more detailed analysis for FRU (Filariasis Research Unit), the biscuit also contains vitamin B_1 μg% 183, vitamin B_2 μg% 60, and iron mg% 12.94.

the culture dishes with a muslin net. Simply removing newly deposited rafts each day is not sufficient, since adults quite commonly scatter their eggs and such eggs are not easily seen.

C. PUPAE

Males pupate first, and are smaller than female pupae; this difference in size may be used for separating the sexes in the pupal stage. For a normal-sized laboratory colony, 250 to 300 pupae—males and females in approximately equal numbers—are placed in an adult cage which is provided with water and raisins or any other source of sugar. The pupal stage lasts about 48 hours at $29° \pm 1°C$ temperature.

Pupae which come from healthy and well-nourished larval cultures are larger than those coming from undernourished and/or overcrowded cultures. Pupae are separated from larvae by hand-picking with a pipette. If pupation is uniform and completed within 24 hours, a small screen-wire scooper or a muslin strainer may be used to collect them from the rearing water. In large cultures, however, the pupation is often spread over 2 or more days and faster methods have to be used (see Section V, A).

D. ADULTS

Emergence from pupae is spread over about 30 hours, with the males emerging first. Although the larval and pupal stages are usually completed in a relatively straightforward manner, the feeding and ovarian cycles of the adults are more complicated. There are a number of physiological and environmental factors which stimulate or arrest these cycles completely or partially. These factors, their interrelationships, or the extent to which each factor alone or in combination with others is responsible for the activities of the females are not yet fully understood.

1. Cages

The size of the cages should depend upon the number of adults that is maintained for each colony. These cages should be easily constructed and durable. It should be easy to feed the adult mosquitoes and insert materials such as pupae, water, sugar, and host animals, and to remove egg rafts. There should be sufficient visibility to permit detection of even slight blood meals in mosquitoes. It must be possible to remove fed or unfed adults from cages for experimental purposes. The opportunity for the adults to escape during these various operations should be minimal. Finally, it should be easy to clean the cages.

Various types of cages incorporating some or many of these features have been described by Young and Burgess (1946), Boyd (1949), Trembley (1955), and Chao (1959). These are either glass or plastic cylinders or cages covered with screen netting all around. Most of these are provided with suitable lengths of sleeves in front which make possible all required manipulations inside the cage.

For routine maintenance purposes, simple cages, preferably with a plywood base, supported on four short legs to take ant guards, and a wooden and metal frame with nylon netting screen on all three sides and top are very satisfactory. It is useful to have the back of the cage provided with a removable plywood up-and-down sliding door which greatly facilitates cleaning. Nylon netting is the most suitable material because it is lighter than wire, more durable than cloth, and more important, offers better visibility than either. The front of this cage is provided with a port of 8-inch diameter which is guarded by a suitable length of sleeve made of the same netting. Such a cage, approximately $1 \times 1 \times 1$ ft, or larger, seems to be ideal for maintaining 250 to 300 adults. These dimensions can be altered to suit the requirements; the figures are intended to serve merely as a guide. Such cages are cheap, durable, and easily constructed and cleaned. The only disadvantage is that there is a possibility of adults escaping during handling. If a little care is taken while opening the sleeves, the number of adults escaping can be minimized to an insignificant level.

Pollard (1960) has described a cage with a built-in compartment for the host animal. Such a cage prevents the escape of adults during insertion and removal of the host. During other operations, the possibility of escape remains the same.

When genetic, resistance, or infectivity studies are carried out, the number of available adults is often small. It is then essential to prevent the escape or entry of any adult mosquito. For this, the intricately designed mosquito-tight cage (Bar-Zeev and Galun, 1960) can be used. These cages are expensive and complicated and practice is required in learning to handle them.

2. Mating

In confinement, mating occurs a day or two after emergence. Adults mate readily in cages of 1 ft³ which seems to be an ideal and practical size for maintaining colonies of 250 to 300 adults. Many strains mate in smaller cages and some may even mate in small cages of $8 \times 4 \times 4$ inches. Successful artificial insemination has not been reported.

3. Feeding

a. Males. Raisins, diluted honey, or any other type of sugar provides their needs and they start feeding shortly after emergence.

b. Females. The females feed on blood and sugar solution. While in confinement, females feed readily on chicken, guinea pig, rabbit, or man. They feed on the blood host only at night or in darkness. Some females can sometimes be fed during daytime if the cage is kept in a dark room or covered with a black cotton shroud.

A number of extrinsic and intrinsic factors affect the feeding cycle of females. The more important of these seem to be the state of hunger and age of the females. Usually the young females do not feed on the blood host until the third or fourth night after emergence. After the first feeding, a chicken or guinea pig, held in a restrainer, is put overnight in the cage, twice a week.

In almost every generation and strain there are some exceptional females which do not feed until 14 to 17 days after emergence, even though a host is placed in the cage twice a week. A far greater number of adults emerging from DDT-selected larvae show reluctance to feed. Removal of sugar supply from cages 12 to 18 hours prior to the introduction of host helps a greater number of females to feed on blood. The factors—intrinsic or extrinsic—that are responsible for this sort of reluctance are not known.

4. Oviposition

The gonatrophic cycle, that is, the time taken from blood meal to oviposition, depends on temperature. At $29 \pm 1°C$ it is 3 days provided the adult has no access to sugar solutions after the blood meal, since this is known to delay oviposition (de Meillon and Sebastian, 1964).

Culex fatigans is anautogenous and a minimum quantity of blood —approximately one third of the mosquito body weight—is required to initiate ovarian development. Normally a single blood meal is sufficient to cause maturation of the ovaries. In occasional specimens more than one blood meal is required for this purpose.

The size of the egg raft depends on the size of the adult and the quantity and quality of the blood meal. After a feed on man about 50% of the follicles develop, whereas after chicken this percentage is increased to 80% (Ikeshoji, 1965b).

Other irregularities have been noted in maturation and development of the eggs. After deposition of the main part of the raft, some females retain a variable number of mature eggs in one or both ovaries. Mature eggs which have been retained may be deposited later. Retention of eggs in a full ovary for too long a period causes them to become hardened and impacted (de Meillon and Sebastian, 1965).

Peculiarities of development and behavior seem to be aggravated among adults which have emerged from DDT-resistant selected larvae. This may be due to direct toxic aftereffects of the insecticide which is inevitably present in various tissues of the body, or to selection of lethal and sublethal factors.

Difficulty in inducing the females to feed and lay eggs over a short period can be a serious drawback in studies on infectivity, genetics, and insecticide resistance.

a. Oviposition Water. The chemical and physical properties of water available for oviposition are of great importance in egg laying. The adults oviposit freely on organically polluted waters such as infusions of dog biscuit, dung, grass, and rice straw which have a strong smell. It is also waters of this type which provide the best growing media for the larvae. In the absence of such attractive waters the adults will, of course, oviposit on tap or even distilled water. It has been found that highly polluted breeding waters from the field contain an ether-soluble, highly volatile attractant for gravid females. Such waters also contain an arrestant and an oviposition stimulant (Ikeshoji, 1965c).

The presence of some chemicals, such as 2 ppm Triton X-55, which is a surfactant (Gjullin, 1961), and 1% sodium chloride (de Zulueta, 1950) in distilled water, has been shown to repel ovipositing females. Beachwood creosote and N-ethyl N-heptyl-O-veratrylamine, on the other hand, were shown to increase the attractiveness of distilled water (Gjullin, 1961).

Visual stimuli also play a part in the selection of the oviposition site. Gravid females prefer a dark surface to a light one and a broken, rugged, uneven surface with scum and floating materials to one which is light, perfectly smooth, and free of debris.

In the laboratory, the female inspects the available water by exploratory flights which consist of darting rapidly up and down and touching the water with some part of its body (de Meillon and Sebastian, 1965). When satisfied, she either lands directly or crawls from the wall of the container or any other material protruding above the surface of the water onto the ovipositing medium. The female usually takes from 10 to 20 minutes to begin ovipositing which is then completed in 10 to 15 minutes. As the eggs are laid, they are carefully packed together into a raft (Wallis, 1954). Once the female starts egg laying, she is not easily disturbed.

b. Oviposition Time. Females normally lay their eggs at night but oviposition during the daytime in the laboratory is not uncommon. Eggs may be deposited in complete darkness (Jobling, 1937). In complete darkness the gravid female is reported to be guided by the chemical condition of the water or of the water vapor which is given off from the dishes or by the combined action of these two factors (Jobling, 1935; Ikeshoji, 1965c).

Newly laid eggs are white or creamish-white in color. Within about an hour they turn black. The time taken for this color change, depends, among other things, on the strain and environmental factors such as temperature, oxygen tension, and the concentration of ammonia and its salts in the water (Ikeshoji, 1965d). Females will feed again on the blood host soon after oviposition is completed on the same night.

The average number of eggs per raft is about 200 when the adult has fed on chicken and about 110 when fed on man. A female may lay up to 5 rafts; the first raft is often the largest. In the laboratory, females often live up to 8 to 10 weeks, but males are shorter lived. Sugar solutions of more than about 2% when taken by adults increase the longevity but delay oviposition (de Meillon and Sebastian, 1964).

5. *Removing Adults for Experimental Purposes*

For general routine experiment adults are removed from the cage with a suction tube attached to a compressed air line or with a mouth suction tube. With a little practice and care adults are easily picked up without injury.

6. *Anesthesia*

For anesthetic purposes carbon dioxide gas is preferable to either ether or chloroform as it does not have an area of high concentration in a closed cup or bottle that will kill the mosquito falling close by. However, with ordinary care individual mosquitoes may be anesthetized repeatedly with ether. It should be noted that gravid females are more sensitive to ether and carbon dioxide.

III. MAINTAINING COLONIES FOR HIGH VARIABILITY IN STOCK

When colonies are maintained with a limited number of adults derived from a few egg rafts, some degree of selection occurs. In such stock colonies, the initial genetic variability is lost over generations. These inbred colonies are not of much value for studies on susceptibility to infectivity and development of resistance to insecticides.

When a representative colony is needed with as much genetic variability as possible, the original colony should be established from large numbers of adults or egg rafts. These should be collected from as many different places as possible. In all later generations larvae from all available egg rafts should be used. The rafts collected on each day should be kept together to hatch. When hatching is complete in each batch, about 200 larvae should be taken out at random and reared. This process should be repeated every day to obtain larvae from the maximum number of egg rafts. When adults emerge from these larval cultures, a sufficient number of them can be taken at random for maintaining the colonies. Since all adults do not feed and lay eggs on the same day, several days have to be spent collecting all the egg rafts and rearing representative larvae in each generation.

A far superior method of maintaining the variability of the original colony is as follows. In this method, rafts are kept individually to hatch. When hatched, a few larvae from each individual raft are reared to adulthood. A sufficient number of adults are then selected at random from all these. This method of rearing a few larvae from individual rafts allows one to observe and study carefully the performance of larvae of every raft. Then one can exclude those which show a high percentage of lethality, lack of vitality, or any other disturbance in the normal development. However, this method is slow, and the process of maintenance is more time-consuming and laborious. In addition, it requires much larger laboratory space.

IV. MAINTENANCE OF PURE STRAINS FOR GENETIC STUDIES

When absolutely pure strains are needed for genetic studies, strict brother-sister mating and inbreeding are necessary. In most cases, such strictly inbred lines will show inbreeding depressions such as lowered vitality and heavy mortality in various stages. Therefore it may be necessary to maintain a number of single-raft lines simultaneously in each generation. This helps to select the most promising lines in each generation and to eliminate others. If, after a few generations, two closely related lines show heavy lethality or other signs of inbreeding depressions, it may be possible to overcome these by crossing them together for hybrid vigor. This method of colonization needs strict care and skill. It can be done only by trained personnel in specialized laboratories. However, as these pure lines are of extreme genetic value, it is worth taking the trouble to maintain them.

V. MASS REARING

Mass rearing is undertaken when extremely large numbers are required for one reason or another. Special types of rearing dishes, devices to separate larvae from pupae and to sex pupae, and special colony cages to maintain adults are required.

Very large numbers of egg rafts have to be obtained either from field or from stock colonies. Larvae are reared in large trays made of galvanized metal (Fay *et al.*, 1963). The number of such trays will depend upon the number of larvae required. The trays are provided with an outlet for draining and cleaning. Each tray should be large enough to rear at least 15,000 larvae. This is managed by allowing the larvae from about 75 to 80 egg rafts to grow in the tray. Larvae are fed daily and excessive scum formation may be prevented, if necessary, by bubbling air through the water or by stirring vigorously. Pupation commences when the larvae are about 6 or 7 days old.

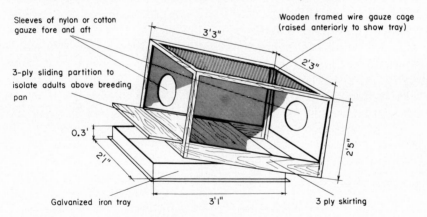

FIG. 1. Cage for mass breeding and transportation of adult mosquitoes.

A suitable cage which serves both for rearing large numbers of larvae and holding the emerging adults is shown in Fig. 1. The galvanized iron tray measures 3 ft 1 in. × 2 ft 1 in. × 0.3 ft and holds about 10 gal of water. It will accommodate with ease 15,000 larvae. The wire cage which covers the breeding tray measures 3 ft 3 inches × 2 ft 3 inches × 2 ft 5 inches and has a removable sliding plywood bottom which can be inserted over the tray when required thus confining the adults in the cage. The cage may then be lifted off the tray and transported to the field if desired.

A. Fast Method of Separating Pupae from Larvae

Separating pupae from larvae is one of the most laborious and time-consuming tasks in mosquito rearing. For a trained person, it takes more than 30 minutes to pick up 1000 pupae from an equal number of larvae with a wide-mouth pipette. This becomes impractical in mass rearing when hundreds of thousands of pupae have to be separated daily.

Various methods of separating these two stages in large-scale rearing of mosquitoes have been reported (Fay and Morlan, 1959; McKiel, 1957; Bar-Zeev and Galun, 1961). The fastest and most satisfactory method of separating them is with ice water (Ramakrishnan *et al.*, 1963; Weathersby, 1963). In this method, the culture with larvae and pupae is drained through the outlet into a muslin strainer by tilting the culture trays. These are then quickly immersed in a large bucket of ice water (3°–4°C). The larvae sink immediately to the bottom of the bucket and remain there for some time, whereas the pupae float. These may be poured or aspirated from the surface. The larvae are then redistributed to the culture dishes and the pupae are left in adult cages. The sudden change of temperature to which these animals are submitted does not affect them adversely or cause any undue mortality among them. Moreover, it is a very fast process. The time required to separate about 10,000 or more pupae from an equal number of larvae does not exceed 5 minutes.

In this method, a very small percentage of larvae may be carried over with the pupae and a few pupae may remain at the bottom of the bucket with larvae. These are later hand collected with a pipette.

B. Sexing Pupae

In colonies maintained for routine purposes, it is not necessary to sex the pupae. When colonies are maintained for crossing experiments or for obtaining only males for incompatibility or sterilization experiments, sexing is important. In small cultures, it is possible to confine pupae individually in small vials until they emerge. After emerging, males and females are kept in separate cages.

This method, however, is not practical or possible when very large numbers of males have to be separated from an equal number of female pupae.

McCray (1961) has devised an apparatus which makes use of the differential sex size of *Aedes aegypti*. This device seems to be satisfactory for *C. fatigans* also. It consists of an inclined aluminum screen with louvered slits 1 inch long (17 per linear inch) and openings of 0.039 inch. The screen is attached to a wooden frame that in turn rests upon an inclined metal tray. The larvae and pupae are gently flushed over the screen with a fan-shaped stream of water. Female pupae are retained by the screen while larvae and male pupae readily pass through. The male pupae later are separated from larvae by using ice water.

C. Adults for Stock Colonies

The pupae which are used for stock colonies are not sexed. Very large numbers of male and female pupae are put in special escape-proof colony cages (McCray, 1963). The cages should be large enough to accommodate at least 30,000 adults. If necessary, the colony should be supplemented with adults at weekly intervals for about 5 weeks. The total number of colonies maintained at any one time depends upon the number of adults required. In the stock colony, the adults are fed thrice a week and eggs are collected daily.

Three of the most important enemies of *Culex fatigans* maintained in laboratory culture in the tropics are ants, jumping spiders, and geckos. These creatures can wreak great havoc in a cage of mosquitoes in one night. Constant guard against them has to be kept.

REFERENCES

Asahina, S. (1964). Food material and feeding procedures for Mosquito larvae. *Bull. World Health Organ.* **31**, 465.

Bar-Zeev, M., and Galun, R. (1960). A mosquito-tight cage. *Mosquito News* **20**, 316–318.

Bar-Zeev, M., and Galun, R. (1961). A magnetic method of separating mosquito pupae from larvae. *Mosquito News* **21**, 225–228.

Boyd, M. F. (1949). "Malariology," Vol. 1, 787 pp. Saunders, Philadelphia, Pennsylvania.

Chao, J. (1959). Notes on the techniques of handling mosquitoes in the laboratory. *Mosquito News* **19**, 191–193.

de Meillon, B., and Sebastian, A. (1964). The effect of cane sugar on oviposition and longevity in *Culex pipiens fatigans*. WHO/Vector Control 72.64.

de Meillon, B., and Sebastian, A. (1965). Some characteristics of ovarian development and oviposition in *Culex pipiens fatigans*. WHO/Vector Control 128.65.

de Zulueta, J. (1950). Comparative oviposition experiments with caged mosquitoes. *Am. J. Hyg.* **52**, 133–142.

Fay, R. W., and Morlan, H. B. (1959). A mechanical device for separating the development stages, sexes and species of mosquitos. *Mosquito News* **19**, 144–147.

Fay, R. W., McCray, E. M., Jr., and Kilpatrick, J. W. (1963). Mass production of sterilized male *Aedes aegypti*. *Mosquito News* **23**, 210–214.

Gjullin, C. M. (1961). Oviposition responses of *Culex pipiens quinquefasciatus* Say to water treated with various chemicals. *Mosquito News* **21**, 109–113.

Ikeshoji, T. (1965a). The influence of larvae breeding conditions on the fecundity of *Culex pipiens fatigans* Wied. WHO/Vector Control 135.65.

Ikeshoji, T. (1965b). Fecundity of *Culex pipiens fatigans* Wied. fed on various amounts of blood and on different hosts. WHO/Vector Control 133.65.

Ikeshoji, T. (1965c). An attractant for ovipositing *Culex pipiens fatigans* Wied. occurring in breeding field waters. WHO/Vector Control 130.65.

Ikeshoji, T. (1965d). A factor controlling the population of *Culex pipiens fatigans* Wied. in pit latrines in Rangoon. WHO/Vector Control 132.65.

Jobling, B. (1935). The effect of light and darkness on oviposition in mosquitos. *Trans. Roy. Soc. Trop. Med. Hyg.* **29**, 157–166.

Jobling, B. (1937). The development of mosquitos in complete darkness. *Trans. Roy. Soc. Trop. Med. Hyg.* **30**, 467–474.

Ramakrishnan, S. P., Krishnamurthy, B. S., and Singh, N. N. (1963). A simple technique for rapid separation of mosquito pupae by sudden chilling. *Indian J. Malariol.* **17**, 119–121.

Mattingly, P. F. (1962). Population increases in *Culex pipiens fatigans* Wied. *Bull. World Health Organ.* **27**, 579–584.

McCray, E. M., Jr. (1961). A mechanical device for the rapid sexing of *Aedes aegypti* pupae. *J. Econ. Entomol.* **54**, 819.

McCray, E. M., Jr. (1963). Escape-proof colony cage (*Aedes aegypti*). *Mosquito News* **23**, 309–311.

McKiel, J. A. (1957). A simplified method for large scale laboratory rearing of *Aedes aegypti* (L). *Mosquito News* **17**, 25–29.

Pollard, D. G. (1960). A cage suitable for holding and feeding blood sucking mosquitos. *Mosquito News* **20**, 56–57.

Trembley, H. L. (1955). Mosquito culture, techniques and experimental procedures. *Am. Mosquito Control Assoc. Bull.* **3**, 1–73.

Wallis, R. C. (1954). A study of oviposition activity of mosquitos. *Am. J. Hyg.* **60**, 135–168.

Weathersby, A. B. (1963). Harvesting mosquito pupae with cold water. *Mosquito News* **23**, 249–251.

Young, M. D., and Burgess, R. W. (1946). Plastic cages for insects. *Science* **104**, 375.

Chapter 8

Culicoides Biting Midges

Robert Henry Jones

Entomology Research Division,
Agricultural Research Service,
U. S. Department of Agriculture,
Denver, Colorado

I. INTRODUCTION

The small, bloodsucking flies that comprise the genera *Culicoides, Leptoconops,* and *Lasiohelea* of the family Ceratopogonidae have not been studied very thoroughly in comparison to most biting flies. With respect to *Culicoides,* the lack of published information is particularly evident for basic studies in the laboratory, a situation that has come about, not only because of the difficulty of working with such minute and relatively unknown flies, but more directly because of the unavailability of established colonies from which to obtain a supply of insects. Even though *Culicoides* have been incriminated, or in some instances proved, as vectors of disease in both human beings and livestock, they have usually been overlooked as possible vectors of most diseases—especially since biting insects that are both large and relatively easy to handle, and at the same time successful transmitters of the disease involved, have been available. A reluctance to work with *Culicoides* is also inherent in most field studies. Although they are commonly serious pests of livestock, large numbers of these flies on an animal are relatively inconspicuous, and research to promote efficient control of livestock insects is directed almost entirely toward more obvious pests. This, of course, is not to say that important research has not been accomplished with this group of insects, especially those species that attack man. Nevertheless, even though two species of *Culicoides* have been colonized, it is apparent that a lack of colonization studies has been a major deterrent to initiating other research.

Since only two species of *Culicoides* have been colonized, this article is restricted to them. No attempt has been made here to digest the bulk of biological information that has accumulated for other species, though these data should be evaluated for a particular species before attempting to colonize it. For this purpose one should consult some of the recent review papers on *Culicoides* in general (Downes, 1958b; Kettle, 1962), or consult papers dealing with more specialized aspects of their activity, such as mating (Downes, 1955, 1958a). Similarly, this article only outlines established colonization procedures, since further details can be found in the listed references.

II. HISTORY

The first species of *Culicoides* to be colonized was *Culicoides nubeculosus* (Meigen) in Britain (Downes, 1950). A few years later *Culicoides variipennis* (Coquillett) was colonized in the United States (Jones, 1957). In a review of the literature for the biology of *Culicoides*, Hill (1947) summarizes the data of previous workers and remarks that "none have maintained any species of *Culicoides* in the laboratory through more than one generation," this statement also being applicable to her own studies. Megahed (1956) states, "The only species which, up to now, has been maintained successfully in the laboratory is *C. nubeculosus*. A strain of this species, collected near Chideock, Dorset, was established in the Department of Zoology, University of Glasgow, by Mr. J. A. Downes in 1947." The *C. nubeculosus* colony was first referred to by Downes (1950), who simply states, "The Chideock strain of *C. nubeculosus* is being maintained in the laboratory . . . ." The remark of Roberts (1950), that ". . . a strain has been maintained . . ." also refers to the establishment of this colony.

References in the literature to the accomplished colonization of *C. variipennis* refer to the colonies that were established at the

Kerrville, Texas, laboratory of the U. S. Department of Agriculture, Entomology Research Division (Jones, 1957, 1960). Attempts at colonization were initiated in 1955, and in 1962 the present colony (Jones, 1964) was relocated at Denver, Colorado. A subcolony of this stock was maintained at the University of Wisconsin by Lee (1961) from February, 1959, to early in 1961.

III. GENERAL CONSIDERATIONS FOR COLONIZATION

A. SELECTION OF WILD MATERIAL

Not only is a knowledge of the basic biology of any species essential for colonizing it, but this knowledge is also desirable in selecting the exact species most likely to lend itself to colonization, or in selecting the most feasible approach for colonization of any certain species. After a species has been selected, one should keep in mind that the exact strain or race used, together with the exact composition of the gene pool at the time of collection, will have at least some bearing on the initial degree of success in colonization work in the laboratory. Research data obtained from a strain collected as larvae about to go into some form of diapause for overwintering would be different from that obtained for the same strain collected in summer when the population was expanding under optimum conditions. Furthermore, if at all possible, colonization work should be started with a large number of wild flies, thus allowing for selection of enough survivors suited to the laboratory conditions imposed. The general approach to colonization of a species should be an initial process of determining biological information by the preliminary colonization of one or more strains, and subsequently the establishment of the permanent colony from wild material when conditions are favorable.

B. LENGTH OF LIFE CYCLE

A main consideration when first initiating colonization research would be the length of the life cycle, since it follows that the more generations there are per year, the more opportunity there is to work with the species, and the greater are the chances of success. Perhaps because of a misconception in the interpretation of field data, information on the length of the life cycle for species of *Culicoides* has at best been vague. Downes (1958b) observes, "Many species have only a single generation in the year whereas others produce one or more additional generations during the summer.

In tropical areas there may be a succession of generations almost throughout the year, the full life-cycle occupying a period of about a month." Kettle (1962) says, "In most species of *Culicoides*, development proceeds steadily from egg to adult without any resting or diapausing stage. Under temperate conditions, one or two generations are produced a year . . . although some species are multivoltine. . . . In the tropics, adult *Culicoides* can be present constantly . . . and seasonal fluctuations are related to tides or rainfall. . . ." Many other authors have supported the concept of only a few generations per year as typical for *Culicoides* in the temperate zone. For example, Foote and Pratt (1954) state, "Observations of the authors have indicated that many inland species in most localities produced two generations a year." The notion of a long life cycle as typical for *Culicoides* is even further enhanced by statements such as that of Anthony (1963) that "Some species produce two or more generations each year but others may require one or two years to complete development." If these observations are correct, very few species indeed would lend themselves to colonization. It appears likely, however, that field data have often been used as if they were a direct indicator of the number of generations occurring each season, rather than for the interpretation of population peaks. Although it can be expected that some species will have a long life cycle, for example, such as is indicated for *Culicoides impunctatus* Goetghebuer by Kettle (1950), my field observations (1959, 1961, 1965) indicate that for many species of *Culicoides*, even those occurring in the northern regions of the United States, the length of the life cycle is rather short under field conditions that promote population increase. This seems at least evident for species in which dense concentrations of larvae occur in soft-mud habitats of stream beds that are regularly subject to washout by rainfall, for example (Jones, 1961), *Culicoides haematopotus* Malloch, *Culicoides hieroglyphicus* Malloch, and *Culicoides multipunctatus* Malloch, as well as *C. variipennis*. The occurrence in a habitat of only one or two generations per season does not mean that the species, either *in toto*, as a strain, or as a genetically distinct part of a population, lacks the capability of producing more generations under better conditions. My laboratory research with early generations during the colonization of *C. variipennis* showed that broods of eggs reared at 80°F and 100% relative humidity produced flies with a life cycle of only about 14 days; the minimum duration of the larval stage was only about 7 days as compared to about 15 days at 75°F. When one considers that laboratory conditions are at best a poor approximation of optimum field conditions, it is probable that *C. variipennis* can complete a full life cycle in even less than 14 days under optimum summer conditions. It seems likely that, even when subjected to poorer environmental conditions, the life cycle of many species will be reasonably short, and overlapping generations will form a population capable of responding with a sharp increase in numbers when conditions are substantially improved.

C. STANDARDIZATION OF *C. nubeculosus* AND *C. variipennis* COLONIES

The initial approach to colonization for both *C. nubeculosus* and *C. variipennis* was the preparation of conditions in the laboratory that simulated optimum natural conditions. These conditions were improved from time to time, and for *C. variipennis* were eventually improved sufficiently so that a laboratory population could be established and maintained by mass-production methods. Evidently, no particular effort was made to standardize conditions for the *C. nubeculosus* colony; for example, laboratory temperatures fluctuated considerably and long-lived larvae were apparently not selected against (Megahed, 1956). In adapting the *C. variipennis* colony to laboratory conditions the main objective was to obtain large numbers of healthy flies. With the use of mass-production techniques, not only was there selection against long-lived larvae, but there was similar selection for uniformity in all phases of colony behavior. Thus, because of the standardization achieved for *C. variipennis*, neither the various procedural details nor much of the biological data are comparable between *C. nubeculosus* and *C. variipennis*.

After the initial start of a colony, the requirements of the investigators determine to a great extent the colony's progress toward establishment on a firm, self-perpetuating basis. It appears from the papers reporting research with flies from the *C. nubeculosus* colony that large numbers of flies were not required, and therefore not reared, for research. Megahed (1956) states, "The strain of *C. nubeculosus* established was successfully maintained, except for one hiatus, from 1947 to mid-1953, when it began to show symptoms of deterioration. The gravid females refused to lay their eggs, and the size of egg-batch and the percentage that hatched became smaller. This deterioration may have been an after-effect of the culture method described below, but it is more probably due to prolonged inbreeding without introduction of new blood. The culture is now (January 1955) extinct." Although this statement can be interpreted to mean that the *C. nubeculosus* colony was not firmly established, it seems more likely that it was firmly established at first, but was later lost because of insufficient numbers of flies to sustain a heterogeneous population in a nonstandard environment, thus producing too few individuals adapted to the conditions prevailing at any given time. With *C. variipennis*, it was fortunate that the desire for large numbers of flies for use in a program to determine the vectors of bluetongue disease of sheep (Foster *et al.*, 1963) exerted pressure to stabilize the colony at some initial point that would ensure, at least periodically, large numbers of flies. Once colonization procedures were arbitrarily stabilized, any further change in the colony was gradual. In addition, modifications to the laboratory environment were made through a succession of slight changes toward conditions felt to be more suitable for the existent colony, rather than a series of changes being made toward conditions determined as more suitable by biological studies with wild or newly colonized strains of the species. My statement (1964) that ". . . at least 20 generations are necessary for full adaptation of wild strains to a colony environment," was based on experience with the colony at Kerrville. Although second-generation eggs were first obtained by September, 1955, it was not until some 3 years later, and after the loss of several colonies that had had from 6 to 12 successive generations in the laboratory, that a strain collected in late 1957 did well enough to be considered successfully colonized. Certainly it is to be expected, after a period of over 7 years without the introduction of wild flies, that the character of the gene pool of the colonized strain has changed from that possessed by the original wild strain (SONORA-1957). However, it is likely that any change has been minimized, since the policy for establishing this colony was to maintain large numbers of insects as a population rather than as a succession of discrete generations. Thus, although the colony has undergone drastic fluctuations in size, the population level has never declined to a point at which the gene frequency might be radically shifted as a result of any one generation arising from only a few females or from females that emerged from the same larval pan. Constant inbreeding does not seem to have had any detrimental effect to date; at least, this is indicated by the normally healthy response of the colony flies and by the uniformity of the data collected with them in several research programs (Harris and Jones, 1962; Foster *et al.*, 1963; Jones, 1967). In addition, two other recently completed programs in cooperation with the U. S. Department of Agriculture, Animal Disease and Parasite Research Division's Denver Laboratory (Jochim and Jones, 1966; Jones and Foster, 1966) have shown that the present colony strain is representative of the species with respect to both virus multiplication and disease transmission of bluetongue disease of sheep, since the results obtained with the colony (SONORA) and a representative wild strain (HUDSON) (Jones, 1965) were equivalent.

IV. COLONIZATION PROCEDURES

A. LIFE HISTORY

Given conditions of standard maintenance similar to those used for *C. variipennis*, it is likely that the life cycle for *C. nubeculosus* (Megahed, 1956) would much more closely approximate that given for *C. variipennis* (Jones, 1964) than might be thought likely from published data. Megahed notes for *C. nubeculosus* that "The eggs commonly hatched 3–4 days, but sometimes up to 6 days, after oviposition . . . the pupal stage [occupied] about 4 days, though in rare cases it lasted about a week . . . the earliest-emerging adults completed their life-cycle in from three to six weeks, and the latest-emerging adults completed it in from 4½ to 8½ weeks." I give the life cycle for the standardized *C. variipennis* colony at Denver as, ". . . about 24 days—egg two, larva 15 (12 days and up), pupa three, period prior to blood ingestion one, and preoviposition period three."

In *Culicoides* only the female takes blood, and most species require a blood meal for the development of eggs, though a few do not (see review by Kettle, 1962). Downes (1950) states for *C. nubeculosus* that "Egg-laying takes place, if the females are suitably concentrated, four to five days after the blood meal, and the insect is then ready to bite again immediately and in due course to lay. As many as five successive batches of eggs have been obtained from a single female; mating in this case had taken place once only (at the time of the first blood meal), but more than 80 per cent of each batch hatched." For *C. variipennis* I earlier stated (1957) that "As most females require more than one blood meal for the production of eggs, it is necessary to blood-feed the colony every day." It now appears that this earlier requirement for several blood meals per egg batch was a result of frequent "abortion" of blood meals under laboratory conditions to which the flies were not yet well adapted. In later studies with a stabilized colony (Jones, 1967), females usually deposited an egg batch for each single blood meal taken. For this test work I state that ". . . normal females lived for up to 44 days. The maximum number of eggs deposited in one egg batch was 243, and the maximum number from one female over her lifetime was 1,143, a total from seven egg batches." It was also shown that both the male and the female can mate repeatedly, and that the female can usually use stored sperm from a single mating for at least three egg batches without any appreciable reduction in egg viability; females usually deposited egg batches 3–6 days after a blood meal (range 3–16).

B. LARVAL MEDIUM

In his review paper, Kettle (1962) states, ". . . the only two species colonised—*C. variipennis* and *C. nubeculosus*—have surface mud-dwelling larvae and belong to a small section of the genus whose larvae have heavily built pharynges and feed on algae, fungi, and bacterial films. . . . Those with light pharynges may feed on algae . . . or detritus . . . or be carnivorous. . . ." Downes (1958b) says of *Culicoides* that "They are probably unselective in their feeding, and the gut contents often consist of a mixture of organic fragments and soil particles. . . ." Megahed (1956) observed the feeding habits of *C. nubeculosus* larvae and described them in detail. The laboratory larval medium for *C. nubeculosus* (Megahed, 1956) was a simulated natural one, requiring a quantity of dried, powdered soil from the original source, together with some auto-lyzed yeast and powdered charcoal. Although the larval medium for the *C. variipennis* colony simulates a natural one in physical aspect and in using a small amount of some suitable soil to provide microorganisms, it is somewhat more artificial in that the other constituents are vermiculite as a substrate, and cow manure (field collected from range-fed cattle, blended, and stored as frozen blocks) as a source of detritus and nourishment for the microorganisms. Since algae and fungi are not available in any quantity in this medium, it would appear that colony *C. variipennis* larvae feed on bacteria, other small microorganisms, and small pieces of detritus.

C. COLONIZATION PROCEDURES FOR *C. variipennis*

Except for several recent innovations, the procedures and techniques now in use are as described in an earlier paper (Jones, 1964). Modifications incorporated over past years have been small ones, since virtually no research has been done on colonization per se since 1958. Early in colonization work, a constant temperature of about 75°F was adopted, because higher temperatures produced a smaller fly than was considered normal. At present, both the adult and larval colonies are kept at standard conditions of temperature and relative humidity, but are maintained in the dark at night.

Larval-rearing facilities have recently been increased, and a production level of well over 1000 flies per day has now been reached. Colony work totals about 14 hours a week for one experienced person, with weekend work limited to from a few minutes of maintenance to almost an hour when blood feeding is necessary.

Twice a week flies are blood fed on the clipped belly of a rabbit by inserting the top of the colony cage through a hole in a rabbit-restraining rack. This cylindrical holding and blood-feeding cage has a conical upper portion leading to a blood-feeding aperture closed by a sliding lid. Additional nourishment consists of a 5% sugar solution supplied through a cotton wick and raisins compressed in a small piece of cloth. Water is provided by the paper-covered wet cotton of the egging dish. Females deposit eggs overnight, and both sugar vials and egging dishes are changed daily. Eggs are examined for viability, and used the same day or stored on wet cotton at 40°–50°F. Eggs can be stored as long as 1 month without hatching (pupae and larvae can also be refrigerated to delay development). The size of an adult colony cage varies, but is kept sufficiently small so that some degree of crowding is provided to stimulate mating activity. Especially during periods of low production, a system of cage handling is used that entails blood feeding every day. Three small cages are alternated so that each night only one cage gets an egging dish, and the next morning the same cage is placed for blood feeding after the addition of recently emerged flies 24–48 hours old.

Larval pans, 30 × 25 × 2-1/2 inches, are held in a rack accommodating five pans on each of five shelves. Initially, the interior of the pan is lined with polyethylene sheeting that is folded and then taped at the corners. A pan is prepared by forming two long central islands and several posterior and lateral banks, of presoaked, cleaned vermiculite, and then adding 200 ml of homogenized cow manure and 2 ml of soil in enough water so that the islands can later be adjusted to leave them slightly above water level. Additional manure is added as needed, usually 100 ml for the first 3 days and 50 ml thereafter on alternate days. The water level, 7/8 to 1 inch from the pan bottom, is maintained either by an automatic float system or by adding the necessary water daily. To keep the liquid medium stirred and therefore assist in the formation of soft mud margins, a moderate water current is maintained in each pan by a small paddle fastened to a slowly rotating rod, one of which runs the length of each shelf. Paddle action prevents the formation of surface scum; but because of this disturbance of the water, the front and inside margins of the two central islands are supported by half-inch metal stripping. The area between and in front of the islands is kept clear by occasional hand stirring of deposited material so that it will settle out elsewhere.

Twice a week larval pans are prepared so that each day one or two are available for egg placement. At present 5000 or more viable eggs are placed per pan. A larger number of larvae, consistent with the available food supply, promotes a better condition of the sub- strate so that it does not scum over readily. After about 14 days, when substantial numbers of pupae are present, they are recovered by flooding: the pan is drained of about half the liquid medium for later replacement, flooded for 2 hours for pupae to float to the surface, overflooded through a notch at the rear to recover the pupae, drained, and refilled with the liquid medium. Pupae are blown through the notch of the overflooded pan with a small air jet; they then flow down a trough at the rear of the rack and are collected in a 100-mesh sieve close to floor level. Pupae are separated from larvae in a 35-mesh sieve slanted through the surface of the water in a shallow pan. Larvae swim through the sieve and, together with those recovered from discarded pans, can be placed on larval pans still in production. Pans are flooded on Monday, Wednesday, and Friday, and the least productive are discarded two or three at a time; pans over 10 days old are sometimes discarded without normal flooding if it appears they will be poor producers. When desired, the contents of discarded pans can be placed in a 10-gal tub pro- vided with a mid-height drain and an overflow spout for the recovery of larvae.

As I recently stated (1964), "These colonization techniques and equipment are designed to maintain a large colony with minimum labour and expense; therefore procedures are followed without any attempt to recover all specimens or to prevent the escape of a few individuals. Security precautions, if employed, must be applied to the entire rearing room and premises, although small colonies can be maintained under more stringent conditions. However, some security precautions are essential to exclude competing in- sects from the larval rearing room. During past years, the larval colony has been almost eliminated on different occasions by blood worms (Tendipedidae) or sewage flies (Psychodidae)."

REFERENCES

Anthony, D. W. (1963). Arthropod vectors of some livestock and poultry diseases. *67th Ann. Proc. U. S. Livestock Sanit. Assoc., 1963* pp. 588–596.

Downes, J. A. (1950). Habits and life-cycle of *Culicoides nubeculosus* Mg. *Nature* **166**, 510–511.

Downes, J. A. (1955). Observations on the swarming flight and mating of *Culicoides* (Diptera: Ceratopogonidae). *Trans. Roy. Entomol. Soc. London* **106**, 213–236.

Downes, J. A. (1958a). Assembly and mating in the biting Nematocera. *Proc. 10th Intern. Congr. Entomol., Montreal, 1956* Vol. 2, pp. 425–434.

Downes, J. A. (1958b). The genus *Culicoides* (Diptera: Ceratopogonidae) in Canada; an introductory review. *Proc. 10th Intern. Congr. Entomol., Montreal, 1956* Vol. 3, pp. 801–808.

Foote, R. H., and Pratt, H. D. (1954). The *Culicoides* of the eastern United States. *U. S. Public Health Serv., Public Health Monograph* **18**.

Foster, N. M., Jones, R. H., and McCrory, B. R. (1963). Preliminary investigations on insect transmission of bluetongue virus in sheep. *Am. J. Vet. Res.* **24**, 1195–1200.

Harris, R. L., and Jones, R. H. (1962). Larvicide tests with colony-reared *Culicoides variipennis*. *J. Econ. Entomol.* **55**, 575–576.

Hill, M. A. (1947). The life-cycle and habits of *Culicoides impunctatus* Goetghebuer and *Culicoides obsoletus* Meigen, together with some observations on the life-cycle of *Culicoides odibilis* Austen, *Culicoides pallidicornis* Kieffer, *Culicoides cubitalis* Edwards and *Culicoides chiopterus* Meigen. *Ann. Trop. Med. Parasitol.* **41**, 55–115.

Jochim, M. M., and Jones, R. H. (1966). Multiplication of bluetongue virus in *Culicoides variipennis* following artificial infection. *Am. J. Epidemiol.* **84** (in press).

Jones, R. H. (1957). The laboratory colonization of *Culicoides variipennis* (Coq.). *J. Econ. Entomol.* **50**, 107–108.

Jones, R. H. (1959). *Culicoides* breeding in human sewage sites of dwellings in Texas. *Mosquito News* **19**, 164–167.

Jones, R. H. (1960). Mass-production methods for the colonization of *Culicoides variipennis sonorensis*. *J. Econ. Entomol.* **53**, 731–735.

Jones, R. H. (1961). Observations on the larval habitats of some North American species of *Culicoides* (Diptera: Ceratopogonidae). *Ann. Entomol. Soc. Am.* **54**, 702–710.

Jones, R. H. (1964). Mass production methods in rearing *Culicoides variipennis* (Coquillett). *Bull. World Health Organ.* **31**, 571–572.

Jones, R. H. (1965). Epidemiological notes: Incidence of *Culicoides variipennis* in an outbreak of bluetongue disease. *Mosquito News* **25**, 217–218.

Jones, R. H. (1967). Some irradiation studies and related biological data for *Culicoides variipennis* (Diptera: Ceratopogonidae). In manuscript.

Jones, R. H., and Foster, N. M. (1966). The transmission of bluetongue virus to embryonating chicken eggs by *Culicoides variipennis* (Diptera: Ceratopogonidae) infected by intrathoracic inoculation. *Mosquito News* **26** (in press).

Kettle, D. S. (1950). The seasonal distribution of *Culicoides impunctatus* Goetghebuer [Diptera: Heleidae (Ceratopogonidae)] with a discussion on the possibility that it may be composed of two or more biological races. *Trans. Roy. Entomol. Soc. London* **101**, 125–146.

Kettle, D. S. (1962). The bionomics and control of *Culicoides* and *Leptoconops* (Diptera, Ceratopogonidae = Heleidae). *Ann. Rev. Entomol.* **7**, 401–418.

Lee, V. H. (1961). Univ. of Wisconsin. Personal correspondence.

Megahed, M. M. (1956). A culture method for *Culicoides nubeculosus* (Meigen) (Diptera: Ceratopogonidae) in the laboratory, with notes on the biology. *Bull. Entomol. Res.* **47**, 107–114.

Roberts, E. W. (1950). Artificial feeding of *Culicoides nubeculosus* in the laboratory. *Nature* **166**, 700.

Chapter 9

Black Flies

R. C. MUIRHEAD-THOMSON

Division of Communicable Diseases,
World Health Organization,
Geneva, Switzerland

I. INTRODUCTION

In nearly every part of its wide distribution in temperate and tropical countries, *Simulium* has long been the subject of the most careful and systematic studies bearing on all aspects of its biology. In some countries these studies owe their main impetus to the role of *Simulium* as a blood-sucking pest of man or of his domestic animals; in other countries the main stimulus has been the importance of some species as vectors of avian parasites or as vectors of onchocerciasis in man; elsewhere, *Simulium* has continued to attract the most skilled investigators purely for the fascination of its biology and breeding habits.

The experience from all those different sources tallies on one important point which is the keystone of this present review, namely, that despite their robustness and aggresion in nature and their remarkable success in invading and dominating the notoriously hazardous torrential habitat, in captivity both as adults and larvae *Simulium* appears as unexpectedly delicate and uncooperative, succumbing readily even under the most careful treatment. This experience has been particularly marked in the case of investigations on *Simulium* as a vector of human onchocerciasis in tropical Africa and Central America where critical work on vector biology has long been handicapped by the great difficulty in maintaining stocks of adult *Simulium* in captivity, or even in persuading it to take a blood feed. Most present-day investigators have run into precisely the same difficulties experienced, for example, by Strong and others (1934) in their classic investigations in Guatemala over thirty years ago. The fact that these basic difficulties are common to a wide range of climatic zones from tropical to subarctic is strikingly brought out in the experiences reported by Dalmat (1955) in Central America and by Hocking and Pickering (1954) in Canada.

When we come to the more ambitious objective of maintaining *Simulium* for successive generations in captivity, we find that there are a series of obstacles to be overcome, any one of which could defeat our object. First, the apparently simple process of successfully rearing larvae from eggs or from young larval instars, through to the pupal and adult stage is usually marked by such a high mortality that only a few adults may finally be obtained from large egg masses or large collections of young larvae. Second, even when large numbers of adults can be reared successfully from wild-caught, full grown larvae and pupae there is normally great difficulty in persuading females to take a blood meal; mating only rarely takes place in captivity, and viable eggs have only exceptionally been obtained from laboratory-reared females.

However, the last few years have been marked by a new and more vigorous approach to the technique of culturing *Simulium* in captivity. Progress along different lines has been reported by several different investigators. Even more important is the increasing collaboration between formerly isolated research workers, and the round-table exchange of information and opinion between groups of investigators working under very different temperate and tropical conditions. This new spirit of coordination is exemplified by three international meetings within the last few years. First, the Third Conference on Black Flies (Diptera, Simuliidae), Ontario, September,

1962. Secondly, the Symposium on Culture procedures for arthropod
vectors and their biological control agents, Gainesville, Florida,
October, 1963 (West, 1963; Muirhead-Thomson, 1963); and third,
the Blackfly Colloquium following the 12th International Congress
on Entomology, London, July, 1964.

The present occasion is therefore a most appropriate one to
attempt a first synthesis of recent developments, although at the
same time there is a great deal of recent information still in unpublished form which may call for an early revision of the present review.

II. INITIATING CULTURES WITH MATERIAL FROM LARVAL HABITATS

It would perhaps be most useful to start with the straightforward
first step of building up a stock of *Simulium* in the laboratory, providing adult material for further investigations on mating, blood
feeding, longevity, etc.

A. HABITATS CLOSE TO LABORATORY

Under the most favorable conditions, where productive *Simulium*
habitats exist in close proximity to the laboratory, stocks of *Simulium*
adults have been built up by the artificial isolation or diversion of

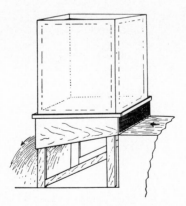

FIG. 1. Breeding cage used for the study of early stages of Simuliidae in Guatemala
(Strong *et al.*, 1934).

the natural larval habitat. In its simplest form this method consists
essentially of isolating part of the breeding stream, or an artificial
diversion, in a channel with continuously flowing water, the channel
being screened in the lower section of the cage (Fig. 1). This method

was used in the classic investigations in Guatemala by the Harvard expedition 1931–1932 (Strong *et al.*, 1934). The object of their work was to obtain large numbers of adults for experimental purposes. No egg batches were introduced into the cage, and the complete egg-to-adult cycle was not aimed at. The same general methods have also been used in Central America by Hoffman (1930) and by Dalmat (1955).

A further perfection of essentially the same principle is the introduction into the screened cage of batches of *Simulium* eggs from the natural habitat, attached to twigs or vegetation. This has recently been done very successfully with *Simulium damnosum* in West Africa by Marr (1962). In this case the supply of egg masses was supplemented by suspending trap sticks from a rope stretched across narrow gaps in the river rapids.

B. HABITATS DISTANT FROM LABORATORY

In the more frequent case where the laboratory is many miles distant from the nearest productive larval habitat, e.g., in a large town, large stocks can still be maintained provided that certain simple precautions are taken with regard to transfer of live material from the field. Very large numbers of larvae and pupae attached to vegetation can normally be found in known habitats for many months

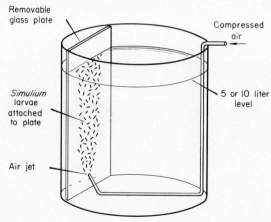

FIG. 2. Rearing chamber used for several species of *Simulium* in West Africa, southern Rhodesia, and England (Muirhead-Thomson, 1957b, 1962).

of the year. This vegetation with attached larvae and pupae is kept wet—but not immersed in water—in a polythene bag or similar container and transported straight away to the central laboratory, where the vegetation can then be immersed in the type of larval-rearing apparatus shown in Fig. 2 or in other types of apparatus described below.

This method provided ample supplies of laboratory-reared adult *Simulium* under three very different conditions: *S. damnosum* Theobald, *Simulium cervicornutum* Pomeroy and *Simulium unicornutum* Pomeroy in Liberia; *S. damnosum* and *Simulium medusaeformis* Pomeroy in Salisbury on the southern Rhodesian plateau, and *Simulium venustum* Say and *Simulium equinum* (Linnaeus) in the London School of Hygiene and Tropical Medicine (Muirhead-Thomson, 1957b, 1962). Similar successes with transporting larvae in polythene containers have been reported by Noamesi (1962) and by Ovazza (1962). Judicious choice of collecting sites can even ensure a fairly pure culture of a particular species, which can be checked or refined by identifying and separating pupae in the laboratory prior to eclosion of adults. The pupae with their attached piece of vegetation can then be put on damp filter paper in labeled containers. Even under tropical conditions larvae can survive long journeys for a period of up to 2 to 3 hours if treated in this way.

III. LABORATORY-REARING TECHNIQUES

A great deal of ingenuity on the part of different investigators has gone into developing techniques by which *Simulium* larvae can be maintained under the same conditions of flow or turbulence as exist in their natural habitat. It would be instructive to consider these under two headings: (a) methods depending on a continuous flow of water pumped or replaced from a natural source, and (b) methods based on agitation and oxygenation of water in a closed system by a stream of air bubbles from a compressed air source.

A. METHODS USING CONTINUOUS FLOW OF WATER

This was the method used successfully by Hartley (1955) for rearing *S. venustum* from eggs to adults. Fresh water was continuously pumped from a lake into an aquarium, and then run off by means of a syphon into 4-oz packer jars (Fig. 3). Egg masses, usually on grass blades, were suspended in the stream of water in the packer jars. Adults were produced in 20–25 days at 60°–70°F.

In this same category is the method used by Wright (1957) in attempting to rear *S. damnosum* in West Africa. River water in a large aquarium tank was circulated over an inclined trough of corrugated asbestos by means of a water circulating pump arranged so as to pro-

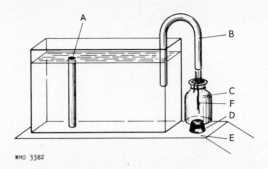

WHO 3382

FIG. 3. Apparatus used for rearing aquatic stages of *Simulium venustum*. A: overflow from aquarium; B: siphon; C: packer jar; D: rubber stopper; E: runoff board; F: grass (Hartley, 1955).

duce maximum aeration (see also Thomas, 1946). Egg masses of S. *damnosum* attached to vegetation in natural larval habitats were introduced into the trough. Water in the tank was replaced at frequent intervals by fresh water in which the plankton and suspended matter had been concentrated approximately 500 times by filtering through fine plankton netting. Eight pupae—producing 7 adults—were finally obtained from approximately 10,000 eggs.

The same principle has been used more recently by Hall and

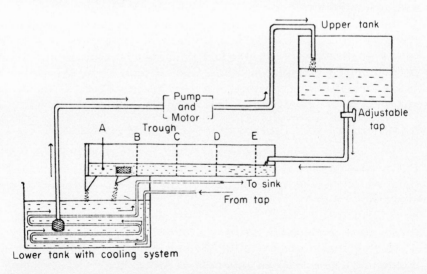

FIG. 4. Apparatus with circulating water system used with *Simulium ornatum* in England A: thermometer; B–E: grids. (Hall and Harrod, 1963).

Harrod (1963) in an apparatus (Fig. 4) designed to simulate natural conditions with regard to constant flow and abundant food supply. In this apparatus, natural stream water is circulated by means of an electric pump through a large tin trough 140 cm long, 10 cm wide, and 15 cm deep, initially filled with water from a natural habitat. Various rates of circulation from 20–80 cm per second could be obtained. The larval food consisted of a mixed culture of diatoms and desmids. *Simulium* eggs obtained from a natural habitat were placed in a short length of wide-bore glass tubing with muslin-covered ends, hatching larvae being released into the main trough when they had passed the delicate first instar. In experiments with *Simulium ornatum* var. *nitidifrons* Edwards, 145 pupae were obtained from approximately 1000 first-instar larvae.

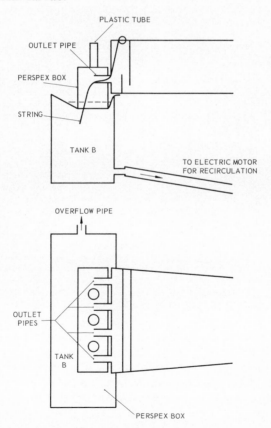

FIG. 5. Terminal part of flowing water trough used in rearing *Simulium damnosum* in Tanzania, showing string for larval attachment and adult trapping device (see Fig. 6) (Raybould, 1965).

A trough technique based on a natural supply of stream water has also been developed successfully by Raybould (1965) in his investigations in Tanzania on methods of culturing *S. damnosum* and *Simulium woodi* de Meillon (*S. "neavei"* group) the larvae of the latter living attached to certain fresh-water crabs in nature. Water from the main tank flows through narrow tubular outlets through each of which a string is suspended (Fig. 5). Larvae of *S. damnosum* introduced into the main tank congregate on the strings where there is a maximum flow of water. The outlet portion of the tank is enclosed in a Perspex chamber surmounted by vertical tubes into which emerging adults are attracted and trapped when the rest of the chamber is covered with shading cloth (Fig. 6).

FIG. 6. Outlet tubes from tank showing larvae of *Simulium damnosum* attached to strings, and adult trapping device (see Fig. 5) (Raybould, 1965).

A further modification of the trough technique has been developed by Jamnback (1964) in the course of studies aimed at methods for testing insecticides. This trough is about 13½ ft long, 13 inches wide, and 6 inches deep. Water enters the trough at the upper end through a valve which can be adjusted to regulate the flow. Stones with attached larvae are placed in the trough, and these larvae eventually congregate on the terminal lip, which is 10 inches wide and 4 inches long. Although in routine testing the water runs through the trough once and then passes out of the system, it is considered that, with recirculating water, storage reservoirs, pumps, valves, and filter, this method might be developed for mass rearing large numbers of *Simulium*.

One of the latest refinements of the running water or trough technique is that developed for Canadian species of *Simulium* by Wood and Davies (1964).

This apparatus consisted of (1) a filter containing 12 ft³ of highly activated granular carbon, sand, and gravel; (2) a head tank; (3) troughs containing larvae; and (4) a device for dispensing a dilute yeast suspension. The rearing troughs (Fig. 7) were ½ inch wide,

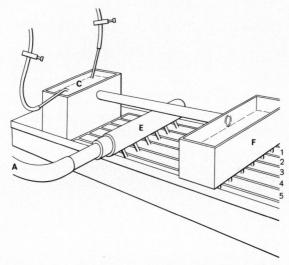

FIG. 7. Apparatus with circulating water system used with several Canadian species of *Simulium* (Wood and Davies, 1964). See text for explanation.

1 inch deep, and 4 ft long, each with a flat bottom and vertical sides and usually inclined at a grade of 1 in 36. Troughs were assembled into units which were supported, 2–3 ft below the head tank, in a galvanized iron pan. To prevent larval escape, each trough was deepened into a reservoir terminating in a stainless steel screen (100 mesh/inch). Filtered dechlorinated tap water (A) entered each trough from a manifold (E) at a constant volume of flow set by the head tank. Each manifold, an acrylic plastic tube (diameter, 1 inch), had a row of 1/16-inch holes, each fitted with a 1-inch plastic tube supplying each trough. The little tubes were clear of the sides and bottom of the troughs, thus preventing larvae from migrating into the manifold.

Baker's yeast was suspended in filtered water with a blender and kept in suspension in a flask with a stirrer. From there the suspension was diluted with more water in small tanks. Larvae were fed this dilute yeast (C), which dripped into each trough from a separate manifold (F). The feeding apparatus was frequently dismantled and cleaned without disturbing the water flow or larvae.

With this apparatus adults of 12 Canadian species were reared from eggs or young larvae. The yield of *Simulium aureum* Fries adults from eggs reached 80% and was usually over 50–60%. Even some larvae of *Simulium pictipes* Hagen, which inhabits large water-falls, were successfully reared.

Pupae were removed from their substrate in natural or artificial streams and mass-reared on wet filter paper in Petri dishes, or individually reared under single tubes with the upper end plugged with cotton. Adults, after their cuticle hardened, were killed in a deep freezer, quickly glued to the side of a pin, and replaced in the freezer for several weeks until they were freeze-dried into a lifelike appearance.

B. Methods Using Compressed Air Jet

In an endeavor to develop larval-rearing techniques independent of a continuous supply or flow of natural water, compressed air has been an effective method of producing agitation combined with aeration in a closed container (Puri, 1925; Wagner, 1926; Smart, 1934). In recent years this technique has been used and further developed by Muirhead-Thomson (1957b), Fredeen (1959), Doby *et al.* (1959), Doby (1964), and others. Muirhead-Thomson (1957b) used a jet of air bubbles from a compressed air source to induce larvae of *S. damnosum* and other African species to leave their attachment on submerged vegetation—brought in from natural habitats—and concentrate on the wall of a 5-liter glass vessel. Later, a vertical detachable glass plate was found more convenient for transferring the congregated larvae to fresh vessels (Fig. 3). This technique was very useful for rearing out adults from late-instar larvae taken in the field, but failed to maintain first-instar larvae hatching from egg batches through complete growth. No special provision was made for adding supplementary food to the water originally collected from the natural stream.

Essentially the same basic principle was used by Doby and his colleagues (1959); it has since been developed and extended to form a most impressive culture technique for rearing many species of European *Simulium* (Fig. 8). (*S. ornatum* Meigen, *S. aureum*, and *S. erythrocephalum* DeGeer) from egg batches to adults (Doby, 1964).

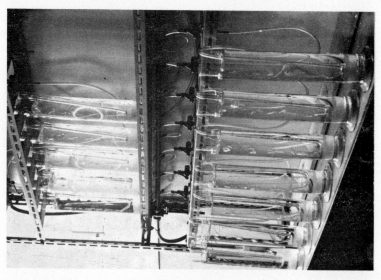

FIG. 8. Batteries of rearing jars provided with continuous jet of compressed air for rearing various species of *Simulium* in France (Doby *et al.*, 1959; Doby, 1964).

Careful attention to the nutritional needs of the *Simulium* larvae in these tall vessels, involving the regular addition of measured quantities of brewer's yeast, and to the fact that larvae of some species are more sensitive to pollution than others, has evidently contributed to a much higher survival rate of larvae than is usually experienced in the laboratory. For example, from 33 egg batches of *S. ornatum* containing from 200–2000 eggs each, the mean recovery of adults per batch was 114.

The compressed air jet technique has also been thoroughly studied with regard to Canadian species by Fredeen (1959) to try and increase the survival of larvae and to facilitate observation. In the technique developed, the fine jet of air bubbles was allowed to rise either through a chimney or under a sloping glass plate, achieving a continuous circulation of water at speeds up to 1.4 ft per second (43 cm per second). This technique was found to allow for a wide range in size and shape of aquaria that could be used, and also enabled emerging adults to be collected with ease when a cage was fitted at the top of the vessel.

An ingenious use of the compressed air technique has been reported from Australia by Mackerras and Mackerras (1948) in which a powerful air pressure—sufficient to bubble air through at least 8 jars—is produced in a "reverse suction" apparatus based on a water pump attached to a tap. In this apparatus *Simulium ornatipes* was successfully reared from egg to adult in the laboratory; other species, however, did not prove so adaptable.

IV. THE INITIATION OF *SIMULIUM* CULTURES FROM EGGS

There are two main sources of *Simulium* eggs for initiating and maintaining cultures: the collections of eggs from natural habitats and collections of eggs laid by female *Simulium* in captivity.

A. EGGS FROM NATURAL HABITATS

Workers with temperate climate *Simulium*, e.g., in Canada and Europe, have in most cases been able to obtain adequate and regular supplies of *Simulium* eggs from natural streams (Davies and Peterson, 1956; Fredeen, 1959; Doby *et al.*, 1959; Wood and Davies, 1964). With tropical species, particularly the much investigated *S. damnosum* in Africa, experiences have varied and although egg masses have been collected by several workers (Wanson and Henrard, 1945; Crisp, 1956; Muirhead-Thomson, 1956; Marr, 1962), in general they are rather difficult to find, and few places can be relied on to provide anything approaching a regular supply. For this species the use of artificial oviposition sites in the form of twigs or leaves suspended at favored places (Muirhead-Thomson, 1956; Marr, 1962) seems to offer the best prospect for ensuring regular supplies of eggs from the field, especially when mass oviposition may provide anything up to 50,000 eggs on a single suspended leaf. The possibility of collecting such egg masses and transporting them for subsequent rearing in European laboratories is being actively explored at the moment.

Nothing is known about the eggs or ovipositing habits of the *S. neavei* group—vectors of onchocerciasis in parts of Africa—whose larvae live attached to crabs.

B. Eggs Laid in Captivity

In the laboratory the most likely sources of eggs at present are those laid in captivity by wild-caught, engorged females. In Canada oviposition by gravid females of *Simulium arcticum* Malloch, *Simulium vittatum* Zetterstedt, *Simulium dacotensis* (D. and S.), and *S. venustum* collected in the field has been obtained by Fredeen (1959) and with *S. aureum* by Wood and Davies (1964).

Again, experience with tropical *Simulium* has been discouraging; *S. damnosum* caught in nature rarely being persuaded to lay viable eggs without artificial inducement. On the other hand, wild-caught *S. woodi* (of the *S. neavei* group) oviposit much more easily in confinement (Raybould, 1965). In the case of *S. damnosum*, Lewis *et al.* (1961) had much more success using two different methods, in the most successful of which oviposition was artificially induced in a tube by decapitation of gravid females, viable larvae being obtained from the eggs laid. The technique of decapitation-initiated oviposition has been used successfully with other types of Diptera such as *Aedes* mosquitos (de Coursey and Webster, 1952) and crane flies (Chiang and Young, 1962), and seems well worth wider investigation in the case of *Simulium*.

The possibility of inducing oviposition by CO_2 has been explored by Dalmat (1950) and has been further investigated in the case of cage-reared *S. damnosum* by Marr (1962). Complete oviposition could be obtained in this way, but none of the eggs developed, presumably because the cage-reared females had not been fertilized.

With regard to obtaining viable eggs from laboratory-reared female *Simulium* which have been induced to mate and to take a blood meal in captivity, it appears that the only success reported is that of Wenk (1963) with *S. erythrocephala*.

V. PHYSIOLOGICAL ACTIVITY IN CONFINEMENT

A. BLOOD FEEDING

One of the main obstacles in the chain of events leading to laboratory colonization is inducing laboratory-reared females to take a blood meal. The biting and blood-feeding activities of *Simulium* in general have recently been reviewed by Fallis (1964), and it is clear that there is still a very wide gap between the considerable amount of data from the field, and the comparative dearth of observations on biting in captivity (Hocking and Pickering, 1954; Fredeen, 1959). In studies on *S. damnosum* induced blood feeding on the part of individual laboratory-reared females could be obtained occasionally, but only with great difficulty, by means of small glass feeding tubes applied to the skin (Muirhead-Thomson, 1957a). Scarification of the skin and the addition of a little sugar solution were found to be a necessary preliminary by Wanson *et al.* (1945) when dealing with this species, although they found that another species in the Congo, *Simulium albivirgulatum* Wanson and Henrard, fed readily in captivity.

Wenk (1963, 1965) has had much more success with *S. erythrocephala*, inducing them to feed on man, rabbit's ear, or on citrated or defibrinated blood.

In large open-air cages, Marr (1962) has had more success with *S. damnosum* in captivity, in which an arm and leg of a fly-boy inside the cage were applied to the netting at the side of the cage where the sun was striking and to which the flies were attracted.

B. MATING AND FERTILIZATION

Successful mating of laboratory-reared *Simulium* has only been reported by Wenk (1963) with *S. erythrocephala* so far, although there are odd records of *Simulium* having been observed to mate in captivity (Hocking and Pickering, 1954; Doby, 1964). No success has yet been reported from the many Canadian investigations. The problem of fertilization in captivity may yet yield to one or another of the new artificial techniques which have been so successfully developed in the case of refractory species of mosquito. There is also the possibility that mating and blood-feeding activities are interrelated, and that fertilized females might prove to feed much more readily on blood in captivity than unfertilized ones.

C. LONGEVITY

The experience of different workers with regard to maintaining *Simulium* adults alive in captivity shows a great degree of variation. Some Canadian workers have successfully kept field-collected, blood-engorged adults alive for several weeks (Davies, 1953; Fallis and Bennett, 1962). On the other hand, workers with tropical *Simulium* have had much less success either with wild-caught adults or with laboratory-reared ones.

Despite refractory behavior with regard to blood feeding in captivity, *Simulium* will readily feed on sugar solution in cages and may be maintained alive in this way for several days. However, a high mortality soon sets in, and it is normally increasingly difficult to keep flies alive much longer than a week or two at most after emergence. This question has received particular attention in the case of *S. damnosum*—main vector of onchocerciasis in Africa—where maintenance of transmission in the field is clearly dependent on longevity of infected flies (Wanson *et al.*, 1945; Muirhead-Thomson, 1957a; Lewis *et al.*, 1961; Marr, 1962).

The question of optimum conditions for adults in captivity has yet to be studied with the attention it merits; it is not yet possible to indicate the relative importance of the factors involved—temperature, humidity, light, nature of food, importance of fertilization, size of cage or container, etc.

VI. DISCUSSION

From this review it appears that while the work of individual *Simulium* workers has run into difficulties in one way or another, the sum total of their efforts reveals that each step leading to complete colonization has been successfully overcome by someone somewhere. One worker or group of workers has had marked success in rearing some species from egg to adult; other workers have been repeatedly frustrated by high larval mortality, but have had success with inducing laboratory-reared females to mate and take a blood feed in captivity. Others again have been unable to find the eggs of their particular species in nature, but have had marked success in inducing wild-caught, blood-engorged females to develop their ovaries and lay viable eggs in captivity.

With regard to larval-rearing techniques, a striking feature has been the progress and perfection along two very different lines, namely, the flowing water trough and the compressed air jet methods.

Success along both lines appears to be related to the meticulous care in providing measured quantities of suitable larval food. The impression persists that we are still very ignorant about the as yet unresolved ecological significance of torrential water and the extent to which factors of water movement, aeration, or continuous food supply determine the habitat and perhaps provide the key to successful culture (Macan, 1961; Phillipson, 1956).

When full allowance is made for variations in technique and differences in approach by different workers, it becomes evident that different species of *Simulium* may react very differently to the same treatment. When successful colonization is ultimately achieved by one or another of these research workers, it would therefore perhaps be too optimistic to expect that this would automatically solve the problem for other species. In tropical countries the greatest attention has rather naturally been devoted to established vectors of human onchocerciasis. Other common nonvector species, however, which have received much less attention in those areas might well prove much more amenable to colonization. The experience gained in such success might provide necessary guidance as to the methods of tackling the more refractory species of economic importance.

It is encouraging to know that many of these problems in culture and colonization of *Simulium* are being vigorously tackled at present, and that there is a growing tendency for research workers to meet and discuss their experiences without necessarily waiting for their findings to remain frozen during the delay and time-consuming process of publication.

There is little doubt that many aspects of *Simulium* biology will remain obscure until successful culturing or colonization can be achieved. Questions of longevity, number of blood feeds, length of gonotrophic cycle, number of ovipositions, effect of temperature, humidity, and light, etc., all need critical examination. Considerable advance in knowledge of species complexes may also be expected once the technique of mating and cross-mating with pure laboratory strains has been mastered. Most important is the fact that our understanding of the epidemiology of *Simulium*-borne disease will remain very incomplete until laboratory colonies of "clean" flies, able to feed readily on human and animal hosts when required, are available for infectivity studies under controlled conditions.

Acknowledgments

I am greatly indebted to many collaborators who have helped to bring the material in this review up-to-date, or who have kept me in touch with aspects of the work which have not reached the stage of publication. I am particularly indebted to Professor D. M. Davies, Dr. Wood, Dr. Wenk, Professor West, Professor Doby, Dr. Jamn-back, and to Mr. Raybould.

REFERENCES

Chiang, H. C., and Young, H. K. (1962). Decapitation-initiated oviposition in crane flies. *Entomol. Exptl. Appl.* **5**, 289–290.

Crisp, G. (1956). "Simulium and Onchocerciasis in the Northern Territories of the Gold Coast," p. 171. Lewis, London.

de Coursey, J. D., and Webster, A. P. (1952). Effect of insecticides and other substances on oviposition by *Aedes sollicitans. J. Econ. Entomol.* **45**, 1030–1034.

Dalmat, H. T. (1950). Induced oviposition of Simulium flies by exposure to CO_2. *Public Health Rept. (U.S.)* **65**, 545–546.

Dalmat, H. T. (1955). The black flies (Diptera, Simuliidae) of Guatemala and their role as vectors of onchocerciasis. *Smithsonian Inst. Misc. Collections* **125**, No. 1, 425.

Davies, D. M. (1953). Longevity of black flies in captivity. *Can. J. Zool.* **31**, 304–312.

Davies, D. M., and Peterson, B. V. (1956). Observations on the mating, feeding, ovarian development and oviposition of adult black flies (Simuliidae, Diptera). *Can. J. Zool.* **34**, 615–665.

Doby, J. M. (1964). Personal communication.

Doby, J. M., David, F., and Rault, B. (1959). Rearing in the laboratory from egg to adult of *Simulium ornatum, S. aureum, S. erythrocephalum* and *S. decorum*, with biological observations on these species. *Ann. Parasitol. Humaine Comparee* **34**, 676–693.

Fallis, A. M. (1964). Feeding and related behaviour of female Simuliidae (Diptera). *Exptl. Parasitol.* **15**, 439–470.

Fallis, A. M., and Bennett, G. F. (1962). Observations on the sporogony of Leucocytozoon mirandae, L. bonasae, and L. fringillinarum (Sporozoa: Leucocytozoidae). Can. J. Zool. **40**, 395–400.

Fredeen, F. J. H. (1959). Rearing black flies in the laboratory (Diptera, Simuliidae). *Can. Entomologist* **91**, 73–83.

Hall, R. E., and Harrod, J. J. (1963). A method of rearing *Simulium ornatum var nitidifrons* (Diptera, Simuliidae) in the laboratory. *Hydrobiologia* **22**, 197–201.

Hartley, C. F. (1955). Rearing simuliids in the laboratory from eggs to adults, *Proc. Helminthol. Soc. Wash. D.C.* **22**, 93–95.

Hocking, B., and Pickering, L. R. (1954). Observations on the bionomics of some Northern species of Simuliidae (Diptera). *Can. J. Zool.* **32**, 99–119.

Hoffman, C. C. (1930). Los Simulidos de la region de Chiapas. *Anales Inst. Biol. (Univ. Nacl. Mex.)* **1**, 293–306.

Jamnback, H. (1964). Description of a trough testing technique useful in evaluating the effectiveness of chemicals as blackfly larvicides. WHO/Oncho/28.64; WHO/VC/96.64. (Restricted documentary series, available from W.H.O. on request.)

Lewis, D. J. (1957). Aspects of the structure, biology, and study of *Simulium damnosum. Ann. Trop. Med. Parasitol.* **51**, 340–358.

Lewis, D. J., Lyons, G. R. L., and Marr, J. D. M. (1961). Observations on *Simulium damnosum* from the Red Volta in Ghana. *Ann. Trop. Med. Parasitol.* **55**, 202–210.

Macan, T. T. (1961). Factors that limit the range of freshwater animals. *Biol. Rev. Cambridge Phil. Soc.* **36**, 151.

Mackerras, M. J., and Mackerras, I. M. (1948). Simuliidae from Queensland *Australian J. Sci. Res.* **B1**, 232–269.

Marr, J. D. M. (1962). The use of an artificial breeding site and cage in the study of *Simulium damnosum* Theobald. *Bull. World Health Organ.* **27**, 622–629.

Muirhead-Thomson, R. C. (1956). Communal oviposition in *Simulium damnosum* Theobald (Diptera, Simuliidae). *Nature* **178**, 1297–1299.

Muirhead-Thomson, R. C. (1957a). The development of *Onchocerca volvulus* in laboratory reared *Simulium damnosum* Theobald. *Am. J. Trop. Med. Hyg.* **6**, 912–913.

Muirhead-Thomson, R. C. (1957b). Laboratory studies on the reactions of Simulium larvae to insecticides *Am. J. Trop. Med. Hyg.* **6**, 920–925.

Muirhead-Thomson, R. C. (1962). A laboratory technique for testing the reactions of Simulium larvae to insecticides. World Health Organization, 13th Expert Committee on Insecticides, Working Paper No. 5.12.2.

Muirhead-Thomson, R. C. (1963). Culture methods for Diptera using running water as a larval habitat. EBL/Working Paper No. DD11/63. Symposium on culture procedures for arthropod vectors and their biological control agents, Gainesville, Florida. *Bull. World Health Organ.* (1964) 31.4, 479–482.

Noamesi, G. K. (1962). A preliminary study of the susceptibility of Simulium larvae to DDT, y-BHC and Dieldrin. *Bull. World Health Organ.* **27**, 620–622.

Ovazza, M. (1962). A laboratory technique for determining the susceptibility of Simulium larvae to insecticides. World Health Organization, 13th Expert Committee on Insecticides, Working Paper No. 5.12.3.

Phillipson, J. (1956). A study of factors determining the distribution of the larvae of the blackfly, *Simulium ornatum* Mg. *Bull. Entomol. Res.* **47**, 227–238.

Puri, I. M. (1925). On the life history and structure of the early stages of Simulium. *Parasitology* **17**, 295–369.

Raybould, J. N. (1965). Preliminary investigations towards a culture technique for S. *woodi* and S. *damnosum* at Amani, Tanzania. Personal communication.

Smart, J. (1934). On the biology of the black fly, *Simulium ornatum* Mg. (Diptera, Simuliidae). *Proc. Phys. Soc. (London)* **22**, 217–238.

Strong, R. P., Bequaert, J. C., Sandground, J. H., and Munoz Ochoa, M. (1934). "Onchocerciasis with Special Reference to the Central American form of the Disease," Vol. 6, pp. 175–224. Harvard Univ. Press, Cambridge, Massachusetts.

Thomas, L. J. (1946). Black fly incubator-aerator cabinet. *Science* **103**, 21.

Wagner, W. (1926). Bau und Funktion des Atmungssystem der Kriebelmucken larven. *Zool. Jahrb. Abt. Allgem. Zool. Physiol. Tiere* **42**, 441.

Wanson, M., and Henrard, C. (1945). Habitat et comportement larvaire du *Simulium damnosum* Theobald. *Rec. Trav. Sci. Med. Congo Belge* **4**, 113–121.

Wanson, M., Henrard, C., and Peel, E. (1945). *Onchocerca volvulus* Leuckart—Indices d'infection des simulies agressives pour l'homme—Cycle de developpement chez *Simulium damnosum* Theobald. *Rec. Trav. Sci. Med. Congo. Belge* **4**, 122–135.

Wenk, P. (1963). Kopulation, Blutsaugen und Eiablage von *Boophthora erythrocephala* de Geer 1776 (Diptera, Simuliidae) im laboratorium. *Naturwissenschaften* **11**, 409.

Wenk, P. (1965). Personal communication.

West, A. S. (1963). Canadian experience in the handling of blackflies under laboratory conditions. EBL/Working Paper No. 44/63. Symposium on culture procedures for arthropod vectors and their biological control agents, Gainesville, Florida. *Bull. World Health Organ.* (1964) 31.4, 487–489.

Wood, D. M., and Davies, D. M. (1964). The rearing of Simuliids (Diptera). *Proc. 12th Intern. Congr. Entomol., London, 1964.* Unpublished communication.

Wright, F. N. (1957). Rearing of *Simulium damnosum* Theobald (Diptera, Simuliidae) in the laboratory. *Nature* **180**, 1059.

Chapter 10

Stable Flies

CALVIN M. JONES[*]

Entomology Research Division,
Agricultural Research Service,
U. S. Department of Agriculture,
Lincoln, Nebraska

I. INTRODUCTION

Research workers have maintained colonies of *Stomoxys calcitrans* (Linnaeus) with varying degrees of success during the past 40 years. It is generally agreed that this species is more difficult to rear in the laboratory than *Musca domestica* Linnaeus. Published reports include rearing procedures and techniques used by at least twenty individuals. They all differ slightly because each worker endeavored to meet his needs with equipment and materials available to him. The larval habitat of *Stomoxys* is rather specific, and the adults feed solely on blood. Each of the steps or procedures in the maintenance of a colony is important. Adherence to strict standards is necessary to produce test insects of uniform size and vigor.

[*] *Present address:* Insectary, University of Nebraska, Lincoln, Nebraska.

145

II. REARING CONDITIONS

A. TEMPERATURE

Stomoxys will develop at a range of temperatures from 16° to more than 32°C. After having used various constant and fluctuating temperatures, the author has concluded that 28° ± 1°C is the most satisfactory for continuous rearing. This temperature is generally near that which is desirable for rearing other species of insects and is suitable for other laboratory activities.

Some larval media generate more heat than others during the first few days. When the room temperature exceeds 30°C precautions should be taken that young larvae do not die because of excessive heat.

B. HUMIDITY

Relative humidity in the rearing room should be kept at 50% or greater for the well-being of the adults. A mean of 55 or 60% is satisfactory. If natural humidity exceeds this amount the air does not need to be dehumidified. High humidity is desirable but not essential in reducing the rate of evaporation from the adult food supply, egg-collecting dishes, and the larval medium.

C. LIGHT

The amount and source of light are not critical. Either incandescent, fluorescent or natural light, or a combination of these, may be used. Flies caged near a window will get sufficient light. In general, the light intensity deemed desirable by the attendant working with the colony is satisfactory for feeding, mating, and egg-laying activities of the flies. The author prefers to use artificial light and control the source to simulate a 16-hour day. Others prefer to illuminate the room continuously.

III. ADULT CARE

A. CAGES

The size and shape of the cages for confining the adults depend upon the size of the colony and techniques used in feeding and collecting eggs. The population per cage should not exceed approximately 1 fly per square inch of resting surface. The use of cages larger than about 2 ft on a side should be avoided. Cylindrical cages are more desirable than those that are square or rectangular. When used in a horizontal position they have a minimum of vertical surfaces on which the flies can rest, thus reducing contamination of the flies by feces from those directly above. Another apparent advantage is that in their search for food the flies tend to move to the upper area of the cage where the feeding can most conveniently be done. Woodbury (1943) pointed out that flies locate cold, citrated blood by contact only.

The cages are easily constructed by supporting the circular wooden ends with four lengths of strap iron. This frame is covered with screen no larger than 14 × 18 mesh. A 5-inch circular hole is cut in one end, and a cloth sleeve is attached to provide an entryway. The holding capacity of a cage can be increased by use of hardware cloth, 2 × 2 or 4 × 4 mesh, as additional resting surfaces.

B. FEEDING

The only satisfactory diet is blood of such mammals as cattle, horses, and swine. Sheep, guinea-pig, and mouse blood is not satisfactory, according to Pospisil (1961), as females do not lay eggs after being fed with it. Defibrinated whole blood was used by Glaser (1924), Bruce and Eagleson (1938), Eagleson (1943), and others. Prior to 1943 researchers thought that the blood should be warmed to 25° to 40°C before it was offered to the flies. Eagleson stated that defibrinated or acidulated blood may be stored in a refrigerator and need not be warmed when given to the flies. Woodbury (1943) stated that flies feed as readily on ice-cold blood as when it is at room temperature, but that the flies cannot detect its presence except by contact with their tarsi. It is now common practice in almost all laboratories where *Stomoxys* is reared to prevent coagulation of fresh animal blood by adding sodium citrate at the rate of 2 to 3.5 gm per liter of blood. It can be stored at temperatures of 0° to 7°C for as long as 2 weeks or kept for longer periods if frozen (Appleby and Fisk, 1959). Blood containing sodium citrate at the rate of 5 gm per liter is acceptable.

Bruce and Eagleson (1938) utilized the positive phototropism of the flies in feeding them. The flies fed from glass tubes resting in an upright position on top of the cage. Totze (1934) described a method of feeding in which he simulated natural conditions. He permitted the flies to feed through a membrane stretched over a container of warm blood. Other workers prefer to pour the blood on an absorbent material such as cotton or a sponge in a dish and set it in the cage. The most convenient method we have found is to saturate pads of absorbent cotton with citrated blood and lay them on top of the cage. Suitable criteria for determining the amount of blood to provide are that at feeding time the old pads should be dry enough to be lifted from the screen and that a little blood may be squeezed from them.

Glaser (1923) and Tuttle (1961) studied the effect of food on longevity and reproduction of laboratory-reared *S. calcitrans.* Glaser stated that flies fed defibrinated blood oviposited from 3 to 7 times and laid many eggs. He demonstrated that neither serum nor red cell elements fed separately to stable flies induced egg deposition and that longevity of the adults was lessened. When the two blood fractions were artificially combined again longevity and oviposition became normal. Tuttle found that dextrose or similar sugars are very important factors sustaining the life of the adults. Dextrose can be substituted for the factor(s) present in the red cell fraction of beef blood that influences oviposition. Tuttle also found that 50% diluted blood could not support life normally, nor could such a diet result in normal egg production.

IV. COLLECTION AND HANDLING OF EGGS

Gravid females will oviposit readily in a properly prepared dish placed in or beneath the cage. The dish should contain a cloth, preferably black, over a pad saturated with water containing 1 to 5% technical ammonium hydroxide. This solution is a very satisfactory oviposition stimulant. If the dish is placed beneath the cage the pad should be in contact with the screen. The eggs will be relatively free of debris and can be counted, weighed, or measured. When it is not necessary to know the number of eggs for starting cultures a small container of larval medium serves as a suitable oviposition site. Any spent medium, old blood pads or dishes, accumulation of dead flies, and empty pupal cases in the cage must be removed to prevent flies from ovipositing in them.

Some eggs will remain viable for a few days when stored at temperatures low enough to prevent hatching. Champlain *et al.,* (1954) reported that 50% hatched after 1 week if immersed in water and stored at 12°C. Very few hatched after 3 weeks. The author frequently stores eggs under moist conditions or in water at 7° ± 1°C for 1 week. From 50 to 75% of them hatch when returned to room temperature.

V. LARVAL REARING

A. MEDIUM

There are almost as many larval media described in published reports as there are rearing procedures. The availability of materials has usually determined the composition of the medium used.

After trying fermenting oat straw and horse manure alone and in mixtures, Glaser (1924) adopted fresh horse manure as a larval rearing medium. Richardson (1932) used a mixture of wheat bran, alfalfa meal, and oat hulls. To this he added bakers yeast and Diamalt (a product of Fleischman Yeast Co. containing a large percentage of malt sugars). Doty (1937) used the same ingredients in similar proportions. The medium used by Melvin (1937) consisted of crushed oats, water, molasses, and yeast. Eagleson (1943) was not able to rear the number of flies that he needed by the procedures of Doty. He started the larvae in wet, chopped alfalfa hay that had fermented 2 to 4 days. After the larvae had fed for 2 days he sprinkled dry, rolled oats (hulls removed as for human consumption) over the surface as food. He said the medium must have an abundance of concentrated carbohydrate food and must not have an acid reaction. Parr (1959), working in Uganda, did not find the rearing methods of Doty and Eagleson suitable under his conditions. His medium for both egging and larval rearing consisted of dried cow dung, dried blood granules, sugar, and water. Fedder (1958) reared larvae in wheat bran and sawdust.

Champlain et al. (1954), McGregor and Dreiss (1955), Goodhue and Cantrel (1958), Campau et al. (1953), the author, and many others have successfully used the Standard Fly Larval Medium (Chemical Specialties Manufacturers Association, 1963). The medium is composed of 26.67% alfalfa meal, 33.33% soft wheat bran, and 40.00% brewer's dried grain. The latter is the dry extracted residue of barley malt alone or in mixture with other cereal grain products resulting from the manufacture of wort. The medium was developed for use in rearing *Musca domestica,* and the procedure calls for the addition of yeast and Diamalt to be added to the water used in mixing. This practice is routine in some laboratories in which *Stomoxys* is reared. The author feels that the yeast and Diamalt are not necessary.

The Standard Fly Larval Medium is an excellent diet for larval development. The mixture, however, must be made more porous by the addition of wood shavings or another coarse material such as vermiculite (Goodhue and Cantrel, 1958), sawdust (Fedder, 1958), and oat hulls (Richardson, 1932). A suitable mixture for starting larvae is approximately 4 parts Standard Fly Larval Medium and 1 part coarse shavings by weight. The proportion will vary depending upon the texture of the shavings. Water is added until a few drops can be squeezed from a handful. The eggs are then mixed with the top portion.

B. CARE DURING DEVELOPMENT

Rearing should be done in containers large enough so that the medium can be stirred daily until the larvae begin to pupate. Four things should be observed: (1) moisture content, (2) larval food, (3) proper texture (ratio of Standard Fly Larval Medium to shavings), and (4) size of larval population. Each of these factors influences success in consistently rearing *Stomoxys* of uniform size and age. If conditions are not satisfactory, the larvae, even though about the same age, will pupate over a period of perhaps 7 days, and the adults will be small. The medium has sufficient moisture when the particles glisten, but the bottom portion should not be wetter than the top. A deficiency of shavings causes the medium to be compact. The food supply will be depleted from top to bottom if other conditions are satisfactory. By observing where the larvae are concentrated and the difference in appearance of the medium above and below them one can quickly learn to recognize when additional food and water should be added. Too much food causes the mixture to feel gummy and stick to the hand. Larvae that are overcrowded, perhaps to the point of being retarded, can usually be salvaged by giving them more room and food.

Excessive mold development in the medium, particularly during the first 2 or 3 days, is sometimes a problem. Stirring, adjusting the moisture content, and increasing the wood shaving content usually corrects the problem.

VI. SEPARATION AND CARE OF PUPAE

Pupae are easily separated from the larval medium by washing them out. All except the very young ones will float. Goodhue and Linnard (1950) described an air separation apparatus that is useful in cleaning pupae if it is desirable to have them free of trash.

Pupae cannot be stored satisfactorily. A few will remain alive at 5° to 8°C for a maximum of 14 days. Larvae will pupate and adults will emerge at 10°C.

VII. LIFE CYCLE

When speaking of speed of development one must keep in mind that the larval medium may be 5° to 8°C warmer than the room temperature. The amount of heat generated will depend upon the mixture used. At a constant rearing room temperature of 27° ± 0.5°C a pan of Standard Fly Larval Medium and wood shavings may have a temperature of 38°C by the second day after it is mixed and may not reach room temperature until larvae begin to pupate about the seventh day.

Development from egg to egg requires a minimum of 46, 30, and 21 days when reared at room temperatures of 15.5°, 21.1°, and 26.6°C, respectively. The following tabulation indicates the number of days required for each stage of development when reared at these temperatures:

Stage of development	15.5°C	21.1°C	26.6°C
Incubation	2	1	1
Larval	18	13	7
Pupal	8	7	7
Preoviposition	18	9	6

NOTE: Some of the larvae and pupae in a given culture require an additional 5 or 6 days to complete development.

REFERENCES

Appleby, J. E., and Fisk, F. W. (1959). Stable fly (*Stomoxys calcitrans*) rearing. *North Central Branch Entomol. Soc. Am., Proc.* **14**, 41–42.

Bruce, W. G., and Eagleson, C. (1938). A new method of feeding adult hornflies, *Haematobia irritans* L., and stable flies, *Stomoxys calcitrans* L. *J. Kansas Entomol. Soc.* **11**, 144–145.

Campau, E. J., Baker, G. J., and Morrison, F. D. (1953). Rearing stable flies for laboratory tests. *J. Econ. Entomol.* **46**, 524.

Champlain, R. A., Fisk, F. W., and Dowdy, A. C. (1954). Some improvements in rearing stable flies. *J. Econ. Entomol.* **47**, 490–491.

Chemical Specialities Manufacturers Association. (1963). The Peet-Grady method. *In* "Blue Book Catalog (1963) of Soap and Chemical Specialties," pp. 229–231. Soap and Chemical Specialties, New York.

Doty, A. E. (1937). Convenient method of rearing the stable fly. *J. Econ. Entomol.* **30**, 367–369.

Eagleson, C. (1943). Stablefly. *In* "Laboratory Procedures in Studies of the Chemical Control of Insects." Publ. No. 20, pp. 77–78. Am. Assoc. Advance. Sci., Washington, D. C.

Fedder, M. L. (1958). Razvedenie krovososuschchei mukhi zhigalki (*Stomoxys calcitrans* L.) v laboratornykh usloviyakh. *Med. Parazitol. i Parazitarn. Bolezni* **27**, 733. [English translation of summary in *Biol. Abstr.* **45**, 26339 (1964).]

Glaser, R. W. (1923). The effect of food on longevity and reproduction of flies. *J. Exptl. Zool.* **38**, 383–412.

Glaser, R. W. (1924). Rearing flies for experimental purposes with biological notes. *J. Econ. Entomol.* **17**, 486–496.

Goodhue, L. D., and Cantrel, K. E. (1958). The use of vermiculite in medium for stable fly larvae. *J. Econ. Entomol.* **51**, 250.

Goodhue, L. D., and Linnard, C. E. (1950). Air separation apparatus for cleaning fly pupae. *J. Econ. Entomol.* **43**, 228.

McGregor, W. S., and Dreiss, J. M. (1955). Rearing stable flies in the laboratory. *J. Econ. Entomol.* **48**, 327–328.

Melvin, R. (1937). *Stomoxys calcitrans. In* "Culture Methods for Invertebrate Animals" (P. S. Galtsoff *et al.*, eds.), pp. 428–429. Cornell Univ. Press (Comstock), Ithaca, New York.

Parr, H. C. M. (1959). Studies on *Stomoxys calcitrans* (L.) in Uganda, East Africa. I. A method of rearing large numbers of *Stomoxys calcitrans. Bull. Entomol. Res.* **50**, 165–169.

Pospisil, J. (1961). Jednoducha metoda chovu bodalky stajove *Stomoxys calcitrans* L. *Zool. Listy* **10**: 222.

Richardson, H. H. (1932). An efficient medium for rearing house flies throughout the year. *Science* **76**, 350–351.

Totze, R. (1934). Blutsaugen unter rein experimentellen bedingumgen. *Zentr. Bakteriol., Parasitenk., Abt. I. Orig.* **132**, 382–384.

Tuttle, E. L. (1961). Studies of the effect of nutrition on survival and oviposition of laboratory reared stable flies, *Stomoxys calcitrans* L. *Dissertation Abstr.* **22**, 1334.

Woodbury, E. N. (1943). Stablefly, *Stomoxys calcitrans* (L.). *In* "Laboratory Procedures in Studies of the Chemical Control of Insects." Publ. No. 20, pp. 70–71. Am. Assoc. Advance. Sci., Washington, D. C.

Chapter 11

Tsetse Flies

W. H. R. LUMSDEN AND D. S. SAUNDERS

Trypanosomiasis Research Unit,
Department of Animal Health,
Royal (Dick) School of Veterinary Studies, and
Department of Zoology,
University of Edinburgh,
Edinburgh, Scotland

I. INTRODUCTION

The colonization of *Glossina* (tsetse flies) is required for two main purposes: first, to provide uniform material for use in experimental work, and second, to provide flies in large numbers for irradiation and release into natural environments for sterile male control techniques as for *Cochliomyia hominivorax* (Coquerel) (=*Callitroga americana*) (Bushland and Hopkins, 1953).

It is possible that the desirable characteristics of artificial colonies may differ according to the purpose in view. For instance, the genetically uniform inbred population most suitable for the first purpose might be largely composed of individuals unable adequately to compete in natural environments, and so unsuitable for the second application. For it, an artificially maintained population with frequent gene reinforcement from natural populations might be desirable (Nash *et al.*, 1958).

Despite considerable attention, laboratory colonization of *Glossina* has so far been accomplished on only very few occasions and even then usually only precariously and with difficulty. The main reason for this difficulty lies in the method of reproduction—adenotrophic viviparity (Hagan, 1951)—which the tsetse flies share with the Pupipara. The female tsetse fly produces only a very small number of offspring; consequently, the potential rate of increase of a population is low. Furthermore, the entire feeding phase of larval development takes place within the female fly so that adult and larva are dependent upon the same source of food.

De Azevedo and Pinhao (1964) quote the many attempts to maintain *Glossina* spp. in captivity up to that date. They divide the studies into two groups: attempts to establish breeding in the laboratory in Africa under natural conditions, and in Europe under artificial ones. The distinction is perhaps not a real one as even in African laboratories the conditions are clearly fundamentally different from those of the natural *Glossina* habitat. Many of the studies quoted extended to several years' duration and rang the changes on most of the factors likely to be of importance—species of fly, types of container, populations per individual container, species of host, regimes of feeding, microclimatic conditions, degree of disturbance or stimulation, and so on. These studies have produced much of interest in relation to *Glossina* ecology and suggestive of the factors important in the laboratory maintenance of *Glossina*, but it is true to say that in none of them has long-term laboratory maintenance, without reinforcement of the population from the outside, actually been achieved for extended periods except by Willett (1953) with *Glossina swynnertoni* Austen, by McDonald (1960) with *G. morsitans* Westwood, and by Evens and Niemegeers (1954), WAITR (1955, 1956), and Geigy (1946, 1948) with *G. palpalis* Robineau-Desvoidy. Even in these instances continued maintenance was not easy for one reason or another, often simply the incapability of maintaining the level of care and attention necessary to sustain the colony.

De Azevedo and Pinhao (1964) were themselves more successful and report the maintenance of a closed colony of *Glossina morsitans* for a period of about 5 years. This unique accomplishment will attract special attention in the course of this review.

The possible distinction between the two types of *Glossina* colony desired will not be discussed further as the first necessity in either case is a colony of such vitality that it will increase its population at a rate near to the theoretical maximum (Buxton, 1955).

Many of the "colonies" reported are sustained in population only by frequent additions from the field (WAITR, 1957; Nash *et al.*, 1958). The "vitality" of laboratory-bred flies is generally less than that of wild flies (Evens and Niemegeers, 1954). It is to be noted, simply, at this point that introduction of wild material will be most safely accomplished with adult flies derived from wild pupae or from wild flies, to avoid the concurrent introduction of trypanosomes and of pupal parasites.

Possible approaches toward the colonization of *Glossina* appear to be:

(a) By approximation to natural conditions either in the open or in the laboratory.

(b) By the discovery of an artificial regime of maintenance to which the flies will submit.

Most work reported so far falls into category (a), in the laboratory; the possibility of approach (b) being successful should not, however, be overlooked, at least for the establishment of uniform *Glossina* colonies. Although the great mass of field data on *Glossina* contains much of pertinence to the present problem it will be necessary, because of limitations of space, to concentrate on the colonization data and only indicate very briefly the implications of field observations. Also, much of the information available both from the field and from the laboratory is miscellaneous and difficult to collate and assess. Some selection of the data available has been necessary on the part of the authors; it is hoped that the selection has been made with due objectivity.

II. IMPLICATIONS OF THE REPRODUCTIVE PHYSIOLOGY

A. THEORETICAL CONSIDERATIONS

Each ovary contains two ovarioles (Saunders, 1960a). Starting with the right ovary, eggs are produced singly in a sequence which involves alternation of ovaries and ovarioles (Saunders, 1960b). In *G. morsitans* at 26°C the first mature egg is ovulated on the eighth or ninth day of imaginal life and comes to lie in the uterus. As it passes the openings of the spermathecal ducts spermatozoa enter the micropyle and fertilization occurs. There are four larval instars. The first two, and the greater part of the third, are passed within the maternal uterus. The first instar is of short duration (Roubaud, 1909); the larva is provided with an "egg tooth" which splits the chorion at hatching. Very little growth occurs at this stage and the first-instar larva takes little food (Bursell, 1955). Most of the feeding is accomplished by the second-instar larva during a 60-hour period in which the "milk" is secreted by the accessory glands (Hoffmann, 1954); most of the growth takes place in the third instar. At the end of the gestation period the third-stage larva is deposited on the ground, where it burrows and where it forms the puparium without further feeding. The fourth instar is a transient phase before pupation within the sclerotized third-instar integument or puparium (Bursell, 1958). Within 24 hours of larviposition the next mature egg is ovulated and the cycle begins again.

In *G. morsitans* at 26°C the first larva is produced 18 to 20 days after emergence; subsequent interlarval periods are about 10 days (Saunders, 1960b). There seems to be little difference in this respect between different species (Buxton, 1955) but the interlarval period is, of course, affected by temperature. At 30°C the mean interlarval period for *G. morsitans* is 8 days; at 24°C, 11 days; and at 18°C, 25 days (Jack, 1939). For *G. palpalis* it is 9–10 days at 25°C and 11 days at 22°C (Roubaud, 1909). Under field conditions in Uganda the mean interlarval period is about 13.5 days. The maximum number of larvae is uncertain, but de Azevedo and Pinhao (1964) record a *G. morsitans* which produced 20 larvae in 196 days.

The reproductive cycle proceeds with remarkable regularity once it has started, and, provided that abnormalities do not occur, it is possible to calculate theoretical rates of reproduction. For instance, if the first larva is produced on day 18 and subsequent larvae at 10-day intervals, at least 9 larvae should be produced in the first 100 days of imaginal life and 10 in the next 100. Assuming an interlarval period of a fortnight, Buxton (1955) calculated a figure of 7 births per 100 female days. It is also possible to calculate a theoretical population increase. Assuming that alternate offspring are male and female, and zero pupal mortality, a fly must survive at least 30 days to replace itself and its mate, and at least 40 days to produce an increase in the population. If mortality of the pupae and adults is taken into account the mean life span necessary to maintain even a steady population may be at least twice this. Figures from the age determination of trap- and bait-caught samples of *G. pallidipes* Austen (Saunders, 1962) show that 40–60% of females have lived at least 40 days before capture and produced 3 or 4, or more, larvae; this high proportion indicates that a substantial number of flies survive to produce a much greater number of larvae. Buxton (1955) calculated a theoretical rate of increase for

Glossina assuming ample food, a constant soil and air temperature of 24°C, and that each female lived 70 days and produced 6 larvae, 3 of each sex. Commencing with one fertilized female he showed that the rate of increase approximated to a geometrical progression, and that the number of females alive after 128 days was 5; after 178 days, 10; and after 212 days, 21. The number of females in the F_3 generation was 27, and in the F_4, 81, and so on. This demonstrates that a *Glossina* population is capable of increasing itself fivefold in 18 weeks and tenfold in less than 6 months. Glasgow (1963), however, points out that this is an unrealistic model since it assumes zero pupal mortality and does not take into account the daily survival rate of the females and the probable decline in fecundity with age. Nevertheless, it serves as a basis to assess the attempts to colonize and breed *Glossina* in the laboratory.

B. REPRODUCTIVE PHYSIOLOGY

The numerous attempts to colonize tsetse flies include studies on different species, controlled and uncontrolled climatic conditions, and many different feeding methods and regimes. Some colonies have been self-supporting (de Azevedo and Pinhao, 1964; Roubaud, 1917; Mellanby and Mellanby, 1936) others have required periodic additions of wild stock (Geigy, 1948; WAITR, 1953). Only the recent work of de Azevedo and Pinhao approaches the theoretical rate of increase described by Buxton's model; the reasons for this success will be discussed later. The majority of workers describe rates of reproduction far less than this. From their work two obvious difficulties emerge: (1) an intermittent larval production; and (2) a gradual decline in pupal size and in fecundity with succeeding generations. For instance, Potts (1933), Buxton and Lewis (1934), and Willett (1953) found that the number of births per 100 female days varied usually between 2 and 5, figures which suggest an intermittent larval production. Even in his original batch of wild-caught flies Willett found that the mean interlarval period was over 15 days, and in flies maintained on guinea pigs it lengthened to 25 days by the fourth generation. Foster (1957) records interlarval periods varying between 9 and 78 days. Clearly in all these colonies there were gaps in the expected production of larvae. Most of these are probably due to abortion: Willett (1953), for instance, found abortion frequent, possibly of the order of 50%.

It is evident that feeding is of utmost importance in determining the reproductive rate in *Glossina*, since the larva within the uterus is dependent upon the blood taken by the mother. Mellanby (1937) showed a close correlation between the amount of blood taken during pregnancy and the weight of the resulting larva. Furthermore, flies which were only allowed to take small interrupted meals aborted their larvae, although the ovulation sequence was unaffected and the flies survived well. Mellanby also showed that the *timing* of the blood meals during the gestation period was important. She considered that three large meals were sufficient, and that the last should be taken about 3 days before parturition. Foster (1957) was of a similar opinion, and also found a positive correlation between the maximum interval without food and the mean interlarval period. This effect, however, is almost certainly due to undetected abortion. Some workers have claimed that the type of blood is important. Willett (1953), for instance, reported that *G. swynnertoni* maintained on sheep were superior in many respects (shorter interlarval period, greater longevity, etc.) to those fed on guinea pigs. However, these differences were at a very low level of significance and could have been due to other factors such as handling.

Apart from abortion, two other kinds of abnormalities are known: (1) the retention of fully developed eggs in the ovary (Roubaud and Colas-Belcour, 1936; Mellanby, 1937), and (2) the degeneration and resorption of egg follicles (Saunders, 1960b). Both of these are responsible for losses in laboratory colonies. Working with *G. palpalis fuscipes* Newstead, Mellanby (1937) showed that the first egg was retained in the right ovary of virgin females and that virgin females 4–5 weeks old may contain 3 or 4 fully developed eggs, some in the ovaries and some in the uterus. A similar retention of the first egg was reported by Vanderplank (1947) and Saunders (1960b), although these authors found that ovulation usually continued normally once the first egg had left the ovary. The inadvertent inclusion of virgin females in the results from laboratory colonies therefore may have accounted for the low reproductive rates reported by some authors. However, unfertilized females were excluded by most later authors (Willett, 1953; Foster, 1957) by better mating procedures and by the exclusion of virgins by examining the spermathecae at death (Mellanby, 1936).

Degenerating follicles have been found in the ovaries of *G. morsitans* (Saunders, 1960b). These follicles ceased development, became granular in appearance, and were eventually resorbed to leave a well-defined dilatation in the follicular tube. Follicular degeneration causes an obvious gap in the sequence of egg production. Mellanby (1937) observed that females of *G. palpalis fuscipes* were effectively sterilized by a few days exposure to a constant temperature of 29° to 30°C. Nearly all the females showed abnormalities in the ovaries: some contained several unovulated eggs, as in virgin females, and others contained no visible ova. Similar abnormalities were observed by Potts (1958) in flies from irradiated pupae. It is probable that follicular degeneration and resorption had taken place in these flies. Furthermore, continuous high temperature appears to be lethal for embryonic development (Roubaud and Colas-Belcour, 1936; Mellanby, 1937) although larval development can continue (Mellanby, 1937).

We have little evidence of the importance of these abnormalities in natural populations. The retention of mature eggs in the ovaries of virgin females is probably very rare since nearly all nonteneral females are fertilized in the field (Vanderplank, 1947; Mellanby, 1936) even when the population is greatly reduced by successful control programs (Teesdale, 1940; Jackson, 1949). Only one example of a female showing follicular degeneration has been found in several thousand wild *G. pallidipes* dissected (Saunders, 1962), although losses from this cause might be more important under "marginal" conditions. Lastly, we have no information on the natural abortion rate, although this may be important when hosts are not readily available or toward the end of reproductive life. In laboratory colonies these abnormalities are frequent and could be traced to some extent by the examination of the ovaries of newly dead flies for evidence of previous ovulations, follicular degenerations, and supernumerary mature eggs.

III. TECHNIQUES

A. GENERAL CONSIDERATIONS: CRITERIA OF PERFORMANCE AND FACTORS OF IMPORTANCE

The criteria by which attempts to colonize *Glossina* have been judged will be considered first, thereafter the main external factors likely to influence success of colonization will be discussed in general terms. The factors are choice of *Glossina* species, temperature, humidity, light, and disturbance. The particular influence of each factor will be discussed further as necessary in relation to the various developmental stages of *Glossina*.

The absolute criterion of the progress of a *Glossina* colony is the degree to which the rate of population increase, without external addition, approaches to that theoretically possible (Buxton, 1955). In most *Glossina* colonies the rate of population increase is far less than this. Most colonies are not self-maintaining; in these situations the duration of survival of a self-contained colony may be used as a criterion.

Many other criteria have been used to gauge the progress and prospect of a colony over a given period and they may suggest, also, where attention should be directed to improve technique.

1. Longevity and Mortality

Willett (1953) used mean female longevity as a criterion of the general condition of the flies during the course of maintenance. Nash *et al.* (1958), working with *G. palpalis*, considered that the daily mortality figures should be less than 2% and that higher values occurring for more than a few consecutive days indicated something radically wrong.

2. Proportion of Females Inseminated

Willett (1953) used the proportion of spermathecae showing sperm on dissection as an index of the fertility of females in the colony.

3. Female Nutrition and Fecundity

Several criteria in use are basically indicators of the state of these two closely related characteristics:

Mean number of pupae per female (Willett, 1953)
Mean number of pupae per female per month (WAITR, 1954)
Mean number of pupae per week per 100 females (Foster, 1958)
Mean number of pupae per 100 female-days (Willett, 1953)
Mean interlarval period (Willett, 1953)
Pupal weight (Mellanby, 1937; Willett, 1953)

Of these, the first and last two, taken together, seem to be most significant; pupal weight should be measured immediately after puparium formation as rapid losses of weight take place in the next few days (Willett, 1953). All the other values are basically similar to mean interlarval period, and will be affected partly by microclimatic factors, such as temperature, but most importantly by the frequency with which egg retention or resorption and abortion occur. Of these four values, mean interlarval period seems the most convenient.

The main factors which require consideration in relation to the colonization of *Glossina* are:

Glossina species. So far attempts to colonize *Glossina* have been concerned with species of economic importance, *G. palpalis* sspp. of the *palpalis* group (which comprises 5 spp.), *G. morsitans* sspp., *G. pallidipes, G. swynnertoni,* and *G. austeni* Newstead of the *G. morsitans* group (which comprises 5 spp.). Only one attempt to colonize any of the 12 species of the *G. fusca* group has been noticed (WAITR, 1958). For providing standard laboratory material, the species colonized is almost certainly immaterial. Trials with *G. fusca* group species are, therefore, indicated as they, being generally larger than species of the *G. palpalis* and *G. morsitans* groups, may also be less nutritionally demanding (Glasgow, 1963).

Glossina palpalis has already been maintained in colony for extended periods (Geigy, 1946, 1948). Willett (1953), working with *G. morsitans, G. pallidipes, G. swynnertoni,* and *G. austeni,* considered no one of these species markedly less promising than another, except that he found difficulty in inducing *G. pallidipes* to mate in captivity. He was impressed with the results obtained with a small sample of *G. austeni;* longevity and pupal production exceeded the values obtained with the other species, and pupal weight appeared satisfactory. Foster (1957) found the longevity and pupal production of *G. austeni* to exceed those of *G. morsitans.* Bursell (1960a) discusses various species on the basis of the relation between their size and the fat content of the pupa. *Glossina palpalis, G. morsitans,* and *G. swynnertoni* were all similar in this relation, *G. austeni* had relatively more, *G. fuscipleuris* Austen and *G. longipennis* Corti relatively less, fat. Thus there is some indication that, of the species of the *G. morsitans* group, *G. austeni* might be more easily colonized than the others. However, de Azevedo and Pinhao (1964) have been successful with *G. morsitans.*

4. *Temperature*

The relationships between the developmental stages of various species of *Glossina* and temperature are admirably summarized by Glasgow (1963). For colonization we are concerned not with limiting but with optimum values and perhaps with a need for diurnal fluctuation. Glasgow (1963) indicates the tolerated range for *G. palpalis fuscipes,* for constant temperatures, as only 21°–28°C. The lower limit for spontaneous flight for food seeking and copulation was 20°C (Mellanby, 1936). At 30°C the embryonic development (Mellanby, 1937), and at 35°C, blood digestion, are upset. Although mechanisms such as reversal of phototactic reaction at 32°C (Glasgow, 1963) or cooling by tracheal evaporation (Edney and

Barrass, 1962) may be important in the field, for laboratory colonization it appears likely that they can be disregarded and conditions
confined to the well-established optimum temperature zone. Some
workers have used fluctuating temperatures; e.g., Foster (1957)
kept G. *morsitans* at about 26.5°C for 3 hours in the morning during
feeding and allowed the temperature to drop by about 3°C later.
There appear to be no data specifically indicating that fluctuation
is necessary or even that very precise temperature control is needed;
de Azevedo and Pinhao (1964) control their long-established G.
morsitans colony generally to 26°C but leave the window of the
room open for 3–4 hours daily during manipulation of the stock.
Pupae incubated at 22°–24°C produce adults with maximum fat
reserves (Bursell, 1960a).

5. *Humidity*

Glasgow (1963) emphasizes the difference between adult and
pupal *Glossina* in respect of their water relations. Nonfeeding
young stages can only conserve, never replenish, water supplies,
while adults whenever they feed have a surplus of water to dis-
pose of (Bursell, 1957). The conclusion (Bursell, 1958) that it is pupal
susceptibility to desiccation which is mainly responsible for restricting the distribution of some *Glossina* species indicates that
a humid pupal environment is likely to be important for colonization; de Azevedo and Pinhao (1964) indeed ascribed their success
with G. *morsitans* largely to attention to this. As regards adult flies,
survival seems better at higher humidities, but water loss is adjusted in relation to the state of the fly, to the size of the blood meal
ingested, and to the humidity of the atmosphere by spiracular control (Bursell, 1957) and dehydration of the feces (Bursell, 1960b).
The humidity conditions under which adult flies are kept thus
appears unlikely to be critical, unless they are quite abnormally
dry. De Azevedo and Pinhao (1964) control their G. *morsitans* room
to 70% RH (relative humidity), but abandon control for several
hours daily by opening the window during the manipulation of
the stock.

6. *Light*

Few of the workers attempting to colonize *Glossina* discuss light
as a factor in any detail. Most presumably accept the approximately
12:12 hour light regime of the tropical localities in which they

worked, or an artificial 12:12 regimen may be arranged (de Azevedo and Pinhao, 1964).

Although the free-living larva is negatively phototactic it burrows as well in dark as in light so that light is not an essential factor in this context (Glasgow, 1963). Since *Glossina* are generally diurnally active insects most manipulation of them, for feeding and so on, has been carried out in light. But low light intensities may be desirable; Glasgow (1961) found *G. swynnertoni* to prefer shade to sunlight for biting and Foster (1957) found low light intensities and short periods of illumination to be consistent with satisfactory feeding for *G. morsitans* and *G. austeni*. Also some species are crepuscular or nocturnal in their biting activity (Glasgow, 1963).

One notable nocturnal response of *Glossina* to light which is not considered in laboratory colonies is the movement between resting places associated with dusk and dawn (Lumsden, 1966). Possibly some provision for such a movement to take place should be included; Cockings (1961) refers to the fly activity associated with sudden changes in light intensity, as "startling."

7. *Disturbance*

Glasgow (1963) puts at only about 30 to 35 minutes the time spent by a tsetse fly daily in flight. During flight water loss and fat consumption are both increased, by factors of 6 and 22, respectively. In 24 hours a fly which flew for 35 minutes of that period would lose as much water as a resting fly does in about 30 hours and as much fat as a resting fly consumes in about 37 hours.

The avoidance of unnecessary activity of the flies in a colony is, therefore, important. It may be necessary to eliminate visual and olfactory stimuli and to develop methods of transfer of flies between containers with a minimum of disturbance (Cockings, 1959, 1960; Foster, 1957; Evens, 1964). Most important, however, is probably the mutual stimulation occurring among flies confined, many together, in the same container. Glasgow (1963) rejects the suggestion that molestation of females by males in excess in captivity is a cause of abortion; de Azevedo and Pinhao (1964), however, do not exclude the possibility of an effect of this sort. Willett (1953) has described a tool for handling pupae with a minimum risk of trauma.

In concluding this section, it should be noted that exclusion of predators or parasites from the colony is a primary necessity.

B. Developmental Stages of *Glossina*

1. *Pupa**

The fat and water reserves of a tsetse pupa are determined during larval development and have to suffice until the teneral fly obtains its first blood meal. Since these reserves are affected by temperature and humidity, these factors have a direct effect upon survival and should be taken into account in a laboratory colony.

a. Type of Container. Little attention has been paid to the type of pupal container in laboratory colonies. However, satisfactory methods for the transmission of pupae are important for the supply of material from the field for the primary establishment of a laboratory colony, and for the distribution of the produce of an established colony. Kernaghan and Nash (1964) developed a method for protecting pupae from the effects of mechanical shock, extremes of temperature, and desiccation during transit by aircraft. Pupae were packed in nylon shavings in a space about $5 \times 10 \times 10$ cm (containing air humidified by means of a moist plastic sponge) insulated by walls of expanded polystyrene about 4 cm thick. With pupae sent from Africa to Europe by air they obtained an 86% emergence rate in 14-day-old laboratory-bred *G. palpalis* pupae and 68% with wild *G. austeni*. These results bettered those of previous workers. They considered, also, oxygen depletion in their containers as a possible cause of pupal death and found it less important than was expected, probably because their containers were not hermetic.

b. Temperature. Bursell (1960a) showed that the amount of fat consumed by pupal metabolism at 22°–24°C was low enough to ensure adequate fat for survival in normal-sized pupae of *G. morsitans*. At temperatures higher than this, however, the rate of fat consumption increased without a correspondingly great reduction in the duration of the pupal period. Conversely, at temperatures lower than the optimum, the duration of the pupal period was lengthened without a corresponding decrease in the rate of fat consumption. Therefore, at temperatures both above and below 22°–24°C the teneral fly emerged with a less than optimum amount

* The word puparium is reserved here for the sclerotized third-instar larval integument which protects the insect during its metamorphosis. Since most of the period between puparium formation and eclosion of the adult is in fact passed in the pupal state, all this period will be referred to as the pupa, unless specific mention of the fourth-instar larva or the pharate adult is required. This terminology differs from that adopted by Bursell (1960a) but avoids the misapplication of the word puparium to the whole of the coarctate pupa.

of fat and was more likely to succumb before finding its first blood meal. At temperatures above 30° or below 16°C the pupae died of fat exhaustion before emergence. Comparable figures for *G. pallidipes* were 32° and 14°C. Furthermore, small pupae of *G. morsitans* (and in general pupae of smaller species of *Glossina*) have relatively smaller fat reserves than large pupae and are more susceptible to the effects of temperature.

c. Humidity. Bursell (1958) also investigated the water balance of tsetse pupae and the effect of humidity on survival. He showed that transpiration was high during the first 5 days after puparium formation because the third- and fourth-larval instars lost water through the polypneustic lobes and through the integument. Water was lost during this stage also through the larval anus, although this loss was under active control. After pupation, water loss was greatly reduced because the pupal spiracles came under active control, and transpiration through the pupal integument was minimized by the subpuparial air space and the puparium itself. Finally, water loss was again high during the last few days before emergence since the waterproofing capacity of the pupal skin was lost when the ecdysial fluid was resorbed by the pharate adult.

Different species of *Glossina* had different susceptibilities to low humidity. Resistant species, such as *G. swynnertoni*, *G. morsitans*, or *G. longipennis*, which can complete their pupal development at relative humidities of 10% or less, have smaller polypneustic lobes and a less permeable pupal integument. They can also tolerate a loss of water of about 29% of their original weight. Susceptible species, such as *G. palpalis*, *G. brevipalpis* Newstead and *G. austeni*, however, cannot complete their development if they lose more than 24% of their original weight. It is clear, therefore, that a humid pupal environment should be provided for most species in a laboratory colony. De Azevedo and Pinhao (1964) attribute the success of their *G. morsitans* colony to the use of wet sand in the pupal containers. Before wet sand was used the average eclosion rate was 79.8%; after this change in technique, however, the emergence rate rose to 88.9%. Various other authors have stressed the importance of a humid pupal environment (Willett, 1953; Evens and Niemegeers, 1954; Evens, 1964).

2. *Imago*

Eclosion from the pupa occurs mainly between 10:00 and 17:00 hours with a maximum in the period after midday (Willett, 1953; Evens, 1964). As soon as the imago emerges it can run and, within a few hours, fly (Glasgow, 1963). In these teneral flies water loss is controlled by spiracular regulation; even in dry air longevity is from 2–4 days (Glasgow, 1963). There is thus no immediate necessity, because of a danger of desiccation, to provide a blood meal for flies on eclosion, but the need to avoid disturbance suggests that they should be distributed to the containers in which they are to be maintained soon after eclosion.

a. Containers. Although there are many small differences in dimensions and materials, containers fall into two main types: cages about $15 \times 10 \times 5$ cm with the two large sides, or all sides, covered with meshed fabric (variously called Bruce, Geigy, or Roubaud boxes); and celluloid or glass cylinders of about 2.5×7.5 cm or larger, with one or both ends closed by meshed material. The size and dimensions of the containers are first influenced by the need for them to be easily applied to the blood source. The materials comprising the containers require careful selection to avoid lethal or traumatic effects; e.g., some melamine resins are toxic to *Glossina* (Nash and Kernaghan, 1964b); some meshes have loose fibers which may entangle the legs of the flies (Nash, 1963). Nash *et al.* (1958) prefer mosquito netting to wire gauze for *Glossina* cages to avoid damage to the flies proboscides when feeding. Although no direct evidence has been noticed indicating that bacterial contamination of the flies dejecta in the cages is deleterious to them, it is probably wise to take measures to minimize bacterial contamination; Nash *et al.* (1958) disinfect their cages every 3 months with 1% centrimide, de Azevedo and Pinhao (1964) wash their cages periodically with a detergent. Foster (1957) considered that impregnation of the mesh of the container with the odor of the animal used as a host for feeding continually stimulated the contained insects to activity and led to their early exhaustion. He recommended frequent changing of the mesh coverings to avoid this effect.

It is convenient for the mesh used for the container to be large enough, about 2 mm, to allow the deposited larva to escape from the containers (de Azevedo and Pinhao, 1964).

Besides using containers of this sort to breed *Glossina*, it is known that some attempts have been made to establish colonies in large outside cages.[*] Little has been published about this work and it is presumed that it was unsuccessful. In the only instance of which the authors have experience, predators were difficult to

[*] The problems involved in setting up *Glossina* breeding in the natural habitat have been considered in the Annual Report of the Agricultural Research Council of Central Africa for 1964.

exclude and their activity soon determined the *Glossina* population.

The populations confined in the containers have varied from 1 to 20 or so for cages, and from 1 to 8 for tubes; sometimes the population was all female, sometimes of both sexes. There is a qualitative difference between a population of 1 and more and a difference in degree only between a population of 2 and larger populations. Only in containers containing single flies is the insect insulated completely from the disturbing effect of movement on the part of its cage mates. It is to be expected, therefore, that mutual stimulation is absent only in the singly inhabited containers and present in various degrees in containers with larger populations. Willett (1953) found no statistical differences in the mortality among flies contained in cages at various populations, from 5–15 individuals per cage. Although there is apparently no specific study of the effect of mutual stimulation on fly longevity and fecundity it appears, taking into account the basic physiological data summarized by Glasgow (1963), that the avoidance of adventitious disturbance is likely to be of importance. In the successful colony of de Azevedo and Pinhao (1964), females, after mating, are isolated in cages. These workers point out, also, the advantage of the maintenance of flies singly in containers as regards ease of documentation. Further, the performance of individual flies may be followed by post-mortem examination of the reproductive system for follicular relics, resorbed follicles, retained eggs, and state of insemination (Mellanby, 1936; Saunders, 1960b; Vattier, 1964).

The temperature and humidity conditions under which adult *Glossina* may be maintained in a colony have been discussed in general earlier; they do not appear likely to be unduly demanding.

b. Feeding. The hosts attacked by *Glossina* in the field are manifold (Weitz, 1963) and these flies may be induced to feed in the laboratory on almost any mammal as well as on amphibia, reptiles, and birds (Roubaud, 1909; Glasgow, 1963). There is little evidence that any given species will do better if fed on one mammal species rather than another. Foster (1957) found guinea pigs and sheep equally suitable for *G. austeni* and probably also for *G. morsitans.* Willett (1953) found the mean length of life of adult flies and the mean numbers of pupae per fly greater in those fed on sheep than in those fed on guinea pigs, but he suspected that these differences might have been caused by different degrees of disturbance in the two groups, associated with the feeding arrangements. Nash *et al.* (1958), however, obtained higher female longevity and greater pupal weights in *G. morsitans* fed on goats as compared to those fed upon guinea pigs. Several authors (e.g., Foster, 1957; Nash *et al.*, 1958, 1965) discuss the deterioration of individual animals as hosts because of the skin changes consequent on their being frequently bitten. Nash *et al.* (1965) suggest a feeding regime to obviate this deterioration. Efficient application of the container to the host is essential for satisfactory feeding and to avoid damage to the proboscis of the fly by the mesh through which it feeds; Geigy (1948), Willett (1953), Evens (1964), Nash and Kernaghan (1964a), and de Azevedo and Pinhao (1964) describe methods applicable to sheep, goats, and guinea pigs.

Glossina will feed readily on blood lakes contained in membranes (Roubaud, 1909), but colonization has not been accomplished using this method. Nevertheless, it may have some advantages, e.g., the avoidance of infecting host animals with trypanosomes by wild flies. Membrane feeding techniques are described by Cockings (1960); defibrination was the most promising method for preventing the coagulation of the blood lake (Southon and Cockings, 1963a).

As regards the time naturally occupied by the feeding act Glasgow (1963), for *G. swynnertoni,* quotes a minimum period of 57 seconds and a maximum of 10 minutes. Thus prolonged application of cages to hosts appears unnecessary, if the population is normally avid. Glasgow (1961) estimated the interval between successive feeds in *G. swynnertoni* in nature at 3–5 days. Roubaud (1909) found *G. palpalis* to vary in its avidity to feed, being avid immediately after larval parturition, less so when gestation was far advanced. As the maintenance of the nutrition of the females has appeared to be crucial for the survival of the colony, most workers have felt it wise to offer the flies a meal daily, or at least 6 days per week. Although primary excretion (Glasgow, 1963) rapidly reduces the volume of any blood meal some workers (e.g., Mellanby, 1937) have felt it important to induce the fly to take a meal just before the larva grows to a size to impede the intake of blood and that if fed too often the fly will not be able to take a large meal at the right time. Cockings' (1959) observation that female *G. pallidipes* in the middle and later stages of pregnancy would feed more than once per day may be relevant in this context. Foster (1957) and Nash *et al.* (1965) used a 3- or 4-day feeding cycle. De Azevedo and Pinhao (1964) offer a host 6–7 days a week for 20–30 minutes; they do not attempt to encourage individuals refractory to feeding. Evens (1964) considered that flies would feed 6–8 days out of 10 and that they should be offered food daily.

As regards the criteria of satisfactory nutrition, Mellanby (1937) found abortions related to restricted blood intake and also a correlation between the amount of blood taken and the size of the pupa produced. The mean number of pupae produced per female per given period, plus the puparial weight, will indicate the nutritional state of the colony.

c. *Mating.* Males are not fully potent until 4–7 days old (Glasgow, 1963). A female need mate only once in its life span to continue to produce fertile eggs. Mating provides a stimulus for the ovulation of the first egg (Mellanby, 1937; Vanderplank, 1947); unless females are mated before the first egg is due to descend into the uterus, at about day 8 of adult life, the reproductive cycles are disorganized. Foster (1957) obtained nearly complete fertilization using 10- to 14-day-old males and 3- to 4-day-old females. Southon and Cockings (1963b) showed with *G. morsitans* that the age of males at the start of mating and the male:female ratio were the factors significantly affecting fertilization; 10- to 15-day-old males and a male:female ratio of 2:1 gave fertilization ratios of about 90%. Females may remate (WAITR, 1956) but this is irrelevant as regards laboratory colonization. Older, nonvirgin males, 20 or more days old, are more potent than younger males (WAITR, 1957). Mating may be carried out in the usual cages or in larger cubical cages of about 30 cm per side, sometimes at reduced light intensities (WAITR, 1957; Nash *et al.*, 1958). Most workers feel it wise to remove the males after mating has taken place to avoid the risk of continued molestation by males and thus reducing female longevity (WAITR, 1957; Evens, 1964; de Azevedo and Pinhao, 1964). Evens (1964) mentions that females not mated in the first few days do not survive the trauma of later matings.

As regards imagines, it remains to consider if females should be retained in the colony until the end of their life span. WAITR (1954) and Nash *et al.* (1958) on the basis of a reduction in the number of pupae per female per month with increasing age, follow the practice of destroying females at 100 days of age.

3. *Larva*

The act of larviposition and the burrowing of the negatively phototactic larva into the ground are in nature very rapidly accomplished (Glasgow, 1963). In *G. morsitans*, larviposition takes place mainly in the afternoon and evening, though sometimes at night (Bursell, 1958). Lewis (1934) found that larvae of *G. morsitans submorsitans* Newstead burrowed into dry sand but returned to the surface until the sand was moistened. He also showed that particle size of the material provided affected the proportion of larvae burying themselves; they could easily enter coarse sand, especially if small stones were placed on the surface.

The water relations of the third- and fourth-instar larvae of *Glossina morsitans* during the process of the development of the pupa within the puparium have been considered by Bursell (1958). These stages occupy the first 3 days of intrapuparial existence and it is during this time that the insect suffers its greatest water loss (Glasgow, 1963). Bursell (1958), also, considers that disturbance should be minimal.

In many laboratory colonies sand or soil is not provided and the larvae are allowed to pupate at the bottom of the adult containers (Foster, 1957; de Azevedo and Pinhao, 1964). It seems probable that such a technique may prolong larval wandering and delay puparium formation at a time when the rate of water loss is at its highest. Improved technique, therefore, could include the provision of damp sand or soil for the larvae to drop into.

IV. CONCLUSIONS

The summary of the digestive and reproductive physiology by Glasgow (1963) has been invaluable in the composition of this review. A few points in these fields, important for the colonization of *Glossina,* have been noticed as likely to benefit from further study. These will be discussed first.

The early movements of the blood meal in the gut of *Glossina* are not clearly understood. Glasgow (1963) notes that the blood meal, sucked from the host by the cibarial pump, is passed by the esophagus to the crop, and that as soon as engorgement is complete, or even before, blood begins to pass to the mid-gut. Primary excretion may begin before engorgement is complete; Glasgow presumes that the water from the blood passes to the hemolymph through the walls of the crop. Roubaud (1909) and Buxton (1955) state that the blood goes first to the mid-gut and does not fill the crop until later in the course of the meal. The point is of importance in understanding the function of the anticoagulins present in the *Glossina* saliva (Buxton, 1955). Extraction of water from the blood meal while in the crop would appear likely to render it viscous and impede its subsequent transfer to the mid-gut. The mechanism by which blood is transferred from the crop to the mid-gut is obscure as both are behind the cibarial pump, the crop is nonmuscular, and both crop and mid-gut are enclosed in the abdomen of the fly.

Other areas of investigation, likely to yield information pertinent to the crucial question of maintaining fly nutrition at a satisfactory level, are studies of the function and occurrence of the mid-gut symbionts or bacteroids (Buxton, 1955) in both wild and colonized flies; study of the factors inducing biting and feeding in *Glossina* in captivity; study of the causes of abortion and follicular degeneration in captive flies; and study of membrane-feeding techniques.

In conclusion, the factors which appear most important for the colonization of *Glossina* are the satisfactory nutrition of the adult female; the avoidance of unnecessary disturbance; the avoidance of pupal water loss. De Azevedo and Pinhao may have been successful by their attention to the two latter factors, particularly. Their colony started with 21 males and 22 females of *G. morsitans* which emerged from pupae collected in Moçambique. The flies were kept singly in cages of 26°C and 70% RH and fed exclusively on guinea pigs. The population fluctuated between 20 and 70 flies for the first 16 generations, but then increased in a geometrical progression close to the theoretical rate of population increase as described in Buxton's (1955) model. This increase coincided with a change in technique for pupal maintenance; before the 17th generation the pupae were kept uncovered; after the 17th generation they were kept in moist sand. The authors attribute the success of the population to this change. The average eclosion rate during the first 16 generations was 79.8%, but rose to 88.9–96.7% when the pupae were kept in wet sand. The improved eclosion rate is undoubtedly an important factor in the colony's success, but the authors also seem to have overcome the difficulties of abortion and the other abnormalities which cause gaps in the reproductive sequence. It is also possible that de Azevedo and Pinhao's success is due to the isolation of a strain of *G. morsitans* which is able to adapt to the conditions of laboratory culture.

REFERENCES

Bursell, E. (1955). The polypneustic lobes of the tsetse larva (*Glossina*, Diptera). *Proc. Roy. Soc.* **B144**, 275–286.

Bursell, E. (1957). Spiracular control of water loss in the tsetse fly. *Proc. Roy. Entomol. Soc. London* **A32**, 21–29.

Bursell, E. (1958). The water balance of tsetse pupae. *Phil. Trans. Roy. Soc. London* **B241**, 179–210.

Bursell, E. (1960a). The effect of temperature on the consumption of fat during pupal development in *Glossina. Bull. Entomol. Res.* **51**, 583–598.

Bursell, E. (1960b). Loss of water by excretion and defaecation in the tsetse fly. *J. Exptl. Biol.* **37**, 689–697.

Bushland, R. C., and Hopkins, D. E. (1953). Sterilization of screw-worm flies with X-rays and gamma-rays. *J. Econ. Entomol.* **46**, 648–656.

Buxton, P. A. (1955). "The Natural History of Tsetse Flies," London School of Hygiene and Tropical Medicine, Memoir No. 10. Lewis, London.

Buxton, P. A., and Lewis, D. J. (1934). Climate and tsetse flies: Laboratory studies upon *Glossina submorsitans* and *tachinoides. Phil. Trans. Roy. Soc. London* **B224**, 175–240.

Cockings, K. L. (1959). Laboratory maintenance of *Glossina pallidipes. E. African Trypanosomiasis Res. Organ., Rept., 1958* pp. 26–31. Govt. Printer, Nairobi.

Cockings, K. L. (1960). Laboratory maintenance of *Glossina pallidipes. E. African Trypanosomiasis Res. Organ., Rept., 1959* pp. 13–18. Govt. Printer, Nairobi.

Cockings, K. L. (1961). Laboratory maintenance of *Glossina pallidipes. E. African Trypanosomiasis Res. Organ., Rept., 1960* pp. 32–33. Govt. Printer, Nairobi.

de Azevedo, J. F., and Pinhao, R. da C. (1964). The maintenance in the laboratory of a colony of *Glossina morsitans* (Diptera) since 1959. *Bull. World Health Organ.* **31**, 835–841.

Edney, E. B., and Barrass, R. (1962). The body temperature of the tsetse fly, *Glossina morsitans* Westwood (Diptera, Muscidae). *J. Insect Physiol* **8**, 469–481.

Evens, F. (1964). L'élevage des glossines. *Bull. World Health Organ.* **31**, 521–525.

Evens, F., and Niemegeers, C. (1954). Notes on the breeding and biology of *Glossina palpalis. 5th Intern. Sci. Comm. Trypanosomiasis Res., 1954* pp. 119–120. Commission for Technical Co-operation in Africa South of the Sahara, Leopoldville.

Foster, R. (1957). Observations on laboratory colonies of the tsetse flies *Glossina morsitans* West. and *Glossina austeni* Newstead. *Parasitology* **47**, 361–374.

Foster, R. (1958). Some observations on the breeding of *Glossina morsitans* in the laboratory. *7th Intern. Sci. Comm. Trypanosomiasis Res., 1958* pp. 351–355. Commission for Technical Co-operation in Africa South of the Sahara, London.

Geigy, R. (1946). Beobachtungen an einer Zucht von *Glossina palpalis. Verhandl. Schweiz. Naturforsch. Ges.* 155–158. Aarau, H. R. Sauerländer & Co.

Geigy, R. (1948). Elevage de *Glossina palpalis. Acta Trop.* **5**, 201–218.

Glasgow, J. P. (1961). The feeding habits of *Glossina swynnertoni* Austen. *J. Animal Ecol.* **30**, 77–85.

Glasgow, J. P. (1963). "The Distribution and Abundance of Tsetse." Pergamon Press, Oxford.

Hagan, H. R. (1951). "Embryology of the Viviparous Insects." Ronald Press, New York.

Hoffmann, R. (1954). Zur Fortpflanzungensbiologie und zur intrauterinen Entwicklung von *Glossina palpalis. Acta Trop.* **11**, 1–57.

Jack, R. W. (1939). Studies in the physiology and behaviour of *Glossina morsitans* Westw. *Southern Rhodesia, Mem. Dept. Agr.* **1**, 1–203.

Jackson, C. H. N. (1949). The biology of tsetse flies. *Biol. Rev. Cambridge Phil. Soc.* **24**, 174–199.

Kernaghan, R. J., and Nash, T. A. M. (1964). A technique for the despatch of pupae of *Glossina* and other insects by air from the tropics. *Ann. Trop. Med. Parasitol.* **58**, 355–358.

Lewis, D. J. (1934). The behaviour of the larvae of tsetse flies before pupation. *Bull. Entomol. Res.* **25**, 195–199.

Lumsden, W. H. R. (1966). Light, forest insects, arboviruses and trypanosomes. *Brit. Ecol. Soc. Symp. Light Ecol. Factor, Cambridge, 1965* (in press).

McDonald, W. A. (1960). The laboratory rearing of *Glossina morsitans submorsitans* Newst., in Northern Nigeria. *8th Intern. Sci. Comm. Trypanosomiasis Res., 1960* p. 247. Commission for Technical Co-operation in Africa South of the Sahara, London.

Mellanby, H. (1937). Experimental work on reproduction in the tsetse fly, *Glossina palpalis*. *Parasitology* **29**, 131–141.

Mellanby, H., and Mellanby, K. (1936). Rearing tsetse flies in captivity. *Proc. Roy. Entomol. Soc. London* **A12**, 1–3.

Mellanby, K. (1936). Experimental work with the tsetse fly, *Glossina palpalis*, in Uganda. *Bull. Entomol. Res.* **27**, 611–633.

Nash, T. A. M. (1963). Personal communication.

Nash, T. A. M., and Kernaghan, R. J. (1964a). The feeding of haematophagous insects on goats and sheep: Techniques for host restraint and cage application. *Ann. Trop. Med. Parasitol.* **58**, 168–170.

Nash, T. A. M., and Kernaghan, R. J. (1964b). Danger of spraying wooden insect cages with melamine resins. *Nature* **203**, 1195.

Nash, T. A. M., Kernaghan, R. J., and Wright, A. I. (1965). A method for the prevention of skin reactions in goats used for feeding tsetse flies. *Ann. Trop. Med. Parasitol.* **59**, 88–94.

Nash, T. A. M., Page, W. A., Jordan, A. M., and Petana, W. (1958). The rearing of *Glossina palpalis* in the laboratory for experimental work. *7th Intern. Sci. Comm. Trypanosomiasis Res., 1958* pp. 343–355. Commission for Technical Co-operation in Africa South of the Sahara, London.

Potts, W. H. (1933). Observations on *Glossina morsitans* Westw. in East Africa. *Bull. Entomol. Res.* **24**, 293–300.

Potts, W. H. (1958). Sterilization of tsetse-flies (*Glossina*) by gamma irradiation. *Ann. Trop. Med. Parasitol.* **52**, 484–499.

Rodhain, J., and Van Hoof, M. J.[*] (1944). Au sujet d'un élevage de *Glossina palpalis* en Europe et de quelques essais d'evolution chez cette glossine des *Trypanosoma lewisi* et *cruzi*. *Ann. Soc. Belge Med. Trop.* **24**, 54–57.

Roubaud, E. (1909). La "*Glossina palpalis*," R. Desv.; sa biologie, son rôle dans l'étiologie des trypanosomiases. Thesis presented to the Faculty of Sciences of Paris, Barnéoud, Laval.

Roubaud, E.[*] (1913). Sur un essai d'élevage de Glossines dans le laboratoire d'Europe. *Bull. Soc. Pathol. Exotique* **8**, 34–36.

Roubaud, E. (1917). Histoire d'un élevage de *Glossina morsitans* á l'Institut Pasteur de Paris. *Bull. Soc. Pathol. Exotique* **10**, 629–640.

Roubaud, E., and Colas-Belcour, J. (1936). Observations biologiques sur les Glossines (*Gl. palpalis, Gl. morsitans*). *Bull. Soc. Pathol. Exotique* **29**, 691–696.

Saunders, D. S. (1960a). Ovaries of *Glossina morsitans*. *Nature* **185**, 121–122.

Saunders, D. S. (1960b). The ovulation cycle in *Glossina morsitans* Westwood (Diptera: Muscidae) and a possible method of age determination for female tsetse flies by the examination of their ovaries. *Trans. Roy. Entomol. Soc. London* **112**, 221–238.

Saunders, D. S. (1962). Age determination for female tsetse flies and the age compo-

* These references have not been quoted in the text but are included here to complete the bibliography.

sition of samples of *Glossina pallidipes* Aust., *G. palpalis fuscipes* Newst. and *G. brevipalpis* Newst. *Bull. Entomol. Res.* **53,** 579–595.

Southon, H. A. W., and Cockings, K. L. (1963a). Laboratory Maintenance of *Glossina. E. African Trypanosomiasis Res. Organ., Rept., 1961* pp. 30–33. Govt. Printer, Nairobi.

Southon, H. A. W., and Cockings, K. L. (1963b). Fertilization of *G. morsitans* in the laboratory. *E. African Trypanosomiasis Res. Organ., Rept., 1962–1963* pp. 33–37. Govt. Printer, Nairobi.

Teesdale, C. (1940). Fertilization in the tsetse fly, *Glossina palpalis,* in a population of low density. *J. Animal Ecol.* **9,** 24–26.

Vanderplank, F. L. (1947). Experiments in the hybridisation of tsetse flies (*Glossina,* Diptera). *Trans. Roy. Entomol. Soc. London* **98,** 1–18.

Vattier, G. (1964). Etude de caractères morphologiques et anatomiques en relation avec l'age physiologique des femelles de Glossines. Cahier, Office de la Recherche Scientifique et Technique Outre-Mer, Brazzaville.

WAITR (1953–1958). West African Institute for Trypanosomiasis Research, Annual Reports. Kaduna, Northern Nigeria.

Weitz, B. (1963). The feeding habits of *Glossina. Bull. World Health Organ.* **28,** 711–729.

Willett, K. C. (1953). The laboratory maintenance of *Glossina.* I. *Parasitology* **43,** 110-130.

Chapter 12

Bed Bugs

G. S. BURDEN

Entomology Research Division,
Agriculture Research Service,
U. S. Department of Agriculture,
Gainesville, Florida

I. INTRODUCTION

The problems encountered in insect control are diversified in nature; consequently, entomologists must maintain efficient and practical research programs in order to produce control measures applicable for a given species. Laboratory research programs in entomology demand the use of trained personnel, assorted laboratory equipment and supplies, and most important of all, vigorous colonies of insects. The establishment and maintenance of insect colonies in a laboratory sometimes involves considerable research in order to determine optimum conditions and procedures necessary for the production of sufficient specimens for assorted programs of biological testing. Whether the rearing of insects under laboratory conditions is for the purpose of developing practical control measures or for using the insects as basic test animals, the success of either program is dependent upon the quality and quantity of production within the insectary.

Bed bugs (*Cimex lectularius* Linnaeus and *Cimex hemipterus* Fabricius) have been a scourge to mankind from a pestiferous and social standpoint. With the advent of DDT, the infestations of bed bugs in private and public environments has decreased in past years; however, this pest continues to be a problem in many areas of the world and has developed resistance to several of the chlorinated hydrocarbon insecticides (Brown, 1958). Many techniques have been described in past years by workers engaged in using the bed bug as an experimental animal; however, the development of improved methods of colonization is a constant necessity in insectaries.

II. REARING AND FEEDING CHAMBERS

Small glass vials stoppered with cotton (Girault, 1910) or covered with bolting cloth (Janisch, 1933) have been used as rearing chambers for bed bugs. The same vials were used as feeding chambers simply by placing the open mouth or cloth-covered mouth against a host animal. Rendtorff (1938) used Petri dishes as rearing chambers for adult bugs, but he placed the small nymphs of each colony into shell vials for direct feeding on the host animal. The adults were separated into 30-ml beakers, covered with fine batiste cloth, that were placed on the host for feeding. Large Petri dishes with covers of 60-mesh organdy stretched over and cemented between metal embroidery hoops functioned as rearing and feeding chambers for the research of Woodbury and Barnhart (1939).

Wide-mouth specimen jars (2 inches diameter × 4 inches high) covered with nylon net (Davis, 1956) or 5 × 5 cm glass tubes covered with gauze (Busvine, 1958) have functioned as combination rearing and feeding chambers for all stages of bed bugs. Adkins and Arant (1959) used feeding chambers made from Pyrex glass cylinders (85 mm diameter × 60 mm high) and half-pint ice cream containers with the bottoms removed. Nylon hosiery material, glued and taped over one end of the cylinders, served as the floor of the chambers. The centers of lids from ice cream containers were removed and replaced with hosiery material to form covers for the open ends of the cylinders. These same workers used large glass beakers (250-ml) for holding the adults between feeding periods and for rearing the nymphs. Gratz (1959) used small beakers covered with fine bolting-silk for rearing and feeding bed bugs used in his studies on resistance.

Gilbert (1964) described rearing and feeding chambers as used by our research project of the Entomology Research Division, U. S. Department of Agriculture, Gainesville, Florida. The chambers consist of screw-top plastic dishes (10 cm diameter × 7 cm high) covered with 60-mesh organdy held in place and stretched tight by means of open-center tops (Fig. 1). The original tops of the dishes are modified for this use by cutting out a circular portion (8.5 cm diameter) of the solid top. This leaves sufficient area for the tightly stretched organdy to serve as a "feeding floor" when each dish is inverted onto a host animal. This allows all stages of bed bugs to insert their proboscises through the weave of the cloth to the host's skin. The cutting

FIG. 1. Rearing and feeding chamber for bed bugs. Components shown on the left: plastic dish, plastic screw top, organdy cover, and Whatman No. 3 filter paper. Assembled chamber is shown on the right.

of each top is easily accomplished by means of an off-set cutter mounted in a slow-speed drill press. Pressure of the cutter on the plastic should be gradual to avoid possible splitting or cracking of each top. Following this process, the cut edges of the open-center tops should be sanded smooth with emery cloth to eliminate all rough areas. Each finished rearing and feeding chamber will accommodate several hundred bed bugs.

III. REPOSITORY MATERIALS AND EGG COLLECTIONS

The literature cites numerous materials used for repositories in the rearing of bed bug colonies. Paper, in various forms, has been the principal item used by researchers in their colonization procedures. Blotting paper, filter paper, mimeograph paper, and paper toweling, in assorted shapes and sizes, have been used extensively for the deposition and collection of bed bug eggs in the laboratory.

It would seem possible that pieces of cloth could be used, but with the extensive use of pesticides there is some possibility that cloth could become contaminated during the numerous stages of manufacture. This problem would of course necessitate a process of decontamination prior to the use of such material in the bug colonies. As with cloth, the same problem could occur with paper but the likelihood is more remote. In view of the afore-mentioned possibilities, we have found it desirable and practical to use filter paper in our colonization for assurance of a chemical-free material. Whatman No. 3 filter paper (9 cm diameter) cut into half pieces serves as excellent repository material; the extra thickness of this grade absorbs appreciable amounts of moisture present in each rearing chamber.

Eggs may be collected from the colonies at weekly intervals, or more frequently if desired. To accomplish this, each chamber is exposed to a small dose of CO_2 gas sufficient to immobilize the adults and nymphs, the cloth top is unfastened, and the filter papers on which eggs have been deposited are removed with forceps. These papers are then placed in a separate rearing chamber. The new chambers should be labeled and dated in order to know the expected times of hatch, nymphal development, and maturity. Prior to closing the old chamber of mature adults, four to six pieces of new filter paper are placed in the chamber for future oviposition.

IV. NUTRITIONAL REQUIREMENTS AND REARING ENVIRONMENTS

The nutritional requirements of bed bugs used in laboratory experiments are flexible to some extent. For maintenance purposes, colonies may be limited to one blood meal per week. However, for maximum egg production, rapid development of the nymphal stages, and availability of large numbers of bugs for experiments designed on various degrees of engorgement, blood meals should be offered two or three times per week. All bugs within a colony will not feed at every offering of a blood meal.

The time necessary for each colony to feed to repletion is dependent on the size of the feeding chamber and the number of bugs within each chamber. Davis (1956) subjected his colonies to a feeding period of 2 hours on a host animal whereas Adkins and Arant (1959) allowed feeding periods of 30 minutes. As described by Gilbert (1964), we have been successful with feeding periods of 15 minutes per colony chamber. Each colony thrives on two feeding periods per week at intervals of 3 to 4 days (Mondays and Fridays).

The temperature and relative humidity necessary to rear abundant and vigorous bed bugs in the laboratory should be carefully selected and maintained. In searching the literature, it can be found that temperatures of 23.9° to 29.4°C and relative humidities of 26 to 70% have been used for colonization. Our colonies have been perpetuated very successfully for numerous years in a constant laboratory environment of 27°C and 50% relative humidity. Care should be taken to avoid extremely low humidities (20% or less) as the longevity of bed bugs is greatly shortened by such conditions at a temperature of 29°C.

V. LABORATORY HOST ANIMALS

Various warm-blooded animals have been used in the laboratory colonization of bed bugs. Girault (1910) fed his colonies by placing the open mouth of each rearing chamber against the lower forearm of a man. Janisch (1933) placed his cloth-covered rearing chambers on the shaved abdomens of guinea pigs to allow the bugs to obtain their blood meals. Each guinea pig was tied to a special board during the feeding. Rendtorff (1938) also fed his colonies on the shaved abdomens of guinea pigs which were restrained in specially designed wooden stanchions.

In 1939, Woodbury and Barnhart described their technique for feeding bed bugs on rabbits strapped to wooden racks. Since that time, several scientists have employed various techniques for feeding bed bug colonies on rabbits. Davis (1956) clipped the fur from the sides of rabbits and strapped his bug-rearing jars to these areas, thereby obviating immobilization of the host animal. Busvine (1958) fed his colonies by clipping small rearing tubes to the ears of lop-eared rabbits, whereas Adkins and Arant (1959), Gratz (1959), and Gilbert (1964) described the feeding of bug colonies on shaved or closely clipped abdomens of rabbits confined in wooden stanchions.

We use rabbits for feeding our colonies of *C. lectularius* and *C. hemipterus* and have found these animals to be very satisfactory for the rearing of large numbers of bed bugs necessary for our research programs. To feed the bugs, a rabbit is restrained on its back in a wooden stanchion (Smith and Eddy, 1954) designed specifically for this purpose (Fig. 2). The abdominal area of the rabbit is then closely clipped with electric animal clippers and the shorn fur is removed

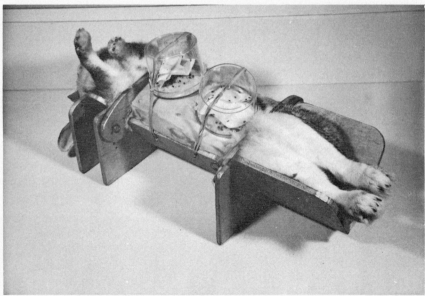

Fig. 2. Stanchion for restraining rabbits during engorging of bed bugs.

by means of a small portable vacuum cleaner. After the rabbit has been clipped, two of the plastic rearing and feeding chambers are inverted (cloth top down) onto the abdomen for a period of 15 minutes. Each feeding chamber is held in place on the rabbit's abdomen by means of a large rubber band secured to opposite walls of the stanchion. The rubber band is not pulled tightly on each chamber, but is firm enough to allow close contact between the cloth top and the skin of the rabbit. To afford some degree of darkness for the bugs during their probing and engorging, a small black cloth is placed over the feeding chambers while they are on the rabbit. This procedure tends to quiet the stimulated bed bugs and hasten their feeding.

The wooden stanchions used for restraining the rabbits are 65 cm in length and 17 cm high (Fig. 2). Each rabbit is held in position by an anterior arm of the stanchion that is secured behind the front pair of legs and a posterior arm that is secured in front of the hind pair of legs. One end of each arm is hinged to the frame of the stanchion, thereby allowing the arm to be swung across the supine rabbit and secured to the opposite or receiving side of the stanchion by means of a metal pin. Each arm is 26 cm long, curved in shape, and can be adjusted to varied degrees of tightness, depending on the size of the host rabbit. The adjustment is made by placing the metal pin through the free end of the arm and into one of a series of vertical holes in the receiving side of the stanchion. The anterior and posterior arms are mounted 21.5 cm and 18.5 cm, respectively, from the ends of the stanchion. The walls of the stanchion distal to each arm are 13 cm high from the bed of the stanchion, whereas the walls between the arms are 8 cm high. The lesser height of the center walls facilitates clipping the abdominal area of the rabbit.

If large numbers of bed bugs are to be colonized it is advisable to use two or more rabbits at each feeding. Also, sufficient host rabbits should be designated for the colonies in order that each rabbit is not subjected to engorgements more often than once every 2 or 3 weeks. This practice will prolong the longevity of each host when large colonies of bugs are maintained. If possible, large rabbits should be used as these afford greater abdominal feeding areas. Any species of rabbit can be used for this process, but we have found that pure white rabbits do not withstand the rigors of bed bug colonization as well as other breeds.

VI. DISCUSSION

The rearing of bed bugs in the laboratory need not be a laborious task if definite procedures and techniques are established and observed. Cleanliness should be maintained at all times in the colonies; it can be achieved by changing the rearing and feeding chambers frequently as well as the cloth tops, which soon become stained and encrusted with excrement. When handling individual bugs for experiments, care should be taken lest they be injured. Featherweight forceps with smooth tips are excellent for this purpose as they exert minimum pressure. Forceps with serrated tips are suitable for removing repository papers at designated times. Low-pressure aspirators of assorted types also can be used for handling bed bugs of various developmental stages.

The host animals (rabbits, guinea pigs, etc.) used for rearing the bugs should be given maximum care as they are the foundation for the colonies. All host animals should be kept in clean and sanitary environments to minimize odors and possible disease or sickness. Adequate food and water should be supplied daily and each animal should be checked at regular intervals for physical fitness.

As with any research program, the successful rearing of robust bed bugs in the laboratory is dependent upon the diligence of responsible personnel. If the rearing task is to be delegated, it is the obligation of the supervisor to initiate a program of instruction for the assigned person(s) responsible for the colonies. The rearing procedures should not be static, but should be subject to improvements whenever necessary and possible.

REFERENCES

Adkins, T. R., Jr., and Arant, F. S. (1959). A technique for the maintenance of a laboratory colony of *Cimex lectularius* L. on rabbits. *J. Econ. Entomol.* **52,** 685–686.

Brown, A. W. A. (1958). Insecticide resistance in arthropods. *World Health Organ., Monograph Ser.* **38.**

Busvine, J. R. (1958). Insecticide resistance in bed bugs. *Bull. World Health Organ.* **19,** 1041–1052.

Davis, N. T. (1956). The morphology and functional anatomy of the male and female reproductive systems of *Cimex lectularius* L. (Heteroptera, Cimicidae). *Ann. Entomol. Soc. Am.* **49,** 466–493.

Gilbert, I. H. (1964). Laboratory rearing of cockroaches, bed bugs, human lice, and fleas. *Bull. World Health Organ.* **31,** 561–563.

Girault, A. A. (1910). Preliminary studies on the biology of the bed bug, *Cimex lectularius* Linn. *J. Econ. Biol.* **5,** 88–91.

Gratz, N. G. (1959). A survey of bed bug resistance in Israel. *Bull. World Health Organ.* **20,** 835–840.

Janisch, E. (1933). Beobachtungen bei der Aufzucht von Bettmanzen. I. Über das Verhalten von Populationen bei verschiedenen Zuchtbedingungen. *Z. Parasitenk.* **5,** 460–514.

Rendtorff, B. C. (1938). A method of rearing the bed bug, *Cimex lectularius* L., for studies in toxicology and medical entomology. *J. Econ. Entomol.* **31,** 781.

Smith, C. N., and Eddy, G. W. (1954). Techniques for rearing and handling body lice, oriental rat fleas, and cat fleas. *Bull. World Health Organ.* **10,** 127–137.

Woodbury, E. N., and Barnhart, C. S. (1939). Tests on crawling insects, tenative methods for evaluating liquid household insecticides against the German cockroach and the bed bug. *Soap Sanit. Chem.* **15,** 93–107 and 113.

Chapter 13

Reduviid Bugs

RAYMOND E. RYCKMAN AND ALBERT E. RYCKMAN

Department of Microbiology,
School of Medicine, and Biology Department,
Graduate School, Loma Linda University,
Loma Linda, California, and
Department of Microbiology,
Loma Linda University,
Loma Linda, California

The family Reduviidae is composed of two biological groups, the hemophagous species of the subfamily Triatominae which are ectoparasites on vertebrates, and the nineteen or more additional subfamiles which are predaceous on arthropods. The ecology of these two groups is quite diverse and in certain respects the methods of laboratory rearing are quite different.

I. LABORATORY CULTURE OF TRIATOMINAE

The subfamily Triatominae consists of 79 species in 14 genera; 74 species and 13 genera are found in the New World; one of the 74 species (*Triatoma rubrofasciata* DeGeer) is tropicopolitan. The monotypic genus *Linshcosteus* is outside the New World.

The Triatominae are known by a number of common names in the several countries where they occur in the New World. Since 1899 the name, kissing bug, has probably been the most frequently used

183

common name in the United States. It was believed that the Triatominae bugs preferred to feed about the mouth; hence, the name
kissing bug. Actually these bugs will readily feed on almost any part
of the anatomy that is exposed to them. Because these bugs usually
feed at night when the prospective victims are sleeping, it is under-
standable why a large percentage of the bites occurs about the neck
and head—they are the most exposed parts of the body. In South
America the bugs are known as *vinchucas;* in Mexico they are known
by a number of names, e.g., *chinche palota, chinche grande, chinche
tigre, chinche picuda, chinche voladora, chinche hocicona,* and
chinche chupa sangre.

All Triatominae known are obligate blood feeders on vertebrate
hosts; however, under laboratory conditions a few have been induced
to feed on invertebrates. The Triatominae are of considerable economic importance because of their vicious biting habits and their
transmission of Chagas' disease. There are approximately 8,000,000
clinical cases of Chagas' disease in the New World. The etiological
agent of this disease is *Trypanosoma cruzi* Chagas, a protozoan blood
flagellate in the vertebrate hosts; the infective metacyclic forms
multiply in the hind-gut of Triatominae bugs and are transmitted to
man by fecal contamination following the bite of infected bugs. In
addition to being vectors of a serious infective disease to man, they
also produce severe allergic reactions in those individuals who have
become hypersensitized to the saliva injected when the bugs feed.

There are a number of reasons why Triatominae have been and
should be cultured in the laboratory. (1) Because these bugs are of
medical and public health importance, they are reared in the laboratory to determine their life cycle and vector potential. (2) Due to
their large size and the relative ease by which they may be cultured
in the laboratory, they are excellent subjects for physiological, genetic, and transmission studies. Perhaps the most serious objection to
using Triatominae as experimental animals is the fact that they have
a rather long life cycle; in addition, a colony of vertebrate animals
must be maintained to serve as a blood source for the bugs.

A. FIELD COLLECTING

Because of the nature of Triatominae research, this chapter would
not be complete without at least an introductory section concerned
with the problems involved in their collection and transportation in
the field. All laboratory colonies must originate directly from field
collections or secondarily from cultures that others have established
from the field. Hence, it is important to understand field collection

methods and practical shipping procedures for the transportation of the bugs from one laboratory to another. Except for those species which are "domesticated" and breeding in man-made dwellings in Latin America, the collection of Triatominae is largely a pick-and-shovel operation. In southwestern United States and northern Mexico, these bugs are most frequently found in association with *Neotoma* spp., or wood rats; *Citellus* spp., burrowing ground squirrels; *Didelphis* spp., opossums; and *Dasypus novemcinctus*, the armadillo. These animals often make their dens in cacti and thorn bushes, thus compounding the burden of excavating their burrows. It is important to bear in mind that the physical collection of live bugs is only the beginning of the total effort. The bugs must be transported in a healthy condition to the laboratory and there become acclimated to the new environment. With respect to temperature and humidity, the laboratory environment should approximate the optimum of the microclimate of the field.

Live bugs in plastic or glass collecting vials will die very quickly after only a very few minutes' exposure to the sun during the hot summer months. Live collections should at all times be protected from elevated temperatures (above 90°F or 32.2°C) or relatively cold temperatures (below 59°F or 15°C). Collections left in the sun inside cloth or metal carrying cases or in parked cars may soon perish. On field trips under the most adverse climatic conditions, live bugs have been carried in plastic vials in our shirt pockets (with button down flaps) or trouser pockets without a fatality. The cooling action effected from a perspiring body affords excellent protection to the bugs. It is important that each collecting vial be furnished with a dry substrate (e.g., paper towel) to take up the moisture from fecal droplets and furnish the bugs with surface footing. Live green twigs or even dead leaves and twigs are very poor substrate material for closed plastic vials because of moisture condensation. The new insulated food and beverage containers of foam plastic are ideal units, but on long hot field trips the limitations of even these efficient units must be taken into consideration.

If it is necessary to mail live colonies from the field to the laboratory or from one laboratory to another, one should try to mentally visualize the conditions to which the package will be subjected. Hence, the package should be well prepared with insulating material, well wrapped and labeled. The package should not be mailed from a rural route mail box, nor an urban letter or package drop because of the possible adverse exposure which may ensue in the postal collection box, or its subsequent handling by the postal carrier. All packages of live materials should be taken directly to a post office. If the shipment is by air, it is much better to mail the bugs in a large city where the package will go directly from the post office to the airport. If it becomes necessary to mail live insects from a city that does not have a large airport, it is helpful to mail the package at a time of day which will ensure their transportation to the airport during favorable hours with respect to prevailing temperatures. If possible, it is preferable to make shipments during a season when adverse temperature conditions do not prevail. For additional information concerning field collections and shipping instructions, consult the publications of Wood (1941a), Usinger (1944), and Ryckman (1962).

B. COLLECTING PERMITS

In many states there are regulations controlling the movement of medically important insects into and within the state. Persons planning on engaging in the transportation of live insects should be acquainted with the laws and regulations of the state or states concerned. There are strict federal regulations concerning the importation of live insects into the United States and their subsequent movement from state to state in the United States.

Federal permits may be requested from the Chief, Epidemiology & Domestic Operations Branch, Division of Foreign Quarantine, U. S. Public Health Service, U. S. Department of Health, Education, and Welfare, Washington 25, D. C. Scientists planning on collecting in Mexico are required to obtain a federal permit from the Republic of Mexico. This permit may be requested from the Direccion General De Caza; Departmento De Conservacion De La Fauna Silvestre; Secretaria De Agricultura Y Ganaderia; Mexico D.F., Mexico. All correspondence should be sent by air mail; several months should be allowed for completion of the negotiations. In addition to the above, each foreign adult collector will need to obtain a tourist permit. All persons traveling in Mexico should also be able to show proof of citizenship and small pox vaccination. If the vehicle to be driven in Mexico is not owned by one of the collecting party, a permit to drive the vehicle must be secured from the registered owner. A collecting party may be denied entry into Mexico if any one of the above entry regulations are not complied with; such delays at the border can be financially costly, and emotionally disturbing.

C. LABORATORY REARING

Many investigators have reared Triatominae and almost as many rearing modifications have been employed. A method of efficient handling and feeding is of paramount importance in the rearing of large numbers of Triatominae. Laboratory culture methods have been described by Larrousse (1927), Galliard (1935), Dias and Philip (1938), Wood (1941b), Usinger (1944), Grundemann (1947), Abalos and Wygodzinsky (1951), Ames *et al.* (1954), Ryckman (1952, 1954, 1962), and Ryckman *et al.* (1965). During the past 15 years the authors have reared over 100,000 kissing bugs for research purposes. During the perfection of rearing techniques a number of time and labor-saving short cuts have been instituted. One of the greatest problems in rearing kissing bugs is the feeding operation; this procedure should possess the following attributes: (1) The host animal must be securely restrained; (2) the bugs must be prevented from escaping during the feeding operation; (3) if the bugs are infected, they should not be permitted to contaminate the normal laboratory host; (4) the bugs should be brought in contact with the host in such a manner that they can feed quickly and to repletion. In addition to the above, the ambient temperatures and the relative humidity are important factors. For most species, 30°C is very satisfactory; colonies reared at 35°C are definitely suppressed as evidenced by a high mortality rate and lowered reproduction. Triatominae will live in a wide range of relative humidities from very low to very high, i.e., from 10% to 96%; however, if the relative humidity is low, the bugs will need to be fed more frequently, and if too high, mold will grow on the bugs and the substrate.

We have found that a relative humidity of 50–60% at 30°C is most satisfactory for the rapid growth and reproduction of most species of Triatominae. Adverse combinations of temperature and relative humidity will not only retard growth and reproduction, but will directly contribute to mortality during molting; this is particularly true when fifth-instar nymphs attempt to molt to the adult. During the critical act of molting, many of the nymphs may be unable to extricate themselves from the skin they are attempting to shed; hence, they soon die in the act of ecdysis. Different species of kissing bugs collected from diverse ecological habitats, e.g., the arid deserts and moist tropical regions, will obviously have different optimum requirements with respect to temperature and relative humidity; if molting or other difficulties arise, it is well to give first consideration to altering these factors in the appropriate and usually obvious direction.

Some species of Triatominae will go into diapause as fifth-instar nymphs during the winter and will not molt to breeding adults until spring; *Triatoma rubida* (Uhler) is an excellent example of a species possessing this characteristic. Data obtained by the writers would appear to indicate that the length of day may be an important factor in speeding up the developmental cycle in Triatominae. A given inbred line of Triatominae, reared under controlled and similar conditions with respect to temperature and humidity, developed at a much faster rate in a long-day incubator than did those in a short-day incubator.

There are essentially three fundamental methods of feeding hemophagous reduviids. (*a*) A frequently used method for small colonies consists of immobilizing the laboratory host animal in a tube of hardware cloth or screening and then placing the tube and animal in a large vessel. The bugs are then released into the vessel and permitted to feed on the animal through the restraining cylinder. (*b*) A glass or screen box is used by placing stiff paper in accordian-like folds or wooden laths in the bottom of the box and covering these supports with hardware cloth. The bugs are then released into the supports beneath the wire screening or hardware cloth. At feeding time guinea pigs or other hosts are confined above the wire netting

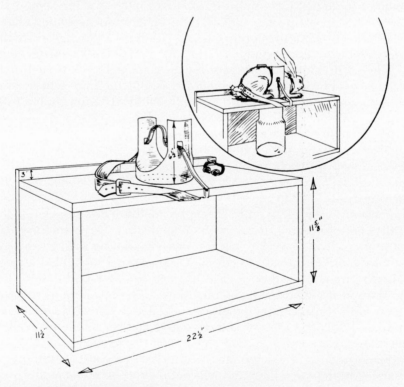

FIG. 1. Feeding device for mass culture of Triatominae [after Ryckman, *J. Parasitol.* **38**, 213 (1952)].

for a period of 15 to 30 minutes (Abalos and Wygodzinsky, 1951). In this method the guinea pig is actually placed into the rearing unit for a short time. (c) A third method, and the one preferred by the authors, consists of holding the rearing jars, which are covered with cloth, against the host; modifications of this method are illustrated in Figs. 1 and 2. The method illustrated in Fig. 1 is best suited for production

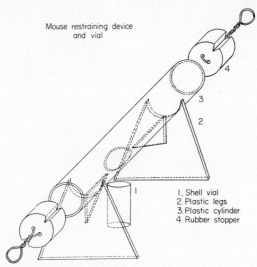

Mouse restraining device
and vial

1. Shell vial
2. Plastic legs
3. Plastic cylinder
4 Rubber stopper

FIG. 2. Feeding device for xenodiagnoses. This unit may be used for rearing small colonies of bugs on mice or for xenodiagnoses [after Ames, Quan, and Ryckman, *Am. J. Trop. Med. Hyg.* **3**, 891 (1954)].

of large colonies of Triatominae; the method illustrated in Fig. 2 is ideal for xenodiagnosis and for feeding a few small colonies of bugs on a relatively small host.

There are several important factors that a rearing and feeding program should offer to culture Triatominae efficiently. These factors are as follows (Ryckman, 1952, pp. 212–213);

1. A minimum amount of handling and opening of the rearing jars to reduce the possibility of escape and to eliminate unnecessary labor.

2. Rearing units which are uniform in size, adapted to the requirements and size of the colony.

3. Provision for the collection of eggs when desired with a minimum of time and procedures.

4. A means whereby the actual feeding operation can be accomplished quickly and efficiently.

5. Prevention of insect feces from contaminating the host should members of the colony be infected with *Trypanosoma cruzi*.

For the past 12 years the authors have used the feeding device illustrated in Fig. 1. This method of feeding has been found to have the following advantages;

1. The laboratory animal is in a natural and comfortable position. Rabbits confined in this device do not show signs of discomfort nor do they struggle to become free after they have become accustomed to the restraints placed on them.

2. The feeding unit is economical to build and facilitates rapid immobilization of the laboratory animal.

3. The possibility of insects escaping is reduced because the jars are not opened during the feeding operation. The bugs feed through the nylon cloth. Nylon is used because it does not tear or stretch as many other materials do if snagged while handling.

4. Constant observation is possible; thus the insects are removed when the blood meal is completed and a maximum of efficiency is obtained in a minimum of time. It was in this type of feeding unit that four species of *Triatoma* were studied while practicing "cannibalism" (kleptohemodeipnonism).

5. Less time is required to feed a number of colonies because bugs are not removed from their rearing jars to be fed.

6. Since bugs feed upward, their fecal material cannot contaminate the rabbit while the jars are in contact with the animal. Because transmission of *Trypanosoma cruzi* is by posterior station, keeping the laboratory animal free of fecal contamination is an important consideration if field-collected material is reared or if infected specimens are maintained for research purposes. *Triatoma* on perpendicular sheets of paper toweling will invariably face upward before defecating; this keeps the feces away from the host so that not even the nylon jar covers are stained by feces.

D. CONSTRUCTION OF LABORATORY EQUIPMENT

Rearing jars should be made to accommodate the colonies being reared with consideration given to the species and number of bugs present and their stage of development. Obviously, a given-size rearing unit could not accommodate as many adults of a large species as of a small species, nor as many adults as young nymphs. The criteria to use in determining the size of rearing unit should be in direct relation to the size of the colony and should be based on the following observable factors; (1) Can all of the bugs present feed readily and to repletion in 15–20 minutes? If overcrowding occurs, they will not all be able to feed at one time. (2) Soon after feeding, most bugs defecate and eliminate a relatively large amount of moisture. After feeding, the bugs should not be so crowded that they appear drenched with fecal material from their colony mates. Excessive, repeated, and prolonged wetting with fecal material increases mortality directly and may also result in death by contributing to molting difficulties. (3) The absorbent paper substrate should become relatively dry 12 hours after feeding.

Using the host-restraining device shown in Fig. 1, several sizes of rearing jars can be used to accommodate the size of the colonies being cultured. Glass or plastic jars 5 × 11 cm are ideal for small colonies; four of these units may be held together with a heavy rubber band and all fed at once under one host rabbit. For larger colonies, wide-mouth, half-pint glass jars or museum jars of similar size are ideal. For very large colonies of a large species, wide-mouth gallon jars may be used. However, these tall jars result in considerable fecal wetting of the bugs resting below those that have recently fed. Hence, shallower rearing units are preferable. The colony unit shown in Fig. 3 is designed for the collection of infective fecal material as indicated in the illustration; if the absorbent blotter paper is extended to

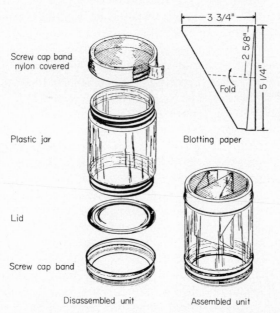

FIG. 3. Rearing units for Triatominae colonies. This rearing unit consists of a plastic cylinder threaded on each end; the metal screw bands and lids are from wide mouth half-pint jars. If the folded blotting paper inside the rearing unit is shortened, as shown in the illustration, this unit may also be used for the collection of large quantities of infective fecal material [after Ryckman, *J. Econ. Entomol.* **47**, 170 (1954)].

the bottom it can be used as a standard rearing unit. Rearing units usually are made like the unit shown in Fig. 3; inexpensive units may be made by using glass or plastic jars with nylon-covered screw cap bands and blotting paper or paper toweling as the supporting material. The screw cap bands or cut-out lids should be covered with nylon cloth of at least 40 threads per inch; other light, strong material may be used. It is important that this covering material does not readily tear. The fine mesh cloth is necessary to keep the unfed first-instar nymphs from escaping through the cloth; ovipositing females will frequently push their eggs through the cloth if the mesh is wide enough to allow an egg to pass through.

An absorbent substrate is essential in each colony for a number of reasons: (1) To soak up the feces produced in relatively large amounts after feeding. (2) To act as a support for the bugs to walk on and a means of reaching the host. (3) To furnish an egg-laying surface for those species which glue their eggs to a substrate. (4) To assist in removal of debris and fecal material. The absorbent substrate can consist of blotting paper, filter paper, or paper toweling. The main requisite is that it should be stiff enough to stand upright in the jar for a period of months with weekly moistening from fecal material. Desk-weight blotting paper or four thicknesses of a heavy grade of paper toweling is quite adequate. Several thicknesses of paper toweling may be held together by stapling. A circular disc should completely cover the bottom of each rearing jar to serve as a blotting surface.

Figure 1 illustrates the dimensions and general plan of the feeding unit. The lumber consists of 1×10 inch pine. All wood surfaces are painted white. The leather straps are adjustable to the size of the rabbit. The galvanized metal retainer is 5 inches in diameter; the surface in contact with the rabbit's body is rolled or covered with white masking tape. This circular metal retainer is held in place by small finishing nails driven into the wooden box on which the rabbit is strapped. All jars used have a diameter less than that of the metal retainer; this allows the nylon-covered jars to be brought up in contact with the rabbit's abdomen. For best results, hair on the rabbit's abdomen should be clipped; shaving is not necessary. Shell vials and smaller jars than the one illustrated may be held in place by a set of blocks cut to accommodate the standardized rearing units used.

This feeding device is the result of research with *Triatoma* colonies over a 12-year period and has proved to be a practical, safe, and efficient method where large colonies are reared. It is at present being used in several laboratories.

E. LABORATORY TECHNIQUES

In almost every science there are methods, techniques, and manipulations that are well known to the specialists, but are not generally known by others. Some of these relatively simple techniques may save hours of laborious work; this section is devoted to just such activities which have been found over the years to be of considerable advantage in the culture of Triatominae.

1. *Inspection of Colonies*

From time to time it is necessary to inspect the colonies for the collection of eggs, removal or addition of bugs, and for cleaning operations. It is important that a suitable vessel be used when the bugs are removed from the rearing units for inspection. If kissing bugs manage to escape from their handler, they will rapidly run in all directions and readily hide under, in, or behind any objects that are available. Consequently, one should always open a rearing unit into a vessel with perpendicular, smooth sides. Large glass bowls, large glazed crucibles, or white enameled pans serve most needs very well. The adults are winged and can fly, but rarely attempt to do so under laboratory conditions. We have used white enameled pans measuring 25×40 cm and 6 cm in depth for many years and find them very effective in retaining nymphs of all ages and for most adults with the exception of *Rhodnius* spp. Adults of *Rhodnius* possess a climbing organ that enables them to climb a perpendicular glass or enameled surface readily. Adults of this species should be anesthetized with CO_2 before being handled.

2. *Removal of Debris*

Removal of debris from an active colony of kissing bugs can be a rather bothersome problem. The debris consists of cast skins, fecal material, hatched eggs, and possibly a few dead bugs; mixed with this material will be found the viable eggs and some small nymphs. If there are several hundred eggs and small nymphs present, their separation from the debris can be no small problem. The illustration in Fig. 4 indicates the condition existing in a colony before and after removal of the debris. Removal of most of the material may be accomplished in a few seconds by holding a white enameled pan above a laboratory sink containing hot water and gently blowing into the pan. Most of the light debris consisting of cast skins and hatched eggs will rise and flow over the edge of the pan and into the hot-water bath. For best results the pan should be moved up and down in short

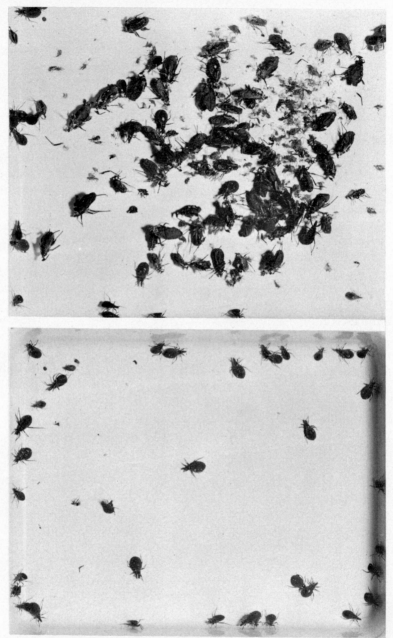

FIG. 4. A technique for removing debris from Triatominae colonies. (Upper) A white enameled pan containing a colony of *Triatoma rubida* with associated debris consisting of cast skins and dried fecal material. (Lower) The same pan 30 seconds later after the debris has been blown out, leaving the live nymphs behind.

quick motions to add to the buoyancy of the debris. With a little practice one can expertly remove most of the debris. The hot-water bath is recommended to kill the occasional small nymph or egg that may be blown out of the pan if the blast of air or breath is too strong. The heavier debris, which is not removed by the above method, may be picked out with forceps or scooped out with a card. This is best achieved by tipping the enameled pan and shaking all of the remaining debris and bugs to one end. The debris and live bugs should then be placed some 6 inches below a lighted 75- or 100-watt electric light bulb; because of the heat and the light the bugs will run to the clean end of the pan and leave the debris behind to be scooped out or removed with forceps. Tapping on the pan will speed up this operation.

Eggs may be collected by using a series of screens; the size of the screens of course will vary, depending upon the size of the eggs being collected. The largest screen should readily allow the eggs to pass, but hold back larger pieces of debris such as broken fragments of cast skins; the second screen should have a mesh small enough to retain the eggs, but allow the finer dust-like particles to pass through. In this manner relatively large numbers of eggs may be separated readily from the debris. The eggs of most species of Triatominae will hatch in approximately 20–25 days at 30°C; hence, it is well to collect the eggs from breeding colonies at least every 3 weeks.

3. Sexing

In some research activities it is necessary to isolate male and female nymphs to obtain virgin specimens. If each nymph must be isolated in individual rearing vials and then fed and inspected until it reaches the adult much time and effort would be involved. Fifth-instar Triatominae can be readily sexed as indicated in Fig. 5. When this method is employed, any number of male or female nymphs may be isolated into their respective sexes with a great saving in time, effort, and material.

4. Preserving

Eggs, nymphs, and adults of Triatominae should be preserved in 75% ethyl alcohol. If there are dried droplets of fecal material on otherwise valuable specimens, this material may be readily removed by placing the bugs (dead or alive) in warm water for as much as an hour and changing the water as often as appears necessary. When clean, they should be blotted dry with paper toweling, and immediately preserved in ethyl alcohol and stored in a dark box or cabinet.

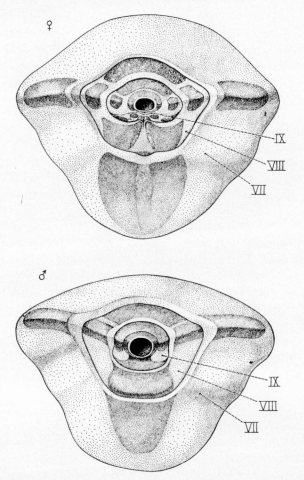

FIG. 5. Sex-determining characters for fifth-instar Triatominae nymphs. The terminal abdominal segments of *Triatoma protracta navajoensis* male and female fifth-instar nymphs are illustrated. Pigmentation of the several sclerotized plates may vary from one species to another; the characters indicated in the 9th segment are the critical morphological structures for sex identification of fifth-instar nymphs [after Ryckman, *Univ. Calif. Publ. Entomol.* **27**, 95 (1962)].

Isopropyl alcohol may cause the bugs to turn red if they have recently had a blood meal. Adults and older nymphs may also be pinned on No. 3 insect pins and stored in insect boxes.

5. *Storage of Colonies in Incubator*

The colonies of bugs in glass or plastic vials with cloth-covered tops should be stored in white enameled pans in the incubator. This is important to prevent the escape of nymphs or the loss of eggs from the jars into the incubator. Occasionally the cloth top may be damaged during handling or during feeding and an undetected small hole may develop which will permit nymphs to slip through or eggs to be pushed through by the ovipositors of the females. A white enameled pan measuring 25 × 40 cm by 6 cm in depth is a very useful size. It will store 7 or 8 half-pint jars. In addition to the above, the white enameled pans are excellent vessels to "pour" a colony into for inspection purposes.

6. *Humidity*

The proper relative humidity (50–60%) may be realized by using specialized humidity generators or dessicators, or by placing water-filled trays in the incubator. Paper or cloth towels partially suspended in the trays of water will assist in raising the humidity.

II. LABORATORY CULTURE OF PREDACEOUS REDUVIIDAE

The predaceous reduviids comprise some 19 subfamilies, or all but one of the subfamilies of the Reduviidae. These bugs are not parasites on vertebrates but rather feed upon a very wide range of arthropod species.

We have reared species of the genera *Reduvius, Zelus,* and *Apiomerus,* and find they have much in common. They are not only predaceous, but also cannibalistic; therefore, from the first instar to the adult, they must be individually reared in the laboratory or swamped with an abundance of live prey. Cannibalism is an important survival mechanism in nature in the predaceous reduviids; hence, this way of life can not readily be altered in the laboratory.

A. FIELD COLLECTING

In collecting live material in the field, the same precautions apply with respect to protection from heat as mentioned in Section I,A. The added step which must be taken is that the nymphs and adults must be immediately placed in individual vials to prevent cannibalism. In collecting predaceous reduviid bugs, one must know the ecology and host relationships of each group to collect them intelligently. For example, native North American species of the genus *Reduvius* appear to be most readily collected in the lodges of *Neotoma* spp., the pack rat; nymphs of *Rasahus* are usually taken under rocks;

Apiomerus in flowers, and many other genera such as *Zelus, Sinea,* and *Arilus* in vegetation waiting for an appropriate host to come along. Many of these bugs can be taken in light traps with incandescent or black light bulbs.

B. ECONOMIC IMPORTANCE

The predaceous reduviid bugs are of considerable economic importance because of their reduction of insect numbers. They kill their prey by grasping them with their strong legs and beak and then inserting their stylets. Within less than a minute the victim of such an attack ceases to struggle. Proteolytic saliva is pumped into the prey and in a few minutes all proteinaceous tissues are dissolved, including the muscles, and the mid-gut and its contents. The liquefied contents are then sucked out at leisure by the reduviid bug; only a chitinous shell remains. Most of the predaceous reduviids which are large enough and capable of biting man inflict a very painful bite; this is because the proteolytic saliva readily lyses human tissues as well as insect tissues. It is necessary to handle these bugs with considerable care to prevent being bitten. This is certainly not true of the Triatominae, which very rarely will attempt to bite while being handled. The bite of the kissing bug is very benign because to be a successful parasite it is to their advantage not to cause discomfort to their host. However, on the part of the predaceous bug, the faster they can kill their host with the most highly proteolytic saliva, the more likely they are of obtaining a meal and surviving in the battle for protein.

C. LABORATORY CULTURE

Reduvius senilis Vanduzee, *R. vanduzeei* Wygodzinsky and Usinger, *R. sonoraensis* Usinger, and *R. personatus* (Linnaeus) have been readily reared in the laboratory. They may be cultured in glass or plastic vials. Each vial should be furnished with a cloth top to permit ventilation and a strip of paper toweling. The latter is important for the absorption of moisture and serves as a substrate for the bugs to walk on. *Reduvius* bugs were readily reared through a complete life cycle on several species of Triatominae or kissing bugs. An indication of the power of the bugs and the strength of their proteolytic saliva may be judged from the following: An unfed fourth-instar nymph of *R. senilis* weighing 2.2 mg killed a fifth-instar nymph of *Triatoma protracta* (Uhler) which weighed 141.3 mg.

Mating of *Reduvius* bugs in the laboratory may be accomplished by feeding them well and then bringing the sexually mature males and females together; one pair per vial is preferred. With plenty of food, a mating pair may share the same vial for several days without cannibalistic activities. In the presence of plenty of food, sexually mature adults more readily attack the prey they are supplied with than each other. But if starvation conditions should prevail, they will resort to cannibalism. Because one or a limited number of copulations will permit the female to lay fertile eggs for many weeks, the best policy is to remove the males from the breeding vials after a few days. Eggs of *Reduvius* hatch in 15–20 days at 30°C; therefore, the eggs should be collected every 2 weeks and the nymphs isolated in individual rearing vials.

If a batch of 50 unfed first-instar nymphs are left together, cannibalism soon begins and there is a progressive diminution until only one second- or third-instar nymph remains. Small first- and second-instar nymphs must be fed prey of an appropriate size; kissing bugs of the same instars serve very well. If the kissing bugs have recently fed on a rabbit and are full of rabbit blood, 3 or 4 such nymphs per *Reduvius* bug are adequate for at least 2 weeks; at that time additional well-fed prey should be added. In the absence of kissing bugs many other species of laboratory-reared insects can serve as prey for predaceous bugs. An important factor to be considered in rearing predaceous bugs is that they strike out at moving objects and therefore must be furnished with live prey.

ACKNOWLEDGMENTS

The authors appreciate the permission given to reproduce four figures from the following publications: Fig. 1., *J. Parasitol.* **38**, 213 (American Society of Parasitologists); Fig. 2., *Am. J. Trop. Med. Hyg.* **3**, 891 (American Society of Tropical Medicine and Hygiene); Fig. 3., *J. Econ. Entomol.* **47**, 170 (Entomological Society of America); Fig. 5., *Univ. Calif. (Berkeley) Publ. Entomol.* **27**, 95 (University of California Press, Berkeley, California). Dr. Robert L. Usinger kindly read the manuscript.

Original development of the rearing techniques and supplementary information was made possible in part by a grant-in-aid (E-173) from the National Institute of Allergy and Infectious Diseases, National Institutes of Health; and a grant (DA-MD-49-193-62-G45) from the Research and Development Command, Office of The Surgeon General, Department of The Army.

REFERENCES

Abalos, J. W., and Wygodzinsky, P. (1951). Las Triatominae Argentinas. *Univ. Nacl. Tucuman, Monograf.* **601**, No. 2, 178.

Ames, C. T., Quan, S. F., and Ryckman, R. E. (1954). Triatominae in experimental transmission of plague. *Am. J. Trop. Med. Hyg.* **3**, 890–896.

Dias, E., and Philip, C. B. (1938). Criação de Triatomideos no laboratorio. *Mem. Inst. Oswaldo Cruz* **33**, 407–412.

Galliard, H. (1935). Recherches sur les réduvidés hématophages *Rhodnius* et *Triatoma*. *Ann. Parasitol. Humaine Comparee* **13**, 522–526.

Grundemann, A. W. (1947). Studies on the biology of *Triatoma sanguisuga* (LeConte) in Kansas. *J. Kansas Entomol. Soc.* **20**, 77–85.

Larrousse, F. (1927). Etude biologique et systématique du genre *Rhodnius* Stål. *Ann. Parasitol. Humaine Comparee* **5**, 63–88.

Ryckman, R. E. (1952). Laboratory culture of Triatominae with observations on behavior and a new feeding device. *J. Parasitol.* **38**, 210–214.

Ryckman, R. E. (1954). A method of collecting large quantities of feces from Triatominae infected with *Trypanosoma cruzi*. *J. Econ. Entomol.* **47**, 170–171.

Ryckman, R. E. (1962). Biosystematics and hosts of the *Triatoma protracta* complex in North America. *Univ. Calif. (Berkeley) Publ. Entomol.* **27**, 93–240.

Ryckman, R. E., Folkes, D. L., Olsen, L. E., Robb, P. L., and Ryckman, A. E. (1965). Epizootiology of *Trypanosoma cruzi* in Southwestern North America. *J. Med. Entomol.* **2**, 87–108.

Usinger, R. L. (1944). The Triatominae of North and Central America and the West Indies and their public health significance. *Public Health Bull.* **288**, 81.

Wood, S. F. (1941a). A method of collecting and transporting cone-nosed bugs. *Bull. Brooklyn Entomol. Soc.* **36**, 137–139.

Wood, S. F. (1941b). Notes on the distribution and habits of reduviid vectors of Chagas' disease in the Southwestern United States. *Pan.-Pacific Entomologist* **17**, 85–94.

Section B

Domestic and Stored Product Insects

Chapter 14

House Flies

D. Spiller

Plant Diseases Division,
Department of Scientific and Industrial Research,
Auckland, New Zealand

I. INTRODUCTION

The first successful colonization of house flies (*Musca domestica* L.) appears to have been that recorded by Lodge (1918), who bred both house flies and *Fannia* for 14 months, in London, England. He used a mixture of casein, bread, water, and banana surrounded by a layer of dry rubbish in which maggots could pupate, the whole being placed in very large earthenware saucers. The photograph of the arrangements (Fig. 1) serves as a vivid comparison with present-day procedures which are all based on multiple cages and are clean and highly organized.

In America the early attempts to rear a continuous supply of house flies were less successful (Glaser, 1924). The rearing medium was usually fresh horse manure, but in winter in New York and

FIG. 1. The fly rearing room at the London School of Hygiene and Tropical Medicine, about 1916 (reproduced from the *Bull. Entomol. Res.* 9 (Part VIII) by permission of the Commonwealth Institute of Entomology).

Pennsylvania it was impossible to rear flies from mid-December to mid-April, although laboratory conditions appeared to be adequate (Glaser, 1927; Grady, 1928). It was thought that the horse manure was deficient in food value during the winter months but there was uncertainty whether this was due to "changes in bacterial flora on which maggots reared in some foods primarily feed or to a reduction in number of bacteria" (Glaser, 1927). Addition of a heavy suspension of autoclaved yeast cells every few days enabled the maggots to grow and mature throughout the year (Glaser, 1927). This permitted colonization, that is, continuous culture in the laboratory, and all further developments of house fly colonization stem from Glaser's rearing medium of horse manure and yeast rather than the earlier successful medium—casein, bread, water, and banana.

Apart from some uncertainty in the supply* the use of horse manure resulted in frequent introduction of parasites into the fly cultures. Later it was found that the manure could be pasteurized at 70°C for 2 hours without reducing its value. If this was not done, a mite parasitic on flies was often brought in and was difficult to eliminate from the culture.

These difficulties led to the introduction of rearing media which are essentially artificial horse manures: first, a medium containing wheat bran, alfalfa meal, yeast, and malt (Richardson, 1932); and later the CSMA (Chemical Specialties Manufacturers Association) medium which contained, in addition, spent brewers' grains (Peterson, 1953; Anonymous, 1956). There is also a simple bran, straw, and bacteria mix used to rear *Musca domestica vicina* (Macq.) (Silverman and Silverman, 1953). These types of rearing medium have been, are, and very possibly will continue to be, used in the majority of laboratories where house flies are reared.

More recently diets based on milk and milk products have been gaining acceptance. In general, these are cleaner, easier to prepare, and more suitable for standardization (Spiller, 1963a, 1964a).

The present stage of laboratory culture of house flies is that there are now no major difficulties in maintaining cultures and that increasingly attention is being directed (a) to improving the over-all ease and efficiency of the rearing procedures (Spiller, 1963a, 1964a,b), (b) to quality control of the reared product (Spiller, 1964b), and (c) to ecological and evolutionary aspects of competition, selection, and fitness of and between house fly strains.

* Ecologists may ponder whether horses and the Model T Ford were an example of competitive exclusion with significant mortality (Hardin, 1960).

The traditional methods of house fly colonization have been described and redescribed by numerous authors; they were adequately reviewed by Sawicki and Holbrook (1961), and in various modifications and aspects at the World Health Organization, *Symposium on Cultural Procedures for Arthropod Vectors and Their Biological Control Agents,* at Gainesville, Florida, 1963 (Louw, 1964; Schoof, 1964; Spiller, 1964a). Thus, the details of the CSMA procedure and variants are readily available, the system is widely known and used, medium can be purchased from a commercial source, and in all probability the procedures will not be supplanted in those laboratories where house fly rearing is an established procedure. Laboratories considering the introduction of house fly rearing for the first time might prefer to adopt the cleaner and more efficient procedures evolved in the writer's laboratory (Spiller, 1963a). These procedures are described below.

II. REARING AND HANDLING LABORATORY COLONIES

A. ADULTS

1. *Cages*

Stock flies are kept in simple cylinder cages formed from a pipe of wire fly-screening closed top and bottom by insertion of cake tin lids, suitably modified (Fig. 2). Our dimensions are set entirely by the size of the available lids and the width of the fly screening; lids 8.5 inches diameter, screening 3 ft wide.

The screening is split lengthwise and perhaps a half inch of the cut edge folded over to what is to be the inside of the cage. The side join is now formed by an inverted lap or clasp joint into what is technically a run-and-fell seam. This is fixed in position by some 20 wire stitches from a standard, long-arm, paper stapler (see Figs. 3 and 4).

Both ends of the cage are modified by soldering a 0.75 inch length of 1.0 inch ϕ copper pipe to the center of what is usually the inside of the lid, but is to be the outside of the cage. A hole concentric with the pipe is then produced with a 0.875 inch ϕ drill (Fig. 3c). The lid, which is the bottom of the cage, has in addition a much larger hole, approximately 2 inches ϕ, into which a 0.75 inch length of 2.0 inch ϕ copper pipe is soldered. The outer end of this

---

* The symposium contributions were published as Part 4, *Bull. World Health Organ.* **31**, 433–622 (1964).

FIG. 2. The cylindrical cage used for feeding and holding adult house flies.

pipe is slightly expanded by a suitable swage to allow easy insertion of the food cup (Fig. 3d).

These ends are inserted into the wire cylinder (Fig. 3a). If the cylinder has been made with due care the rolled edge of the lid abuts the cylinder end and prevents slippage caused by the lid entering the gauze cylinder. Each end is easily held in position by some 8–10 wire clips (Fig. 3a) passed under the lid edge and through the screening (Figs. 2 and 4). In my laboratory these clips are made by half unfolding the major arm of a glide wire paper clip.

Each cage is hung from a ceiling hook by a single wire hooked through a hole in the lip of the upper lid. This method of supporting the cages leaves the floor of the room entirely free for cleaning and greatly restricts entry of ants into the cages. If ants invade cages via the ceiling and wires, it is both easy and clean to hang oil cups from the ceiling hooks and the cages from the oil cups.

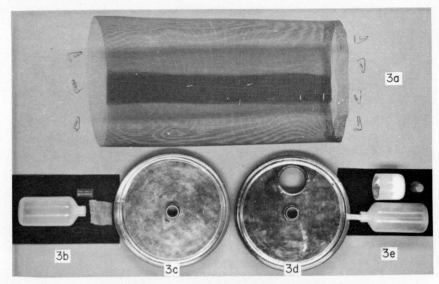

FIG. 3. Various parts of the cylindrical cage used for holding and feeding adult house flies. (a) Gauze cylinder and wire clips; (b) bottle for feeding sugar-water; (c) the cage top; (d) the cage bottom; (e) upper, the feeding cup; and lower, the bottle used for emergence of adults and for egg collection.

These cages are cheap, easy to make, assemble and disassemble, are readily cleaned by washing, and are sterilized by dry heat. All parts are interchangeable. Few flies escape, unless, as happens on rare occasions, the cork falls out of the bottom central hole. There are no reasons to believe that foreign flies ever find their way into these cages.

2. Emergence

Twenty grams of cleaned and dry pupae are placed in a 6-oz polyethylene bottle. A strip of card 0.5 inch wide and 6–7 inches long (a fly-walk) is inserted through the mouth of the bottle (Fig. 3e). One end of the card is placed among the pupae, the other end protrudes from the bottle. The bottle with pupae and card is then attached to the central hole of the bottom of the fly cage. This hole is usually closed by a cork. Flies emerge from the pupae, proceed up the fly-walk and into the cage. Obviously the bottle with remaining pupae can be removed after any interval and attached to a new cage or the remaining pupae destroyed. Thus it is easy to segregate early emerging or late emerging flies, or to produce flies of known age interval.

FIG. 4. Lower portion of cage used for feeding and holding adult house flies. Note the feeding cup (right), the bottle for emergence of adults or egg collection, and the wire clips holding the end into the gauze cylinder.

3. Removal and Disposal

When flies need to be removed from cages for sexing or for insecticide tests, a 0.5-inch diameter rigid plastic tube is inserted through the central bottom opening of the cage and the flies sucked into a suitable container attached to a domestic vacuum cleaner. They are then anesthetized with carbon dioxide.

Old or excess flies are killed by placing the whole cage in a deep freeze.

4. Feeding

Many older procedures supply liquid milk daily. In other feeding procedures, including my own, this is replaced by water and dry food.

Experience suggests that water supplied as tap water is rather unacceptable to adult flies. A dilute (2.5%) sugar solution is acceptable (Spiller, 1963a, Morrison and Davies, 1964a). This is fed from a 6-oz polyethylene bottle, into the neck of which is inserted a short length of thick wall polyethylene tubing (vacuum tubing) over one end of which is stretched a piece of organdy held in place by a rubber band or bands (Fig. 5). Properly assembled bottles do not

FIG. 5. The sugar-water feeder. Left, components disassembled; right, feeder assembled.

drip when inverted. The inverted assembly is inserted into the central hole of the top of the cage (Fig. 2) and supplies sugar-water *ad libitum*. Bottles are changed once a week, or more frequently if the organdy becomes grossly soiled.

Solid food is supplied in feeding cups (Fig. 3e). These are the bottom halves of the 6-oz polyethylene bottles used for sugar solutions and for holding pupae until adults have emerged. These cups fit snugly into the large hole in the cage bottom (Fig. 4). Flies for insecticide tests are fed dry cane sugar. Stock flies are fed a 1:1 dry mix of whole cream dried milk, and cane sugar supplemented with 10% autolyzed yeast and 0.1% cholesterol. Some 20 gm (2 tea-spoonfuls) of this mix is placed in the feeding cups daily except Saturday and Sunday.

B. EGGS

Some female flies will produce their first eggs 4 days after emer-gence; considerable egglaying can occur by the sixth day and full egglaying by the seventh and subsequent days. Flies are routinely egged by the seventh day after emergence and then at 3- to 4-day intervals until the sixteenth day, when they are discarded.

Eggs are collected in the following manner. A small piece of loosely woven muslin is dipped into thick milk (from whole cream dried milk, and water) and dropped into a 6-oz polyethylene bottle. A few drops of a saturated solution of ammonium carbonate and a fly-walk are added and the bottle is attached to the central hole of the bottom of the cage (Fig. 4). The following morning the bottle is removed, half filled with water, the eggs, milk, and muslin are tipped into a beaker, and the bottle is rinsed with further water. The muslin is held with forceps and lightly shaken in the water to free attached eggs, and then the beaker contents are poured on to and through a brass screen sitting on a 1-liter beaker. The origi-nal beaker is rinsed and this water is used to rinse the screen. The muslin is picked off and later washed, dried, and heat-sterilized for reuse. Eggs are allowed to settle, the milky water is poured off, more water is added, settled, and decanted. Eggs are then trans-ferred to smaller labeled beakers.

Eggs are measured by volume. The required amount is obtained by sucking up eggs into a medicine dropper and filling a conical centrifuge tube to the required volume. The centrifuge tube is then brought to the 5-ml mark with water, the end closed with the thumb, inverted to suspend eggs, and eggs and water dropped onto the rearing medium.

C. LARVAE

Larvae are reared in a medium comprised of equal weights of whole cream dried milk, and flocked paper to which is added 5% by weight of dried yeast and 2.1 ml water per gram mix. This medium is exceedingly easy to prepare. The dry ingredients are weighed out and then mixed by stirring with a glass rod; the required amount of water is added and the stirring continued. The medium aggregates into large crumbs and is then transferred to the rearing jars (Fig. 6, left). We find it convenient to rear slightly in excess of 1000

FIG. 6. Rearing jar with rearing medium. Left, medium as introduced into jar; right, approximately 6 days later.

flies from each jar; for this number we use 63 gm of dried mix plus 135 ml tap water for each jar.

D. PUPAE

Pupation occurs in the rearing medium. For normal rearing it begins early on the fifth day and is completed very soon after the end of the sixth day. Pupae have largely darkened and hardened by the seventh day and can then be separated from the spent medium, although this is usually done on the eighth or ninth day.

Pupae are easily separated by flotation. Water is added to the culture jar and the jar contents tipped into a plastic bucket. More water is added and the floating pupae are gathered off the surface with a strip of fly-screening. From this they are easily passed to pieces of screening about 7 inches square, washed under the cold tap, the excess water blotted off from below, and the pupae dried under an air blower. When dry the total mass of pupae is weighed to give *biomass*, 100 random pupae are counted out and weighed to give *average pupal weight*, and the *number of pupae reared* is computed from the biomass and the pupal weight.

III. SOME VARIATIONS AND COMMENTS

A. ADULTS

1. *Emergence*

Special conditions are not required for emergence of adults from pupae which may lie free as individuals or groups in bottles or Petri dishes. When the rearing room is at 25°C the first adults emerge on the tenth day, the majority on the eleventh, and a few on the twelfth. Emergence is easily delayed by allowing pupal development to proceed at ambient rather than rearing room temperatures or by cool-storing the pupae. There is a slight decrease in percentage emergence following cool storage for a few days but longer periods produced major mortality (Bucher *et al.*, 1948).

By Petri dish tests flies emerge from 95% or more of the pupae recovered and dried. This value is not increased or decreased more than 1 or 2% by major variations in larval rearing conditions. For example, I have found no major difference in emergence of adults from pupae from larvae reared from ⅓ to 2.7 times the normal densities or in medium containing from 85 to 145% of normal water content.

2. *Mating*

Male flies are sexually aggressive and frequently mount females but are seldom accepted. Mating may occur within 24 hours of emergence (Barber and Starnes, 1949) and, except in a few cases, is not repeated (Zingrone *et al.*, 1959). There is need for detailed study of how soon mating can occur and of how often it may be repeated. It should be observed that early sexing may not be a dependable way of obtaining virgin females. These are best obtained by isolating individual pupae in small corked or capped bottles or vials. Truly random pairs are best obtained by isolating pairs of pupae in small Petri dishes and sexing after emergence; approximately 50% of the dishes will contain a male and a female, an unbiased pair.

3. *Age Effects*

A few adults die within a few days; at 26.8°C and 45% relative humidity the mean longevity of one strain was 17.4 days (males), 29.4 days (females) (Rockstein and Lieberman, 1958). The age of the parents has some effect on succeeding generations. Average length of adult life decreased when lines were bred exclusively from eggs deposited by young flies (Callahan, 1962; Meister, 1962); average longevity increased when eggs were always taken from females 20 to 30 days of age (Meister, 1962). In another strain, continued use of the last viable eggs decreased longevity and reduced fitness so that no more than three consecutive generations could be reared (Callahan, 1962).

The age of the parents when eggs are laid does not affect the length of the larval or pupal stages (Callahan, 1962), nor are there differences in pupal size or weight which can be directly attributed to parental age. Spurious correlations are easily obtained. In my laboratory eggs were collected from standard cultures at 10, 14, 18, 21, and 25 days after emergence and added in standard measure to standard rearing medium. Neither the biomass nor the average pupal weight (17.8 mg) differed from eggs from parents 10, 14, or 18 days old. However, heavier pupae (19.5 mg) were obtained from eggs from the older flies, but this was clearly a response correlated with the lesser numbers (65.7%) of pupae reared from these eggs. This in its turn probably indicates that aged females produce an increased proportion of infertile eggs, as found previously (Callahan, 1962, Meister, 1962).

4. *Egg Production*

Stock flies must be fed on a diet which will maintain them and allow production of fertile eggs. Further, it is efficient to supply the diet that maximizes fertile egg production, in that this reduces the number of stock cages required to maintain the colony. Until rather recently it had been thought that female house flies required only protein (or amino acids) and possibly cholesterol for egg maturation and production (Spiller, 1964a). However, flies fed a liquid milk diet laid five times as many eggs as flies fed a synthetic diet of known amino acids, sucrose, and mineral salts, with or without B-vitamins and cholesterol (Morrison and Davies, 1964a). On the liquid milk diet half the females had two ovarian cycles and a quarter of the flies had four cycles. On the synthetic diet few achieved a second cycle and none a fourth cycle. When yeast ribonucleic acid (RNA) was added to the diet, egg laying equaled that on the liquid milk diet. Further, the yeast RNA could be replaced with cytidylic acid and adenine and it has been suggested: (*a*) that protein or amino acids, previously considered necessary and sufficient for house fly fecundity, actually allow only limited egg production because certain nutrient reserves are used by the female house fly in maturing eggs of the first ovarian cycle; and (*b*) that when these reserves are replenished by adding RNA or precusor to the diet, more than one ovarian cycle can be accomplished (Morrison and Davies, 1964a,b).

However, I have already obtained indications of other requirements for maximum egg laying. In my earlier procedure (Spiller,
1963a) the adult diet of sugar-water, whole cream dried milk powder,
and dried yeast achieved egg production which was adequate to
maintain stock cultures but was inferior to that obtained on another
dry diet* from CSMA-reared flies (Spiller, 1963b). This became
a major deficiency when it was necessary to rear adequate numbers from single pair matings or from a small nucleus, as, for example, the survivors of insecticide selection trials. When different
sources of yeast were tested in the dry diet, egg production increased
2.7-fold with 10% autolyzed yeast† and 1.9-fold with 10% yeast
extract (Fig. 7). Further, it has been found that neither adenine

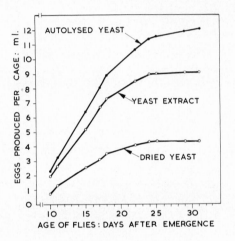

FIG. 7. Cumulative amounts of eggs laid per rearing cage (approximately 500–600
females) when the basic dry diet was supplemented with various yeast preparations.

nor yeast RNA improves egg laying. Thus there are indications
of undefined chemical or physical factors which facilitate high egg
production. Possibly these are feeding stimulants (Robbins *et al.*,
1965), the increased egg production reflecting increased food uptake. From the practical point of view, addition of autolyzed yeast
to the diet achieves egg production which now equals or surpasses
that obtained on a liquid milk diet; adequate egg production is no
longer a difficulty with single pair matings and small lots. Eggs
mature earlier than previously and flies are now egged on the fifth,
sixth, or seventh day rather than on the ninth or tenth. This earlier

---

* Granulated sugar, 6 parts; non-fat dry milk, 6 parts; powdered egg yolk, 1 part;
with water *ab libitum* (LaBrecque *et al.*, 1960).

† "Difco" brand.

and increased egg production has brought an attendant difficulty, for now many eggs are laid in the feeding cups and it is often necessary to change them daily when egg laying is at its peak.

B. Eggs

Eggs are obtained by the method described in the procedure, and no difficulties are now encountered. However, the technique is one that exerts strong positive selection of flies exhibiting the response; there can be little doubt that in such a situation considerable selection will have occurred. Therefore it will not be surprising if the technique is less effective when first applied to other strains.

Experience suggests that use of additional ammonium carbonate will increase the egg harvest at any one collection; there is no evidence that the total egg laying can be increased.

Detailed procedures of washing and recovery of eggs can be worked out as required. Violent shaking during recovery appears to reduce egg hatching. After recovery eggs are routinely held in water for an hour or two while medium is prepared. This delay has no adverse effect and experimentally has been extended to 3, 6, and even 8 hours without affecting either biomass or pupal weight.

Usually more than 90% of the eggs hatch; if the adult diet is deficient in cholesterol, egg hatching is depressed and may be low in later egg clutches (Monroe, 1960).

Eggs are usually measured by volume, commonly in the end of a graduated centrifuge tube. In our experience the initial graduations are often inaccurate, and large differences may occur when a tube is broken and then replaced. The egg-measuring device described by Sawicki and Holbrook (1961) would certainly be more consistent but is rather cumbersome. Reversing their procedure by sucking the eggs into a measuring cup or filter stick of the required volume and then dislodging the eggs by reversing the water flow may be as accurate and as convenient for house flies as it has proved for mosquito larvae (Bar-Zeev, 1962), but has the disadvantage that it is difficult to make the minor variations in egg volume necessary for quality control.

In some laboratories a fixed weight of eggs, or sometimes newly hatched larvae, is added to each rearing jar, and this is likely to be more accurate than present volumetric methods.

However, there is need for a rapid and accurate egg counter, which could both count total eggs and shut off at predetermined counts. If such an instrument were available it would markedly increase the precision of work on egg laying, on competition, and some genetic studies. Perhaps a modification of the cell counter developed by Cornwall and Davidson (1960) would prove suitable.

In most laboratory-rearing procedures where eggs are collected separately and pupae are separated from the rearing medium, the oviposition materials, the egg-catching device, and the eggs, provide the only link between the microorganisms of the adult gut and the microorganisms of the rearing medium. This association is via microbial contamination of these by feeding and ovipositing flies (Spiller, 1964c) and could be broken by surface sterilization of the eggs, which is readily accomplished (Dutky, 1962).

C. LARVAE

1. *Rearing Medium*

The various ingredients and proportions in the original rearing medium (Spiller, 1963a) were arrived at fairly arbitrarily. Some modifications which might improve, cheapen, or simplify the medium have since been tested; the results are summarized below.

a. Paper. The paper used by my laboratory is facial tissue bought in bulk, usually as seconds or offcuts. The grinding mill is a medium-speed cutting mill of local design and manufacture; presumably other laboratory cutting mills would give a similar product. The exit sieve is 12 meshes/linear inch. When the paper was shredded with a document shredder, and the shreds used in the rearing medium there were no real differences in biomass or average pupal weight between the flies reared on the shredded and the ground paper media. Recovery of pupae from the shredded paper medium was difficult.

b. Milk Powder. Substituting dried skim milk for dried whole cream milk gave a 13.7% increase in numbers of pupae recovered, a 23% decrease in biomass, and a 31.5% decrease in average weight of pupae (Spiller, 1963a). The increased survival is of considerable importance as indication of apparent avoidable mortality and selection pressure exerted by the standard rearing medium. On the other hand, very few pupae were obtained when milk powder was replaced by casein.

c. Microorganisms. i. *Bacteria.* As shown in Fig. 8 the rearing medium contains large numbers of microorganisms increasing to 10^9 per gram by the first day. Bacteria isolated and identified were *Proteus vulgaris* (or *mirabilis*), *Proteus rettgeri*, *Escherichia freundii*, *Aerobacter aerogenes*, and *Streptococcus faecalis*. When inoculated in sterile or unsterilized rearing medium most of these microorganisms either depressed production or were without effect. An exception was *A. aerogenes,* which gave marked gains in both biomass and pupal weight. This has suggested that standardization of the microbial flora may be desirable for adequate quality control of house fly rearing (Spiller, 1964a,b,c).

ii. *Yeast.* Omitting the dried brewers' yeast reduced both biomass and average pupal weight.

d. Additions. Replacing the dried yeast weight for weight with autolyzed yeast or yeast extract reduced both biomass and average

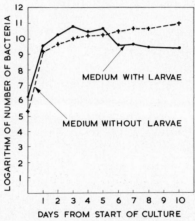

FIG. 8. Numbers of bacteria per gram of larval rearing medium at various times after mixing (from Spiller, 1964c, by permission Editor, New Zealand Entomologist).

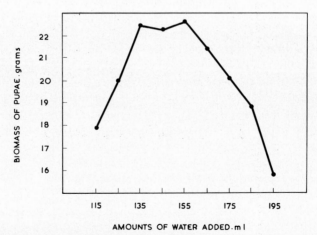

FIG. 9. Average pupal biomass values when larvae were reared in medium drier or wetter than the standard medium (135 ml).

pupal weight. When yeast extract was used almost half the maggots had not pupated by the eighth day. Cholesterol added at 1% of dry weight of milk and yeast did not improve pupal yield or weight or total egg yield (Spiller, 1963a).

e. Water. A standard mix of rearing medium contains 135 ml water. This may be varied within the range 115 ml–195 ml and the medium will still be acceptable to larvae. However, as is seen from Figs. 9, 10, and 11, the relationship can be complex. The biomass

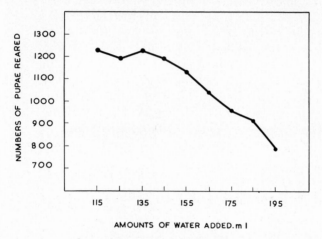

FIG. 10. Average numbers of pupae reared when larvae were reared in medium drier or wetter than the standard medium (135 ml).

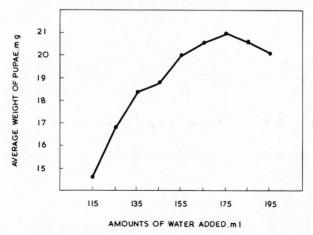

FIG. 11. Average weights of pupae when larvae were reared in medium drier or wetter than the standard medium (135 ml).

is maximal in the range 135–155 ml, but the number of pupae reared is greatest at 115–135 ml; the weight of individual pupae increases up to 175 ml water. These results emphasize that there is no "optimum" moisture content, only an optimum in relation to some particular biological measure. If it is intended that the rearing medium exert minimum selection pressure, then the drier mediums are preferable and the attendant deficiency in larval size could probably be met by seeding the rearing jar with fewer eggs. If, as is thought, the biomass is the most efficient of these measures, then the evidence suggests that present water content could be increased to 145 ml (2.23 ml/gm dry mix), with advantage.

f. Competition. When larvae are reared at different densities on standard medium, the numbers of pupae obtained are approximately a fixed proportion of the numbers of eggs used (Vladimirova and Smirnov, 1938), but the size of individual pupae decreases as the rearing density increases. Figure 12 shows the magnitude of this latter effect in our standard laboratory strain.

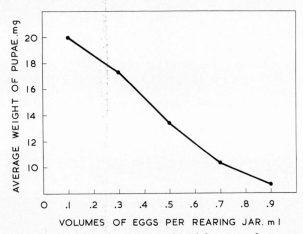

FIG. 12. The inverse relationship between larval density and average pupal weight for standard rearing jars with standard medium.

The importance of this in laboratory rearing is that it provides a ready means for quality control of the size of reared flies. Even under apparently constant conditions and with careful standardization of materials and methods there are sometimes downward trends in average pupal weight. When these appear they seem to become progressive, a result which could be readily explained if average egg size were proportional to body size. Whatever the cause, these trends can be disastrous if repeated batches of house flies fail to meet the quality control limits that have been established. In our laboratory such downward trends are now met by the simple expedient of fractionally reducing the volume of eggs added to the rearing medium so that the resulting flies are proportionally larger, returning to the standard egg volume as the average pupal weight reaches 18 to 19 mg. In this way no real difficulties are experienced in obtaining pupae with average weight greater than 15 mg.

IV. REARING FROM SINGLE PAIRS AND SMALL GROUPS

Many house fly rearers have experienced difficulties in obtaining adequate numbers of eggs from single pairs or from small-group matings of house flies. Many pairs lay few or no eggs. Often this has been attributed to lack of social or gregarious factors, and several ingenious techniques have been elaborated to supply these social factors without impairing the sexual isolation of the single pair. Most of these techniques have failed and details are not available except as part of the folklore of the house fly-rearing coterie. However, Lichtwardt *et al.* (1955), Barbesgaard and Keiding (1955), Buei (1958), Sawicki and Holbrook (1961), and Nagasawa and Asano (1963) have described methods for rearing from single-pair matings.

In the method of Nagasawa and Asano (1963), each single pair is kept in a glass vial 9 cm in diameter and 7 cm high, the top being closed with vinyl net. Food is supplied via a cotton ball moistened with 1:1:10 mix of whole dried milk, sugar, and tap water. After 4 to 5 days the pair are anesthetized and some 220 gm of Tofu rearing mixture is introduced. The container is then covered with a cotton cloth. Flies remain in the container until dead, no attempts being made to rear more than a single egg mass from each female. About 90% of the females produce offspring with this procedure (Nagasawa and Asano, 1963).

In our laboratory there has been an initial trial of a single-pair rearing procedure that is perhaps simpler and has the advantage of obtaining successive egg batches from each female. The container used is a wax-paper, 1 pint, ice-cream container or honey pot which normally has a press-in wax-paper lid. This lid is discarded and replaced by an identical-sized circle of wire fly-screening. About half a teaspoonful of adult food is placed in a container or spread on the bottom of the pot, a small (2.8 cm × 1.5 cm) polyethylene cup containing a twist of dry muslin is added, and then the anesthetized male and female. The pot is closed by pressing in the circle of fly-

screening. Sugar-water is supplied *ab libitum* from a small chicken
feeder laid on the fly-screening (Fig. 13). These units are placed in
the rearing room for 5 to 6 days; then the twist of muslin is thoroughly
soaked with the thick milk and ammonium carbonate mixture, which
is introduced directly into the cup from a hypodermic syringe fitted
with a long, wide-bore veterinary needle. The following morning

FIG. 13. The single-pair breeding cage described in Section IV. Left to right: the
egg-laying cup with twist of dry muslin; the food cup; the honey pot and screen lid;
the chicken feeder for sugar-water with a hole punched in the functional bottom and
a square of organdy which covers this hole. Adhesive is unnecessary. (Photo by F. E.
Skinner.)

the flies are lightly anesthetized, the egg-laying cup is removed
and replaced, and the cage closed. Eggs are recovered by the usual
procedures; they are counted and seeded onto suitable amounts of
rearing medium. At appropriate times further batches of eggs are
obtained until the female dies.

Some people have found difficulty in rearing small numbers of
larvae on the traditional CSMA rearing medium. In our laboratory
no difficulties were experienced in rearing the small numbers of
larvae on the milk-yeast-paper medium described in Section II.
With fewer eggs there was always excess food and minimum competition so that large pupae were usually obtained.

Twenty-one single pairs were tested in the initial trial of this technique. Pupae and adults were obtained from 17 (81%) of the pairs, which were egged on three occasions and discarded 21 days after emergence. Average number of pupae was 82.5, actual values being 21, 24, 26, 38, 40, 47, 50, 55, 60, 86, 90, 100, 122, 136, 136, 185, and 187.

This rearing technique has also been used with consistent success with groups of from a few up to 40–50 flies for controlled matings or from insecticide selection experiments, and there is now no difficulty breeding house flies from any number down to a single pair.

V. MASS CULTURE

There have not been any published reports of the culture of house flies in lots of more than a few thousand a week. However, if continuous mass culture (for example, a million or more a week) of house flies became desirable—as, for example, to mass rear tsetse fly parasites—there do not appear to be any major difficulties. A simple multiplication of facilities would almost suffice, but more economic procedures could readily be evolved.

Dr. G. C. LaBrecque, in a personal communication (1965), informs me that the Gainesville Laboratory of the Entomology Research Division, Agricultural Research Service, U. S. Department of Agriculture, has been producing house flies for one year at the rate of 2 million per week for use in release experiments. The methods are similar to those described in Section I, using the CSMA larval medium and a dry adult diet (see footnote on p. 215). Only a few changes were necessary to adapt the method to mass rearing. The rearing cages measured 0.23 cubic meters and held approximately 20,000 adult flies. The adults were egged twice weekly with used CSMA medium. Approximately 30,000 to 33,000 eggs were measured and placed in a 1-liter container of prepared CSMA medium 24 hours old. Two hours later, the eggs and medium were transferred into a galvanized iron tub (100-liter capacity) that had been partially filled with a mixture composed of 8 liters of water and 3200 gm of dry CSMA medium. On the seventh day the pupae were floated, strained off, and dried in an air dryer. Approximately 25,000 to 30,000 pupae were obtained from each tub. At present the cost is $111.73 per million, and it could be appreciably lowered by mechanization should it become necessary to rear even larger numbers.

224   D. SPILLER

REFERENCES

Anonymous (1956). The Peet-Grady method. *Soap Chem. Specialties* **32**, 243–244 and 267.

Barber, G. W., and Starnes, E. B. (1949). The activities of house flies. *J. N. Y. Entomol. Soc.* **52**, 203–214.

Barbesgaard, P., and Keiding, J. (1955). Crossing experiments with insecticide resistant housefly (*Musca domestica* L.). *Vidensk. Medd. Dansk Naturhist. Foren. Kjøbenhavn* **117**, 83–116.

Bar-Zeev, M. (1962). A simple technique for obtaining standard numbers of newly hatched mosquito larvae. *Mosquito News* **22**, 171–175.

Bucher, G. E., MacB. Cameron, J. W., and Wilkes, A. (1948). Studies on the housefly (*Musca domestica* L.). II. The effects of low temperatures on laboratory reared puparia. *Can. J. Res.* **D26**, 25–56.

Buei, K. (1958). On the single pair culture of the common housefly, *Musca domestica vicina* Macq. *Botyu-Kagaku* **23**, 177–181.

Callahan, R. F. (1962). Effects of parental age on the life cycle of the house fly, *Musca domestica* Linnaeus (Diptera: Muscidae). *J. N. Y. Entomol. Soc.* **70**, 150–158.

Cornwall, J. B., and Davidson, R. M. (1960). Rapid counter for small particles in suspension. *J. Sci. Instr.* **37**, 414–417.

Dutky, S. R. (1962). Quoted by R. E. Monroe (1962). A method for rearing house fly larvae aseptically on a synthetic medium. *Ann. Entomol. Soc. Am.* **55**, 140.

Glaser, R. W. (1924). Rearing flies for experimental purposes with biological notes. *J. Econ. Entomol.* **17**, 486–496.

Glaser, R. W. (1927). Note on the continuous breeding of *Musca domestica*. *J. Econ. Entomol.* **20**, 432–433.

Grady, A. G. (1928). Studies in breeding insects throughout the year for insecticide tests. *J. Econ. Entomol.* **21**, 598–604.

Hardin, G. (1960). The competitive exclusion principle. *Science* **131**, 1292–1297.

LaBrecque, G. C. (1965). Personal communication.

LaBrecque, G. C., Adcock, P. H., and Smith, C. N. (1960). Tests with compounds affecting housefly metabolism. *J. Econ. Entomol.* **53**, 802–805.

Lichtwardt, E. T., Bruce, W. N., and Decker, G. C. (1955). Notes on the inbreeding of houseflies. *J. Econ. Entomol.* **48**, 301–303.

Lodge, O. C. (1918). An examination of the sense relations of flies. *Bull. Entomol. Res.* **9**, 141–151.

Louw, B. K. (1964). Physical aspects of laboratory maintenance of muscoid fly colonies. *Bull. World Health Organ.* **31**, 529–533.

Meister, G. (1962). Biologische Beobachtungen bei der Laboratoriumszucht von *Musca domestica* L. *Z. Tropenmed. Parasitol.* **13**, 102–133.

Monroe, R. E. (1960). Effect of dietary cholesterol on house fly reproduction. *Ann. Entomol. Soc. Am.* **53**, 821–824.

Morrison, P. E., and Davies, D. M. (1964a). Feeding of dry chemically defined diets, and egg production in the adult house-fly. *Nature* **201**, 104–105.

Morrison, P. E., and Davies, D. M. (1964b). Repeated ovarian cycles with ribonucleic acid in the diet of adult house-flies. *Nature* **201**, 948–949.

Nagasawa, S., and Asano, S. (1963). An inbreeding method of rearing the house fly. *J. Econ. Entomol.* **56**, 714.

Peterson, A. (1953). "A Manual of Entomological Techniques," p. 62. Edwards, Ann Arbor, Michigan.

Richardson, H. H. (1932). An efficient medium for rearing house flies throughout the year. *Science* **76**, 350–351.

Robbins, W. E., Thompson, M. J., Yamamoto, R. T., and Shortino, T. J. (1965). Feeding stimulants for the female house fly, *Musca domestica* Linnaeus. *Science* **147**, 628–630.

Rockstein, M., and Lieberman, H. M. (1958). Survival curves for male and female house-flies (*Musca domestica* L.). *Nature* **181**, 787–788.

Sawicki, R. M., and Holbrook, D. V. (1961). The rearing, handling and biology of house flies (*Musca domestica* L.) for assay of insecticides by the application of measured drops. *Pyrethrum Post* **6** (2), 3–18.

Schoof, H. F. (1964). Laboratory culture of *Musca, Fannia* and *Stomoxys. Bull. World Health Organ.* **31**, 539–544.

Silverman, P. H., and Silverman, L. (1953). Growth measurements on *Musca vicina* (Macq.) reared with a known bacterial flora. *Riv. Parassitol.* **14**, 89–95.

Spiller, D. (1963a). Procedure for rearing houseflies. *Nature* **199**, 405.

Spiller, D. (1963b). Personal observations at Gainesville and Savannah.

Spiller, D. (1964a). Nutrition and diet of muscoid flies. *Bull. World Health Organ.* **31**, 551–554.

Spiller, D. (1964b). Discussion on muscoid flies. *Bull.World Health Organ.* **31**, 612–615.

Spiller, D. (1964c). Bacterial status of a housefly rearing medium. *New Zealand Entomologist* **3** (3), 33–38.

Vladimirova, M. A., and Smirnov, E. S. (1938). Concurrence vitale dans une population homogenè de *Musca domestica* L. de *Phormia groenlandica* et entre ces deux especes. *Med. Parazitol. i Parazitarn. Bolezni* **7**, 755–777 [In Russian, French summary: Translation by Jackson, J. D. (1952). For Bureau of Animal Population, Oxford Univ., England. Trans. 245 F1050A].

Zingrone, L. D., Bruce, W. N., and Decker, G. C. (1959). A mating study of the female house fly. *J. Econ. Entomol.* **52**, 236.

Chapter 15

Cockroaches

BURRELL J. SMITTLE

Entomology Research Division,
Agriculture Research Service,
U. S. Department of Agriculture,
Gainesville, Florida

I. INTRODUCTION

Cockroaches of today are direct descendants of huge, ancient cockroaches which infested the earth 250 million years ago. Modern cockroaches are smaller but have changed very little in structure. Cockroaches have adapted themselves so well to the changes in environment brought about by man that it appears that some could not survive without man. No doubt cockroaches have plagued man from his first appearance on earth and they continue to do so to this day. Not only do they compete with man for food, but they feed on his clothing and other possessions. Cockroaches also endanger the health of mankind. Several species of cockroaches have been shown to be capable of carrying and transmitting various microorganisms which are pathogenic to man. As the cockroach is as much at home in the sewer as the kitchen pantry, this is becoming more important.

There are over 3500 described species of cockroaches; fortunately for man, less than 1% of these are domiciliary pests. There is almost a complete void of information about all cockroaches except a few domestic species and, to a much lesser degree, a few other wood-inhabiting species. There is still much to be learned about the most common and pestiferous species. Many laboratories all over the world are continually studying these insects in an attempt to find new and better ways of controlling them. The importance of cockroach control is illustrated by the fact that cockroaches are the No. 1 problem for pest control operators, who were paid an estimated 350 million dollars for their services in the United States during 1964.

In addition to the use of cockroaches in evaluation of insecticides, they are widely used in nutritional, physiological, and resistance studies. In modern research in these fields of study there is a great need for large numbers of specimens of a uniform quality. Cockroaches have a long life cycle; therefore, to provide large numbers for experimental purposes it is necessary to plan ahead. It may take a year or more to obtain a supply and build up a colony of sufficient size for laboratory experiments. It is advantageous to maintain laboratory cultures under controlled conditions and on a known-age basis.

Most of the methods used to rear cockroaches are very similar. Basically, all that is needed to rear cockroaches is a rearing room, preferably with temperature and relative humidity control, and a rearing container in which is placed the required food, water, and harborages. The rearing methods used at the U. S. Department of Agriculture, Insects Affecting Man and Animals Research Laboratory, Gainesville, Florida, will be the basis for most of the procedures discussed.

II. GENERAL REQUIREMENTS

A. REARING ROOMS

Most biological research laboratories have a room or a series of rooms equipped to serve as rearing rooms for the species under study. These rooms often may be used for many different species. To prevent killing a susceptible insect colony, rearing rooms should not be used for insecticide testing or connected to a room used for storage or testing of volatile insecticides.

The temperature and relative humidity (RH) are important factors affecting the maintenance of a continuous supply of uniform specimens. The most frequently used temperatures for rearing cockroaches range between 70° and 85°F, while the relative humidities range between 50 and 80%. Gould and Deay (1940) reared cockroaches at temperatures ranging between 60° and 95°F with humidity often as low as 10%. However, they report that temperature and humidity greatly affect the developmental time. For example, they report a 1° rise in the average temperature will shorten the incubation period by 1 to 5 days, depending on the species.

To provide maximum utilization of space, shelves should be provided to store the rearing containers. Other desirable features are a sink for washing equipment, a work table, a source of carbon dioxide if this is used as an anesthetic, and a storage area.

The rooms used to rear cockroaches at this laboratory are approximately 10 feet square. One room is used only for *Periplaneta americana* (L.), a second room is used for the nonresistant *Blattella germanica* (L.) as well as other nonresistant colonies, and a third room is used for resistant *B. germanica* (L.) colonies. Each room has individual temperature and humidity controls; however, all rooms are maintained at 80°F ±1° and 50% ±1% RH. All rooms are provided with a sink and storage cabinets. Stainless steel shelving that can be adjusted to accommodate any size containers is provided in all rooms. Connections for carbon dioxide and a vacuum line are provided for use in anesthetizing and handling cockroaches.

B. Rearing Containers

Cockroaches have been reared in metal, glass, wood, or plastic containers ranging from an 80-ml test tube (Noland, 1956) to a large barrel (Piquett and Fales, 1952). The container used may vary depending on cost, availability, space, species to be reared, and the size of colony to be maintained. Glass battery jars are used by many laboratories; however, these are expensive. It is desirable to have a jar constricted at the top to provide a nonperpendicular surface inside that can be lightly greased with petrolatum or a mixture of petrolatum and mineral oil (1:1) to prevent the cockroaches from escaping. Less grease is required in a jar of this shape than in a jar with straight sides, and the neck of the jar can be left ungreased. A lip on the outside of the top of the jar aids in holding a cloth over the jar with a rubber band. One- and two-gallon jars with these features may be obtained from Anchor Hocking Glass Company at

FIG. 1. Cockroach rearing jars. On the right is an empty jar and on the left is a jar set up for rearing.

FIG. 2. Rearing container for American cockroaches.

about one quarter the cost of battery jars (see Fig. 1). Wide mouth jars used for canning and preserving purposes are also satisfactory.

For large colonies, 20- to 30-gallon trash cans (Fig. 2) or 15½-gallon rectangular tubs (Fig. 3) make good rearing containers. These may be either plastic or galvanized metal. A metal flange, 4 inches wide, that extends 4 inches from the edge toward the center of the container, can be taped to the top of each container. The under surface of this flange and the top two inches of the container should be greased to prevent the cockroaches from escaping. Wagner *et al.* (1964) used an electric barrier to confine cockroaches in large metal cans.

Other rearing containers such as aquaria, ½-pint milk bottles, plastic containers, and assorted sizes and shapes of screen and metal cages have been used by Cummings and Menn (1959), Dold (1964), Heal (1948), McCay (1938), Melampy and Maynard (1937), and Piquett and Fales (1952).

C. FOOD

The common domiciliary species can be reared satisfactorily on a variety of diets. Purina laboratory chow checkers are currently

FIG. 3. Rearing container for German cockroaches.

the most popular diet and is the diet recommended by the Chemical Specialty Manufacturers Association (Anonymous, 1964). Most types of compressed dog food are satisfactory and have been the most commonly used food for laboratory colonies in past years. Gould and Deay (1940) used raw potato, dog biscuit, Haydak's Mixture (Haydak, 1936) and Pablum, a prepared baby food. House (1949) used a synthetic diet for *B. germanica* (L.). Piquett and Fales (1952) report that commercially prepared foods for guinea pigs or rabbits are not suitable for cockroaches.

For some of the tropical or wood-inhabiting species the above-mentioned diets may have to be supplemented with other foodstuffs. Young nymphs of *Panchlora nivea* (L.) seem to need bananas to survive in the laboratory. McKittrick (1964) recommends wheat germ, yeast, lettuce, raw carrot slices, and bananas as supplements to compressed dog food to establish and maintain laboratory colonies.

Other diets have been used and examples may be found in Edmunds (1957), Fischer and Juric (1958), Gier (1947), McCay (1938), Qadri (1938), Siakotos and Dewey (1959), and Tuma (1938).

D. WATER

Many different types of devices have been used to supply water to laboratory cockroach colonies. Glass or plastic vials of various sizes make excellent watering devices for small colonies. The tubes are filled with water, plugged with moist cotton, and placed in a horizontal position in the colony jar. As the cockroaches drink, the plug recedes down the tube. For large colonies, gravity waterers (such as chicken waterers available in glass, metal, or plastic that incorporate jars ranging in size from ½ pint to ½-gallon) are more desirable. These waterers are available at most feed stores. The jars are filled with water, the waterer attached, and inverted. The trough is filled with cotton strips to prevent free-standing water, and the cotton strips are replaced as necessary. Waterers consisting of a pint jar or small bottle inverted on a synthetic sponge or cotton placed in a Petri dish also work satisfactorily. Many different types of watering devices have been used; a few examples may be found in Cummings and Menn (1959), Dold (1964), and Heal (1948). Water is very essential for cockroaches. Willis and Lewis (1957) report that water alone enabled most species to live significantly longer in 36–46% relative humidity than did dry food alone.

E. HARBORAGES AND LITTER

The placing of harborages in the rearing container greatly increases the number of cockroaches that can be reared in the container. Single-face, flexible corrugated cardboard, cut to the desired size, rolled loosely to leave harborage spaces between the coils, and taped or held with a rubber band placed around the roll, can be used for most species. Piquett and Fales (1952) used inverted pint-size cartons with V-shaped openings in the open end. Heal (1948) used masonite platforms with ¼-inch legs stacked one on top of the other. Coiled or bent pieces of hardware cloth can be used to provide additional resting surfaces.

For some species it is desirable to place a thin layer of litter in the bottom of each container to absorb excess moisture emitted by the cockroaches or from accidental leakage from the watering devices. The litter also helps keep the oöthecae from being eaten by other cockroaches in the colony. Sawdust, after it has been heated for 4 hours at 100°C, serves very well for this purpose. Wood shavings, shredded paper, or crushed sugar cane pulp are also satisfactory. Since some species, such as *Pycnoscelus surinamensis* (L.), burrow into the litter, enough litter should be placed in the rearing containers to enable all of the specimens to hide. McKittrick (1964) recommends peat moss as litter for many of the tropical species.

III. REARING PROCEDURE FOR *PERIPLANETA AMERICANA* (L.)

To start a colony of American cockroaches, specimens can be collected from infested areas or a supply of egg capsules obtained from another laboratory. At this laboratory, small colonies are maintained in 2-gallon containers. Food, water, corrugated cardboard harborages, and a 1-inch layer of sawdust are placed in the rearing container. The food is placed in a shallow box so as not to be mixed with the sawdust. The food and water are replenished at weekly intervals. At 2-week or 1-month intervals the cockroaches are transferred to a new rearing container. This can be done by shaking the cockroaches out of the rolls of corrugated cardboard into the new rearing set-up. The oöthecae may be removed from the sawdust and placed in a rearing container to hatch for starting additional colonies. A rearing container of this size, with adequate harborages, can be used to maintain approximately 100 adults.

For maintenance of large colonies or for mass production, American cockroaches are reared in 30-gallon plastic trash cans fitted with a greased ring (described in Section II,B and shown in Fig. 2). In the bottom of each can 1–2 inches of sawdust serves as litter. The water is supplied by gravity-flow waterers equipped with a 1-quart jar. A supply of food is contained in ½-pint cartons. Approximately

6 rolls of corrugated cardboard 5 inches in circumference and 15 inches long serve as harborages. Unhatched oöthecae are collected from the litter in containers with adults and placed in a new container. This can be a large can, as described above, or, if space is a problem, 1- or 2-gallon jars can be used for the first two months after hatching. The oöthecae are removed after approximately 2 weeks, depending on the number of nymphs that have hatched. At 80°F the incubation period is about 5 weeks; therefore, the unhatched oöthecae can be removed at weekly or biweekly intervals and stored until it is about time for hatch to occur before placing them in the rearing containers. Each week food and water are replenished if necessary. When the cotton strips in the trough of the waterer or the cardboard harborages get dirty they are replaced. Under these rearing conditions, the nymphal stage takes 4 to 6 months. About 1000 adults are considered maximum for rearing containers of this size.

Rearing containers may be set up in groups of 4 or 5 to provide a large number of any one stage at a given time. For a continuous supply of cockroaches, rearing containers may be set up on a monthly or bimonthly schedule.

IV. REARING PROCEDURE FOR *BLATTELLA GERMANICA* (L.)

The best way to start a colony of German cockroaches is to obtain a supply of gravid females from another laboratory. This is especially true if nonresistant strains or strains having a known level of resistance are desired. If the susceptibility level is not important, cockroaches may be collected from infested areas and taken to the laboratory for colonization.

Small colonies are reared in 1- or 2-gallon glass jars by the same procedure used for *P. americana* (L.). With adequate harborages, a 1-gallon container can be used for up to 400 adults. When it is desirable to keep the generations separate, as with resistant colonies being selected and tested each generation, the following method is used. A brood chamber (Fig. 4) is constructed of a cylinder of galvanized metal that will fit snugly into the top of the rearing container. A circle of 12- by 16-mesh screen wire is soldered inside the end fitting into the rearing container, a ¼-inch flange is soldered around the outside, 1½ inches from the bottom, to support the cylinder and provide a tight fit with the top of the rearing container. At the top of the cylinder a flange 1½ inches wide, with an outside diameter the same as the cylinder, is held in place with masking tape. The under side of this flange and the top 1½ inches of the cylinder are greased. A piece of cheesecloth or white organdy rather than a dark cloth is placed over the top so that light will enter the chamber. A small vial of water and few cubes of dog food are placed on the screen bottom of the cylinder. No harborages are provided. This chamber is placed on a rearing jar that has been darkened with a

FIG. 4. Brood chamber for small colonies. Unassembled on the right and assembled (except for cloth covers) on the left.

black cloth or black paint and contains food, water, and harborages. When the young hatch they crawl through the screen wire and fall into the rearing container. The brood chamber is removed when enough nymphs for the next generation have hatched.

For rearing large colonies or mass production, German cockroaches are reared in 15½-gallon galvanized metal tubs (Fig. 3) similar to those used by Dahm (1955). A sheet of heavy kraft paper is used in lieu of the sawdust to cover the bottom of the tub. This facilitates the frequent collection of specimens for daily laboratory experiments. Food, water, and harborages are supplied in each tub as in the rearing containers for large colonies of American cockroaches.

To obtain a continuous and adequate supply of nymphs, two brood chambers (Fig. 5) are stocked with gravid females. The cham-

FIG. 5. Brood chamber for large colonies. Unassembled on the right and assembled (except for cloth covers) on the left.

bers are constructed similar to the ones described above except that below the screen the chamber is cone-shaped and tapers to the bottom, where a large-mouth mason screw cap is soldered in place. The inside of the cone should be as smooth as possible to prevent the small nymphs from staying in the cone. A ½-gallon jar is screwed onto the cap at the bottom of the cone and covered with a black cloth. This jar contains food, water, and harborages. It is greased at the top to prevent the cockroaches that fall into the jar from climbing back into the cone. Food and water are placed in the upper chamber. To provide resting surfaces for the adults, 3 × 5-inch cards folded in the shape of a Z are placed in the chamber.

Each week the dead cockroaches and hatched egg capsules are removed from the chamber. This normally activates the newly hatched nymphs, which may have remained with the adults, to crawl through the screen and go into the jar below. The brood chamber is placed over the rearing tub and the jar removed. The nymphs that remain in the cone can be shaken into the rearing tub by tapping on the side of the chamber. Gravid females are added to the chamber to replace those that have died and to ensure a constant supply of nymphs.

Under these conditions the nymphs normally become adults in 5 to 7 weeks after hatching. The rearing tubs will support 2000 to 3000 German cockroaches. This procedure may be expanded to provide more specimens if desired.

V. PROCEDURES USED FOR OTHER SPECIES

The procedures outlined above for American and German cockroaches have been used successfully for other species. The diet may need to be supplemented for some species, as previously mentioned. For wood-inhabiting species, Edmunds (1953) says it is necessary to place some strips of the infested wood in rearing containers.

When attempting to colonize a new species, one should endeavor to maintain the approximate temperature and humidity conditions found in the natural habitat and also to provide the cockroaches with a supply of their natural diet.

Since some of the wood-inhabiting species are much better fliers than the German and American cockroaches, more care must be taken to prevent their escape.

VI. PARASITES

There are several parasites which occasionally become a problem in the laboratory colonies. Piquett and Fales (1952) report that a red mite, *Pimeliaphilus podapolipophagus* Tragardh, a true parasite, can wipe out a cageful of American cockroaches and that a white mite, *Caloglyphus* sp., which feeds on organic matter, can reduce the vigor of a colony. For control of these mites, they recommended fumigating all food with methyl bromide (3 lb/1000 ft³) for 2 hours, transferring the cockroaches to a clean cage, and dust the shelves with flowers of sulfur. Fisk (1951) used ovex to control mites in a *P. americana* colony.

There are several hymenopterous species that parasitize cockroach egg capsules. Piquett and Fales (1952) report *Evania appendigaster* L. as a parasite from an American cockroach colony. Edmunds (1955) reared *Tetrastichus hagenowii* (Ratzenburg) on egg capsules of *P. americana*. Edmunds (1952, 1953) lists other parasites collected from wood cockroaches. Damage from most of the species that parasitize egg capsules can be prevented by covering the rearing containers with tightly woven cloth. These parasites will normally be a problem only when capsules are collected in nature and returned to the laboratory. Therefore, close observations of these capsules should be made to prevent the adults from escaping and infesting other capsules.

To prevent the introduction of mites, all harborages, food, and litter used in the colonies maintained at this laboratory are placed in a dry-heat oven at 150°C for 1, 4, and 4 hours, respectively. In addition, each week the shelves are wiped off with mineral oil and then with 70% alcohol; the cloth tops are rinsed in acetone, dried, and placed back on the rearing containers. The frequent changing of rearing containers also helps prevent a build-up of mites. In the past, when mites became a problem, the cockroaches were transferred to a clean colony jar containing a thin layer of precipitated sulfur. After the cockroaches have crawled through the sulfur and are partly covered with it, litter, food, water, and harborages are placed in the rearing container.

Booklice are occasionally observed in cockroach colonies but are not a problem when the above procedures are followed.

Serratia marcescens Bizio, a bacterium that frequently produces a red color in cockroaches after they die, is reported by Heimpel and West (1959) not to be normally pathogenic *per os* to *Blattella germanica* (L.).

All equipment used in cockroach colonization is washed in hot soapy water, rinsed in clear water, and dried. Glass and metal are rinsed in acetone, and plastic is rinsed in 70% alcohol. Glass and metal are heated in a dry-heat oven at 150°C for 24 hours.

VII. METHODS USED TO HANDLE COCKROACHES

Most laboratories use anesthetics, such as chloroform or carbon dioxide, or short exposure to low temperature to facilitate the handling of cockroaches. Piquett and Fales (1952) preferred to capture cockroaches by placing a small vial over them and not use anything to reduce their movement. At this laboratory carbon dioxide is used to anesthetize cockroaches when necessary. For routine maintenance and transferring procedures it is not necessary to anesthetize the cockroaches. However, when large numbers are used for testing anesthetization with carbon dioxide is used as it permits faster collection of test specimens.

In the collection procedure the cockroaches are shaken from the rolls of corrugated cardboard into round plastic refrigerator dishes that have been dusted with pyrophyllite. The dust keeps the cockroaches from escaping. Petrolatum also may be used to keep the cockroaches in the cups. The dish is then inverted in a "knock-down" chamber and the cockroaches are exposed to carbon dioxide. Knock-down chambers can be made from a cardboard carton containing cotton balls and covered with organdy or a modified large, plastic Büchner funnel connected to a carbon dioxide source. While the cockroaches are anesthetized they are transferred to other dusted plastic dishes to recover. The length of exposure to carbon dioxide is kept as short as possible.

After the cockroaches begin to move around, a period of at least 10 minutes is allowed before any tests are begun. The cockroaches may be transferred from the dusted dishes to other test chambers without being anesthetized again. These plastic dishes also are used to contain cockroaches during exposure to treated surfaces.

Great care must be taken during handling procedures to prevent the cockroaches from escaping. Some laboratories do all handling of cockroaches on a surface surrounded by an oil moat so that any escaping insects are trapped in the oil. This or any method that prevents the escape of cockroaches should be used in all cockroach colonization procedures.

REFERENCES

Anonymous (1964). Cockroach spray method. *Soap Chem. Specialties Blue Book* pp. 231–232.

Cummings, E. C., and Menn, J. J. (1959). An American cockroach rearing cage. *J. Econ. Entomol.* **52**, 1227–1228.

Dahm, P. A. (1955). A convenient method for rearing large cockroaches. *J. Econ. Entomol.* **48**, 480–482.

Dold, J. (1964). How to trap and rear roaches for display and resistance testing. *Pest Control* **32**, 18–20.

Edmunds, L. R. (1952). *Parcoblatta pennsylvania, P. virginica. Entomol. News* **63**, 141–144.

Edmunds, L. R. (1953). Collecting and culturing native wood roaches in Ohio, with some additional notes on their parasites. *Entomol. News* **64**, 225–230.

Edmunds, L. R. (1955). Biological notes on *Tetrastichus hagenowii* (Ratzeburg). A Chalcidoid parasite of cockroach eggs. (Hymenoptera: Eulophidae; Orthoptera: Blattidae.) *Ann. Entomol. Soc. Am.* **48**, 210–213.

Edmunds, L. R. (1957). Observations of the biology and life history of the brown cockroach *Periplaneta brunnea* Burmeister. *Proc. Entomol. Soc. Wash.* **59**, 283–286.

Fischer, R. W., and Juric, F. (1958). Rearing houseflies and roaches for physiological research. *Can. Entomologist* **90**, 1–7.

Fisk, F. W. (1951). Use of a specific mite control in roach and mouse culture. *J. Econ. Entomol.* **44**, 1016.

Gier, H. T. (1947). Growth rate in the cockroach *Periplaneta americana* (Linn.). *Ann. Entomol. Soc. Am.* **40**, 303–317.

Gould, G. E., and Deay, H. O. (1940). The biology of six species of cockroaches which infest buildings. *Indiana Agr. Expt. Sta. Bull.* **451,** 1–31.

Haydak, M. H. (1936). A food for rearing laboratory animals. *J. Econ. Entomol.* **29,** 1026.

Heal, R. E. (1948). Rearing methods for German and American cockroaches. *J. Econ. Entomol.* **41,** 329–330.

Heimpel, A. M., and West, A. S. (1959). Notes on the pathogenicity of *Serratia marcescens* Bizio for the cockroach, *Blattella germanica* (L.). *Can. J. Zool.* **37,** 169–172.

House, H. L. (1949). Nutritional studies with *Blattella germanica* (L.) reared under aseptic conditions. II. A chemically defined diet. *Can. Entomologist* **81,** 105–112.

McCay, C. M. (1938). The nutritional requirements of *Blattella germanica. Physiol. Zool.* **11,** 89–103.

McKittrick, F. A. (1964). Personal communication.

Melampy, R. M., and Maynard, L. A. (1937). Nutritional studies with the cockroach *Blattella germanica. Physiol. Zool.* **10,** 36–44.

Noland, J. L. (1956). An improved method for rearing cockroaches. *J. Econ. Entomol.* **49,** 411–412.

Piquett, P. G., and Fales, J. H. (1952). Rearing cockroaches for experimental purposes. *U. S. Dept. Agr. Bur. Entomol. Plant Quarantine,* **ET301,** 1–12.

Qadri, M. A. H. (1938). The life history and growth of *Blatta orientalis* Linn. *Bull. Entomol. Res.* **29,** 263–276.

Siakotos, A. N., and Dewey, J. E. (1959). The effects of a diet containing gibberellic acid on the growth and food consumption of *Periplaneta americana. J. Econ. Entomol.* **56,** 1214–1215.

Tuma, V. (1938). Roaches-resistance to insecticides. *Soap* **14,** 109.

Wagner, R. E., Ebeling, W., and Clark, W. R. (1964). An electric barrier for confining cockroaches in large rearing or field collecting cans. *J. Econ. Entomol.* **57,** 1007–1009.

Willis, E. R., and Lewis, N. (1957). The longevity of starved cockroaches. *J. Econ. Entomol.* **50,** 438–440.

Chapter 16

Coleoptera Infesting Stored Products

Phillip K. Harein* and Edwin L. Soderstrom

Stored-Product Insects Research and Development Laboratory,
U. S. Department of Agriculture,
Savannah, Georgia

I. INTRODUCTION

Many species of weevils and beetles that infest stored products are popular laboratory test animals for basic research in ecology, behavior, reproduction, and genetics and for applied research on developing new or improved methods of insect control.

The rice weevil, *Sitophilus oryzae* (L.), and the granary weevil, *Sitophilus granarius* (L.), are major pests of stored grain. The immature weevils of both species develop within grain kernels and, subsequently, are not adapted to ordinary ecological and toxicological studies. However, new and improved methods of monitoring and studying these early stages have been developed. Confused flour beetles, *Tribolium confusum* Jacquelin du Val, and red flour beetles, *Tribolium castaneum* (Hbst.), are serious pests of milled products. Although they are frequently present in grain shipments, they confine their attack to grain dust and the surfaces of broken grains. One of the

* *Present address:* Department of Entomology, Fisheries, and Wildlife, University of Minnesota, St. Paul, Minnesota.

largest grain-infesting beetles is the cadelle, *Tenebroides mauritanicus* (L.). This insect is widespread over the world and infests grain and grain products. Damage results from chewing out the germ end of kernels, boring into wooden storage structures, and cutting holes in packages and bags to allow entrance for other insect species. Until recently, studies on the cadelle were limited because of the difficulty of rearing large numbers in the laboratory.

Considering new and improved rearing methods, most of the stored-product Coleoptera are easy to obtain and rear for testing. In general, they do not require sophisticated diets although each species may have specific requirements for certain carbohydrates, proteins, fats, vitamins, and other nutritional factors. All have short life cycles and relatively long life spans. Both the adults and immature forms can generally be isolated for study under controlled environmental conditions. Precautions must be taken to separate closely related insects to maintain species-specific cultures, and to isolate and protect the cultures from parasites, predators, and diseases. Some of the developmental stages, such as eggs or young larvae, may be damaged easily if not handled carefully. The temperature and humidity in the rearing area should be controlled as a basic step in the attempt to maintain uniform insect cultures. The amount or duration of light in the rearing room is usually of less importance than temperature and humidity.

No attempt will be made to cite or deal with every paper written that pertains completely or in part to rearing Coleoptera. Instead, emphasis will be given to current information that is likely to be used by future workers, especially in confined experimental research.

The Coleoptera that damage stored products can be divided into two general groups. One group (internal feeders) spends the majority of its life feeding within a kernel of grain; the second group (external feeders) spends the majority of its life feeding on the surface of grain kernels or in the milled products of grain.

II. INTERNAL FEEDERS

This group of insects include the granary weevil; rice weevil; corn weevil, *Sitophilus zeamais* (Mots.); lesser grain borer, *Rhyzopertha dominica* (F.); bean weevil, *Acanthoscelides obtectus* (Say); pea weevil, *Bruchus pisorum* (L.); broad-nosed grain weevil, *Caulophilus latinasus;* and Angoumois grain moth, *Sitotroga cerealella* (Olivier).

The rice weevil, corn weevil, and the granary weevil are normally reared under similar conditions. However, the granary weevil prefers slightly lower temperatures. All discussions will refer to the rice and granary weevil unless otherwise specified.

A. Culture Medium

1. Source

Care should be taken to obtain grain that is free of insecticide residues, insects, and mites. Insecticide residues may result from soil applications before or during the growing season, plant applications before harvest, and grain applications after harvest. Many researchers prefer to obtain their supply of grain directly from the farmer in order to avoid the biological or chemical contamination that may occur after the grain is in storage. Rice and granary weevils are generally reared in wheat, corn (maize), rice, and sorghum; however, wheat is the most universal culture medium for these species.

2. Preparation and Storage

Since dockage affects the infestation of grain (McGregor, 1964), grain should be cleaned of dirt, chaff, and other foreign matter before use as culture media for rice and granary weevils. Grain is generally cleaned by screening and/or by aspiration. Grain may also be sized by screening during or after the cleaning process. Morrison (1964) and Surtees (1965) reported that the food-particle size affected weevil development, and concluded that the larger the particle, the heavier the insect.

Although precautions may have been taken to avoid or prevent insect and mite infestations of grain, new grain should be sterilized. Sterilization may be accomplished by (1) heating the grain to 60°C for 10 minutes (Cotton, 1964); (2) heating the grain in an autoclave to 60°C at a pressure of 12 to 16 lb/square inch for 90 minutes (Stored-Product Insects Research and Development Laboratory, Savannah, Georgia[*]); or (3) by cooling the grain below −17.8°C. for 1 week (Entomology Department, Kansas State University, Manhattan, Kansas[†]). Cooling is the preferred method unless diseases are a problem, in which case the autoclave method must be used. Heating of grain is more critical than cooling because of the small temperature differential between killing of insects and killing of the seed. The germination of grain is not affected by freezing (Branton et al., 1961).

[*] Hereafter referred to as the Savannah Laboratory.
[†] Hereafter referred to as the Kansas State Laboratory.

3. *Moisture Adjustment*

Grain may be tempered to the desired moisture level by many methods including (1) drying in a forced-air oven or similar apparatus, (2) adding water, (3) mixing (blending) grain of different moistures in the proper proportions or placing small sacks of grain into a large mass of grain of the desired moisture and allowing it to reach equilibrium.

Moisture content may be determined by the air oven method as presented in the Official Methods of Analysis of the Association of Official Agricultural Chemists (1960). Various electronic moisture testers are also useful for this purpose (Zeleny, 1960), but they may not be as accurate as the air oven method. The Motomco Moisture Meter is currently used by the Savannah Laboratory. Electronic moisture detectors should be checked frequently to determine their accuracy. The calculations used by entomologists at the Kansas State Laboratory to determine the amount of water to add to grain for tempering are as follows:

$$\frac{100 - \% \text{ of present moisture}}{100 - \% \text{ of desired moisture}} - 1 = F$$

$F \times$ gm of grain = ml of water needed to bring the grain to the desired moisture. Tempered grain should be stored in air-tight containers and maintained at 40°C.

B. STOCK CULTURES

1. *Collection of Weevils*

Rice and granary weevils are cosmopolitan in distribution; thus they may be collected from stored grains throughout the world. Adult weevils may be collected by sifting grains through a No. 6 or 8 sieve.[*] Samples of infested grain should be collected if the immature stages of the weevils are desired.

Whether insects are obtained from the field or from established cultures from another institution, they must be isolated until it is determined that they are free of parasites, predators, and/or diseases. Isolation should be in an area that is separated from the stock culture room. Jars containing infested cultures may be placed in containers of mineral oil to prevent crawling insects and mites from escaping and infesting the surrounding area. Mites may be controlled by placing dicofol on the grain, as described by Strong *et al.* (1959).

[*] This and all future references to sieves will be based on the U. S. Standard Sieve Series.

2. Identifying Characteristics

Rice weevil adults may be identified by four light spots on the elytra and by round pits on the prothorax. The granary weevil has unicolorous elytra and oval pits on the prothorax. Larvae may be identified by the number of folds per body segment, the rice weevil having one fold and the granary weevil two. Pupae may be identified by the pits on the prothorax as given for adult identification.

3. Sexing

Rice and granary weevils may be sexed using the characteristics described by Reddy (1951). Females have small pits on the proboscis while the males have large pits. Consequently, the female's snout appears shiny compared to the male's snout.

4. Life Cycle

The adult chews a hole into a kernel of grain, deposits an egg inside the hole, and seals it with a gelatinous material. The egg hatches, and the larva feeds within the kernel until it is ready to pupate. Pupation takes place in a cavity formed by the last larval instar. The adult may remain in the kernel for several days before chewing its way out. Mating of rice weevils may occur within 42 hours after they emerge from the kernel (Singh and Soderstrom, 1963).

Soderstrom (1960) showed that rice weevil larvae emerged from the egg in 6 to 9 days from the date of oviposition; the larval stage lasted 6 to 25 days; the prepupal stage, 1 day; the pupal stage, 20 to 25 days; pre-emerged adults, 2 to 3 days; the adults lived 4 to 5 months. Development from egg to adult required 28 to 31 days. These cultures were reared in wheat stored in a room maintained at 26.6°C and 70% relative humidity. The granary weevil's rate of development is slower than that of the rice weevil. Granary weevil larvae emerged from the egg in 6 to 9 days; the larval stage lasted 6 to 33 days; the prepupal stage, 1 day; the pupal stage, 25 to over 33 days; the adults lived 5 to 8 months.

5. Monitoring Development

Special methods have been devised to locate and observe internal infestations in grain. Flotation of grain in a solution of sodium silicate and water with a specific gravity of 1.160 or in a mixture of methyl chloroform and deodorized kerosene with a specific gravity of 1.30 were used by White (1956) to locate infested kernels. Egg plugs in kernels may be detected by staining with acid fuchsin (Frankenfeld, 1948); gentian violet (Goossens, 1949); berberine sulfate (Milner *et al.*, 1950), or iodine (Walkden, 1957). Acid fuchsin is preferred by the authors since solutions of the stain may be stored for long periods without deterioration and the stained egg plugs are easier to locate. If infested grain is to be used in experiments, flotation and staining may be undesirable.

Close observation of magnified kernels will disclose the presence of egg plugs without staining; however, they are difficult to locate. An X-ray microscope has been developed for observing weevil eggs, larvae, prepupae, pupae, and pre-emerged adults (Pedersen and Brown, 1960). Kirkpatrick (1962a) used a General Electric Grain Inspection Unit to study the biology of the granary weevil. Similar studies were conducted with the rice weevil (Pedersen, 1960). Eggs and first-instar larvae are difficult to see, but larval instars 2, 3, and 4, prepupae, pupae, and pre-emerged adults may be observed readily. Soderstrom (1960) removed rice and granary weevil larvae from wheat kernels and determined instars by head capsule measurement, using Dyars' law as given by Imms (1957). Egg plugs and larval development have been observed in corn by holding kernels in an intense beam of light. In corn many larvae tunnel in the endosperm just beneath the seed coat and are readily visible. Change of larval instars may be determined by a change in the tunnel size and by the presence of the dark-colored mandibles in the frass packed in the larval tunnel. Once information has been obtained on stages, the age of cultures from the first date adults were placed for oviposition may be used to obtain a high percentage of a given stage.

6. *Dissection and Handling*

Eggs may be obtained by dissection from a kernel of grain, or by allowing weevils to oviposit in lumps of starch. The eggs may then be washed out of the starch with lukewarm water (Dal Monte, 1964). Weevil larvae are usually used for tests while they are within a kernel of grain. However, if larvae are desired out of the kernel they may be located by X-ray or staining and then removed by dissection. Larvae will live and pupate in flour (Kirkpatrick, 1965), but many do not completely escape their pupal case and die.

Prepupae and pupae may also be removed from the kernels by dissection. The most satisfactory method of dissection is by cutting a notch in the kernel and cracking the kernel open with a twist of the knife. After adults have emerged from the kernel they may be obtained by sifting grain with a No. 6 sieve.

7. Rearing

Rice and granary weevils are generally reared in glass jars closed with a paper or cloth cover to allow air interchange and to prevent other insects from entering the culture.

At the Savannah Laboratory, 1-quart wide-mouth glass jars are half-filled with wheat; 150 adults are introduced into each jar and allowed to oviposit for 1 week, at which time the adults are removed by screening. The cultures are stored in a room maintained at about 26°C and 70% relative humidity. If not used within 3 weeks from the date of adult weevil emergence, the cultures should be isolated to reduce the possibility of mite infestations.

III. EXTERNAL FEEDERS

A. Confused Flour Beetle and Red Flour Beetle

These two species are representative of stored-product Coleoptera that feed on the outside of cracked or broken kernels of grain, or in grain dust or the products of milled grain. Based on these general feeding characteristics, these insects may be reared in almost any kind of cracked grain, meal, or flour. These materials are easily obtained from commercial sources or by grinding the whole-kernel grain obtained for the weevil cultures.

1. Preparing Culture Medium

The material selected for the culture medium should be ground evenly or it should be sifted through appropriate screens to provide a standard particle size of all components. This is necessary to obtain a uniform and reproducible total environment for the insects and to facilitate removal of the insects from the medium. The influence of food particle size on the rate of larval and pupal development of confused flour beetles was investigated by Hampton (1949) and the effect of flour particle size on pupal body weight of red flour beetles was studied by Bartlett (1962). Bartlett found that the pupae reared in flour sifted through a No. 2 silk bolting cloth had a mean body weight of 2.323 mg ± 0.015 mg; in flour sifted through a No. 8 cloth, body weight was 2.229 mg ± 0.014 mg.

The culture medium currently used for rearing the confused flour beetle and the red flour beetle at the Savannah Laboratory consists of white flour and corn meal (47.5% each) and brewer's yeast (5.0%). Before mixing these components, the flour is sifted through a No. 14 sieve and then the flour and corn meal are autoclaved 90 minutes at 12 to 16 lb pressure and 116°C to kill infesting insects or mites. After the materials have cooled to room temperature, they are mixed in the proportions by weight as stated above and stored at 4.4°C in sealed 5-gallon jars until needed. Both species of *Tribolium* are also reared successfully at the Kansas State Laboratory, using medium consisting of 95% wheat shorts and 5% dry yeast (w/w). This medium is sifted through a No. 20 sieve and then stored at 32°C in sealed metal cans for 7 days to eliminate any infestation.

The moisture content of these prepared mixtures should be between 11.5 and 14.5%; the optimum being about 12.5%. The moisture content can be adjusted by tempering with water or drying in an oven. There are several air oven and electrical methods available for determining the moisture content of grain and milled products. If facilities are available, the moisture content of culture medium may be maintained at the desired level by storing it in a room with controlled relative humidity in equilibrium with the percentage moisture desired.

Although confused flour beetles and red flour beetles have been successfully reared on a wide variety of culture media, these insects apparently have specific food preferences and nutritional requirements. Loschiavo (1952) reported that foods containing the highest percentage of wheat germ attracted the greatest number of confused flour beetles. He also noted that fine bran attracted significantly more insects than coarse bran, and that rancid bran was less attractive than fresh bran. Although bran was relatively unattractive to adults, it was a suitable medium for the normal development of larvae. There was evidence that, given sufficient time, the insects gradually became conditioned to an otherwise unattractive food. Wheat middlings and flour containing 5% ground wheat germ were the most attractive foods; bran, sawdust, and sawdust containing 5% wheat germ oil were significantly less attractive. In 1954, Magis reported that red flour beetles' order of preference to three types of cereal flour was wheat > barley > corn. He believes that these food preferences were attributed primarily to a particular chemical response rather than to humidity or thigmotaxis. Studies conducted by Loschiavo (1959) confirmed that confused flour beetles and red flour beetles are attracted short distances toward preferred foods, probably in response to olfactory stimuli. Additional information on specific nutritional requirements for confused flour beetles include a study on (1) the effect of vitamin-B complex on metamorphosis, growth, and vitality (Schneider, 1943), (2) growth factors in brewer's yeast (Charbonmeau and Lemonde, 1960), (3) amino acid requirements (Fraenkel and Printy, 1954), and (4) responses to various protein sources (Chirigos *et al.*, 1960; Naylor, 1964).

2. *Obtaining Pure Stock Cultures*

Most species of Coleoptera that infest stored products can easily be obtained from several sources. Many laboratories or organizations that use insects for research or training purposes usually maintain their own cultures. An ample supply of insects can be obtained from such sources upon request. Various standardized, wild, and mutant strains of stored-product insects are listed with their sources in each issue of the Tribolium Information Bulletin published by the Department of Genetics, University of California, Berkeley, California.

Many species can easily be collected by sifting infested materials from various grain, seed handling, or storage sites. Any point where grain accumulates is a potential source of stored-product insects. Augers, spouts, elevator boots, and elevator legs are examples of these areas. Grain dust that has accumulated on ledges is especially attractive to the larval stages of these insects.

Various traps have been devised to collect *Tribolium* spp. Graham (1962) described a trap consisting of a glass vial enclosed in an envelope of wire gauze 70–80 mesh per inch. The top edge of the gauze is folded tightly over the lip and into the mouth of the vial. The vials are placed upright in small samples of infested grain. The trap works on the principle that the insects congregate at the highest accessible point and attempt to fly. The highest point would be at the top of the vial into which they eventually fall. Another type of trap, called the "triboliotrap," was designed and tested by Stanley (1962) for collecting insects from flour. This is a plastic vial about 2 inches in height by ¾ inch in diameter. A narrow rim of Plexiglass is cemented around the open end and the slope is roughened. The trap is pushed into the flour until the rim is touching the flour surface. Insects that fall into the vial cannot escape.

3. *Purifying Cultures*

Obtaining official identification of representative insects from a newly acquired wild population is recommended considering the time lost if there is a chance of cross-contamination with closely related species. Cultures of saw-toothed grain beetle, *Oryzaephilus surinamensis* (L.), may be contaminated with the merchant grain beetle, *Oryzaephilus mercator* (Fauvell), and it is difficult to keep cultures of the red flour beetle and the confused flour beetle from cross-contamination especially if both species are reared in the same laboratory.

Confused flour beetles and red flour beetles are frequently used in the same laboratory in toxicological, ecological, and population studies. Because of their common use, identification of the species in each stage is required. Characteristics have been reported for separating these species in the adult stage (Good, 1936; Hinton, 1948), in the pupal stage (Ho, 1960; Mertz, 1961), and in the larval stage (Ho, 1964).

Preventing the entrance of disease or parasites into insect cultures is worthy of careful consideration. *Adelina tribolii* is a coccidian parasite that frequently invades cultures of flour beetles. Heavily infested larvae or adults are relatively inactive and do not respond to stimuli such as light or vibrations as readily as do healthy insects. Various protozoa including *Mattesia dispora, Farinocystis tribolii*, and *Triboliocystis garnhami* are parasitic to *Tribolium* spp. (Laird, 1959). As these parasites are not localized in the gut, evacuation of the gut at pupation is no help in controlling them in laboratory stocks. Strict laboratory sanitation and the frequent transfer of colonies to fresh media are generally effective methods of control. Insects from a highly infested culture may be saved by collecting the insect eggs and subjecting them to the washing technique described by Park (1948). Sokoloff (1962) described a dilution technique for ridding *Tribolium* spp. cultures of *Triboliocystis garnhami*. He transferred adult insects every 2 days into fresh medium to dilute any spores clinging to the adults. After about five transfers, the adults and eggs were sifted out of the flour. The adults were discarded and the eggs were introduced into fresh flour. Stanley (1961, 1964) published data on a procedure to control *Tribolium garnhami* in *Tribolium* spp. cultures. The parasites were removed by following stringent aseptic precautions in the laboratory, involving heat-sterilization of culture media and glassware, and by starting cultures with disinfected eggs. It should be understood, however, that the eradication of all micro flora associated with stored-product Coleoptera will not and perhaps should not occur. Van Wyk *et al.* (1959) report that both bacteria and fungi may be isolated from larval and adult confused flour beetles; they found that the bacteria were more numerous in the insects than in the food from which they were taken. The beetles preferred flour containing fungi and bacteria and the larvae would not develop normally in a vitamin-free diet unless bacteria were added to the medium.

The cereal psocid, *Troctes divinatorius* (Muller), may be found in large numbers in *Tribolium* spp. cultures. They compete against the beetles for food and they may be vectors of disease. Flour, grain, or cheese mites in the family Tyroglyphidae sometimes become abundant in culture media and in rearing rooms. To prevent their infestations or to suppress their migration to other cultures, 10% ovex powder should be sprinkled over the surfaces of the culture jar lids when paper lids are used. Keeping the culture jars on dicofol-treated paper towels will also help minimize mite infestations. If mite infestations become established, it may be necessary to sacrifice the cultures, disinfect the rearing area, and start over with mite-free medium and insects. A basic requirement to keep the insect cultures and the rearing area free of disease, parasites, and predators is to transfer a standard number of insects to fresh medium periodically and discard the old cultures. Fresh cultures of confused flour beetles should be started every 7 days using 7- to 9-week-old adults selected from several culture jars to minimize inbreeding. About 100 adults should be placed in 1-quart glass jars half-filled with medium. Each jar can be closed with a No. 1 filter paper to keep the insects from escaping and still allow adequate ventilation. The parent adults should be removed after a 7-day ovipositioning period by sifting the medium through a No. 20 sieve. The medium and insect eggs should then be transferred into the desired rearing container and stored in a room maintained at about 26°C and 60% relative humidity. Red flour beetles may be reared the same as the confused flour beetles.

4. *Determining Age, Stage, and Sex*

The first requirement in obtaining stored-product insects at a given age or stage is to determine accurately the life cycle of the insect under the rearing conditions provided.

Although many references on the life cycle of *Tribolium* spp. can be found in the literature, only a few references will be cited in this chapter. One of the earliest and most complete references on the biology of confused flour beetle was published by Park (1934). His paper includes information on taxonomic and historical considerations, food relationships and nutritional requirements, life cycle and productivity, behavior reactions, parasites, and techniques of culturing and studying populations.

Determining the life cycle of stored-product insects under specific environmental conditions can be a tedious and time-consuming job. The development of an apparatus for the automatic determination of the incubation period of insect eggs (Stanley, 1939) has been valuable in providing the necessary information on life cycles with a minimum of attention. Using this same equipment, Stanley (1946) determined the mean times required for the development of eggs, larvae, and pupae of confused flour beetles at 17°, 22°, 27°, 28°, 29°, 31°, 32°, 33°, and 35°C, with percentages of survival at these temperatures. In 1951, Stanley published information on the "autotrephon," an apparatus for rearing stored-product insects under controlled conditions with automatic time-controlled withdrawal of insect culture samples. The samples were stored at reduced temperatures where little, if any, growth would occur. Thus the samples could be examined at the convenience of the researcher. Using the autotrephon, Stanley (1953) collected and reported data on the life cycle of the confused flour beetle reared at 30°C and 75% relative humidity in whole wheat flour plus 3% ground wheat germ.

The effects of temperature and humidity on the life cycle of confused flour beetles and red flour beetles were reported by Howe (1956, 1960). The observations on the red flour beetle revealed the following:

1. The shortest time required for eggs to hatch was 2.6 days at 37.8°C. Humidity had no effect on the length of the incubation period.

2. The rate of larval development on wheat feed was shortest (12 days) at 35°C and 90% relative humidity and was longest (109 days) at 20°C and 70% relative humidity. The rate of larval development was affected by both temperature and humidity. At any temperature, the highest humidity tested produced the shortest larval period.

3. The shortest pupal period (3.9 days) was obtained at 37.8°C. Humidity did not affect the length of the pupal period.

Howe's work on the confused flour beetle indicated that the temperatures required for the maximum and minimum egg hatching time was about 1.4°C below that required for the red flour beetle eggs. The same difference applied to the optimum temperature for larval development. The shortest egg, larval, and pupal periods for the confused flour beetle were 3.9, 15.5, and 4.9 days, respectively. They occurred at 70% relative humidity. Confused flour beetle adults averaged 0.1 to 0.4 mg heavier than red flour beetle adults of the same sex when reared under similar conditions.

Ho (1961) determined the age of confused flour beetles and red flour beetles by observing characteristics of their optic organs. Two pairs of stemmata are present in all larval instars and in the early pupa. As the compound eyes begin to develop in the pupa, the stemmata degenerate. The larval instars are determined by the distance between the two pairs of stemmata as this distance increases with each successive molt until the latter part of the last larval instar. During this time the distance decreases as the stemmata migrate to a position near the vertex. The degree of migration can be used as an index for determining the age of the last larval instar. The pupal age can be estimated by the number of rows and the degree of development of the ommatidia of the compound eye.

Adult confused flour beetles can be sexed by examination of the elytra where the keels and strial grooves form a pattern (Hope, 1953). In the female, the keels on the seventh and third intervals are united distally, as are those on the sixth and the fourth. In the male, the keels on the sixth and the fourth intervals are not united distally and the sixth strial groove is never continuous with the third.

5. Handling and Collecting Eggs and Larvae

Insect eggs are generally delicate and difficult to handle. Backs (1955) suggested the use of Saran Wrap, made by the Dow Chemical Company. The eggs were spread on a sheet of this material where the static charge was strong enough to hold the eggs securely. They could be removed easily with a moist brush. Kirkpatrick (1962b) designed a rubber-bulb aspirator for handling eggs and young larvae of the lesser grain borer.

A method commonly used for separating the larvae of various beetles from rearing medium is simply to roll the medium on rough paper such as paper towels (Fletcher, 1942). The larvae cling to the paper when it is tilted to remove the medium. A modification of this method was developed by Saunders and Krueger (1957) to speed up the collecting technique.

B. CADELLE

1. Life Cycle

The final rearing method to be discussed in this chapter is designed to provide information on specific stages and ages of the cadelle. The use of the cadelle as a test insect has been limited because of the difficulty of rearing these insects in large numbers. The female lays her eggs (about 1000) in small clusters in the commodity being infested or she packs them in small protected areas such as crevices or holes in solid material. The larvae complete their development in about 50 days and generally have four instars. The full-grown larvae bore into wood or some other available material to form a pupal cell. The time for pupal development varies from 8 to 25 days.

Development from egg to adult may take place within 70 days but may be as long as 668 days, as observed by Back and Cotton (1926).

2. Rearing

Bond and Monro (1954) developed a procedure for rearing large numbers of cadelle. Two types of medium were used successfully: the "moldy oatmeal culture" and the "yeast oatmeal culture." Sites for egg laying were provided by placing two squares of plastic together with a thin spacer of paper between them. The female places her eggs in the crevice between the plastic blocks where they are easily observed and removed for rearing. The cadelle is reared successfully at the Savannah Laboratory in an oatmeal-base medium for the adults and in a whole wheat flour-base medium for the larvae. The oatmeal medium is prepared by mixing 95 parts of oatmeal with 5 parts of brewer's yeast (w/w). Thirty ml of water, containing 2 gm of agar, is heated to boiling, and then added to each 100 gm of the oatmeal-yeast mixture. The whole wheat flour medium contains 95 parts whole wheat flour and 5 parts brewer's yeast (w/w). The flour is autoclaved 90 minutes at 116°C and cooled to room temperatures before being mixed with the brewer's yeast.

To start the cultures, 3 gm of the oatmeal medium is placed in a Petri dish containing 3 adult males, 3 adult females, and a plastic "egg-laying" block as described by Bond and Monro (1954). After the desired time, the cadelle eggs are removed from the plastic blocks and are transferred to the larval culture containers.

The larval culture containers are 1-qt Mason jars containing 1 pint of the whole wheat flour medium and closed with filter paper lids. About 100 cadelle eggs are placed in each jar. After 10 weeks, the larvae are sifted out of the medium. About 50 larvae are placed in each pupation container. The pupation containers are 1-qt Mason jars containing 1-inch cubes of coarse building cork and 150 gm of the whole wheat flour medium. After 7 weeks, the cubes of cork are broken open to collect the adults. All rearing containers are stored in a room maintained at 26.7°C ± 1° and 60% relative humidity ±5.

3. Protecting against Mite and Disease Contamination

To provide a barrier for mite or disease contamination in these cultures, 10% ovex should be sprinkled on the paper covers of the cultures and cadelle larvae are treated with ovex before they are placed in the pupation containers. The larvae are treated by covering them with a mixture of ovex and wheat flour (1 pint of wheat flour with 2 tablespoons of ovex) in a wide-mouth 1-qt jar. All cultures should be examined periodically for mites, spoilage, and disease.

REFERENCES

Back, E. A., and Cotton, R. T. (1926). The cadelle. *U. S. Dept. Agr., Bull.* **1428**.

Backs, R. H. (1955). A new method for handling insect eggs. *Can. Entomologist* **87**, 344.

Bartlett, A. C. (1962). The effect of flour particle size on pupa body weight. *Tribolium Info. Bull.* **5**, 20.

Bond, E. J., and Monro, H. A. U. (1954). Rearing the cadelle, *Tenebriodes mauritanicus* (L.) (Coleoptera: Ostomidae) as a test insect for insecticidal research. *Can. Entomologist* **86**, 402–408.

Branton, I. C., Logsdon, C. E., Allen, L., and Pollock, D. (1961). Freezing as a factor in storing grain seed. *Alaska, Univ., Agr. Expt. Sta. Leaflet*, p. 2.

Charbonmeau, R., and Lemonde, A. (1960). Unidentified growth factors in brewer's yeast. I. Necessity of these factors for *Tribolium confusum* Duval. *Can. J. Zool.* **38**, 87–90.

Chirigos, M. A., Meiss, A. N., Pisano, J. J., and Taylor, M. W. (1960). Growth response of the confused flour beetle, *Tribolium confusum* Duval, to six selected protein sources. *J. Nutr.* **72**, 121–130.

Cotton, R. T. (1964). High temperatures: How they affect insect pests. *Northwest. Miller* **270**, 30–32.

Dal Monte, G. (1964). Ricerche sull' infestazione da insetti delle paste alimentari: Metodo per "liberare" le uova di punteruoli (Investigations on insect infestation of pastos: A method for "releasing" the eggs of weevils). *Molini Italia* **15**, 173–175.

Fletcher, F. W. (1942). Fabric pests. *Soap Sanit. Chem.* **18**, 117, 119, 121, and 123.

Fraenkel, G., and Printy, G. E. (1954). The amino acid requirement of the confused flour beetle, *Tribolium confusum* Duval. *Biol. Bull.* **106**, 149–157.

Frankenfeld, J. C. (1948). Staining methods for detecting weevil infestations in grain. *U. S. Dept. Agr., Bur. Entomol. Plant Quarantine*, **ET256**.

Good, N. E. (1936). The flour beetles of the genus Tribolium. *U. S. Dept. Agr., Bull.* **498**.

Goossens, H. J. (1949). A method for staining insect egg-plugs in wheat. *Cereal Chem.* **26**, 419–420.

Graham, W. M. (1962). Trapping Tribolium in storage experiments. *Trop. Agr. (London)* **39**, 53–56.

Hampton, W. F. (1949). Effect of food particle size on the rate of larval and pupal development of *Tribolium confusum* Duv. Unpublished report of a problem conducted for Stored Product Insect Investigations, Dept. of Entomology, Dept. of Agr., Ottawa.

Hinton, H. E. (1948). A synopsis of the genus *Tribolium* Macley, with some remarks on the evolution of its species-groups (Coleoptera, Tenebrionidae). *Bull. Entomol. Res.* **39**, 13–56.

Ho, F. K. (1960). Discrimination between the pupae of *Tribolium confusum* Duv. and *T. castaneum* (Hbst.) (Coleoptera: Tenebrionidae). *Ann. Entomol. Soc. Am.* **53**, 280–281.

Ho, F. K. (1961). Optic organs of *Tribolium confusum* and *T. castaneum* and their usefulness in age determination (Coleoptera: Tenebrionidae). *Ann. Entomol. Soc. Am.* **54**, 921–925.

Ho, F. K. (1964). Identification of mature larvae of *Tribolium confusum* and *T. castaneum*. *Tribolium Info. Bull.* **7**, 59–65.

Hope, J. A. (1953). A simple method for sexing the confused flour beetle, *Tribolium confusum*. *Nature* **171**, 265–266.

Howe, R. W. (1956). The effect of temperature and humidity on the rate of development and mortality of *Tribolium castaneum* (Herbst) (Coleoptera, Tenebrionidae). *Ann. Appl. Biol.* **44**, 356–368.

Howe, R. W. (1960). The effects of temperature and humidity on the rate of development and the mortality of *Tribolium confusum* Duval (Coleoptera, Tenebrionidae). *Ann. Appl. Biol.* **48**, 363–376.

Imms, A. D. (1957). "A General Textbook of Entomology." E. P. Dutton, New York.

Kirkpatrick, R. L. (1962a). The development and habits of the granary weevil *Sitophilus granarius* (L.) within the kernel of wheat. M.S. Thesis, Kansas State University, Manhattan, Kansas.

Kirkpatrick, R. L. (1962b). Rubber-bulb aspirators to handle minute insects. *J. Econ. Entomol.* **55**, 411.

Kirkpatrick, R. L. (1965). Personal communication.

Laird, M. (1959). Gregarines from laboratory colonies of flour beetles, *Tribolium castaneum* Herbst and *T. confusum* Duval at Montreal. *Can. J. Zool.* **37**, 378–381.

Loschiavo, S. R. (1952). A study of some food preferences of *Tribolium confusum* Duv. *Cereal Chem.* **29**, 91–107.

Loschiavo, S. R. (1959). Observations on food preferences of five species of stored-product insects. *Cereal Chem.* **36**, 299–307.

McGregor, H. E. (1964). Preference of *Tribolium castaneum* for wheat containing various percentages of dockage. *J. Econ. Entomol.* **57**, 511–513.

Magis, N. (1954). Misé en évidence de préférences alimentaires chez *Tribolium castaneum* Herbst (Coléoptére Tenebrionidae). *Arch. Intern. Physiol.* **62**, 22–32.

Mertz, D. B. (1961). Identification of *Tribolium* species by pupal characteristics. *Ecology* **42**, 811.

Milner, M., Barney, D. L., and Shellenberger, J. A. (1950). Use of selective fluorescent stains to detect insect egg plugs on grain kernels. *Science* **112**, 791–792.

Morrison, E. O. (1964). The effect of particle size of sorghum grain on development of the weevil *Sitophilus zeamais*. *J. Econ. Entomol.* **57**, 390–391.

Naylor, A. F. (1964). Possible value of cassin, gluten, egg albumin or fibrin as whole protein in the diet of two strains of the flour beetle, *Tribolium confusum* (Tenebrionidae). *Can. J. Zool.* **42**, 1–9.

Official Methods of Analysis of the Association of Official Chemists. (1960). p. 158.

Park, T. (1934). Observations on the general biology of the flour beetle, *Tribolium confusum*. *Quart. Rev. Biol.* **9**, 36–54.

Park, T. (1948). Experimental studies of interspecies competition. I. Competition between populations of the flour beetles, *Tribolium confusum* Duv. and *T. castaneum* Herbst. *Ecol. Monographs* **18**, 265–308.

Pedersen, J. R. (1960). Personal communication.

Pedersen, J. R., and Brown, R. A. (1960). X-ray microscope to study behavior of internal-infesting grain insects. *J. Econ. Entomol.* **53**, 678–679.

Reddy, B. D. (1951). Determination of sex in adult rice and granary weevils. *Pan-Pacific Entomologist* **27**, 13–16.

Saunders, J. P., and Krueger, H. (1957). A rapid method for counting larvae of the confused flour beetle. *J. Econ. Entomol.* **50**, 693.

Schneider, B. A. (1943). The nutritional requirements of *T. confusum*. II. The effect of vitamin B complex on metamorphosis, growth, and adult vitality. *Am. J. Hyg.* **37**, 179–192.

Singh, Shiv Raj, and Soderstrom, E. L. (1963). Sexual maturity of the rice weevil, *Sitophilus oryzae* (L.) indicated by sperm transfer and viable eggs. *J. Kansas Entomol. Soc.* **36**, 32–34.

Soderstrom, E. L. (1960). Recognition and duration of larval instars of the rice weevil and the granary weevil. *J. Kansas Entomol. Soc.* **33**, 157–161.

Sokoloff, A. (1962). A simple technique for ridding Tribolium cultures of parasites. *Tribolium Info. Bull.* **5**, 48.

Stanley, J. (1939). Time required for the development of Tribolium eggs at 27°C. *Ann. Entomol. Soc. Am.* **32**, 564–569.

Stanley, J. (1946). The environmental index, a new perameter, as applied to Tribolium. *Ecology* **27**, 303–314.

Stanley. J. (1951). The autotrephon: An apparatus for rearing insects under controlled conditions with automatic time-controlled withdrawal of samples. *Ecology* **32**, 413–442.

Stanley, J. (1953). Studies from the autotrephon, II. The analysis of autotrephon data. *Ecology* **34**, 29–43.

Stanley, J. (1961). Two techniques for use in the control of Triboliocystis garnhami. *Can. J. Zool.* **39**, 121–122.

Stanley, J. (1962). The tribioliotrap. *Can. J. Zool.* **40**, 1313.

Stanley, J. (1964). Washing the eggs of *Tribolium* for Gregarine control. *Can. J. Zool.* **42**, 920.

Strong, R. G., Pieper, G. R., and Sbur, D. E. (1959). Control and prevention of mites in granary and rice weevil cultures. *J. Econ. Entomol.* **52**, 443–446.

Surtees, G. (1965). Effect of grain size on development of the weevil *Sitophilus granarius* (L.) (Coleoptera: Curculionidae). *Proc. Roy. Entomol. Soc. London.* **A40**, 38–40.

Van Wyk, J. H., Hodson, A. C., and Christensen, C. M. (1959). Microflora associated with the confused flour beetle, *Tribolium confusum*. *Ann. Entomol. Soc. Am.* **52**, 452–463.

Walkden, H. H. (1957). Detecting hidden infestation. *Grain & Feed J.* **114**, 37–38.

White, G. D. (1956). Studies on separation of weevil-infested from non-infested wheat by flotation. *U. S. Dept. Agr., AMS* **101**, 1–9.

Zeleny, L. (1960). Moisture measurement in the grain industry. *Cereal Sci. Today* **5**, 130–136.

Chapter 17

Lepidoptera Infesting Stored Products

H. P. BOLES* AND F. O. MARZKE

Stored-Product Insects Research and Development Laboratory,
U. S. Department of Agriculture,
Savannah, Georgia

The major stored-product insects, which include some of the most destructive to man, are found among various species of Coleoptera and Lepidoptera. The rearing of such insects is of importance in finding methods for preventing damage to man's food supply, but some species are also ideally suited for genetic studies and for parasite rearing. The colonization of selected coleopterous species is described in the preceding chapter. The statements in the introduction to that chapter on the ease as well as the precautions for rearing the coleopterous species are, in general, also applicable to rearing the lepidopterous species. Lepidoptera species are cosmopolitan and easily collected, insects are easily handled, culture media are relatively easy to prepare, rearing can be done under a range of environmental conditions although an optimum

* *Present address:* Mid-West Grain Insects Investigations, Stored-Products Insects Branch, Marked Quality Research Division, Agricultural Research Service, Manhattan, Kansas.

must be selected if rearing is for research purposes, and culturing techniques require little space.

Among the most important Lepidoptera infesting stored foods are the Indian-meal moth, *Plodia interpunctella* (Hbn.); Mediterranean flour moth, *Anagasta kühniella* Zeller; and almond moth, *Cadra cautella* Walker; it is the rearing of these species that will be discussed in this chapter. Shepard (1943) notes "the suggestions for rearing one species may apply to others, particularly within the same group." This is generally true of these three species.

I. NUTRITIONAL REQUIREMENTS

Each species has specific nutritional requirements. According to Fraenkel and Blewett (1946a), larvae of all three species can be grown successfully on diets containing 50 parts casein, 50 parts glucose, 5 parts yeast, 1 part cholesterol, 1 part wheat germ oil, 2 parts McCollum's salt mixture, and 10 parts water. Any reduction in the amount of glucose seriously affects growth of the Mediterranean flour moth, but satisfactory growth of the Indian-meal moth and almond moth occurs when the glucose is reduced as much as one third. In diets for the Mediterranean flour moth glucose can be replaced by starch, but such media are unsuitable for the other species.

If all known factors of the vitamin-B complex are substituted for the yeast, the insects grow relatively well but the growth rate is slowed. Thiamine, nicotinic acid, pyridoxine, and pantothenic acid are essential for the Mediterranean flour moth; in the absence of riboflavin it grows slowly. Inositol generally improves the growth of the Mediterranean flour moth. Biotin is an important growth factor for the Mediterranean flour moth and the Indian-meal moth. If wheat germ oil is omitted, the Mediterranean flour moth grows poorly (Fraenkel and Blewett, 1946b). The active substance in the saponifiable portion of the oil is linoleic acid and in the unsaponifiable fraction, vitamin E (α-tocopherol).

II. REARING MEDIA

Many rearing media have been described for the three species, most of which are based on food the insects were found to infest. However, the efficiency of these "natural food" media varies considerably. For example, those that contain all parts of the cereal are better than those from which the bran has been removed. Provision of an adequately balanced diet, or at least one containing the essential growth substances described previously, is necessary.

Haydak's mixture (Haydak, 1936) has been widely used for rearing many stored-product insects, especially the moths. This is composed of a dry mix of 4 gm of corn flour, 2 gm of whole wheat flour, 2 gm of wheat middlings or bran, 1 gm of dried powdered yeast, and a fluid mix of equal parts of honey and glycerine by volume. When ready to use, equal parts of the dry and fluid mixes are combined and allowed to stand for 24 hours before use. Peterson (1953) apparently rates this medium the most satisfactory for rearing Indian-meal moths and notes that it also is satisfactory for other moth species.

At the Stored-Product Insects Research and Development Laboratory, Savannah, Georgia, a formulated medium that has many of the characteristics of Haydak's medium is used. This medium is satisfactory for all three species; it is reproduced in Table I.

TABLE I

FORMULA FOR REARING MEDIUM

Ingredients	Pints
Cornmeal	4
Whole wheat flour	4
Gaines meal[a]	2
Dried yeast	1
Honey	1
Glycerine	1
Wheat germ	$\frac{1}{2}$
Oat meal	1

[a] Hominy feed, soybean meal, wheat middlings, meat and bone meal, wheat red dog, animal fat preserved in BHA, fish meal, iodized salt, riboflavin supplement, U.S. certified food color, vitamin B_{12} supplement, vitamin E supplement, vitamin A supplement, and vitamin D_2 supplement.

The whole wheat flour and cornmeal portions are autoclaved for 90 minutes at 12–16 lb of pressure at 240°F. Metal pans, 5 to 6 inches deep, which are shallow enough to allow even and complete heat penetration, are used to hold the materials during autoclaving. This treatment eliminates any mites and insects that might be present and at the same time conditions the ingredients to a favorable moisture level. After autoclaving, the materials are cooled to a temperature that will permit hand-mixing. The two ingredients are then combined and hand-mixed until all "cakiness" is removed and the ingredients thoroughly mixed. The mixture, after further cooling to room temperature, may be held as stock for future use. If this is done, it should be stored at about 40°F, in sealed containers. The remaining ingredients do not require autoclaving and are added and mixed in at the time of culture preparation. However, as Gaines meal may become infested with insects, it should be carefully examined; if found to be infested the insects should be removed and the material autoclaved or new material should be obtained. No additional moisture is required for the finished medium since the glycerine-honey combination performs the same function as it does for Haydak's basic medium. The honey absorbs moisture from the air and the glycerine prevents molding as well as contributing to the softness of the medium. The prevention of mold is important, because mold competes with the larvae. However, Abdel-Rahman (1963) and Misra (1961) found the Indian-meal moth could complete its life cycle on several species of *Aspergillus*. The Savannah laboratory has also used a medium composed of whole wheat flour containing 5% glycerine. This medium is satisfactory for maintaining stock cultures, but adult production usually averages less than 25% of the potential production.

Successful rearing of the three species on a variety of media has been described by a number of researchers. The U. S. Department of Agriculture Stored-Product Insects Laboratory in Fresno, California, rears the Indian-meal moth on a medium consisting of 1 gallon of chicken mash to 1 pint of equal parts of honey and glycerine (Nelson, 1964). Tzanakakis (1959) used a medium of 7 parts chicken mash,* ½ part glycerine, and ½ part honey by volume. He also used raisins and walnut meats. Hamlin *et al.* (1931) raised Indian-meal moths on figs, prunes, and raisins. Shepard (1943) reported that the insects developed well on moist, shelled corn and even on wheat. Abdel-Rahman (1963) found that the larvae preferred the germ of the kernels of corn, and Dal Monte (1960) reported that 40 to 50 germs were the estimated number required for each larva to reach maturity. Williams (1964), investigating a number of stored commodities, found No. 3 N. Manitoba Tough wheat induced the quickest development of the Indian-meal moth,

* Composition in pounds:

Corn	300	Liver and glandular meal	20
Wheat	135	Ground limestone	15
Barley	100	Bone meal	12
Alfalfa meal	40	Salt	5
Wheat bran	150	Technical $MnSO_4$	0.5
Fish meal	100	Fortified fish oil	2.5
Soybean oil meal	100	Riboflavin	1 (gm)
Dried whey	25		

while maize meal gave the poorest results. Gerhardt and Lindgren (1954) reared the Indian-meal moth on a mixture of whole wheat flour and powdered milk. Russell (1961) found salted pistachio nuts were useful in rearing relatively small numbers of larvae.

Shepard (1943) reported that the Mediterranean flour moth can be reared successfully on a coarse cereal mixture such as whole wheat flour and rolled oats. Mansbridge (1933) also reared them on coarse whole wheat. Richardson (1926) found that high-grade flour produced small larvae with a long development period. Kunike (1938) reports that the speed of development was highest in flours, wastes, and flakes that contain the bran components. Large moths were reared from larvae fed on bean waste, sweet almonds, and oatmeal, while small ones developed on barley, oats, and buckwheat. Gray (1943) used corn meal with a small quantity of whole wheat flour in the center top of the meal. Eggs were added to the wheat flour to give the young larvae a "good start" before they spread into the corn meal. Peterson (1953) states that the larvae should be kept in whole wheat flour during the development of the first instar and then transferred to corn meal or other suitable material. Whiting (1937) used rolled wheat breakfast food. Ullyett and Merwe (1947) cultured the moth on various portions of bran and flour and obtained only slight differences in body weight without a measurable change in development time.

Norris (1934) reared the almond moth on corn flakes or coarsely ground peanuts. Burges (1956) used a wheat feed plus 5% glycerine mixture as a rearing medium.

The final choice of a medium will be determined by the number of insects desired and the purpose for which the insects are being reared. If only a few moths are required in a short time, a more expensive medium adapted for a particular species may be used; e.g., Russell's (1961) pistachio nut medium for the Indian-meal moth. For mass culturing a cheaper medium or a medium for which the ingredients are readily obtained is preferable. When several species are being reared, the medium selected should be suitable for use with as many of the species as possible. Whatever medium is selected, it must have the required nutrients and the proper consistency (Lipke, 1957).

III. OBTAINING CULTURE STOCKS

Field strains of moths attacking stored products can be easily collected as they are cosmopolitan. Because of the possibility that many of the field strains may have been exposed to insecticide residues, extreme care should be taken to prevent contamination of any established laboratory stocks. Therefore, when field stocks are to be colonized, an isolation area and a rearing area completely separated from each other and from any area where standardized laboratory cultures are being maintained should be available. The wild stocks should be carefully examined for evidence of disease, injury, and predators. Symptoms and evidence of possible abnormal conditions are described by Steinhaus (1953). Affected insects should be removed and destroyed. Individuals that appear free of such symptoms should be placed on a clean medium and held in the isolation area through at least one generation of rearing before moving them into the rearing area.

Established laboratory strains of moths are also available. The use of such strains has many advantages. The long period of laboratory rearing has resulted in (1) considerable standardization of each strain, (2) knowledge of the reproductive potential on a standard medium, (3) elimination of mites, parasites, and disease, and (4) freedom from exposure to insecticide residues. The chief disadvantage is that such strains may not respond in the same manner as wild stocks in toxicological and other studies. For specialized strains, such as those that are insecticide-resistant and those that are mutants useful for genetic studies a laboratory may be the only source. Stocks obtained from other laboratories should also be quarantined through at least one generation unless the sanitary conditions of the supplying laboratory are known. If it is necessary to rear the cultures under aseptic conditions, the method of Jacobs and Raichoudhury (1937) may be used; in this method the eggs are immersed for 10 minutes in 0.1% mercuric chloride solution and then rinsed three times in distilled water. The medium in which the insects are to be reared should be sterilized by heat.

IV. REARING CHAMBERS

All three moths can be mass reared with moderate success under normal room conditions, provided there are no periods of extremely high and low temperatures. However, completely satisfactory results will be obtained only when the rearing is done in chambers in which constant temperatures and humidities can be maintained. At the Savannah Laboratory the moths are reared in rooms maintained at a temperature of 80°F ±2° and a relative humidity of 60 ±5%. A number of commercial environmental chambers that provide various temperatures and humidities are available. If price is the limiting factor, Bare *et al.* (1955) describe the construction of a chamber for rearing the tobacco moth [*Ephestia elutella* (Hubner)] that can be built inexpensively. Wagner *et al.* (1965) also describe a low-cost portable environmental chamber that can be built by laboratory personnel.

V. REARING CONTAINERS

At the Savannah Laboratory, 1-gallon wide-mouth jars have been found to be the most satisfactory type of mass-rearing container. They are easily obtained, decontaminated, cleaned, and stored. In jars having a two-piece screw top the center lid is replaced with filter paper to provide a tight cover that still permits adequate air exchange. If the lid is of one-piece construction, the center portion of the lid is removed and replaced with a kraft paper insert. Tsuji (1963) used Petri dishes for rearing the Indian-meal moth and Burges (1956) used 2 by 1 inch tubes as rearing chambers for the almond moth.

VI. SEEDING WITH ADULTS

One- to three-day-old adult moths selected from several cultures should be used for egg-laying. Collections should be made by gentle aspiration or by anesthetization with CO_2. At the Savannah Laboratory approximately 600 gm of rearing medium is placed in each 1-gallon jar and arranged to expose the greatest surface area. Fifty seeding adults are placed in each jar, and the jar sealed with a lid whose center has been replaced with kraft paper to permit sufficient air exchange. If rearing chambers of other sizes are desired, they should be stocked with the same ratio of moths to chamber space. Fifty seeding adults should produce about 1000 to 1500 next generation adults. If the seeding adults are selected at random, about a 50-50 sex ratio is usually obtained. The sexes of the moths are readily distinguished. The two claspers at the end of the male abdomen are easily recognized. When virgin males and females are desired, sexing can be done while the insects are still in the larval or pupal stages. The male larvae, especially in the almond moth, can be identified by the dark testes that are easily seen without the aid of a microscope. The pupal stages can be sexed according to the characters described by Butt and Cantu (1962). If cultures of an exact age are not required, the adults need not be removed from the rearing chambers since they will all die before the next generation emerges. However, when an exact age range of the next generation is desired, the adults should be removed by aspiration after the required egg-laying period. Only one species should be handled at a time to prevent cross-contamination of cultures should any adults escape. When free moths are present, they may lay eggs around the edges of the culture jar lids and the young larvae when they hatch crawl into the culture medium and contaminate it.

VII. SEEDING WITH EGGS

The use of eggs for seeding a culture permits closer control over the expected larval density and over the age range of the adults of the next generation. Eggs may be collected by several methods. At the Savannah Laboratory sufficient eggs of all species are collected by use of an oviposition chamber similar to the one used by Bare *et al.* (1955) to obtain tobacco moth eggs. A quart or gallon jar containing adults is inverted over a 20-mesh screen and the screen is then placed over an egg-collecting container from which the eggs can be easily removed. A small box with a black bottom functions well as the collecting unit. A hole in the bottom of the box allows the eggs to be rolled out and counted as they drop onto the surface of the medium. The screen surface is carefully brushed between each collecting time to prevent older eggs from dropping down during the next collecting period. In this manner, the age of the eggs can be controlled within very narrow limits. All unnecessary handling should be eliminated to prevent injury to the eggs. If desired, the eggs can be placed in small containers with low rims and the containers then put on the surface of the medium. The moisture of the medium prevents the eggs from drying out; as the larvae hatch, they will crawl out of the container and into the food. A count of the unhatched eggs can then be used to determine percentage of hatch.

When large numbers of eggs are involved, they may be collected on a flat sheet of paper and then poured into a marked glass tube measured for the desired number. The moth scales, appendages, and other contaminating material that may also pass through the screen can be removed by screening the eggs onto a paper towel and then rolling the towel from side to side. The scales that pass through even a fine screen will adhere to the rough towel surface, whereas the eggs will not. The collected eggs then should be sprinkled over the medium surface to ensure that the newly hatched larvae are adequately spread throughout the medium.

For mass rearing the Savannah Laboratory uses a ratio of about 0.5 gm of medium per egg. Tzanakakis (1959) used a ratio of 1.5 gm of medium to each egg. Burges (1956) used not more than 36 eggs and 3 gm of medium per 2 by 1 inch tube. Kunike (1938) used 1000 eggs in a 1-liter jar filled one third with food. If too many eggs are used for the size of the culture container chosen or for the amount of medium used, the size of the larvae and emerging adults will be affected. Moreover, the expected number of emerging adults may be reduced through excessive moisture and heat production by the larvae, which increases molding and spoilage of the culture medium and the possibility of a disease or mite infestation.

Shepard (1943) reports that eggs of the Mediterranean flour moth are easily obtained by confining several moths in a small wide-mouth bottle plugged with cotton. The eggs are laid on the cotton, which is then removed and placed on the surface of the rearing medium. Gray (1943) obtained the eggs of this moth by confining them in a wire-screen oviposition cage with a screen bottom placed over bolting cloth.

VIII. SEEDING WITH LARVAE

If larvae are desired as starting stock, they should be taken from cultures started with adults or eggs, as described previously, since such larvae will be of about uniform age. The ratio of larvae to medium should be the same as for the eggs. Larvae selected between the second and last instar must be separated from the medium. This can be done in part by removing the medium from the container and spreading it evenly over a sheet of paper which is then placed under a light. The light will cause many of the larvae to crawl onto the paper surface. The remaining larvae will then have to be hand separated from the medium. Larvae near pupation may be collected by placing rolls of the corrugated portions of corrugated cardboard on the surface of the medium. The larvae will crawl inside the roll, which is then unrolled and the insects collected. Care again must be taken at all times to prevent injury to the larvae.

IX. SEEDING WITH PUPAE

Pupae may be collected by waiting until the larvae that crawl into the corrugated cardboard described in the previous section have pupated. Most of the pupae will drop free when the cardboard is unrolled. Collection and separation of pupae directly from the medium must be done with extreme care. A pupal cell collected from medium can be held with one pair of forceps and the cell pulled open with another pair. If the cell is formed against the side of the culture container, a gentle pulling with a pair of forceps will usually open the cell without damage to the pupa.

X. LIFE HISTORY

Under the rearing conditions of 80°F and 60% relative humidity maintained at the Savannah Laboratory the development time from egg to adult for the Indian-meal moth ranges from 23 to 30 days with maximum emergence occurring between 23 and 27 days. The life history for the other two species is somewhat similar. The females lay an average of 90 eggs, which hatch in about 4 days. The moths remain in the larval stage for about 17 days and in the pupal stage for about 7 days. The adult moths live an average of 13 days. However, according to Tsuji (1963), stocks of Indian-meal moths may also be obtained that enter diapause. The onset of diapause is governed by temperature and larval density. The cocoon of the diapausing larva is dense and completely closed while the regular pupal cocoon is flimsy and open anteriorly to provide an exit for the adult. If cultures show extremes in development time, the possibility of diapause occurring should be investigated.

XI. REARING PRECAUTIONS

With due precautions the rearing of moths infesting stored products is not difficult. However, as mentioned previously, the presence of disease, parasites, or predators is always a potential hazard. If permitted to get out of hand, any one of these factors can result in complete loss of the cultures. Cleanliness should be practiced at all times. Rearing equipment used on a regular basis should be sterilized frequently. Stock cultures kept for maintenance purposes should be examined as frequently as are the test cultures. No culture should be kept longer than necessary, and, if possible, should be discarded immediately after serving its purpose. Although insects may have to be sent to a specialist for identification of suspected disease or other factors, the eradication program should be started at once on the assumption that the condition may be due to a virulent organism. An effective program for disease eradication has been described by Steinhaus (1953). Mites can also be as great a danger as disease, as they spread rapidly and will attack all stages of stored-product insects. A frequent turnover of cultures and a liberal use of a miticide such as ovex on the culture shelves and on the jar lids will keep the mite problem at a minimum. However, should a mite infestation become widespread, other measures will be required to eradicate them. Strong *et al.* (1959) describe procedures to follow should this occur.

REFERENCES

Abdel-Rahman, H. A. (1963). A study on the ecology of the Indian-meal moth *Plodia interpunctella* Hb. with emphasis on its relation to stored grain fungi. *Dissertation Abstr.* **24**, 911.

Bare, C. O., Tenhet, J., and Brubacker, R. W. (1955). Improved techniques for mass-rearing of the cigarette beetle and the tobacco moth. *U. S. Dept. Agr., AMS* **33**.

Burges, H. D. (1956). Some effects of the British climate and constant temperature on the life cycle of *Ephestia cautella* (Wlk.). *Bull. Entomol. Res.* **46**, 813–835.

Butt, B. A., and Cantu, E. (1962). Sex determination of lepidopterous pupae. *U. S. Dept. Agr., ARS* **ARS 33-75**.

Dal Monte, G. (1960). The habits of the moth *Plodia interpunctella*. *Molini Italia* **11**, 211–217.

Fraenkel, G., and Blewett, M. (1946a). The dietetics of the caterpillars of three *Ephestia* species, *E. kuhniella*, *E. elutella*, and *E. cautella*, and of a closely related species *Plodia interpunctella. J. Exptl. Biol.* **22**, 162–171.

Fraenkel, G., and Blewett, M. (1946b). Linoleic acid, vitamin E and other fat-soluble substances in the nutrition of certain insects, *Ephestia kuehniella*, *E. elutella*, *E. cautella* and *Plodia interpunctella* (Lep.). *J. Exptl. Biol.* **22**, 172–190.

Gerhardt, P. D., and Lindgren, D. L. (1954). Penetration of various packaging films by common stored-product insects. *J. Econ. Entomol.* **47**, 282–287.

Gray, H. E. (1943). Stored-food insects. *In* "Rearing Insects that Attack Plants," Publ. No. 20, pp. 54–56. Am. Assoc. Advance. Sci., Washington, D. C.

Hamlin, J. C., Reed, W. D., and Phillips, M. E. (1931). Biology of the Indian-meal moth on dried fruit in California. *U. S. Dept. Agr., Tech. Bull.* **242**.

Haydak, M. H. (1936). A food for rearing laboratory insects. *J. Econ. Entomol.* **29**, 1026.

Jacobs, S. E., and Raichoudhury, D. P. (1937). Some characteristics of *Ephestia kühniella* reared under aseptic conditions. *Ann. Appl. Biol.* **24**, 632–650.

Kunike, G. (1938). The determination of the food value of various materials by feed tests with granary pests. *Anz. Schädlingskunde* **1**, 101–105.

Lipke, H. (1957). Nutritional considerations for rearing insects. *Proc. Entomol. Soc. Am. North Central Branch* **12**, 90–91.

Mansbridge, G. H. (1933). The breeding of *Ephestia kuhniella* Zell. in large numbers for experimental work. *Ann. Appl. Biol.* **20**, 771–774.

Misra, C. P. (1961). Studies on the relationship between *Sitotroga cerealella* Oliv. (Angoumois grain moth), *Plodia interpunctella* Hbn. (Indian meal moth) and storage fungi. *Dissertation Abstr.* **21**, 1680.

Nelson, H. (1964). Personal communication.

Norris, M. J. (1934). Contributions towards the study of insect fertility. III. Adult nutrition, fecundity and longevity in the genus *Ephestia* (Lepidoptera, Phycitidae). *Proc. Zool. Soc. London* Part 2, 333–360.

Peterson, A. (1953). "A Manual of Entomological Techniques," 7th ed. Edwards, Ann Arbor, Michigan.

Richardson, C. H. (1926). A physiological study of the growth of the Mediterranean flour moth *Ephestia kühniella* Zell. *J. Agr. Res.* **32**, 895–929.

Russell, M. P. (1961). A simple rearing medium for the Indian-meal moth, *Plodia interpunctella*. *J. Econ. Entomol.* **54**, 812–813.

Shepard, H. H. (1943). Rearing insects that attack stored products. *In* "Rearing Insects that Attack Plants," Publ. No. 20, pp. 36–51. Am. Assoc. Advance. Sci., Washington, D. C.

Steinhaus, E. A. (1953). Diseases of insects reared in the laboratory or insectary. *Calif. Agr. Expt. Sta. Ext. Serv. Leaflet* **9**, 1–26.

Strong, R. G., Pieper, G. R., and Sbur, D. E. (1959). Control and prevention of mites in granary and rice weevil cultures. *J. Econ. Entomol.* **52**, 443–446.

Tsuji, H. (1963). Experimental studies on the larval diapause of the Indian-meal moth *Plodia interpunctella* Hübner (Lepidoptera, Pyralidae). Publisher not known, Tokyo.

Tzanakakis, M. E. (1959). An ecological study of the Indian-meal moth, *Plodia interpunctella* (Hübner) with emphasis on diapause. *Hilgardia* **29**, 205–246.

Ullyett, G. C., and Merwe, J. S. (1947). Some factors influencing population growth of *Ephestia kühniella* Zell. (Lepidoptera, Phycitidae). *J. Entomol. Soc. S. Africa* **10**, 46–63.

Wagner, R. E., Ebeling, W., and Clark, W. R. (1965). Controlled environment chambers for the biological laboratory. *J. Econ. Entomol.* **58**, 236–240.

Whiting, P. W. (1937). Rearing *Ephestia kühniella* larvae in quantity. "Culture Methods for Invertebrate Animals," p. 355. Cornell Univ. Press (Comstock), Ithaca, New York.

Williams, G. C. (1964). The life history of the Indian meal moth *Plodia interpunctella* (Hübner) (Lep. Phycitidae) in a warehouse in Britain and on different foods. *Ann. Appl. Biol.* **53**, 459–475.

Section C

Phytophagous Insects and Mites

Chapter 18

Defined Diets for Phytophagous Insects

ERMA S. VANDERZANT

Entomology Research Division,
Agricultural Research Service,
U. S. Department of Agriculture*
Texas A & M University,
College Station, Texas

* In cooperation with the Texas Agricultural Experiment Station.

I. INTRODUCTION

Insects with omnivorous food habits and those that live on stored food are adaptable to laboratory culture and have been used for many years as experimental animals. Insects that feed on growing plants have more discriminating tastes. In devising laboratory rearing diets for these insects radical changes in composition and physical properties from the natural food are required. Most of these insects are highly selective in their food habits; some choose only a single species of plant or a family of plants or feed on a single part, leaves, fruit, or stems. In general, they thrive best on diets with high water content. This review is limited to phytophagous insects, classified as those that feed on growing plants. Excluded are many insects that feed largely on dry or decaying vegetable matter and are not classified as phytophagous even though their food is of plant origin.

Historically, the first attempt to rear a phytophagous insect on an artificial diet is credited to Bottger (1942), who compounded a diet for the European corn borer, *Ostrinia nubilalis* (Hübner), consisting of casein, sugars, fat, salts, vitamins, cellulose, agar, and water. In 1949, Beck *et al.* reported a diet used for the successful rearing of the European corn borer that was composed largely of pure chemicals and highly purified natural products but included a corn leaf extract to provide unidentified growth factors. The rearing was also successful under aseptic conditions (Beck and Stauffer, 1950). Subsequently, many other investigators modeled their experimental diets after the corn borer diet. Ishii (1952) and Matsumoto (1954) used diets containing extracts of host plants in diets for the Asiatic rice borer, *Chilo suppressalis* (Walker), and the oriental fruit moth, *Grapholitha molesta* (Busck), whereas Vanderzant and Reiser (1956a) were able to rear the pink bollworm, *Pectinophora gossypiella* (Saunders), on a diet without any plant extracts. Since these early experiments, a number of insects have been reared on diets consisting entirely of pure chemicals and other nutritive substances that are completely foreign to the natural food of the test insects.

Diets of known composition offer several obvious advantages. Laboratory rearing is greatly facilitated. Insects of known and reproducible nutrition are available for various tests. Studies of nutrition and metabolism can be regulated through variations in chemical and physical characteristics of diets and environmental conditions.

Nutritive substances needed by all insects have been discussed in recent reviews (House, 1961, 1962). Nutritional requirements of phytophagous insects were discussed by Friend (1958), Legay (1958), and Auclair (1963). Although this information is quite helpful as a guide to the nutrients needed for growth of insects, the application of this information to successful and sustained rearing over many generations has not been attained for very many insects because of the many other factors involved. A number of concepts with selected illustrations are presented herein. These should assist the investigator in devising diets for phytophagous insects and answer some of the problems that arise.

II. DEFINITION OF DEFINED DIET

The terminology used to describe diets for insects is extremely confusing. The terms artificial, synthetic, purified, and chemically defined are used by different investigators to describe diets containing substances that vary greatly in purity. Thus, one can find a diet called "completely chemically defined" that contains the nutrients, starch, and casein—large molecules likely to vary in purity depending upon the manner in which they were produced and processed. To some a synthetic diet is a mixture of nutritive substances, perhaps a plant preparation with vitamins, yeast, or sugar added; to others a synthetic diet is a mixture of pure chemicals only. Purified is usually applied to diets containing pure chemicals and natural products such as casein that have been extracted with solvents to remove fats, vitamins, and other trace substances. Artificial, a more general term, usually refers to any diet that is not the natural food of the insect.

In an attempt to resolve some of the confusion, Dougherty (1959) suggested the terms "holidic" to describe diets composed of pure chemicals and "meridic" to describe diets containing one substance of unknown structure such as a protein. Useful as these terms might be, they have not been widely accepted by investigators rearing insects. He considers diets containing agar to be meridic even though agar is of doubtful importance as a nutrient, and can be obtained in pure enough form to permit the study of amino acids, lipids, and many other nutrients. By the same reasoning one must also include in the meridic category all diets whether or not they contain agar because they may contain trace contaminants, especially minerals; Gordon (1959) has discussed rather fully the occurrence of trace substances in so-called pure chemicals.

A defined diet is merely a diet in which the constituents can be described. To define means *to set the limits of something*. Ideally a defined diet should consist of only chemically pure constituents. Nutrients that can be obtained in pure form are almost all small molecules. Insect diets consisting of only small molecules have not been very successful. In the broadest sense, a defined diet may be considered as one that contains chemically pure nutrient substances and one or more specially purified natural products. For example, casein can be made essentially free of vitamins for tests on vitamin requirements or can be extracted exhaustively with organic solvents for tests of lipid requirements. If amino acids are to be tested, however, the casein must be replaced by amino acids. Finally, no diet can be defined if microorganisms are not excluded.

III. CHEMICAL, PHYSICAL, AND BIOLOGICAL REQUIREMENTS FOR FEEDING

A. GENERAL CONSIDERATIONS

No defined diet will permit growth if the insect will not feed on it. Consequently, a diet that has an adequate amount of nutrients may fail to support growth if the stimuli that initiate feeding are lacking.

Although many plants contain specific odorous chemicals that apparently attract insects from a distance, such chemicals may be of little importance as feeding stimulants when the insect is located on the plant or confined in close proximity with an artificial diet. There is some evidence that non-nutritive chemicals cause feeding responses in certain leaf-feeding insects, but the successful rearing of many plant species without any unique plant chemicals indicates that most insects can be reared without these chemicals if all other feeding requirements are met.

The physical requirements for feeding are numerous and are different for each species. Beck *et al.* (1958) found that the milkweed bug, *Oncopeltus fasciatus* (Dallas), fed on pelleted diets if the diet was covered with milkweed seed husks. The only part of the husk apparently eaten was that part removed during the penetration. The response appeared to be tactile, although chemicals in the seed coat enhanced the tactile response (Feir and Beck, 1963). Vanderzant and Davich (1961) reported that shape of the diet was important in inducing oviposition in the boll weevil, *Anthonomus grandis* Boheman. Up to twice as many eggs were collected if food was cast in the form of cylindrical pieces, thus presenting a curved surface, as were obtained from diets with a flat surface. The design of suitable membranes for plant-sucking insects was a problem until Mittler and Dadd (1962, 1963a) and Auclair and Cartier (1963) succeeded in feeding aphids through Parafilm membranes.

Many chewing insects exhibit improved feeding and growth if cellulose is added to their diets. Growth is apparently improved by an increased intake of food caused by stimulation in feeding. Such an effect was observed for the silkworm, *Bombyx mori* (Linnaeus) (Mukaiyama and Ito, 1962). By including cellulose in the diets of the locusts, *Schistocerca gregaria* (Forskal) and *Locusta migratoria* Linnaeus, Dadd (1960c) found that the amount of diet eaten increased with the amount of cellulose incorporated. The amount of food eaten appeared to be regulated by its utilizable nutrient; the cellulose caused a diluting effect and more food had to be consumed. *Melanoplus bivittatus* (Say) also grew better if cellulose was included in the diet (Nayar, 1964a). Cellulose, agar, and other non-nutritive inert materials have been included in the diets of many other insects primarily to furnish a carrier for nutrient substances or to thicken the diet.

Many of the biological requirements of insects are peculiar to the species and are not directly related to nutrition. However, physiological conditions such as age and diapause should not be overlooked in evaluating the results of nutritional experiments.

B. NUTRIENTS AS FEEDING STIMULANTS

When biological and physical feeding requirements have been met, providing suitable nutrients that will induce feeding is the most important problem to be solved. Since special plant chemicals are not included in defined diets, chemical stimulation of feeding depends entirely upon the nutrients. On natural foods and artificial diets in the laboratory, nutrients play a very important role in initiating and sustaining feeding. Thus, unsatisfactory growth may be obtained with a diet having sufficient utilizable nutrients but lacking one that causes optimum feeding.

Sugars are perhaps the most important feeding stimulants for phytophagous insects. Beck (1956a) found that the feeding of O. *nubilalis* larvae was stimulated by glucose, and that fructose and sucrose were also stimulatory. *Bombyx mori* larvae, however, were stimulated by sucrose and little if any stimulation resulted from glucose (Ito, 1960b). Adults of A. *grandis* also preferred sucrose to glucose (Vanderzant and Davich, 1961). Scheel *et al.* (1957) found that starch stimulated the feeding of O. *fasciatus*, whereas glucose, fructose, and sucrose did not. Sugars also affected feeding in locusts; sucrose, glucose, fructose, and soluble starch solutions caused more feeding than water alone (Dadd, 1960c). Sucrose was definitely phagostimulatory to aphids because they imbibed sucrose solutions at a faster rate and in a greater quantity than water (Mittler and Dadd, 1963a).

In rearing tests, glucose, fructose, sucrose, starch, and many other carbohydrates could be used. But the rate and efficiency of growth depend on the special gustatory properties of the carbohydrate substance, and the effect on feeding should be considered when diets are devised.

Proteins and amino acids are perhaps the second most important class of nutrients that stimulate feeding. The effect of proteins is most likely related to their amino acid content, although impurities might exert an effect. Beck (1956a) found that casein was slightly stimulatory to feeding of *O. nubilalis* larvae.

Effects of amino acids upon feeding were tested by incorporating each of them into an agar-based purified diet containing casein and glucose as the only other nutrients (Beck and Hanec, 1958). In a series of choice experiments, the feeding of *O. nubilalis* larvae was increased most by L-alanine, DL-α-amino-*n*-butyric acid, L-serine, and L-threonine. A negative feeding effect was caused by L-tryptophan, L-arginine, and β-alanine.

Lipid substances are also feeding stimulants. Wheat-germ oil increased feeding in locusts, although Dadd (1960c) believed that feeding was regulated by utilizability rather than by special gustatory stimuli. Plant phospholipids isolated from wheat-germ oil evoked strong feeding responses in the grasshoppers, *M. bivittatus* and *Camnula pellucida* (Scudder) (Thorsteinson and Nayar, 1963). Lecithins and phosphatidyl inositol were the most active components. Many other nutrients undoubtedly affect feeding. A striking example was shown by the response of *B. mori* to diets containing the plant sterols, β-sitosterol, stigmasterol, and campesterol which caused more feeding by the larvae than cholesterol (Ito *et al.*, 1964).

IV. COMPOSITION OF DIETS

A. GENERAL

Insects in general do not differ greatly in qualitative nutritional requirements from other laboratory test animals such as rats. Differences between species of insects vary widely especially in quantitative requirements. Given an adequate assortment of nutrients, the greatest problem perhaps lies in satisfying the physical and chemical feeding requirements (Section III).

In devising diets for insects having complex dietary requirements, it is desirable to include all known nutrients with enough accessory substances to provide the proper physical properties. Some important dietary substances and their major and minor functions as determined from the diets for phytophagous insects re-

TABLE I

SUBSTANCES USED IN INSECT DIETS AND THE MAJOR AND
MINOR NUTRIENTS THEY PROVIDE

Dietary ingredient	Major nutrient furnished	Important trace substances[a]
Proteins		
Casein, Soybean	Amino acids	Fatty acids, cholesterol, sugars, vitamins, minerals
Albumin	Amino acids	Vitamins, minerals
Amino acids	Amino acids	Other amino acids, isomers
Carbohydrates		
Sugars	Simple sugar	—
Starch	Simple sugars	Amino acids, vitamins
Lipid substances		
Vegetable oils	Fatty acids	Sterols, carotene, tocopherol
Phospholipids	Fatty acids, choline, inositol	Sterols, carotene, biotin, tocopherol
Fatty acids	Fatty acid	Isomers
Sterols	Sterol	Other sterols
Salt mixtures	Cations, anions	Other minerals
Vitamin mixtures	Vitamins	—
Cellulose	None	Minerals
Agar	None	Minerals

[a] Traces of minerals may occur in all constituents of diets.

ported herein are listed in Table I. Substances are designated as nutrients even though they have been proved to affect the development of a single species. Obviously, polymeric substances may contain trace nutrients the presence of which is not detected until replacement with simple molecules is successful. These problems will be discussed under individual nutrients.

B. PROTEINS AND AMINO ACIDS

Several proteins used for animal test diets are satisfactory for insect diets. Casein has been widely used. It contains all the essential amino acids, is water-soluble, and does not coagulate or precipitate on heating. It can be obtained from biochemical supply companies in a highly purified form suitable for studies of deficiencies of many nutrients. Traces of vitamins and lipids, however, may interfere with tests involving the functions of trace amounts of substances such as biotin, vitamin B_{12}, cholesterol, and fatty acids.

Egg albumin also has been used successfully in insect diets (Vanderzant and Reiser, 1956a). It furnishes adequate amounts of the amino acids essential for growth and it contains no lipids. The presence of traces of B-vitamins makes it unsuitable for vitamin deficiency tests. Its main disadvantage, however, is that it coagulates upon heating; this makes the addition of other substances to such diets after sterilization virtually impossible.

Protein from soybeans was used in a diet for *A. grandis* larvae (Vanderzant and Davich, 1958). Soybean protein preparations may vary considerably in their amounts of amino acids and impurities. In general, they supply all the essential amino acids, but supplementary amounts of several amino acids may be needed. The main disadvantage of soybean proteins is their low solubility in water. The addition of alkali will effect solution. Soybean protein like other plant proteins contains high amounts of basic amino acids believed to be more favorable for the growth of plant-feeding insects. Ito (1961b,d) used a product called "soybean casein" in diets for the silkworm.

Numerous other substances—yeasts, protein hydrolyzates, and crude plant preparations—have been used in diets for insects. Although diets containing these substances cannot be called defined, it is unlikely that they contribute significant amounts of protein and amino acids to the diet when they are added in small amounts. Their major function is to supply trace nutrient substances.

Diets containing amino acids instead of protein have rarely been as successful as natural food or artificial diets containing protein. A notable exception is the diet devised for the onion maggot, *Hylemya antiqua* (Meigen), by Friend and Patton (1956). They obtained faster growth and larger yields of the insect on their defined diet than on onions.

Several reasons why insects fail to grow well on amino acid diets include a deficiency of one or more important amino acids, an amino acid imbalance, and an increase in the osmotic properties of the diet caused by a large number of small molecules. With such diets the digestive system is presented simultaneously with a group of similar molecules which compete with each other for sites in the absorption system. In a pool of free amino acids interferences may occur between like molecules; leucine, isoleucine, and valine or lysine and arginine. Small changes in concentration of an individual amino acid may upset the balance. During the digestion of proteins not all amino acids are released at the same time, nor is all protein completely hydrolyzed. Therefore, certain concentrations of amino acids which might not be satisfactory in a mixture might produce excellent growth when they occur as part of a protein.

Amino acids are small molecules, ionic in character, and may change the osmotic properties of the diet greatly when they are used to replace protein. House and Barlow (1964) tested the effects of various levels of casein and a mixture of amino acids on the growth of *Agria affinis* (Fallen). At the 2% level, development was similar for both, while at a 4% level of amino acids growth was unsatisfactory. Casein gave good growth up to 10%. The freezing point depression of the diet increased very little as the concentration of casein increased and never exceeded that caused by the larval blood. On amino acid diets, however, at concentrations between 3 and 4% amino acids, the freezing point depression of the diets exceeded that of the larval blood. Growth and development were seriously retarded when the concentration of dietary amino acids in the food was increased beyond the point at which the diet was isosmotic with the insect's normal blood. They also found that *A. affinis* larvae reared on amino acid diets contained more water than those reared on liver diets. Growth and development were retarded also when dietary levels of glucose exceeded 1%.

If plant-feeding insects are affected by the osmotic properties of the diet, then providing the right proportion of amino acids in a mixture would become a very critical problem. The use of DL-forms would also increase the number of molecules since the D-isomers are used little (if at all) for growth, and the total amount of amino acids must be increased to provide sufficient amounts of active isomers.

Other possible failures of amino acid diets are lack of gustatory stimuli and physical properties that encourage feeding, or the omission of a growth factor included accidentally when protein was used. This could be a vitamin, mineral, or lipid which occurs as a trace contaminant in purified proteins. The effect of trace nutrients accidentally included with proteins can usually be eliminated if care is taken to include all known nutrients in amino acid diets. Still not known is the possible effect on growth of incompletely hydrolyzed proteins or the peptides that are produced in digestion of proteins. Naylor (1964) believes that they are responsible for the improved growth on diets with protein as compared to diets with amino acids only. However, this is difficult to prove without intensive studies on the effects of amino acid balance, osmotic properties of diets, and other nutrients in the diets.

Inferior growth is not always caused by a deficiency of some dietary amino acid. Adequate amounts of indispensable amino acids were present in a mixture that gave inferior growth of *A. grandis* larvae (Vanderzant, 1965a). Little or no change occurred in development when the concentration of each amino acid was doubled or decreased by half, one at a time. Lysine at half concentration was the only one that failed to produce satisfactory growth. After the concentration of lysine was adjusted (Table III), additional improvements in growth were obtained by changing some of the other constituents of the diet.

The amino acid mixtures (Table II) included in diets for plant-feeding insects have many origins. An amino acid mixture partially modeled after the composition of casein was used by Friend and Patton (1956). Vanderzant (1957, 1958) could not get the pink bollworm to grow with amino acid mixtures based on casein, but a mixture based on cottonseed protein was satisfactory. A similar mixture was also used for *A. grandis* larvae (Vanderzant, 1965a) and adults (Vanderzant, 1963b). Mittler and Dadd (1962) fed the green peach aphid, *Myzus persicae* (Sulzer), a diet containing twenty amino acids based on the composition of pea juice as reported by Auclair *et al.* (1957). However, they were not as successful as Auclair and Cartier (1963), who reared the pea aphid, *Acyrthosiphon pisum* (Harris), on diets containing an amino acid mixture based on the concentrations of amino acids and amides found in pea aphid blood and honeydew, supplemented with arginine, cysteine, histidine, lysine, and tryptophan. These amino acids were not found in their analyses of the insect. The aphids, *Aphis pomi* DeGeer and *Macrosiphum rudbeckiae* (Fitch), also thrived on the pea aphid diet. Fukada *et al.* (1962) based their diet for *B. mori* on the composition of mulberry leaves. Arai and Ito (1964) did not explain how they derived their dietary amino acid mixture for *B. mori*. The diet contained mulberry leaf powder and was used only to determine the amino acids indispensable for growth and survival during a 30-day period. Ishii and Hirano (1955) conducted similar tests with the Asiatic rice borer *C. suppressalis* with individual amino acids at either one of two different levels, 250 and 125 mg per 100 ml of diet to make a total of 3500 mg. This composition was not optimal for

TABLE II: AMOUNTS OF AMINO ACIDS USED IN DIETS FOR VARIOUS PHYTOPHAGOUS INSECTS

Amino acids[a]	Chilo suppressalis Ishii and Hirano (1955) (mg/100 ml)	Hylemya antiqua Friend and Patton (1956) (mg/100 ml)	Pectinophora gossypiella Vanderzant (1957) (mg/100 ml)	Anthonomus grandis Vanderzant (1965) (mg/100 ml)	Bombyx mori Fukada et al. (1962) No. 20 (mg/100 gm)	Bombyx mori Arai and Ito (1964) (mg/100 gm)	Myzus persicae Mittler and Dadd (1963a) (mg/100 ml)	Acyrthosiphon pisum Auclair and Cartier (1963) (mg/100 ml)	Schistocerca gregaria Dadd (1961c) (gm/100 gm dry)
Alanine	(DL) 250	109	150	150	240	280	100	100	1.162
Arginine	250	80	311	(HCl) 150	240	(HCl) 240	270	400	2.490
Aspartic acid	125	122	100	(HCl·H₂O) 100	504	(Na) 440	140	100	0.830
Cysteine	0	48	0	50	0	0	10	50	0
Cystine	125	0	50	0	240	100	0	5	0.498
Glutamic acid	250	442	125	325	552	(Na) 520	140	200	2.988
Glycine	250	175	150	150	288	180	40	20	1.162
Histidine	125	48	(HCl) 75	(HCl·H₂O) 75	(HCl) 168	(HCl) 100	40	200	0.498
Isoleucine	(DL) 125	126	113	113	288	220	30	200	0.996
Leucine	250	235	175	175	432	340	40	200	1.660
Lysine	125	(HCl) 134	(HCl) 113	(HCl) 113	(HCl) 360	(HCl) 240	120	(HCl) 200	(HCl) 0.996
Methionine	(DL) 125	34	75	75	72	100	10	100	0.498
Phenylalanine	125	101	150	150	264	220	10	100	1.328
Proline	250	168	50	50	264	160	40	100	1.162
Serine	(DL) 250	88	50	50	288	140	80	100	(DL) 1.328
Threonine	(DL) 125	38	100	100	264	200	140	200	0.498
Tryptophan	(DL) 250	175	75	75	72	160	40	100	1.162
Tyrosine	125	124	50	50	168	80	40	20	0.830
Valine	(DL) 250	136	138	138	336	240	40	200	0.996
Asparagine							550	300	
Glutamine							150	600	
γ-Aminobutyric acid	125	38						20	
Hydroxyproline						40			0.332
Homoserine								800	
	3500	2421	2050	2089	5040	4000	2030	4315	21.414

[a] L-forms of amino acids were used except as indicated in parentheses.

larval growth although it contained the same total amount by weight as the enzymatic hydrolyzed casein which promoted growth and development of the insect to the adult stage. All diets named above were aqueous mixtures and contained from 2 to 4% amino acids.

For locusts, Dadd (1961c) used an arbitrary mixture of amino acids based essentially on casein but with increased amounts of basic amino acids, particularly arginine. This mixture was incorporated into the diet with other nutrients as a dry mixture. *Schistocerca gregaria* became adults but at a retarded rate and weighed less than those insects fed grass or diets with protein.

The most useful function of amino acid diets is that they provide a system in which the concentration of each amino acid can be controlled. Not only can the absolute dietary requirements for an amino acid be determined, but the effects of changing the concentrations of any one can be measured, and interactions or effects of one upon another can be evaluated.

An example of the effect of a change in lysine concentration on the growth of *A. grandis* is shown in Table III. There was a gradual increase in weight and per cent yield from 0.30 to 2.10 mg of lysine

TABLE III

DEVELOPMENT OF *Anthonomus grandis* FROM EGG TO ADULT ON AN
AMINO ACID DIET CONTAINING DIFFERENT AMOUNTS OF LYSINE

			Adults			
			Avg. weights		No. of days to	
Lysine hydrochloride (mg/ml)	No. of larvae	Yield (%)	Females (mg)	Males (mg)	First Pupa	90% Pupation
0.3	93	0	—	—	—	—
0.6	85	2	4.3	7.8	21	40
0.9	94	24	10.3	6.8	16	30
1.2	92	66	9.7	9.3	11	19
1.5	79	71	10.6	10.1	11	17
2.1	94	75	11.8	11.4	11	16
3.0	90	70	11.7	10.2	10	16

hydrochloride per ml of diet, with best results occurring at a concentration of 1.50 mg and higher. Development was also faster at these higher concentrations. This effect of lysine concentration was very striking.

Friend *et al.* (1959) tested the response of *H. antiqua* to dietary concentrations of tryptophan ranging from 0.25 mg per ml to 2.25

mg per ml. In spite of this ninefold increase in concentration, there was no effect on the rate of growth and the per cent that pupated and became adults. The tryptophan requirement was obviously very low. In addition, a reduction in the amounts of three amino acids—aspartic acid, tryptophan, and tyrosine—resulted in faster growth of larvae and more adults. Thus, small changes in relative concentrations of some amino acids had marked effects on the growth of *H. antiqua.*

V. PREPARATION OF DIETS AND REARING PROCEDURES

A. MIXING

Nutrients that are water-soluble, sugars, vitamins, and minerals are easily mixed homogeneously in diets. Fats, fatty acids, sterols, carotene, and fat-soluble vitamins do not dissolve in water and special care must be taken to ensure homogeneous incorporation. They can be triturated with other nutrients to form finely divided particles that will not separate on mixing; for example, cholesterol was mixed with sucrose (Vanderzant and Reiser, 1956b). Dissolved in alcohol, ether, or other organic solvents, they can be mixed with starch, cellulose, protein, or other ingredients (Dadd, 1960a). The solvent is then evaporated and the water-insoluble substances remain as a coating on the other constituents. Homogeneous mixing of aqueous diets is obtained effectively with a blender. Constituents of dry diets also can be mixed in this way or in a ball mill or other rotating device.

Large molecules used to thicken and/or stabilize dietary mixtures are not considered to have nutritive value. Cellulose, agar, carboxymethylcellulose, and alginates are not digested by the insects studied. Although they are useful adsorbants for nutrients such as fat, they may have certain disadvantages. Alginate had a retarding effect on the growth of the boll weevil (Vanderzant, 1963a). The Tweens used to solubilize lipids are believed to have adverse effects on growth and cause reduced feeding in some insects.

Heating of diets may change the chemical characteristics of some of the nutrients. Some substances included in insect diets are destroyed by the temperature and conditions of sterilization. However, the pH of the dietary mixture, the presence of other substances, as well as the time and temperature of heating determine the degree of destruction. The addition of excess amounts of heat-sensitive nutrients may ensure against a deficiency. It should be noted that the vitamin requirements reported in Section VI were determined in diets sterilized by heat. Even ascorbic acid, which is quite unstable to heat, is not completely destroyed when diets are heat-sterilized.

B. STERILIZATION

Although antiseptic techniques and a sanitary environment can be maintained in rearing insects, exact nutrient requirements can be determined only in the absence of microorganisms. Sterile food can be prepared by heating it to 121°C at 15 lb pressure for 15 minutes or longer and maintaining the insect and its food in an aseptic environment. In the absence of filterable viruses that live in or cause disease in the test insect, soluble portions of diet can also be filter-sterilized through Seitz or membrane filters and then added to other sterile components of diet. Heat-sensitive nutrients are best sterilized this way (Vanderzant *et al.*, 1962). To free egg surfaces from organisms that cause disease and contaminate dietary media, a number of chemical treatments have been used. The choice of chemicals depends on the kind of microorganisms in the environment and the chemical and physical properties of the egg surface. The investigator has a large number of chemical agents from which to choose.

C. REARING TECHNIQUE

The choice of rearing container may also affect the health and nutrition of the insect. If insects are reared individually, the chances of spreading disease and contamination are reduced. Furthermore, this method eliminates cannibalism, a serious complication of nutritional experiments because an insect derives a greater concentration of nutrients by eating another insect than it derives from the diet on which it is feeding. Some species of insects are inherently cannibalistic, but even gregarious species may become so if the insects are crowded or the diet deficient.

Although phytophagous insects feed on food of high water content, successful rearing of several species has been accomplished with food of low moisture content. This success is not surprising because Mellanby and French (1958) reported that many plant-feeding species drink water even though their food contains water. Dadd (1960a) reared locusts on dry dietary mixtures and provided their water separately in cellulose pads. Nayar (1964a) used an amorphous dry diet and found that the availability of free water in the rearing containers or the relative humidity was important for the growth and development of nymphs of *M. bivittatus*, whereas *C. pellucida* nymphs were not affected by the humidity of the environment (Nayar, 1964b). Salt marsh caterpillars, *Estigmene acrea* (Drury), were transferred to cages and given dry wafers of diet when they outgrew their sterile rearing containers. Water with ascorbic acid was offered in vials with paper wicks (Vanderzant *et al.*, 1962). Although these insects were not maintained under aseptic conditions, the absence of water in the diets markedly reduced the chance of interference by ordinary contaminants. Disease and symbiotic organisms can be eliminated in such tests by use of germ-free insects initially.

VI. NUTRITIONAL REQUIREMENTS FOR GROWTH

A. Proteins and Amino Acids

Casein has been widely used in insect diets because it is available in various purified forms for nutritional studies. Excellent growth of many phytophagous insects has been obtained although casein is of animal origin. Several investigators have added amino acids to supply those that occur in insufficient amounts in casein, but occur in plant proteins and are believed to be required by certain insects. Vanderzant and Reiser (1956b) added cystine and glycine to diets for *P. gossypiella*. Cysteine was used in a diet for *A. grandis* (Vanderzant, 1959). Rock *et al.* (1964) added cystine, glycine, arginine, and lysine to a diet for the red-banded leaf roller, *Argyrotaenia velutinana* (Walker). There is no evidence that the concentration of any of these amino acids in casein would seriously limit growth of these insects. However, the efficiency of growth and ability to reproduce may depend on the relative proportions of amino acids present.

Dadd (1961c) found that casein alone regardless of purity was not satisfactory for the growth of *L. migratoria*, but *S. gregaria*, which did not grow with fat and vitamin-free casein as the protein source, grew well with less pure preparations of casein. Both insects developed with a mixture of casein, egg albumin, and peptone. Supplementation of diets with vitamins, various growth factors, seven amino acids, and minerals failed to make the diets with casein as the only protein adequate for rearing the insect. Casein with added amino acids or peptone was used in diets for *Loxostege sticticalis* (Linnaeus), *Heliothis zea* (Boddie), and *Gelechia malvella* Hübner. Increased growth rate occurred with added amino acids (Shumakov *et al.*, 1960).

Nayar (1964a) apparently obtained satisfactory growth with casein as the only nitrogen-containing substance for *M. bivittatus*.

Other relatively pure proteins used as sole source of nitrogen include albumin (Vanderzant and Reiser, 1956a) and soybean protein (Vanderzant and Davich, 1958). The test for adequate amounts and kinds of amino acids in other proteinaceous material depends upon the delineation of the functions of many impure plant products that are added to diets.

If growth on a diet with a single protein is improved with supplemental amino acids, the protein is probably deficient. If another protein is needed, failure of growth may be due to the lack of some non-nitrogen substance included as a trace contaminant. Quantitative studies determine the amounts of protein and other nutrients needed for optimum and minimum growth on a particular diet. Such information is necessary to evaluate nutritional data correctly. For example, it would be unwise to study amino acid metabolism with suboptimal amounts of carbohydrate because many amino acids might then be used as a source of energy.

An insect's nutritive requirements may also change during its growth. Larvae of *O. nubilalis* needed a high dietary level of protein and a low level of sugar in the early stages and a low level of protein and a high level of sugar during the late larval stages (Beck, 1956b).

Insects in general and plant-feeders in particular do not differ significantly from other animals in their dietary requirements for amino acids (House, 1962; Friend, 1958). Although about ten species have been employed in tests with amino acid diets, only five—the onion maggot, *Hylemya antiqua* (Friend and Patton, 1956), the pea aphid, *Acyrthosiphon pisum* (Auclair and Cartier, 1963), the pink bollworm, *Pectinophora gossypiella* (Vanderzant, 1957), the boll weevil, *Anthonomus grandis* (Vanderzant, 1965a), and *Argyrotaenia velutinana* (Rock, 1964)—have been reared successfully on such diets. Of these, the amino acid requirements were determined for *H. antiqua* (Friend *et al.*, 1957), *P. gossypiella* (Vanderzant, 1958), *A. grandis*, and *A. velutinana*. Amino acid diets that permitted only suboptimal growth yet were satisfactory for deletion experiments were used by Ishii and Hirano (1955) to determine the requirements for the Asiatic rice borer, *C. suppressalis*, and by Arai and Ito (1964) for the silkworm, *B. mori*. All six insects required the ten indispensable amino acids arginine, histidine, isoleucine, leucine, lysine, methionine, phenylalanine, threonine, tryptophan, and valine for growth. Proline also was indispensable for *B. mori* and poor growth occurred without aspartic acid. Since the latter is an important metabolic intermediate, substitution of another nitrogen-containing compound would have undoubtedly alleviated this deficiency.

Vanderzant (1958, 1965a) found that larvae of both *P. gossypiella* and *A. grandis* reached the adult stage with only the ten indispensable amino acids. Growth was suboptimal, as was to be expected, because increased demands were placed on the insects' metabolism for synthesis of the missing dietary amino acids.

Ishii and Hirano (1955) did not obtain growth of *C. suppressalis* on diets with the ten indispensable amino acids alone although the omission, one at a time, of each dispensable amino acid caused no appreciable change in growth. These workers analyzed larvae reared from diets lacking alanine, glycine, serine, glutamic acid, proline, tyrosine, aspartic acid, and cystine and found these same amino acids in insect tissues, thus proving that synthesis from other dietary substances occurred.

In view of the difficulty in compounding satisfactory defined diets for certain plant-feeding insects, several investigators (Kasting *et al.*, 1962; Kasting and McGinnis, 1962; Strong and Sakamoto, 1963) used an indirect method to determine amino acid requirements. Glucose-U-C^{14} was injected into larvae and the radioactivity in the amino acid subsequently measured. If little or no radioactivity was found in an amino acid, it was not synthesized by the insect so classed as indispensable in the diet.

B. Carbohydrates

All insects studied have been provided with carbohydrate in their diets. Glucose and sucrose, alone or together, and sometimes also combined with starch or dextrin, are satisfactory for growth of most plant-feeders. Some investigators pay little attention to the role of sugars as feeding stimulants although several examples of marked differences between sugars in this respect are believed to influence the results of nutritional experiments. In a series of experiments in which larvae were given a choice of different diets, Beck (1956a,c) showed that nutrients had markedly different effects on larval feeding. He found sugar to be the most important feeding stimulant for *O. nubilalis*.

Utilization of sugars for growth does not follow any pattern. *Chilo suppressalis* larvae (Hirano and Ishii, 1957) grew well with fructose, glucose, sucrose, maltose, and glycogen; D-ribose, D-arabinose, L-arabinose, D-xylose, L-rhamnose, L-sorbose, D-mannose,

D-galactose, trehalose, cellobiose, melibiose, lactose, melezitose, raffinose, starch, and inulin were not utilized at all or gave poor growth.

In feeding experiments with S. *gregaria* and L. *migratoria,* Dadd (1960d) discovered that these locusts utilized a number of carbohydrates very well including glucose, fructose, maltose, cellobiose, trehalose, sucrose, lactose, melibiose, melezitose, raffinose, dextrins, and starches. Pentoses, D-mannose, L-sorbose, and D-galactose were used sparingly, if at all. Surprisingly, the sugar alcohols— sorbitol, mannitol, and inositol—were utilized for growth. Locusts did not grow without carbohydrate, and neither protein nor fat replaced carbohydrate. Dadd (1960d) also conducted tests on the optimum concentration of carbohydrates needed for growth of the locusts and Ishii and Hirano (1957) did the same for C. *suppressalis.*

The effectiveness of sugars for promoting growth in the boll weevil was tested with an amino acid diet (Vanderzant, 1965a). Fructose promoted the fastest growth although size and yields of adults were similar for both fructose and sucrose. Adults also developed with satisfactory yields when larvae were fed glucose, maltose, lactose, corn starch, cellobiose, and mannose, although the adults were smaller. Galactose, melibiose, and ribose produced poor yields of small adults. Larvae died in the first instar when no carbohydrate was included in the diet.

Lacking a suitable test diet for B. *mori,* Ito (1960a) injected sugar solutions into the gut lumen from the mouth opening by means of a hypodermic needle and measured survival of the larvae. The best results were obtained with xylose, glucose, fructose, mannose, sucrose, maltose, lactose, cellobiose, trehalose, melibiose, raffinose, melezitose, sorbitol, mannitol, and dextrin. There was no correlation between survival and feeding stimulation of carbohydrates. Sucrose stimulated feeding the most, followed by fructose and raffinose, whereas glucose was a very weak stimulant (Ito, 1960b).

For laboratory rearing one or more of the common carbohydrates— glucose, fructose, sucrose, starch, or dextrin—should be suitable for the diet of almost any plant-feeding insect. Utilization experiments with other sugars determine only which carbohydrates in plants can be assimilated by insects feeding on those plants.

C. LIPIDS

Since Fraenkel and Blewett (1945, 1946) discovered the requirement for unsaturated fatty acids in *Ephestia,* almost all plant-feeding insects among the *Lepidoptera* tested were found to require fat in their diets. Linoleic or linolenic acids are the active moieties of the fat. Most vegetable oils contain these two fatty acids.

In 1949, Beck *et al.* reported that linoleic acid could replace corn oil in the diet of *O. nubilalis*. In tests with defined diets, Vanderzant *et al.* (1957) showed that both dietary linoleic and linolenic acids promoted emergence of normal pink bollworm moths. It required about five times as much linoleic acid to produce the same results as linolenic acid. On a more highly defined diet (Vanderzant, 1957) with cholesterol and linoleic acid as the only lipid substances, successful growth and emergence occurred also. However, linoleic acid did not promote emergence in the smaller tea tortrix, *Adoxophyes orana* Fischer von Roeslerstamm (Tamaki, 1961a), but linolenic acid was effective. The author has found that larvae of *H. zea* grew faster with linoleic acid than in the absence of fatty acids, but adults emerged with crumpled wings when larvae were fed linoleic acid. However, with linolenic acid as the only dietary fatty acid normal growth and emergence resulted. Similar results were obtained for *Trichoplusia ni* (Hübner) (Chippendale *et al.*, 1964, 1965). Rock *et al.* (1965) found that either linoleic or linolenic acid was needed for normal emergence of *A. velutinana*. Hirano (1963) found neither a growth-promoting effect nor an improvement in pupation and emergence of *C. suppressalis* by feeding soybean oil, oleic, and linoleic acids. At higher dietary levels they were toxic. At all concentrations linolenic acid was very toxic.

Locusts and grasshoppers also benefited from dietary fatty acids. Growth was retarded and adults of *S. gregaria* and *L. migratoria* had crumpled wings when deprived of linoleic acid. A considerable number of hoppers failed to molt at all (Dadd, 1960a). In *M. bivittatus* the only effect of a dietary lack of unsaturated fatty acids or linoleic acid was a crumpling of wings upon adult emergence (Nayar, 1964a).

Fats, either crude or refined, contain traces of other substances such as sterols, tocopherol, carotene, and essential oils that may affect feeding and nutrition in insects. Phospholipids may contain choline and inositol also. If these trace substances are accounted for, the effects of fatty acids can be determined. Nevertheless, a beneficial effect of fat is frequently noted. This can be explained by an improvement in physical properties of diets and solubilization of other dietary lipids such as sterols.

Because insects are unique in not being able to synthesize the sterol nucleus, a sterol must be included in all diets. Phytophagous insects are very efficient in converting plant sterols to tissue sterols, the major body sterol being cholesterol (Levinson, 1962; Beck and Kapadia, 1957). Insect diets usually include cholesterol, which produces satisfactory growth for most insects tested. However, in *B. mori*, inferior growth was obtained with cholesterol as compared to β-sitosterol and stigmasterol (Ito, 1961a,b). Since plant sterols stimulated feeding and cholesterol did not, retardation of growth was mainly due to the lack of feeding stimulation (Ito *et al.*, 1964). Locusts, *S. gregaria* and *L. migratoria* (Dadd, 1960b), were able to use cholesterol, cholesteryl acetate, β-sitosterol, and dihydrocholesterol, whereas ergosterol, stigmasteryl acetate, 7-dehydrocholesterol, and a number of other steroids were not used. The pink bollworm grew as well on diets containing ergosterol, sitosterol, and stigmasterol as on those with cholesterol (Vanderzant and Reiser, 1956b). Cholesterol, sitosterol, and stigmasterol were equally effective in satisfying the sterol requirements of the boll weevil larva (Vanderzant, 1963a).

Although choline and inositol have several functions and occur in both small and large molecules, their presence in phospholipids justifies their classification in the lipids. In this form they are sometimes overlooked in nutritional tests.

Choline is an indispensable nutrient, although in some species it can be partially replaced by its analogs. It is needed in relatively large amounts as compared to other trace substances and care must be taken to ensure that enough is present in diets.

Inositol was first reported to be required for growth of the German cockroach *Blattella germanica* (Linnaeus) (Forgash, 1958; Gordon, 1959). Early attempts to show that inositol was a growth factor for this insect failed because nymphs were fed a stock diet before being placed on deficient diets. Also, a number of dietary ingredients such as proteins and lipids contain inositol as an impurity.

The boll weevil failed to grow on a defined diet containing casein but grew very well if the diet contained soybean protein or yeast (Vanderzant and Davich, 1958). The latter substances were replaced by inositol (Vanderzant, 1959). No growth at all was observed in casein diets without inositol. Subsequently, Dadd (1961b) found that locusts needed inositol. None survived the fourth instar with diets lacking inositol. This deficiency also interfered with melanization and the yellowing due to carotene.

D. VITAMINS

In 1957, Dadd reported that carotene was needed in the diet of *S. gregaria*. Later, in experiments with *S. gregaria* and *L. migra-*

toria he showed (Dadd, 1961a) that although a slight retardation of growth occurred without dietary carotene, the principal effect of carotene deficiency was on the pigmentation. Melanization was reduced and a marked reduction in the intensity of the colored pigments was observed, indicating that carotene was a precursor of these pigments.

Vitamin A containing pigments have been found in insect eyes Goldsmith (1958). It is likely that the sensitive tests now available for detecting trace substances will reveal a wider distribution of carotene and Vitamin A in insects.

The need for dietary B-vitamins in animals is so universal that it hardly seems necessary to restate it. However, the following insects have been tested with vitamin-deficient diets: *C. suppressalis* (Ishii and Urushibara, 1954), *H. antiqua* (Friend and Patton, 1956), locusts (Dadd, 1961b), *A. grandis* (Vanderzant, 1963a) and *P. gossypiella* (Ouye and Vanderzant, 1964). These insects all required pantothenic acid, nicotinamide, riboflavin, pyridoxine, folic acid, and thiamine.

Obviously, tests on requirements for vitamins should be conducted under axenic conditions because microorganisms are an excellent source of vitamins if allowed to propagate in the diet or in the insect. In the tests cited, the investigators used aseptic techniques except Dadd (1961b), who used dry diets that discourage microbial growth even under nonaseptic conditions.

Biotin requirements are difficult to determine because the levels needed are so low that even purified proteins contain enough biotin to permit growth. Friend and Patton (1956) proved that *H. antiqua* required dietary biotin with an amino acid diet. Similar tests with *P. gossypiella* showed that it also required biotin (Ouye and Vanderzant, 1964). Ishii and Urushibara (1954) took advantage of the irreversible reaction between avidin and biotin to prove a dietary biotin requirement for *C. suppressalis*. No larvae grew when raw egg white was added to the diet. Heated diet permitted larval growth since the compound is destroyed by heat.

Other growth factors reported to improve the growth of *H. antiqua* are vitamin B_{12}, thioctic acid, and coenzyme A (Friend and Patton, 1956). However, these compounds were not indispensable. A requirement for vitamin B_{12} in the diet of the pink bollworm could not be proved (Ouye and Vanderzant, 1964). Nucleic acids improve growth in the *Diptera* (House, 1962).

Quantitative amounts of vitamins needed by various insects may differ greatly. This difference depends in part on the kind of diet fed to an insect. B-vitamins are used as coenzymes in the metabolism of protein, carbohydrate, and fat, and the amounts of vitamins needed may depend upon the amounts and kinds of nutrients in the diet that are metabolized. Sang (1959, 1962) showed that the dietary requirement of *Drosophila* for nicotinic acid and folic acid increased about three- and sixfold, respectively, when the protein content of the diet was increased from 4 to 7%. Analogous relationships exist among many other nutrients.

Fortunately, relatively large excesses of B-vitamins do not have an adverse effect upon insects, and minimum amounts can safely be increased to ensure against additional needs when changes are made in diets.

A dietary requirement for ascorbic acid in insects is one of the most interesting findings that has occurred in recent years. From the data now available the insects that consume dry, stored, or decaying food and carnivorous species need no dietary ascorbic acid, whereas the majority of plant-feeding insects require it. Among phytophagous insects that require ascorbic acid are *S. gregaria*, *L. migratoria* (Dadd, 1957, 1960e), *A. grandis*, *H. zea*, *E. acrea* (Vanderzant *et al.*, 1962), *B. mori* (Ito, 1961c,d), *T. ni* (Chippendale *et al.*, 1965), and *O. nubilalis* (Chippendale and Beck, 1964). In addition to these eight insects, a number of others are now being reared on diets that include ascorbic acid. Not all phytophagous insects require ascorbic acid. Successful rearing and reproduction of two insects, *H. antiqua* and *P. gossypiella* were achieved without dietary ascorbic acid (Friend and Patton, 1956; Vanderzant, 1957).

Circumstantial evidence of a requirement for dietary ascorbic acid in *B. mori* was presented by Gamo (see Legay, 1958) in a series of experiments begun in 1941. Mulberry leaves have a high content of ascorbic acid and the content in the silkworm was related to the insect's feeding on this host plant.

Chemical analyses of insects for ascorbic acid (Dadd, 1960e; Mehrotra, 1963; Vanderzant and Richardson, 1963) show that most insects contain it. Largest amounts were found in eggs and ovaries. Even when the vitamin was not present in the diets, the insects examined contained ascorbic acid. *Pectinophora gossypiella*, a plant-feeder, contained ascorbic acid when fed diets lacking the vitamin, whereas *H. zea* contained no appreciable amount of ascorbic acid when the vitamin was omitted from the diet (Vanderzant and Richardson, 1963). Mehrotra (1963) found it in plant-feeding species, *Dysdercus koenigii* (Fabricius) and *Aulacophora foveicollis* Lucas, and also in insects that consume dry food, *Trogoderma granarium*

Everts and *Tribolium castaneum* (Herbst). These reports and the histological evidence reported by Day (1949) indicate that a large number of insects utilize ascorbic acid and that many can synthesize their own needs.

Ascorbic acid plays an important role in reproduction. *Anthonomus grandis* adults could not lay fertile eggs without it (Vanderzant and Davich, 1961), although larvae could be reared to the adult stage without a dietary supply (Vanderzant *et al.*, 1962). In other insects growth was retarded and molting abnormal without dietary ascorbic acid.

E. MINERAL REQUIREMENTS

Requirements of insects for mineral elements are usually satisfied by including some commercially available salt mixture in the diets. Such mixtures were designed for vertebrates and contain large amounts of calcium, sodium, phosphorus, and other minerals not commonly found in appreciable amounts in plants or in the insects feeding upon them. It is not likely that phytophagous insects require the same proportional amounts of minerals as do the vertebrates. Nevertheless, commercial salt mixtures have been used successfully in insect diets. Most investigators have restricted their studies of mineral requirements of insects to the determination of the optimum levels needed for growth. A wide range of dietary amounts has been reported for various insects discussed herein. Dadd (1961c) observed that a salt mixture fed at a level as high as 11% of the dry constituents of the diet had no apparent deleterious effect on locusts. He also found that very simple mixtures containing only four salts were adequate for growth. It can be assumed that salts present in the other dietary constituents, especially the large molecules, make a substantial contribution to the supply of trace minerals.

No diet has been prepared that will permit an exact evaluation of the effect of trace minerals on insects. Although diets composed of only small molecules would make such studies possible, all constituents would first have to be purified to remove trace elements.

The minerals included in the amino acid diet for *P. gossypiella* consisted of soluble salts except for calcium carbonate (Vanderzant, 1957). A higher content of potassium than sodium was used to conform more closely with the ratios of these elements present in plants. With only slight modifications, the same mixture was used in diets for *A. grandis* (Vanderzant, 1965a). The effects on growth of deleting individual salts was also studied. Prior to these tests no constituents of the diet were purified. The only large molecule was agar, which could be expected to furnish appreciable quantities of calcium and magnesium and traces of other elements. Development from egg to adult was not hindered by omission of any of the elements except magnesium, although tests on the deletion of potassium and phosphate were not run. Improved growth occurred when the concentrations of some of the salts were changed.

F. UNIDENTIFIED NUTRIENTS

A great deal of difficulty has been experienced by some investigators in finding suitable defined diets for rearing insects to the adult stage. It is postulated that unidentified nutrients exist. However, certainly some of the failures must be attributed to suboptimal concentrations of nutrients, lack of feeding stimulants and other factors already mentioned.

One of the first growth factors reported for a phytophagous insect, *O. nubilalis* (Beck, 1953), has now been found to be satisfied largely if not entirely by ascorbic acid (Chippendale and Beck, 1964). *Melanoplus sanguinipes* (Fabricius) and *M. bivittatus* were reported to require a growth factor extractable from lettuce (Kreasky, 1962), but Nayar (1964a) reared the latter insect on defined diets without plant extracts. Kreasky substituted only 1.5 gm of brewer's yeast for the B-vitamins, and it is possible that the yeast did not contain enough B-vitamins for growth. Tamaki (1964) reported that *A. orana* larvae required a water-soluble factor extractable from tea leaves. This factor was not a feeding stimulant (Tamaki, 1961b). An unidentified nutrient was reported for *C. suppressalis* (Ishii, 1952). The silkworm *B. mori* has remained intractable to good growth on defined diets; but there has been some success in rearing it on diets containing no leaf powder (Ito, 1962; Ito and Horie, 1962). The problem appears to be related to the insect's highly specific chemical and physical feeding requirements.

Although yeast extracts, plant extracts, and other natural products are included in the diets of many other phytophagous insects, there is no evidence that these mixtures could not be replaced by ordinary nutrients.

VII. REPRODUCTION

The ultimate test for a nutritionally adequate defined diet is to obtain adult insects that will reproduce normally. Unfortunately, many nutritional experiments are terminated before adults develop or adults are not tested for reproduction. However, a few insects have been reared on defined diets for several generations. *Pectino-phora gossypiella* was reared for four generations on an amino acid diet before the test was ended (Vanderzant, 1957). Friend *et al.* (1957) obtained eggs from *H. antiqua* reared from amino acid diets. *Anthonomus grandis* reproduced when fed amino acid diets both as larvae and adults (Vanderzant, 1965b). *Acyrthosiphon pisum* nymphs reared to adults on amino acid diets gave birth to nymphs which also matured to adults on the same diet (Auclair and Cartier, 1963).

Diets with casein, corn oil, and other nutrients have supported growth of the boll weevil for nine generations (Vanderzant, 1963b). A similar diet was successful for rearing six generations of *A. veluti-nana* (Rock *et al.*, 1964). *Heliothis zea* adults reproduced when larvae were reared from casein diet (Vanderzant *et al.*, 1962).

Except for those adult insects whose dietary requirements are restricted largely to sugar and water, few tests have been conducted of fecundity, fertility, and longevity of adults fed defined diets.

Cavanagh (1963) extended the studies of Dadd (1960a, 1961c) and studied the effects of diet on reproduction of *S. gregaria*. Adults fed diet matured almost as rapidly as adults fed grass but laid very few egg pods. Although eggs from adults fed diet had low fertility, some hatchlings also were reared to adults on diet. Survival of adults of *M. persicae* and production of larvae was greatest when adults were fed a complex diet containing amino acids, sucrose, vitamins, minerals, cholesterol, and water (Mittler and Dadd, 1963b).

Several tests have been conducted of the effects on oviposition of deletion of nutrients from defined diets. Adults of *A. grandis* required a daily dietary supply of the ten indispensable amino acids in order to lay (Vanderzant, 1963b). Oviposition was greatly reduced when corn oil and fat-soluble vitamins, inositol, choline, and cholesterol were omitted from the adult diet (Vanderzant and Richardson, 1964). No eggs from cholesterol-deficient diets hatched after the first 12 days of adult feeding. The effects of deleting ascorbic acid from diet already has been discussed (Section VI).

These few examples clearly indicate that there are many insects that need a complete and well-balanced diet in order to survive and propagate. In the examples cited, the adult diets did not differ greatly from the diets fed to the immature forms.

VIII. NUTRIENT RESERVES

The insect egg is important as a source of trace nutrients that can be carried over from one generation to the next. Adults of *A.*

grandis weigh only about 100 times more on the average than the eggs. A comparison of weights of progeny from parents of different size is shown in Table IV. The F_2 adults were smaller than their parents and their weights correlated also with the size of the eggs (F_2) from which they hatched. The egg of this insect is large as compared to the size of the adult; the materials in the egg could conceivably make a significant contribution to the newly hatched

TABLE IV

EFFECT OF SIZE OF ADULTS AND EGGS OF
Anthonomus grandis ON THE PROGENY

F_1 adults (mg)	F_2 eggs (mg)	Times increase	F_2 adults (mg)	Times increase
22.5	0.163	138	10.2	63
12.2	0.134	91	8.5	63

larvae and hence mask a dietary deficiency of a nutrient. These results also indicate that the larval diets from which the F_2 adults were reared was not adequate for optimum growth. Many insects are not as well supplied with stored reserves; *H. zea* increases in weight about 3000 times from egg to adult.

Possible evidence of trace nutrients carried from adult to egg was illustrated by the findings of the effect of ascorbic acid in *A. grandis* (Vanderzant *et al.*, 1962). Adults fed diets deficient in ascorbic acid laid eggs that hatched into larvae that did not mature on diets lacking ascorbic acid, whereas adults that were given ascorbic acid produced offspring that matured on the deficient diet.

Dadd (1961a) believed that if the concentration of carotene in the locust egg was low, dietary carotene might affect growth. He obtained eggs from parents reared on carotene-deficient diets and observed inferior growth, decreased activity, and abnormal coloration of the hatchlings reared on carotene-deficient diets, whereas improved growth and coloration occurred with similar hatchlings fed diets containing carotene. A masking effect was thus demonstrated for the normal egg which contained enough carotene to permit the insect to develop on carotene-deficient diets.

IX. CONCLUSION

It is evident from the discussion herein that a number of factors other than the nutritional value of dietary ingredients must be considered in devising a satisfactory defined diet for an insect. Further-more, a better understanding of these factors is needed as the use of highly refined dietary substances is attempted. Information on an insect's qualitative and semiquantitative nutritional require-ments is useful in devising a diet from which both good growth and efficient use of nutrients can be obtained. Use of defined diets has revealed several nutrients not heretofore recognized as important for insects. With the present information and the analytical chemical techniques now available, knowledge on nutrition and metabolism of dietary substances can be advanced further.

REFERENCES

Arai, N., and Ito, T. (1964). Amino acid requirements of the silkworm, *Bombyx mori* L. *J. Sericult. Sci. Japan* **33**, 107–110.

Auclair, J. L. (1963). Aphid feeding and nutrition. *Ann. Rev. Entomol.* **8**, 439–490.

Auclair, J. L., and Cartier, J. J. (1963). Pea aphid: Rearing on a chemically defined diet. *Science* **142**, 1068–1069.

Auclair, J. L., Maltais, J. B., and Cartier, J. J. (1957). Factors in resistance of peas to the pea aphid, *Acyrthosiphon pisum* (Harr.) (Homoptera: Aphididae) II. Amino Acids. *Can. Entomologist* **89**, 457–464.

Beck, S. D. (1953). Nutrition of the European corn borer, *Pyrausta nubilalis* (Hübn.). III. An unidentified dietary factor required for larval growth. *J. Gen. Physiol.* **36**, 317–325.

Beck, S. D. (1956a). Nutrition of the European corn borer, *Pyrausta nubilalis* (Hübn.). IV. Feeding reactions of first instar larvae. *Ann. Entomol. Soc. Am.* **49**, 399–405.

Beck, S. D. (1956b). The European corn borer, *Pyrausta nubilalis* (Hübn.), and its principal host plant. II. The influence of nutritional factors on larval establish-ment and development on the corn plant. *Ann. Entomol. Soc. Am.* **49**, 582–588.

Beck, S. D. (1956c). Bimodal response to dietary sugars by an insect. *Biol. Bull.* **110**, 219–228.

Beck, S. D., and Hanec, W. (1958). Effect of amino acids on feeding behaviour of the European corn borer, *Pyrausta nubilalis* (Hübn.). *J. Insect Physiol.* **2**, 85–96.

Beck, S. D., and Kapadia, G. G. (1957). Insect nutrition and metabolism of sterols. *Science* **126**, 258–259.

Beck, S. D., and Stauffer, J. F. (1950). An aseptic method for rearing European corn borer larvae. *J. Econ. Entomol.* **43**, 4–6.

Beck, S. D., Lilly, J. H., and Stauffer, J. F. (1949). Nutrition of the European corn borer, *Pyrausta nubilalis* (Hübn.). I. Development of a satisfactory purified diet for larval growth. *Ann. Entomol. Soc. Am.* **42**, 483–496.

Beck, S. D., Edwards, C. A., and Medler, J. T. (1958). Feeding and nutrition of the milkweed bug, *Oncopeltus fasciatus* (Dallas). *Ann. Entomol. Soc. Am.* **51**, 283–288.

Bottger, G. T. (1942). Development of synthetic food media for use in nutrition studies of the European corn borer. *J. Agr. Res.* **65**, 493–500.

Cavanagh, G. G. (1963). The use of the Dadd synthetic diet as a food for adult *Schisto-cerca gregaria* (Forsk.) and the effects of some additions and modifications to it. *J. Insect Physiol.* **9**, 759–775.

Chippendale, G. M., and Beck, S. D. (1964). Nutrition of the European corn borer, *Ostrinia nubilalis* (Hübn.) V. Ascorbic acid as the corn leaf factor. *Entomol. Exptl. Appl.* **7**, 241–248.

Chippendale, G. M., Beck, S. D., and Strong, F. M. (1964). Methyl linolenate as an essential nutrient for the cabbage looper, *Trichoplusia ni* (Hübner). *Nature* **204**, 710–711.

Chippendale, G. M., Beck, S. D., and Strong, F. M. (1965). Nutrition of the cabbage looper, *Trichoplusia ni* (Hübner). I. Some requirements for larval growth and wing development. *J. Insect Physiol.* **11**, 211–223.

Dadd, R. H. (1957). Ascorbic acid and carotene in the nutrition of the desert locust, *Schistocerca gregaria* (Forsk.). *Nature* **179**, 427–428.

Dadd, R. H. (1960a). The nutritional requirements of locusts. I. Development of synthetic diets and lipid requirements. *J. Insect Physiol.* **4**, 319–347.

Dadd, R. H. (1960b). The nutritional requirements of locusts. II. Utilization of sterols. *J. Insect Physiol.* **5**, 161–168.

Dadd, R. H. (1960c). Observations on the palatability and utilisation of food by locusts, with particular reference to the interpretation of performances in growth trials using synthetic diets. *Entomol. Exptl. Appl.* **3**, 283–304.

Dadd, R. H. (1960d). The nutritional requirements of locusts. III. Carbohydrate requirements and utilization. *J. Insect Physiol.* **5**, 301–316.

Dadd, R. H. (1960e). Some effects of dietary ascorbic acid on locusts. *Proc. Roy. Soc.* **B153**, 128–143.

Dadd, R. H. (1961a). Observations on the effects of carotene on the growth and pigmentation of locusts. *Bull. Entomol. Res.* **52**, 63–81.

Dadd, R. H. (1961b). The nutritional requirements of locusts. IV. Requirements for vitamins of the B complex. *J. Insect Physiol.* **6**, 1–12.

Dadd, R. H. (1961c). The nutritional requirements of locusts. V. Observations on essential fatty acids, chlorophyll, nutritional salt mixtures, and the protein or amino acid components of synthetic diets. *J. Insect Physiol.* **6**, 126–145.

Day, M. F. (1949). The distribution of ascorbic acid in the tissues of insects. *Australian J. Sci. Res.* **B2**, 19–30.

Dougherty, E. C. (1959). Introduction to axenic culture of invertebrate metazoa: A goal. *Ann. N. Y. Acad. Sci.* **77**, 27–54.

Feir, D., and Beck, S. D. (1963). Feeding behavior of the large milkweed bug, *Oncopeltus fasciatus*. *Ann. Entomol. Soc. Am.* **56**, 224–229.

Forgash, A. J. (1958). The effect of inositol on growth, survival, and maturation in *Periplaneta americana* (L.). *Ann. Entomol. Soc. Am.* **51**, 406–409.

Fraenkel, G., and Blewett, M. (1945). Linoleic acid, α-tocopherol and other fat-soluble substances as nutritional factors for insects. *Nature* **155**, 392–393.

Fraenkel, G., and Blewett, M. (1946). Linoleic acid, vitamin E and other fat-soluble substances in the nutrition of certain insects, *Ephestia kuehniella*, *E. elutella*, *E. cautella* and *Plodia interpunctella* (Lep). *J. Exptl. Biol.* **22**, 172–190.

Friend, W. G. (1958). Nutritional requirements of phytophagous insects. *Ann. Rev. Entomol.* **3**, 57–74.

Friend, W. G., and Patton, R. L. (1956). Studies on vitamin requirements of larvae of the onion maggot, *Hylemya antiqua* (Mg.) under aseptic conditions. *Can. J. Zool.* **34**, 152–162.

Friend, W. G., Backs, R. H., and Cass, L. M. (1957). Studies on amino acid requirements of larvae of the onion maggot, *Hylemya antiqua* (Mg.), under aseptic conditions. *Can. J. Zool.* **35**, 535–543.

Friend, W. G., Salkeld, E. H., and Stevenson, I. L. (1959). Nutrition of onion maggots, larvae of *Hylemya antiqua* (Meig.), with reference to other members of the genus *Hylemya*. *Ann. N. Y. Acad. Sci.* **77**, 384–393.

Fukada, T., Suto, M., Kameyama, T., and Kawasugi, S. (1962). Synthetic diet for silkworm raising.*Nature* **196**, 53–54.

Goldsmith, T. H. (1958). The visual system of the honeybee. *Proc. Natl. Acad. Sci. U.S.* **44**, 123–126.

Gordon, H. T. (1959). Minimal nutritional requirements of the German roach, *Blattella germanica* L. *Ann. N. Y. Acad. Sci.* **77**, 290–351.

Hirano, C. (1963). Effect of dietary unsaturated fatty acids on the growth of larvae of *Chilo suppressalis* Walker (Lepidoptera: Pyralidae). *Japan. J. Appl. Entomol. Zool.* **7**, 59–62.

Hirano, C., and Ishii, S. (1957). Nutritive values of carbohydrates for the growth of larvae of the rice stem borer, *Chilo suppressalis* Walker. *Bull. Natl. Inst. Agr. Sci.* **C7**, 89–99.

House, H. L. (1961). Insect nutrition. *Ann. Rev. Entomol.* **6**, 13–26.

House, H. L. (1962). Insect nutrition. *Ann. Rev. Biochem.* **31**, 653–672.

House, H. L., and Barlow, J. S. (1964). Effects on the parasitoid *Agria affinis*, of small molecules in diets. *J. Insect Physiol.* **10**, 255–260.

Ishii, S. (1952). Some problems on the rearing method of rice stem borer by synthetic media under aseptic condition. *Oyo-Kontyu* **8**, 93–98 (English summary).

Ishii, S., and Hirano, C. (1955). Qualitative studies on the essential amino acids for the growth of the larva of the rice stem borer, *Chilo simplex* Butler, under aseptic conditions. *Bull. Natl. Inst. Agr. Sci.* **C5**, 35–48.

Ishii, S., and Hirano, C. (1957). Effect of various concentrations of protein and carbohydrate in a diet on the growth of the rice stem borer larva.*Japan. J. Appl. Entomol. Zool.* **1**, 75–79.

Ishii, S., and Urushibara, H. (1954). On fat-soluble and water-soluble growth factors required by the rice stem borer, *Chilo simplex* Butler. *Bull. Natl. Inst. Agr. Sci.* **C4**, 109–133.

Ito, T. (1960a). Nutritive values of carbohydrates for the silkworm, *Bombyx mori*. *Nature* **187**, 527.

Ito, T. (1960b). Effect of sugars on feeding of larvae of the silkworm, *Bombyx mori*. *J. Insect Physiol.* **5**, 95–107.

Ito, T. (1961a). Sterol requirements of the silkworm, *Bombyx mori*. *Nature* **191**, 882–883.

Ito, T. (1961b). Nutrition of the silkworm, *Bombyx mori*. III. Requirements for sterols and their effects on the feeding. *Bull. Sericult. Exptl. Sta. (Tokyo)* **17**, 91–117 (tables and summary in English).

Ito, T. (1961c). Effect of dietary ascorbic acid on the silkworm, *Bombyx mori*. *Nature* **192**, 951–952.

Ito, T. (1961d). Nutrition of the silkworm, *Bombyx mori*. IV. Effects of ascorbic acid. *Bull. Sericult. Expt. Sta. (Tokyo)* **17**, 119–136 (tables and summary in English).

Ito, T. (1962). Rearing of the silkworm entirely on semi-synthetic diets which do not contain leaf powder.*J. Sericult. Sci.Japan* **31**, 1–6 (tables and summary in English).

Ito, T., and Horie, Y. (1962). Nutrition of the silkworm, *Bombyx mori*. VII. An aseptic culture of larvae on semi-synthetic diets. *J. Insect Physiol.* **8**, 569–578.

Ito, T., Kawashima, K., Nakahara, M., Nakanishi, K., and Terahara, A. (1964). Effects of sterols on feeding and nutrition of the silkworm, *Bombyx mori* L. *J. Insect Physiol.* **10**, 225–238.

Kasting, R., and McGinnis, A. J. (1962). Nutrition of the pale western cutworm, *Agrotis orthogonia* Morr. (Lepidoptera, Noctuidae). IV. Amino acid requirements determined with glucose-U-C[14]. *J. Insect Physiol.* **8**, 97–103.

Kasting, R., Davis, G. R. F., and McGinnis, A. J. (1962). Nutritionally essential and non-essential amino acids for the prairie grain wireworm, *Ctenicera destructor* Brown, determined with glucose-U-C[14]. *J. Insect Physiol.* **8**, 589–596.

Kreasky, J. B. (1962). A growth factor in romaine lettuce for the grasshoppers *Melanoplus sanguinipes* (F.) and *M. bivittatus* (Say). *J. Insect Physiol.* **8**, 493–504.

Legay, J. M. (1958). Recent advances in silkworm nutrition. *Ann. Rev. Entomol.* **3**, 75–86.

Levinson, Z. H. (1962). The function of dietary sterols in phytophagous insects. *J. Insect Physiol.* **8**, 191–198.

Matsumoto, Y. (1954). An aseptic rearing of the oriental fruit moth, *Grapholitha molesta* Busck on synthetic food media. *Ber. Ohara Inst. Landwirtsch. Biol., Okayama Univ.* **10**, 66–71.

Mehrotra, K. N. (1963). Ascorbic acid in insects. *Indian J. Entomol.* **25**, 270–273.

Mellanby, K., and French, R. A. (1958). The importance of drinking water to larval insects. *Entomol. Exptl. Appl.* **1**, 116–124.

Mittler, T. E., and Dadd, R. H. (1962). Artificial feeding and rearing of the aphid, *Myzus persicae* (Sulzer), on a completely defined synthetic diet. *Nature* **195**, 404.

Mittler, T. E., and Dadd, R. H. (1963a). Studies on the artificial feeding of the aphid *Myzus persicae* (Sulzer). I. Relative uptake of water and sucrose solutions. *J. Insect Physiol.* **9**, 623–645.

Mittler, T. E., and Dadd, R. H. (1963b). Studies on the artificial feeding of the aphid *Myzus persicae* (Sulzer). II. Relative survival, development, and larviposition on different diets. *J. Insect Physiol.* **9**, 741–757.

Mukaiyama, F., and Ito, T. (1962). Digestion experiments in the silkworm, *Bombyx mori*, by means of artificial diets. II. Effect of cellulose powder added in diets. *J. Sericult. Sci. Japan* **31**, 398–406 (tables and summary in English).

Nayar, J. K. (1964a). The nutritional requirements of grasshoppers. I. Rearing of the grasshopper, *Melanoplus bivittatus* (Say), on a completely defined synthetic diet and some effects of different concentrations of B-vitamin mixture, linoleic acid, and β-carotene. *Can. J. Zool.* **42**, 11–22.

Nayar, J. K. (1964b). The nutritional requirements of grasshoppers. II. Effects of plant phospholipids and extracts of bran on growth, development, and survival of the grasshoppers *Melanoplus bivittatus* (Say) and *Camnula pellucida* (Scudder). *Can. J. Zool.* **42**, 23–38.

Naylor, A. F. (1964). Possible value of casein, gluten, egg albumin, or fibrin as whole proteins in the diet of two strains of the flour beetle, *Tribolium confusum* (Tenebrionidae). *Can. J. Zool.* **42**, 1–9.

Ouye, M. T., and Vanderzant, E. S. (1964). Vitamin requirements of the pink bollworm. *J. Econ. Entomol.* **57**, 427–430.

Rock, G. C. (1964). Unpublished data.

Rock, G. C., Glass, E. H., and Patton, R. L. (1964). Axenic rearing of the red-banded leaf roller, *Argyrotaenia velutinana* on meridic diets. *Ann. Entomol. Soc. Am.* **57**, 617–621.

Rock, G. C., Patton, R. L., and Glass, E. H. (1965). Studies of the fatty acid requirements of *Argyrotaenia velutinana* (Walker). *J. Insect Physiol.* **11**, 91–101.

Sang, J. H. (1959). Circumstances affecting the nutritional requirements of *Drosophila melanogaster*. *Ann. N. Y. Acad. Sci.* **77**, 352–365.

Sang, J. H. (1962). Relationships between protein supplies and B-vitamin requirements, in axenically cultured *Drosophila. J. Nutr.* **77**, 355–368.

Scheel, C. A., Beck, S. D., and Medler, J. T. (1957). Nutrition of plant-sucking Hemi-
ptera. *Science* **125**, 444–445.

Shumakov, E. M., Edelman, N. M., and Borisova, A. B. (1960). Experiment on raising
phytophagous insects upon artificial media. *Dokl. Akad. Nauk SSSR* **130**, 237–240.

Strong, F. E., and Sakamoto, S. S. (1963). Some amino acid requirements of the green
peach aphid, *Myzus persicae* (Sulzer), determined with glucose-U-C¹⁴. *J. Insect
Physiol.* **9**, 875–879.

Tamaki, Y. (1961a). Studies on nutrition and metabolism of the smaller tea tortrix,
Adoxophyes orana (Fischer von Röslerstamm). II. An essential factor for adult
emergence. *Japan. J. Appl. Entomol. Zool.* **5**, 58–63.

Tamaki, Y. (1961b). Studies on the nutrition and metabolism of the smaller tea tortrix,
Adoxophyes orana (Fischer von Röslerstamm). III. Nature of an unknown dietary
factor for larval growth. *Japan. J. Appl. Entomol. Zool.* **5**, 203–206.

Tamaki, Y. (1964). Studies on the nutrition and metabolism of the smaller tea tortrix
Adoxophyes orana (Fischer von Röslerstamm). IV. Some chemical properties
of an unknown dietary factor responsible for larval growth. *Japan. J. Appl. Entomol.
Zool.* **8**, 55–61.

Thorsteinson, A. J., and Nayar, J. K. (1963). Plant phospholipides as feeding stimulants for grasshoppers. *Can. J. Zool.* **41**, 931–935.

Vanderzant, E. S. (1957). Growth and reproduction of the pink bollworm on an amino
acid medium. *J. Econ. Entomol.* **50**, 219–221.

Vanderzant, E. S. (1958). The amino acid requirements of the pink bollworm. *J. Econ.
Entomol.* **51**, 309–311.

Vanderzant, E. S. (1959). Inositol: An indispensable dietary requirement for the
boll weevil. *J. Econ. Entomol.* **52**, 1018–1019.

Vanderzant, E. S. (1963a). Nutrition of the boll weevil larva. *J. Econ. Entomol.* **56**,
357–362.

Vanderzant, E. S. (1963b). Nutrition of the adult boll weevil: Oviposition on defined
diets and amino acid requirements. *J. Insect Physiol.* **9**, 683–691.

Vanderzant, E. S. (1965a). Axenic rearing of the boll weevil on defined diets: Amino
acid, carbohydrate, and mineral requirements. *J. Insect Physiol.* **11**, 659–670.

Vanderzant, E. S. (1965b). Unpublished data.

Vanderzant, E. S., and Davich, T. B. (1958). Laboratory rearing of the boll weevil:
A satisfactory larval diet and oviposition studies. *J. Econ. Entomol.* **51**, 288–291.

Vanderzant, E. S., and Davich, T. B. (1961). Artificial diets for the adult boll weevil
and techniques for obtaining eggs. *J. Econ. Entomol.* **54**, 923–928.

Vanderzant, E. S., and Reiser, R. (1956a). Aseptic rearing of the pink bollworm on
synthetic media. *J. Econ. Entomol.* **49**, 7–10.

Vanderzant, E. S., and Reiser, R. (1956b). Studies of the nutrition of the pink bollworm using purified casein media. *J. Econ. Entomol.* **49**, 454–458.

Vanderzant, E. S., and Richardson, C. D. (1963). Ascorbic acid in the nutrition of
plant-feeding insects. *Science* **140**, 989–991.

Vanderzant, E. S., and Richardson, C. D. (1964). Nutrition of the adult boll weevil:
Lipid requirements. *J. Insect Physiol.* **10**, 267–272.

Vanderzant, E. S., Kerur, D., and Reiser, R. (1957). The role of dietary fatty acids in
the development of the pink bollworm. *J. Econ. Entomol.* **50**, 606–608.

Vanderzant, E. S., Pool, M. C., and Richardson, C. D. (1962). The role of ascorbic
acid in the nutrition of three cotton insects. *J. Insect Physiol.* **8**, 287–297.

Chapter 19

Southern Pine Beetles

EDGAR W. CLARK AND EBEN A. OSGOOD, JR.

U. S. Forest Service,
Forestry Sciences Laboratory,
Durham, North Carolina, and
Department of Entomology,
University of Maine,
Orono, Maine

Prior to Clark and Osgood (1964b) no laboratory technique for continuously producing large numbers of pine bark beetles had been reported. Further, with the exception of studies conducted by Thatcher (1963), attempts to rear the southern pine beetle (*Dendroctonus frontalis* Zimm.) starting with uninfested material have had little or no success and have briefly been reviewed by Dixon and Osgood (1961). Thatcher, by confining southern pine beetles in screen cages containing 2- to 4-ft-long bolts subjected to various treatments, was able to rear these beetles for seven generations. The only other large-scale rearing technique reported for bark beetles was for the greater and lesser elm bark beetles, *Scolytus multistriatus* Marsh. and *Hylurgopinus rufipes* Eich. (Griswold, 1948).

In the past, techniques for rearing scolytid pine bark beetles have been based almost entirely on the use of natural diet and have been of three general types: on inner bark sandwiches between glass or plastic plates; on short bolts, or sections therefrom, confined in screen, glass, or plastic containers; and, on longer bolts, 2 to 8 ft long, again normally confined in some sort of container. However, for the most part, such techniques consisted of caging infested materials and allowing the beetles to mature and emerge. Attempts to carry the adults through further generations usually failed.

Clark and Osgood (1964a,b,c, 1966) utilized several techniques for rearing the southern pine beetle and the coarse writing engraver (*Ips calligraphus* Germ.); all their methods fall into one of the three types mentioned above, but most of them made use of pine bolts. Each of these techniques serves a specific purpose, such as studying single pairs or obtaining eggs and/or larvae. The rearing technique described herein is one of this group.

This technique is dependent on the use of an emergence-rearing container or collector (Fig. 1) (Clark and Osgood, 1964a). It consists of a 20-gal trash can into which are soldered two short 1/4-inch copper tubes and a modified 6-inch tractor funnel. The large end of this funnel is cut to fit the contour of the can and the lower edge soldered flush with the bottom of the can. A mason jar ring is soldered to the small end of the funnel, which is cut back to make a snug fit.

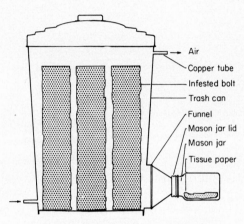

FIG. 1. Rearing-collector container.

A mason jar screwed into this ring provides a light source trap, thus taking advantage of the beetle's strong attraction to light. After assembly this collector is washed thoroughly with hot water and strong detergent to remove any substances toxic to the beetles. A ramp, made by pressing sawdust into wet shellac, extends from the bottom of the can through the funnel and gives the beetles secure footing. Tissue paper is placed in the jar to give the beetles support, footing, and concealment, and for ease in the subsequent handling of the trapped beetles.

Bark beetles are collected by placing infested bolts or other material in the emergence-rearing container. Corks are placed in the copper tubes and all light is excluded except for that passing into the mason jar where the beetles gather as they mature and emerge.

The rearing procedure is initiated by placing two to four fresh pine bolts in the container. The bolts are 4 to 8 inches in diameter by 20 to 22 inches long, which totals about 8 ft² of bark area. The bolts are untreated other than wiping the sticky, fresh pitch off the cut ends and rubbing them with fine sawdust. At this time all light is excluded from the container by inserting a mason jar cap between the jar ring and the jar. Then 30 to 40 adults per square foot of bark area are introduced and the lid placed tightly on the container. It is not necessary to sex the beetles as the normal sex ratio is 1 : 1 (Osgood and Clark, 1963). For maximum rapid attack the only beetles used are those able to cling to tissue paper or to walk, indicating a vigorous, uninjured condition; beetles collected before emergence from infested material fall off greatly.

Five days after this introduction the jar cap is removed and the nonattacking adults are collected. If continuous records are to be maintained the bolts are removed 3 days after introduction, the dead adults counted, and the bolts replaced. Figure 2 is typical of the

Experiment number: 100

Rearing can number: 10

Installation date: 20/2/65

Bolt size and bark area: 4" × 20", 7.5   Date and number introduced: 22/2, 312

% Bark moisture: 65.5 ww   Number dead: 4

Remarks: Fresh loblolly pine   Number not attacking: 30

Number of attacking parents: 278

Periodic record: For example, accumulative daily emergence. 27/2-25, 28/2-5=30, 1/3-0=30, etc.

Termination date: 1/5

Number dead at bottom of can: 35

Number of emerging parents: 169

Number of emerging brood: 2500

Total: 2704

% Terminal bark moisture: 52.9 ww

% Efficiency of can: 98.7

Number introduced/ft^2: 41.6

% Attacking parents: 89.2

Number adults attacking/ft^2: 37

% Reemergence of parents: 60.9

Brood emergence/ft^2: 333.3

Ratio of brood to introduced parents: 8:1

Ratio of brood to attacking parents: 9:1

FIG. 2. Typical rearing record.

records maintained on each rearing container when specific data are required. From the tenth to twentieth day the parent adults emerge. The brood adults commence to emerge in 20 to 25 days and are collected for the next 35 to 45 days. Usually there is a period of a few days with little or no emergence spanning the change from parent to brood emergence.

Pertinent typical results are found in Fig. 2. Generally at least 75% of the surviving parents will attack fresh bolts twice more with approximately the same output/input ratio. Furthermore, the females do not necessarily require mates in these subsequent attacks. The mortality among these reattacking parents is large; about 60% re-emerge following the first attack and about 30% from the second attack. The range of the brood:parent yield for 12 generations was 2:1 to 15:1. The major advantages of this technique are: the beetles attack quickly while in a vigorous condition; daily record mainte-nance is convenient, accurate, and rapid; the method simulates natural conditions; the culture can be manipulated easily; and, it is economical.

Environmental requirements in the rearing room are not particu-larly critical. Natural and/or artificial light is used to give a 9-hour day and averages 35 ft-c at jar level. Roughly controlled diurnal tempera-tures of 22° and 27°C are adequate and the relative humidity of the rearing room is 40 to 60%. However the temperature must be main-tained between 20° and 30°C or the rearing technique becomes extremely inefficient. Below 20°C very poor results are obtained. Time switches equipped with a day dial and trippers to skip opera-tions on selected days are used to make the technique more auto-matic. For example, emergence is delayed over the weekends, holi-days, or for other reasons by maintaining 22°C and no lights. The room itself can be very simple and its size depends upon the output of beetles desired. Twenty such containers can easily be placed in a rearing room 10 × 10 ft using a 2-tier rack. A very functional rack for these containers is made from 1-inch galvanized pipe and slip-on structural fittings. These racks, although more expensive than wooden racks, are simple to assemble or adjust and are very easy to clean and maintain.

Bark moisture is the most critical factor and must be maintained between 50 and 60% wet weight for optimal rearing. The range of 40 to 70% is not optimal but a fair output of southern pine beetles can be obtained. Inner bark moisture measurements are taken imme-diately following the cutting of the bolts and at the close of each experiment. Continual bark moisture determinations are not essential but occasional determinations are desirable, particularly when the rearing system is first started, to assure maintenance in the optimal range. The moisture is determined by taking three 1- to 2-gm samples of inner bark from the bolts, weighing immediately, drying to a con-stant weight at 100°C (about 8 hours), and reweighing. The per cent moisture can be calculated on a wet or dry weight basis, but the former is more useful for this purpose. To avoid excessive moisture a small amount of dry air is continually passed through the container from the fifth to fortieth day. A compressor is the most convenient air source and is necessary in a large operation, the air being passed through the lower copper tube of the emergence-rearing container. If no compressor is available an air source can be installed at the base of each container. Figure 3 illustrates a simple, economical one made by

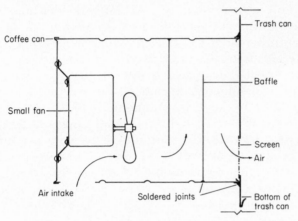

FIG. 3. Individual air source for rearing-collector containers.

mounting a small television-tube cooling fan in a 2-lb metal coffee can which is about 5 inches in diameter by 7 inches long. This source is soldered over a hardware cloth-covered hole in the rearing container. The series of baffles prevent a light leak.

Under these conditions the bark moisture drops about 20% wet weight in the first 2 weeks but then levels off or increases slightly as the infestation develops and remains at about 50 to 60%. With no air the bark moisture rises to over 80% (400% dry weight) accompanied by the development of contaminants such as molds and yeasts, and the destruction of the southern pine beetle culture. Bedard (1961) and Johnson (1962) found that the upper moisture limit for successfully rearing western scolytids was also around 80% wet weight.

As in most insect rearing mites can become a problem. Three species are found in association with the southern pine beetles under these conditions. Therefore cultures are examined periodically. Any new beetles brought in from the field are isolated until the presence of mites can be ascertained and, if present, controlled. The rearing room is not used for any other purpose which might lead to an infestation. Of the available acaricides DMC [1,1-bis(p-chlorophenyl) ethanol] is used, but the beetle mortality is high. Kelthane is very toxic under laboratory conditions and cannot be used. The possibility of contamination by mites, as well as fungi and other organisms, is reduced by washing all rearing cans, mason jars, and other non-disposable rearing equipment thoroughly with very hot water (80°C) and strong detergent after each use. Disposable items such as tissue paper are used once and destroyed.

Precautions against the escape of reared beetles are simple. The rearing room is insect-tight with no leaks around the door. Beetles that escape in handling gather at the window or other light source where they are destroyed or allowed to perish. Discarded infested bolts are heat treated in an oven at 250°C for at least 1 hour to destroy any remaining brood and other organisms.

Injuries must be kept at a minimum and a number of routine precautions are taken. To reduce mutually inflicted injuries tissue paper is always present in the jars, and, if possible, not more than 50 emerging beetles are allowed to accumulate in these jars. Handling, a major source of injuries, is minimized and carefully done. Whenever possible beetles are kept on the tissue paper while being counted and otherwise manipulated.

REFERENCES

Bedard, W. D. (1961). Media for the rearing of immature bark beetles (Scolytidae). Ph.D. Thesis, Univ. of California, Berkeley, California.

Clark, E. W., and Osgood, E. A., Jr. (1964a). An emergence and rearing container for *Dendroctonus frontalis* Zimm. and other bark beetles. *J. Econ. Entomol.* **57**, 783–784.

Clark, E. W., and Osgood, E. A., Jr. (1964b). Mass rearing the southern pine beetle and the coarse writing engraver. *U. S. Dept. Agr., Forest Serv., Southeast. Exp. Sta. Res. Note* **SE-30**, 4 pp.

Clark, E. W., and Osgood, E. A., Jr. (1964c). A simple laboratory technique for rearing *Ips calligraphus. U. S. Dept. Agr., Forest Serv., Southeast. Exp. Sta. Res. Note* **SE-31**.

Clark, E. W., and Osgood, E. A., Jr. (1966). Unpublished data.

Dixon, J. C., and Osgood, E. A., Jr. (1961). Southern Pine Beetle. A review of present knowledge. *U. S. Dept. Agr., Forest Serv., Southeast. Exp. Sta. Paper* **128**, 34 pp.

Griswold, C. L. (1948). Bulk rearing of *Scolytus multistriatus* Marsh. and *Hylurgopinus rufipes* Eich. *U. S. Dept. Agr. B.E.P.Q.* **ET-252**, 5 pp.

Johnson, N. E. (1962). Rearing of Douglas-fir beetle broods in waxed slabs. *Ann. Entomol. Soc. Am.* **55**, 659–663.

Osgood, E. A., Jr., and Clark, E. W. (1963). Methods of sexing and sex ratios of the southern pine beetle, *Dendroctonus frontalis* Zimm. *Can. Entomologist* **95**, 1106–1109.

Thatcher, R. C. (1963). Personal communication.

Chapter 20

Grasshoppers

FRANK T. COWAN

Entomology Research Division,
Agricultural Research Service,
U. S. Department of Agriculture,
Bozeman, Montana

I. INTRODUCTION

Grasshoppers are being used more extensively each year in teaching and for experimental purposes. The demand for adults, nymphs, and eggs and for information on methods of rearing and breeding has increased accordingly.

At the Bozeman Grasshopper Investigations Laboratory of the Entomology Research Division, Agricultural Research Service, U. S. Department of Agriculture, it has been necessary to keep a supply of grasshoppers throughout the winter months for use in insecticide screening tests and other projects. Prior to the advent of the chlorinated hydrocarbon insecticides it was usually possible to gather a supply of eggs from the field each fall for hatching and rearing. Because it was necessary to have a stock of several thousand eggs on hand, the species collected were limited to those which commonly concentrated their eggs around cultivated fields or in the borrow pits of rural roadways. *Melanoplus bivittatus* (Say), *Melanoplus sanguinipes* (F.), and *Melanoplus differentialis* (Thos.), in that order, were the most commonly sought after. When the "new insecticides," used in the form of sprays, became popular in early 1950 the average farmer or rancher found it possible for the first time in history to eliminate the grasshopper threat to crop lands, and the concentrations of eggs dwindled. Since it has become increasingly more difficult to dig eggs each fall, we have resorted to caging young adult hoppers over sand and harvesting the eggs. More recently we have attempted to establish colonies of *M. sanguinipes* and *Schistocerca vaga vaga* (Scudd.) at Bozeman, Montana, and Mesa, Arizona. In both instances we have been moderately successful, but the number of problems which have arisen during these early trials are numerous and each one must be treated individually. The purpose of this paper is to point out as many of these problems as we are now familiar with and to offer solutions where possible.

II. LITERATURE REVIEW

Little has been written on the problem of grasshopper colonization although it is known that much work has been done. The Anti-Locust Research Centre, in London, has maintained a colony of *Schistocerca gregaria* Forsk. for many years. More recently they have promoted colonies of the African migratory locust (*Locusta migratoria migratorioides* R. & F.), the red locust (*Nomadacris septemfasciata* Serv.), and the Egyptian grasshopper (*Anacridium aegyptium* L.). Their methods of rearing were described by Hunter-Jones (1961).

In Canada, a colony of nondiapausing *M. sanguinipes* has been established for several years at the Canadian Department of Agriculture Laboratory, Field Crop Insect Section, at Saskatoon, Saskatchewan (Riegert, 1961).* At the Science Service Laboratory, Field Crop Insect Section, Lethbridge, Alberta, colonies of both *M. bivittatus* and *M. sanguinipes* are maintained.

In the United States the only place, aside from the Bozeman Laboratory, where grasshopper colonies have been maintained is the ARS Entomology Research Laboratory at Mesa, Arizona. O. L. Barnes,† in charge of the Mesa station, has had good success in breed-

* Letter from D. S. Smith, February 12, 1965, to F. T. Cowan.
† Unpublished reports.

ing and rearing *M. sanguinipes* for many years. In much of the work at Mesa the young adults or last instar nymphs of *M. sanguinipes* are brought into the insectary from the field and are allowed to oviposit in dishes filled with sand. The eggs are harvested by screening and kept in refrigeration until needed. In another phase of this work Mr. Barnes has carried *M. sanguinipes, M. differentialis,* and *Trimerotropis pallidipennis* (Burm.) through several generations in the insectary:

III. EQUIPMENT

A. CAGES

The types of cages used in rearing grasshoppers are as varied as the men who, over the years, have used them. To attempt description of all types would be impossible. At the Bozeman Laboratory we have used many types varying in size and form from a ¼ ft³ (6 × 6 × 12 inches) 12- to 16-mesh wire screen to the 6 ft³ (24 × 24 × 18 inches) wire screen cage (Fig. 1). Each cage was built for a special purpose

FIG. 1. The large (6 ft³) cage has an 8-mesh bottom to allow feces to drop through. The 250-watt infrared light mounted on the ring stand is normally placed within 6 inches of the side of the cage. The large cage will hold up to 200 *M. sanguinipes* or 150 of a larger species. The small ¼-ft³ cage is not used in rearing.

but none was ideal as a rearing and breeding cage. For that reason a new cage constructed entirely of aluminum and wire screen has been devised (Mazuranich and Cowan, 1965). This cage (Fig. 2) is 13½ × 13½ inches (measured from the outside of the angle at the top) by

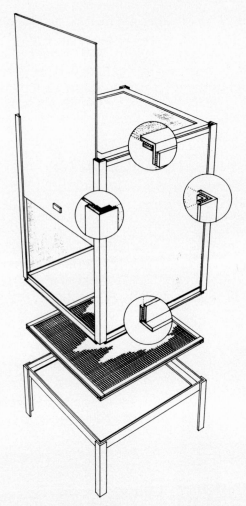

FIG. 2. The metal cage is 13½ × 13½ inches (measured outside the angle at the top) and 18½ inches high. The bottoms are 14 × 14 inches and the base 14½ × 14½ inches inside the angle. The length of the legs is optional. This cage should be populated with not more than 100 small grasshoppers nor more than 50 of a larger species.

18½ inches high, and has many advantages over all the other cages that we have used in grasshopper breeding: (1) All parts are inter-changeable so that the bottoms with 8-mesh screen, which are best for the smaller species such as *M. sanguinipes*, can be exchanged for 4-mesh screen bottoms when the cage is being used for rearing a large grasshopper such as *S. vaga vaga*. Special type bottoms de-signed to hold four display jars* 1⅝ inches in diameter by 4 inches

* Ward's of California Catalogue No. 370.9.

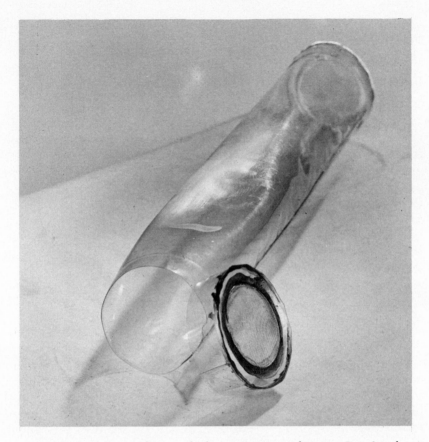

FIG. 3. This cage is used primarily for starting young hoppers. It is 3 inches in diameter and 18 inches long, and is constructed of a clear acetate.

long can also be used. These jars are filled with sand for egg laying. (2) Grasshopper feces, which are prime vehicles for transmitting disease within the cage, fall through the larger mesh screen bottoms into a pan below. There are few ledges on which the droppings can lodge and these can be brushed clean with a minimum of effort. (3) When the cage is emptied the door, which is of clear Plexiglass, can be removed, washed thoroughly, and wiped with a cloth dampened in alcohol. The remainder of the cage is washed and then sterilized in an oven at 450°F for 3 hours. Complete sterilization of the cage periodically is essential to the control of disease in a grasshopper colony.

Another cage that has proved very successful at Bozeman consists of a cylinder of clear acetate 3 inches in diameter and 18 inches long (Fig. 3). The ends are closed with screened caps. This cage is used to confine the young grasshoppers from hatching until they have reached the third instar. They are then transferred to the large cages described above.

B. REARING ENVIRONMENT

Controlled temperature cabinets, growth chambers, and rearing rooms where a uniform temperature of 90°F and the lowest possible relative humidity can be maintained are desirable in any large scale rearing project. However, any room or greenhouse where a fairly uniform temperature can be maintained will suffice. Additional heat can be supplied to each individual cage by a 250-watt infrared heat lamp suspended over the cage or held on a ring stand near one side for 8 to 10 hours a day (Fig. 1). With an arrangement of this type it is inevitable that a temperature gradient within the cage will exist. However, grasshoppers will seek the temperature most suitable to them (approximately 90°F).

IV. METHODS

A. CARE AND HATCHING OF EGGS

Eggs harvested in the field from any of the three species mentioned above are placed in sterile sand moistened with distilled water in clean, plastic freezer cartons, covered to prevent loss of moisture, and refrigerated at approximately 40°F until needed. A good mixture of water to sand for this purpose is 15 to 100 parts by volume. Field eggs harvested in October or November are usually collected after the embryos have gone into diapause and will hatch within a short while, or they may be refrigerated for long periods. Eggs of *M. bivittatus*, *M. sanguinipes*, and *M. differentialis*, held under the proper conditions of moisture and in clean sand, have hatched well and produced healthy grasshoppers after 18 months in refrigeration.

Eggs taken in the laboratory are handled by various methods dictated pretty much by the species. Adults of *Melanoplus* spp. brought in from the field are usually caged over clean wooden flats 12 × 12 inches by 2 inches deep, which are filled with sterile moist sand. The eggs are harvested by sifting the sand through an 8-mesh screen once or twice each week. Harvested eggs are handled in the same manner as field-collected eggs, except they should be incubated at room temperature for 2 to 3 weeks before they are placed in the refrigerator.

When hatching is desired the eggs are transferred to a sterile plaster-of-Paris chamber 12 × 6½ × 4 inches, covered lightly with moist sand, and incubated at 85°F. Glass lids, painted black, are placed over the top opening of the hatching chamber to exclude light. The newly hatched nymphs are collected in glass or acetate tubes inserted in holes in the hatching chamber, and then transferred to rearing tubes (Skoog *et al.*, 1961).

Nondiapausing eggs such as those from *S. vaga vaga* are collected in sterilized ½-pt fruit or display jars filled with sterile sand and incubated at 85°F. Nondiapausing eggs should not be refrigerated nor should the pods be disturbed. Hatching will take place in from 18 to 25 days at 85°F. The jars should be capped to preserve moisture until 4 to 5 days before the time hatching should begin.

B. Nymphal Rearing

Immediately after hatching the young nymphs are transferred to plastic (acetate) cylinders (Fig. 3) which have been thoroughly washed in warm soapy water and sterilized in a solution of 1 part 5.25% hypochlorite (Chlorox) to 9 parts water by volume. Fresh green leaves of head or romaine lettuce which have been thoroughly washed should be supplied along with wheat bran. Each day the surplus food is removed from the tube and replaced with fresh lettuce and bran. The nymphs are held in the tube until they have reached the third instar, at which time they are transferred to the large (6 ft³) or the metal rearing cages to complete their development. After transfer to the larger cages it is desirable, if greenhouse space is available, to supplement the bran-lettuce diet with sprouted grasses such as wheat, barley, or sorghum.

C. Control of Diseases

Grasshoppers reared in the laboratory are subject to attack from many diseases. These include fungus, bacteria, protozoans, and possibly rickettsia and viruses. To date, at least one species of fungus, several species of bacteria, and at least two protozoans have caused epizootics in laboratory cultures at Bozeman. The spores of at least one of the protozoans is known to be carried in the feces of infected grasshoppers.

Fungal and bacterial diseases can be controlled by holding the relative humidity in rearing cabinets and rooms to a minimum. Protozoans, however, cannot be controlled in this fashion; cleanliness is the only method that has had any effect so far. Antibiotics have been tried but have not proved entirely successful; however, this work is continuing in the hope that an antibiotic can be found that will at least minimize the effects of these diseases.

In order to enforce a proper sanitary atmosphere within the rearing cabinets or rooms all cages must be thoroughly cleaned at least once each day. A proper tool for cleaning cages is a household cannister-type vacuum cleaner with disposable dust bags. Floors, cage supports, tables, etc., of the rearing rooms should be gone over with the vacuum in order to remove any droppings which may have fallen outside the cage. At least once each week the cages should be removed from the rearing rooms and the floors, walls, and cage supports thoroughly washed with a strong solution of hot water and Chlorox. In a room used for purposes other than grasshopper rearing such thorough scrubbing is not always possible. It is possible, however, to scrub table tops and floors in the area of the room used for rearing.

When the cages are emptied they should be thoroughly washed with hot water containing a detergent and then treated with a solution of 1 part Chlorox to 9 parts water. The plastic tubes should also be washed and treated with Chlorox solution, but only cool water should be used; hot water softens the acetate and causes the cage to become flattened and otherwise distorted. Metal cages should be washed and then sterilized at 450°F for about 3 hours. This will ensure destruction of protozoan and bacterial spores.

D. ADULTS AND EGG LAYING

Grasshopper adults caged for egg laying are best held in the metal cage with either the 8- or 4-mesh screen bottom. The cage should be thoroughly washed and sterilized with heat. Display jars which have been sterilized in dry heat or an autoclave should be filled with sterile sand moistened with distilled water in the proportion of 15 parts of water to 100 parts of sand by volume. The proper number of grasshoppers will vary somewhat according to size, but probably not more than 25 pairs of the smaller ones, such as *M. sanguinipes*, nor more than 20 pairs of *S. vaga vaga*. Sprouted grasses, kept green by immersing the cut ends in water, along with a dish of wheat bran are preferred as food. The egg-laying jars should be examined each day after the females start ovipositing. The egg pod, if one is present, can generally be brought into view by knocking off the thin layer of dry sand at the top of the jar. Jars found to contain eggs should be removed, capped, and dated. If the sand has lost its moisture around the egg pod it should be remoistened with distilled water. All egg pods should be incubated for 10 days to 2 weeks, but only those from grasshoppers known to produce diapausing eggs should be refrigerated. Others, such as eggs of *S. vaga vaga*, should be continued in incubation until they hatch. All jars should be removed at least twice each week and those found not to contain eggs replaced with fresh ones.

V. DESIRABLE SPECIES FOR COLONIZATION

A. *Melanoplus sanguinipes*

This is a small species weighing from 250 to 300 mg (Parker, 1930), but one that lends itself well to laboratory rearing and colonization. Gurney and Brooks (1959) recognize two races of *M. sanguinipes sanguinipes* covering the United States and most of Canada. It is a strong flyer and in years of heavy concentrations has been known to migrate over 100 miles. It is quite prolific; some individual females producing, under laboratory conditions, 20 or more egg pods of 15 to 20 eggs per pod. The average number of pods, however, would probably be somewhat under 10 per female.

Melanoplus sanguinipes is apparently susceptible to all of the diseases commonly found in the laboratory but is generally thought to be somewhat less susceptible than *M. bivittatus*. They are voracious feeders and will eat most plants. According to Barnes (1955), they do best on a diet of succulent lettuce, Johnson grass, and alfalfa, supplemented with dry bran. At Bozeman they are reared mostly on lettuce and bran supplemented with sprouted grasses until they reach the fifth instar. Through the adult stage, including egg laying, the food is mostly grasses.

According to Shotwell (1930), *M. sanguinipes* normally goes through 5 nymphal instars at a rearing temperature of 90°F. At temperatures lower than 90°F they often go through an extra instar which falls after the normal third or fourth.

B. *Melanoplus bivittatus*

This species is somewhat larger than *M. sanguinipes*, with the females averaging 700 mg and the males 500 mg. *Melanoplus bivittatus* is about as prolific as *M. sanguinipes*, laying a smaller number of pods but pods that contain more than twice the number of eggs.

Melanoplus bivittatus is more susceptible to disease, especially bacterial and fungal, than *M. sanguinipes*. However, these are quite easy to control in the laboratory by decreasing humidity and by holding the temperature to at least 90°F. *Melanoplus bivittatus* thrives on the same diet recommended for *M. sanguinipes*. They also go through the same number of instars.

C. *Melanoplus differentialis*

This grasshopper is a native of the corn-growing states and the Southwest and is often referred to as the "corn grasshopper." Its northern limits are normally the southern part of North Dakota and Minnesota, but occasionally it becomes numerous in the irrigated valleys of eastern and southeastern Montana. It is also a pest of alfalfa and other crops in the irrigated valleys of the Southwest. It is somewhat larger than *M. bivittatus,* with the females weighing nearly 2 gm and the males well over 1 gm.

This species has not been reared extensively at Bozeman, but from work done by Barnes (1963) at Mesa, Arizona, it is believed that it would lend itself well to colonization. Under normal conditions in the field *M. differentialis* eggs will go through a long diapause. Eggs laid in the laboratory will sometimes hatch in 35 to 40 days without going through a period of diapause, but this is believed to be the unusual.

The diet recommended for *M. sanguinipes* is satisfactory for *M. differentialis.* Sprouted corn can be added to the list of grasses recommended for other *Melanoplus* spp.

D. *Schistocerca vaga vaga*

A colony of this grasshopper was established at the Bozeman Laboratory in December 1964. Some 30 wild adult females and an equal number of males were imported from Riverside, California. The colony is now in the F_3 generation and we are hopeful it can be maintained indefinitely.

Schistocerca vaga is a large grasshopper with the females weighing over 2 gm and the males about 700 mg. It is a strong flyer and presumably capable of long-range migration, although we have been unable to find any record of such flights. It is sometimes a pest of grapes and other crops in southern California and other parts of the Southwest, but it seldom becomes numerous enough to be of great economic importance, in spite of the fact that it has great reproductive potential. It was estimated that the 30 original females imported from California each laid over 500 eggs. *Schistocerca vaga* is very susceptible to a protozoan (*Malamoeba locustae* King and Taylor) and to an as-yet unidentified fungus. *Malamoeba locustae* does not kill the host quickly but contributes to a general weakening of the affected individual and, in the case of the female, limits egg production. Little is known at this time concerning the fungus. In attempting to establish a colony of this species from wild adults care should be taken to isolate all individuals until it can be established that they are free from disease.

Schistocerca vaga is an omnivorous feeder and thrives on most grasses except corn. The diet recommended for laboratory strains is the same as that listed for *M. sanguinipes*.

REFERENCES

Barnes, O. L. (1955). Effect of food plants on the lesser migratory grasshopper. *J. Econ. Entomol.* **48**, 119–124.

Barnes, O. L. (1963). Food-plant tests with the differential grasshopper. *J. Econ. Entomol.* **56**, 396–399.

Gurney, A. R., and Brooks, A. R. (1959). Grasshoppers of the *mexicanus* group, genus *Melanoplus* (Orthoptera: Acrididae). *Proc. U. S. Natl. Museum* **110**, 1–93.

Hunter-Jones, P. (1961). "Rearing and Breeding Locusts in the Laboratory." Anti-Locust Research Centre Bull., London, England.

Mazuranich, P. C., and Cowan, F. T. (1965). A metal cage for rearing grasshoppers. *J. Econ. Entomol.* **59**, 232–234.

Parker, J. R. (1930). Some effects of temperature and moisture on *Melanoplus mexicanus mexicanus* Saussure and *Camnula pellucida* Scudder (Orthoptera). *Univ. Montana, Agr. Expt. Stat., Bull.* **223**.

Riegert, P. W. (1961). Embryological development of a nondiapause form of *Melanoplus bilituratus* Walker. *Can. J. Zool.* **39**, 491–494.

Shotwell, R. L. (1930). A study of the lesser migratory grasshopper. *U. S. Dept. Agr., Tech. Bull.* **190**.

Skoog, F. E., Cowan, F. T., and Connin, R. V. (1961). Laboratory and field tests of insecticides for grasshopper control. *J. Econ. Entomol.* **54**, 170–174.

Chapter 21

European Corn Borer

EARLE S. RAUN

Corn Borer Laboratory,
Agricultural Research Service,
U. S. Department of Agriculture,
Ankeny, Iowa

I. INTRODUCTION

The European corn borer, *Ostrinia nubilalis* (Hübner), has been investigated in the United States since its identification as an introduced pest in 1917. Brindley and Dicke (1963) reviewed the significant developments in European corn borer research since that time, including literature citations in the areas of biology, host plants, population statistics, and control.

Colonization of the European corn borer in the laboratory has only been practical the last few years, as laboratory diets were per-

323

fected. Various techniques for rearing the insect have evolved using fresh or living plant material (Surany, 1957) and artificial diets. Bottger (1942) developed a synthetic medium for use in borer nutrition studies. Beck *et al.* (1949) modified this diet and described a successful technique for rearing the borer in the laboratory. Later Beck (1953) indicated that several generations of borers had been raised on the diet without apparent loss in vitality. Wressel (1955) and Becton *et al.* (1962) were the first to suggest the use of artificial media in mass rearing the corn borer. Becton also included data indicating growth responses of larvae reared continuously on an artificial diet. He carried one colony through eleven generations.

II. ARTIFICIAL DIET

A. INGREDIENTS

The artificial diet used at the European Corn Borer Laboratory is similar to that of Becton *et al.* (1962). Becton and his co-workers

TABLE I

COMPLEX VITAMIN SUPPLEMENT USED IN
EUROPEAN CORN BORER LABORATORY DIET[a]

Ingredient	Per cent
Vitamin A (200,000 units/gm)	0.45
Vitamin D (400,000 units/gm)	0.025
α-Tocopherol	0.5
Ascorbic acid	4.5
Inositol	0.5
Choline chloride	7.5
Riboflavin	0.1
Menadione	0.225
p-Aminobenzoic acid	0.5
Niacin	0.45
Pyridoxine hydrochloride	0.1
Thiamine hydrochloride	0.1
Calcium pentothenate	0.3
Biotin	0.002
Folic acid	0.009
B_{12}	0.000135
Dextrose	84.738865
	100

[a] Available from Nutritional Biochemicals Corp., Cleveland, Ohio.

eliminated "runts" from their colony as each generation became 10 days old. Also they stored the leaf powder used in the diet at −4°C. Both of these practices were found to be unnecessary when a complex vitamin mixture was added, and modifications in the method of cooking were made (Guthrie *et al.*, 1965). The vitamin supplement (Table I) is available commercially.

Leaf powder used in the diet can be prepared by either sun- or heat-drying corn plant tissue. The inbreds, WF-9 and M-14, or the single cross of the two, are commonly used since they are suscep- tible to corn borer attack. Plants are cut just below the first full collar of leaves at the stage of growth when the tassel is just entering the boot. The unrolled leaves are dried at 50° to 70°C in an oven provided with ventilation to remove the moisture-laden air. Crop harvesting and drying equipment have been used to handle the tissue from a ½-acre plot (Guthrie *et al.*, 1965). The dried tissue is powdered either in a Wiley mill (Becton *et al.*, 1962) or a portable feed grinder (Guthrie *et al.*, 1965), and sealed in plastic bags to prevent moisture uptake during storage. Becton *et al.* (1962) used alfalfa leaf meal as their leaf factor.

Other dietary ingredients are readily available at biological supply houses or the local drug store. Dietary ingredients and their quantities are listed in Table II.

TABLE II

INGREDIENTS FOR THE LABORATORY DIET USED IN
EUROPEAN CORN BORER REARINGS

Ingredient	Quantity per batch
Distilled H_2O	3000.0 ml
Agar	68.0 gm
Dextrose	98.0 gm
Casein	97.0 gm
Cholesterol	7.5 gm
Salt No. 2[a]	13.0 gm
Brewer's yeast	50.0 gm
Leaf and whorl powder	135.0 gm
Wheat germ oil	7.5 ml
Ascorbic acid	30.0 gm
Vitamin supplement	15.0 gm
Mold inhibitor[b]	40.0 ml

[a] Available from Nutritional Biochemicals Corp., Cleveland, Ohio.
[b] Dissolve 90 gm sorbic acid in 400 ml 95% ethyl alcohol.

It is not desirable to use aseptic technique when rearing large numbers of corn borers. Various workers have utilized microbial inhibitors incorporated into the diet. Beck *et al.* (1949) used *n*-butyl *p*-hydroxybenzoate (Butoben) successfully. Becton *et al.* (1962) tested combinations of Butoben and sorbic acid, finally deciding that 0.2% sorbic acid alone seemed to provide adequate control of microorganisms with less inhibition of larval development. It is likely that other laboratories may be dealing with a different complex of contaminating organisms and will need to determine for themselves which microbial inhibitor(s) to use.

B. PREPARATION

The diet is prepared (Guthrie *et al.*, 1965) by cooking the agar and one half the water in a double boiler for 5 minutes. The leaf powder is then added and the total cooked for 15 minutes. The remainder of the ingredients are not cooked. The vitamins are dissolved in the remaining water, which is placed in a high-speed blender with the other uncooked ingredients and blended for 2 minutes. When cooked, the agar and leaf powder are added and the total blended an additional 2 minutes. The still-liquid diet is poured to a depth of about ¾ inch into containers, varying according to the use to be made of the diet, and allowed to solidify.

If the diet was prepared for individual rearings, plugs of the solidified diet are placed in 3-dram glass vials which have been previously cotton-stoppered and sterilized. The plugs of diet are cut with equipment made by slipping a 15 × 150 mm flanged test tube inside a stainless steel cylinder with an inside diameter of 15.5 mm (16 × 90 mm outside). One technician can fill 3 to 400 vials in an hour.

Various methods of placing the diet in the vials while it is still liquid have been used, although first-instar larvae are apparently unable to feed on the smooth surface of the hardened diet. Becton *et al.* (1962) solved the problem by making a channel down one side of the hardened diet with a spatula. Placing a plug of the already solidified diet into a vial allows the young larva to begin feeding on the side of the plug which was scarified by the cutting operation.

For mass rearing the European corn borer (Guthrie *et al.*, 1965), plastic containers with snap-on friction lids are used at our laboratory. The round containers have a diameter of 10 inches and are 4 inches high. A rectangle, 3 × 4 inches, cut from the lid provides ventilation and prevents humidity in the container from increasing to the point at which larvae cannot survive. Brass screening, 80 × 60 mesh, sealed over the opening, prevents larval escape. Other rearing dishes may be equally suited. Containers made of polyethylene or aluminum foil are unsuitable since full-grown larvae will chew through them and escape.

The diet may be placed in the rearing containers directly, while it is still fluid, or in a chopped or ground state after it has solidified in other containers. Approximately 500 ml of the liquid, or 500 gm of crumbled diet, is an adequate quantity. If the diet is allowed to solidify in the rearing container its surface must be sacrificed for the young larvae to begin feeding uniformly over the surface.

III. HANDLING OF LARVAE

A. INDIVIDUAL REARINGS

Methods for starting larvae individually have included placing either a single egg or a newly hatched larva into the vial onto the diet. Beck and Stauffer (1950) and Becton *et al.* (1962) digested the eggs apart, surface sterilized them, rinsed them in alcohol, then transferred an egg in a drop of alcohol into the vial by means of a medicine dropper. This technique is particularly desirable when aseptic rearing is being carried out. Becton *et al.* (1962) abandoned the aseptic method because it was too cumbersome for most rearing programs. He and his co-workers, and Guthrie *et al.* (1965), placed discs of

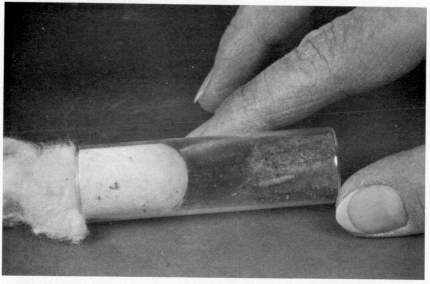

FIG. 1. Three-dram vial, artificial diet, and half-grown larva of the European corn borer.

waxed paper (Section VI), on which the egg masses had been laid, into small screw-capped jars and allowed the eggs to hatch. The larvae were then transferred individually by means of a small camel's-hair brush which had been moistened in sterile, distilled water.

The cotton-stoppered vials, containing the diet (Fig. 1) and newly hatched larvae, can then be incubated. Incubators should contain some means of providing moisture to the air. Unless the relative humidity (RH) remains high the diet will become dehydrated before the larvae can mature. Incubator temperatures can vary according to the rapidity desired for larval growth. If they are maintained at 26.7°C, the first larvae will pupate on day 13, and pupation will be essentially completed by day 20 (Table III). At 23.9°C, first pupation will occur on day 15, with moth emergence beginning on day 23.

TABLE III

First Occurrence of European Corn Borer Developmental Stages When Reared in the Laboratory at a Constant 26.7°C and 75% RH

Stage	Period after oviposition	Period after egg hatch
Black-head	90 hours	—
Hatch	96 hours	—
Instar III	11 days	7 days
Instar IV	13 days	9 days
Instar V	15 days	11 days
Pupa	17 days	13 days
Emergence	24 days	20 days

B. Group Rearings

Either egg masses in the black-head stage (head capsule of the mature embryo showing through the egg chorion) or newly hatched larvae have been placed in mass-rearing containers. There are advantages to both methods.

Placing the egg masses on the diet presents a saving in time and consequently labor costs. Also, larvae that hatch are already on the medium and can begin feeding as soon as they are physiologically able. Two disadvantages attend this method. Unless discs of waxed paper, which contained the egg masses, are removed after egg hatch is complete, fungal growth will begin on the paper. This provides a focal point from which fungi overwhelm the microbial inhibitor present in the diet. Furthermore, the number of larvae to hatch in the container can only be estimated, since not all eggs hatch. This results in the number of larvae being less than the size of container and quantity of food could handle, or inefficient production. As experience is gained in rearing corn borers in this fashion, however, this difficulty is minimized.

Placing larvae in the rearing containers requires more time, but also provides for a maximum use of container space and diet. Eggs are allowed to hatch in small, closed containers, as in individual rearings, and the larvae are transferred to the rearing containers with a camel's-hair brush.

The number of larvae or eggs to be placed in a mass-rearing container will vary according to the quantity of diet it contains. The optimum number appears to be approximately 100 for each 250 gm of diet (Guthrie et al., 1965). Table IV contains data bearing on this point.

TABLE IV

AVERAGE ESTABLISHMENT AND PUPATION OF VARYING NUMBERS
OF EUROPEAN CORN BORERS[a]

Diet	Larvae/dish		Pupae at 20 days	
	No. started	Estab. (%)	No.	%
Poured	100	77.3	70.3	90.9
	150	72.7	94	86.2
	200	75.1	131.8	87.5
Crumbled	150	82.7	96.1	81.7
	200	87.2	129.7	74.4
	250	79	141.3	67.3

[a] Placed in 12-inch diameter dishes containing 500 gm of laboratory diet.

IV. HANDLING OF PUPAE

Various workers have handled pupae according to the needs of their research programs and facilities available. The important criteria followed in all cases were care not to injure the pupa when it is being transferred to another container, and a sufficiently high humidity in the emergence container to allow the moth to inflate its wings and spread them properly. Male larvae are usually the first to pupate but require slightly longer in the pupal condition, so that emergence of the two sexes is well synchronized (Walker, 1962).

A. INDIVIDUAL REARINGS

When larvae have been reared individually, pupation occurs in the rearing vial. The mature larva usually migrates to the top of the vial, spins a protective sling and a thin covering of silk, and pupates.

Guthrie *et al.* (1965) describe how cotton stoppers are removed from vials containing pupae, and the vials are then placed in a cage where moths emerge. About 250 to 300 pupae are placed in the cage they describe, which is 12½ × 18 × 24 inches (Fig. 2).

FIG. 2. Vials racked in cage for moth emergence and oviposition.

The same authors also describe the handling of pupae when mating studies are to be undertaken. Pupae are removed from the rearing vials and placed individually in small containers which are incubated. These are checked daily, and, as moths emerge, they are paired in appropriate mating and oviposition cages.

B. GROUP REARINGS

In rearing large numbers of larvae in a single container, one of the big problems has always been the copious amount of silk left by the larvae during the latter stages of their growth. Fourth- and fifth-instar larvae apparently wander around the surface of the diet and over the inside of the container, leaving a mat of silk. Pupation occurs either in a cell in the diet, or in the mat of silk (Fig. 3). Moths are unable to escape from this mat of silk. Guthrie *et al.* (1965) describe the method used to circumvent this problem. The mat of silk, containing pupae, is removed from each dish and placed in a pan of 1½% sodium hypochlorite. The sodium hypochlorite dissolves the silk and the pupae float free, are skimmed off with a strainer, rinsed in water, and placed on cellucotton in wire baskets. Both the wire baskets and the dishes of diet, which still contain pupae, are placed on racks in a large emergence cage.

FIG. 3. Plastic dish and diet suitable for rearing 200 European corn borers to pupation.

A method currently being tested in our laboratory may eliminate the use of the sodium hypochlorite as a silk solvent. Strips of corrugated paper (cardboard), 1 inch wide and 60 inches long, are fastened around the inside wall of the mass-rearing container on day 12 of larval growth. As the larvae search for a suitable pupation site they crawl into the "tunnels" in the paper, create a prepupal cell, and pupate. These strips of paper, containing the pupae, can then be removed to an emergence cage.

V. HANDLING ADULTS

Adults are allowed to emerge either into a large cage from which they are collected (Guthrie *et al.*, 1965) by means of a modified hair drier and placed into suitable oviposition cages, or they are allowed to emerge into the oviposition cage directly. Both methods have advantages.

If moths are allowed to emerge into the oviposition cage, labor requirements are reduced, and separate strains of borers can be easily maintained. The biggest disadvantage is that moth emergence extends over a week, with the actively ovipositing group of moths at its maximum for only a few days.

When moths emerge into a large cage, from which they are transferred to oviposition cages, those within an individual oviposition cage are of the same age. Egg production from that cage will be quite uniform, maintained at a high level for several days and cease quickly, allowing the cage to be cleaned and readied for another group of moths. This method makes maintenance of separate strains of the borer much more difficult, however, and requires more labor.

It has never been demonstrated that feeding European corn borer moths lengthens their life span or increases egg production. Moths readily take water, however, which can be supplied by spraying the screen of oviposition cages with a fine spray of water twice daily. Water droplets coalesce in the mesh of the screen, from which the moths drink. Sparks (1963) fed a sugar-water solution.

A. OVIPOSITION CAGES

Several sizes of oviposition cage have been used (Guthrie *et al.*, 1965). A cage 12½ × 18 × 24 inches occupies a minimum of space in the incubator or oviposition room and appears to be of sufficient size to accommodate from 100 to 200 female moths and their mates. The sizes, ends, and bottom of the cage consist of wooden frames, covered with 16- or 18-mesh copper or bronze screen, fastened together with the screened surface inside. All wood surfaces must be covered with screen because the moths will oviposit on smooth wood surfaces but not the screen. The top of each cage is covered with 4-mesh hardware cloth. An opening is provided at one end of the hardware cloth through which moths are placed in the cage. Two sheets of heavy waxed paper, 6 × 24 inches, are placed on top of the hardware cloth and held in place with a felt pad. Moths oviposit through the hardware cloth onto the waxed paper, the sheets of which are changed daily.

For smaller numbers of moths various sizes and styles of cage have been used. They all utilize the principle of screen walls, hardware cloth top, and an oviposition sheet of waxed paper.

B. MATING REQUIREMENTS

The oviposition room must provide climatic conditions for both adequate mating and egg production. Sparks (1963) obtained 100% mating in the laboratory by simulating the climatic conditions of a late June day in Iowa. He provided 14 hours of light and temperatures of 31.1° to 18.9°C, day to night, respectively. The relative humidity in his tests varied from 45–55% during the day to 90–95% during the night. He used a 1:1 male to female ratio.

Guthrie *et al.* (1965) obtained satisfactory mating and oviposition using the cycling temperatures of Sparks, but a constant relative humidity of 80 to 85% and continual darkness after Barber's (1925) suggestion.

VI. HANDLING EGG MASSES

Waxed paper sheets removed from the oviposition cages will contain up to 300 masses per sheet, depending on cage size and moth numbers. Egg masses will average about 20 eggs each. If incubated at a constant 26.7°C they will hatch in about 96 hours, having reached the black-head stage in about 90 hours.

For many uses, egg masses are cut from the waxed paper with a specially designed punch (Guthrie *et al.*, 1965). Each egg mass remains on a waxed paper disc ½ inch in diameter. These discs can be placed in small, screw-capped hatching jars, if larvae are to be placed on diets, or the discs can be placed on the diet when the eggs reach the black-head stage.

Guthrie *et al.* (1965) describe the method by which such egg masses are used for field infestations. A straight pin through each egg mass fastens it to a Celotex board. The Celotex board, containing 200 pinned egg masses, is then incubated until eggs reach the black-head stage. They are then taken to the field where the pin is utilized to fasten the mass to the midrib or ear flap of the corn plant.

Raun (1964) indicates that eggs may be incubated at 18.3°C; they will hatch in from 10 to 12 days at that temperature. He also presents data indicating that black-head egg masses can be refrigerated at 4.4°C for 10 days and still hatch when incubated at 26.7°C. Temperature manipulations of this type often facilitate the utilization of egg masses.

Aseptic rearing of the European corn borer has been utilized by many workers, and still will be necessary for some purposes. Beck and Stauffer (1950) described the method for such rearings. Egg masses in the black-head stage are placed in a 2% solution of a commercial 1:300 trypsin preparation and held at 35°C, with agitation every 10 minutes. In approximately 45 minutes the eggs become separated. They are then taken up in a medicine dropper, and transferred through six changes of distilled water to remove the trypsin. From the last water rinse they are transferred to 40% ethyl alcohol for 1 minute, then returned to distilled water. They are surface sterilized by placing them in a solution of 2% sodium hydroxide and 2% formaldehyde for 10 minutes. From the sterilizing solution the eggs are transferred to 70% ethyl alcohol in an aseptic transfer chamber, in which vials of diet prepared in an aseptic manner have been previously placed. Each egg in a drop of the alcohol is then placed in a vial of the diet, where it hatches.

VII. DISEASE PREVENTION

The prevention of disease in laboratory colonies is sometimes difficult. Crowding, and other laboratory conditions to which the insect is not subjected in the field, may provide stress. According to Steinhaus (1958), stress conditions often trigger disease outbreaks. Care must be taken to reduce these stress conditions in laboratory colonies.

There are two diseases which plague European corn borer rearing procedures. The white muscardine fungus, *Beauveria bassiana* (Balsamo), presents the most serious threat to mass rearing this insect. While aseptic techniques are not used in mass rearing programs, extreme cleanliness must be observed throughout the cooking process, and rearing containers should be sterilized, after washing, before the prepared medium is placed in them. All working surfaces, and rearing incubators, should be scrubbed and periodically sterilized with sodium hypochlorite (Ignoffo and Dutky, 1963). Emergence and oviposition cages and the oviposition room should be scrubbed and disinfected at the end of each period of rearing (Guthrie *et al.*, 1965).

The other disease of the European corn borer which can be a problem is microsporidiosis. The taxonomic position of the causative organism is still in doubt. Since much of the literature on this microsporidian refers to it as *Perezia pyraustae* Paillot, I shall do the same in this discussion.

Perezia pyraustae is apparently present in almost all, if not all, wild populations of *O. nubilalis* in the United States. Raun *et al.* (1960) found the organism in groups of larvae collected in eight states. Kramer (1959) suggests that it is found wherever its host occurs. Therefore, any laboratory colony started from a wild stock will contain the microbe. Since one method by which the disease is transmitted from generation to generation is through the egg (Zimmack *et al.*, 1954) the disease will remain in the colony for at least several generations, unless preventive measures are taken.

This disease is not as decimating as the white muscardine fungus, but it is more persistent in a colony. Zimmack *et al.* (1954), Zimmack and Brindley (1957), and Kramer (1959) present evidence showing the debilitating effect of *P. pyraustae* infections in individuals and populations of the European corn borer.

Raun (1961) describes a method for elimination of *P. pyraustae* from laboratory colonies. He immersed corn borer egg masses in a water bath for 30 minutes at 43.3°C. Larvae hatching from these eggs were free of the microsporidian. Higher temperatures prevented egg hatch. Shorter periods of time were not completely reliable in the inactivation of the microorganism. His data also show that infected larvae reared in mass cultures will infect one another, making a *P. pyraustae*-free colony especially important for mass-rearing procedures.

While other fungi and bacteria can cause disease in the European corn borer (Raun and Brooks, 1963; Brooks and Raun, 1965) procedures already outlined will prevent most problems. Apparently virus diseases have never been a problem in laboratory cultures of the corn borer. A virus-like disease has been described from a field population of the insect (Raun, 1963). It is likely that this disease is triggered by some predisposing factor(s) in the insects environment in the field.

VIII. DIAPAUSE

The European corn borer is an insect possessing a facultative diapause. In the field there are one or more nondiapausing generations followed by a generation which diapauses through the winter.

Diapause is apparently induced and terminated in response to environmental stimuli. Beck (1962) found that he could induce diapause in laboratory-reared European corn borer larvae by subjecting them to a dark period of 10 to 14 hours during every 24-hour period (scotophase). He also concluded that the length of photoperiod and the ambient temperature played a part in diapause induction. In 1963, Beck reported that the termination of diapause can be brought about by subjecting the diapause insect to a photophase of 16 or more hours in each 24-hour period.

In maintaining a laboratory colony it is necessary to prevent diapause, as a rule. In our laboratory incubator lights are left on throughout the growth period of the larvae. Essentially 100% pupation occurs under these conditions. If diapause is desired in a particular group, the larvae are grown in an incubator in which a time clock turns the lights off for 12 hours daily.

IX. LABORATORY COLONY

In June of 1963, a group of wild moths, from the Iowa State University Farm at Ankeny, Iowa, were placed in oviposition cages in the Corn Borer Laboratory (Guthrie *et al.*, 1965). Eggs from these moths were utilized to start a laboratory colony which is still continu-

TABLE V

BIOLOGICAL MEASUREMENTS OF THE EUROPEAN CORN BORER COLONY
REARED CONTINUOUSLY UNDER LABORATORY CONDITIONS

		Males		Females		
Generation	Pupation (%) at 20 days	Pupal wt. (mg)	Normal (%)	Pupal wt. (mg)	Normal (%)	Average number egg masses/female
I	96	—	—	—	—	16.9
II	95	78	96	105	92	10.6
III	98	71	100	97	98	7.1
IV	98	74	100	98	100	5.0
V	99	75	98	103	98	9.9
VI	99	71	100	98	97	—
VII	92	70	100	92	96	7.1
VIII	95	74	100	98	100	4.1
IX	90	79	98	105	100	3.7
X	88	79	100	106	100	17.2
XI	90	79	100	107	100	12.6
XII	85	77	96	105	92	11.1
XIII	90	89	100	116	98	—
XIV	83	81	100	116	100	—

ing and is in the thirty-second generation. For each generation approximately 500 newly hatched larvae are placed individually in rearing vials and incubated at 26.7°C and high humidity. Pupation rate on day 20 and weights of 100 pupae are recorded. Moths of these 100 are allowed to emerge from the pupal case in individual isolation. The remainder are placed in racks in an emergence-oviposition cage as previously described. Eggs from this cage are used to continue the colony and for laboratory tests. Data from 14 of these generations are tabulated in Table V. Little change can be noted from the early generations through the fourteenth, although there is a tendency for the pupae to be heavier and pupation to be somewhat slower.

REFERENCES

Barber, G. W. (1925). Observations on the response of adults of the European corn borer to light in egg laying. *Ann. Entomol. Soc. Am.* **18**, 419–431.

Beck, S. D. (1953). Nutrition of the European corn borer, *Pyrausta nubilalis* (Hbn.). III. An unidentified dietary factor required for larval growth. *J. Gen. Physiol.* **36** 317–326.

Beck, S. D. (1962). Photoperiodic induction of diapause in an insect. *Biol. Bull.* **122**, 1–12.

Beck, S. D. (1963). Physiology and ecology of photoperiodism. *Bull. Entomol. Soc. Am.* **9**, 8–16.

Beck, S. D., and Stauffer, J. F. (1950). An aseptic method for rearing corn borer larvae. *J. Econ. Entomol.* **43**, 4–6.

Beck, S. D., Lilly, J. H., and Stauffer, J. F. (1949). Nutrition of the European corn borer, *Pyrausta nubilalis* (Hbn.). I. Development of a satisfactory purified diet for larval growth. *Ann. Entomol. Soc. Am.* **42**, 483–496.

Becton, A. J., George, B. W., and Brindley, T. A. (1962). Continuous rearing of European corn borer larvae on artificial medium. *Iowa State J. Sci.* **37**, 163–172.

Bottger, G. T. (1942). Development of synthetic food media for use in nutrition studies of the European corn borer. *J. Agr. Res.* **65**, 493–500.

Brindley, T. A., and Dicke, F. F. (1963). Significant developments in European corn borer research. *Ann. Rev. Entomol.* **8**, 155–176.

Brooks, D. L., and Raun, E. S. (1965). Entomogenous fungi of corn insects in Iowa. *J. Invert. Pathol.* **7**, 79–81.

Guthrie, W. D., Raun, E. S., Dicke, F. F., Pesho, G. R., and Carter, S. W. (1965). Laboratory production of European corn borer egg masses. *Iowa State J. Sci.* **40**, 65–83.

Ignoffo, C. M., and Dutky, S. (1963). The effect of sodium hypochlorite on the viability and virulence of *Bacillus* and *Beauveria* spores and cabbage looper polyhedral virus. *J. Insect Pathol.* **5**, 422–426.

Kramer, J. P. (1959). Observations on the seasonal incidence of microsporidian in European corn borer populations in Illinois. *Entomophaga* **4**, 37–42.

Raun, E. S. (1961). Elimination of microsporidiosis in laboratory reared European corn borers by the use of heat. *J. Insect Pathol.* **3**, 446–448.

Raun, E. S. (1963). A virus-like disease of the European corn borer. *Proc. Entomol. Soc. Am. N. Central Branch* **18**, 21.

Raun, E. S. (1964). The effects of refrigeration on corn borer egg hatch. *Proc. Entomol. Soc. Am. N. Central Branch* **19**, 59–60.

Raun, E. S., and Brooks, D. L. (1963). Bacterial pathogens in Iowa corn insects. *J. Insect Pathol.* **5**, 66–71.

Raun, E. S., York, G. T., and Brooks, D. L. (1960). Determination of *Perezia pyraustae* infection rates in larvae of the European corn borer. *J. Insect Pathol.* **2**, 254–258.

Sparks, A. N. (1963). Preliminary studies of factors influencing mating of the European corn borer. *Proc. Entomol. Soc. Am. N. Central Branch* **18**, 95.

Steinhaus, E. A. (1958). Crowding as a possible stress factor in insect disease. *Ecology* **39**, 503–514.

Surany, P. (1957). Continuous mass rearing of the European corn borer in the laboratory. *Illinois Nat. Hist. Survey Div., Biol. Notes* **37**.

Walker, J. R. (1962). Evaluation of control of European corn borer, *Ostrinia nubilalis* (Hubner), by X-ray induced sterility. Ph.D. Dissertation, Iowa State University, Ames, Iowa.

Wressel, H. B. (1955). Rearing the European corn borer, *Pyrausta nubilalis* (Hbn.), on artificial diet. *Ann. Rept. Entomol. Soc. Ontario* **86**, 10–13.

Zimmack, H. L., and Brindley, T. A. (1957). The effect of the protozoan parasite *Perezia pyraustae* Paillot on the European corn borer. *J. Econ. Entomol.* **50**, 637–640.

Zimmack, H. L., Arbuthnot, K. D., and Brindley, T. A. (1954). Distribution of the European corn borer parasite *Perezia pyraustae*, and its effect on the host. *J. Econ. Entomol.* **47**, 641–655.

Chapter 22

Codling Moths

D. W. HAMILTON[*] AND D. O. HATHAWAY[†]

Entomology Research Division,
Agricultural Research Service,
U. S. Department of Agriculture,
Vincennes, Indiana;
and †Yakima, Washington

I. INTRODUCTION

Research for controlling the codling moth, *Carpocapsa pomonella* (L.), can be most satisfactorily accomplished when laboratory cultures of this insect are available. The different life history stages of the codling moth are utilized for investigations with sterilants that sometimes involve the release of large numbers of codling moths which have been made sterile by either chemosterilants or $\gamma = 1$ radiation. Different strains of codling moth are colonized to study their resistance to insecticides. They are also employed to screen candidate insecticides and for field-laboratory tests where different insecticides are applied to field plots and sprayed foliage, and fruit is infested in the laboratory after different periods of weathering.

II. METHODS OF COLLECTION

Prior to 1947, codling moth cultures for laboratory use were started from field collections of hibernating larvae. The usual procedure for

[*] *Present address:* Japanese Beetle Investigations, Entomology Research Division, Agricultural Research Service, U. S. Department of Agriculture, Moorestown, New Jersey.

collecting larvae was by removing the rough bark from apple trees and placing a 3- to 4-inch band of burlap, burlap-paper, or corrugated strawboard around the trunk. Larvae, seeking hibernating quarters, crawled under and into these bands (Fig. 1) and later were collected

FIG. 1. Codling moth hibernacula and larvae under trunk bands. (From Entomology Research Division, Agricultural Research Service, U. S. Department of Agriculture, Vincennes, Indiana.)

and concentrated for storage. In our collections we placed galvanized screen, separated from the tree band by ¼-inch sticks of wood, over the bands to prevent the birds from eating the larvae. Although the above method was in general use (Smith, 1926; Farrar and Flint, 1930; Sazama, 1932; Eide, 1936; Waters, 1937; Steiner, 1939; Harris and Waters, 1943), large numbers of larvae were also sometimes collected during the winter months by sawing off jagged limb stubs in which many larvae had pupated. Adults were sometimes collected in large numbers during their emergence period in closed or screened packing sheds or other buildings where field crates containing hibernating larvae were stored.

L. F. Steiner and his co-workers also collected large numbers of larvae in Indiana and Illinois by placing strawboard bands on and in bins of cider and vinegar processing plants. When trunk bands were used they were placed in the orchards during late summer (about August 1) and removed in the fall or early winter after the apple harvest was completed. Larvae were sometimes concentrated in rolls of corrugated paper ¾ to 1 inch wide that were about 6 inches in diameter. A known number could be stored in each roll in a coffee can or 2-lb plastic cheese container. Bands containing larvae were stored at temperatures between 36° and 38°F and 60–80% relative humidity (RH). Larvae hibernating for the winter, collected from apple trees, were stored at low temperatures for a period in order to break diapause. We often stored them in an insectary until January so that they would be exposed to the early winter temperatures, but refrigeration in a cold storage is just as satisfactory. The larvae should always be protected from mice, and mortality increases rapidly when larvae are exposed to temperatures of 0°F or less. Larvae can be stored for about a year in this manner; however, improved control of codling moths in most apple orchards since the introduction of organic insecticides and reduction in acreage of uncared for or poorly sprayed orchards has made it impractical to obtain larvae in large quantities by this method. When a limited number of larvae is needed and personnel is limited, this method can still be used by keeping a small orchard that is isolated from commercial plantings free of diseases and other insects by treating it with sprays that are nontoxic to the codling moth.

III. THE GREEN APPLE METHOD OF REARING

Dickson *et al.* (1952) first reported on a method of continuously rearing codling moths in the laboratory. Other investigators had difficulty in breaking diapause. Dickson (1949) solved this problem by maintaining cultures under constant light, thus prolonging the photoperiod. In this method, moths were collected in the laboratory with a suction device made of a metal tube 1.25 inches in diameter connected to a vacuum source with flexible tubing and opening into a 1-inch diameter glass tube, which was screened at one end and contained a stopper with a 9-mm glass tube inserted through it at the other end. Collected moths were transferred to the oviposition cages.

The cage used was a 6 × 11-inch celluloid cylinder screened at each end. Wax paper 12 inches wide was used to line the cage, and was held in place by folding it back ½ inch on each end under the caps of the cage. A pad of wet cotton wrapped in cheesecloth was placed in a dish in each cage for water for the moths. Moths oviposited best when exposed to natural twilight, below 50 ft-c. Evening light from a west window or in a greenhouse proved most satisfactory for maximum oviposition. Sazama (1932) showed that egg yields were most satisfactory when each cage contained 100 moths. About 20 eggs were produced per female.

Dickson *et al.* (1952) reared the larvae on small green apples 1 to 1.5 inches in diameter, obtained from growers at thinning time and stored up to 1 year at 32°F. They reported Winesap and Rome Beauty as the better varieties. Rearing trays 12 × 13 inches by 4 inches deep were made of galvanized iron painted white. A felt-fitted metal frame containing 28-mesh brass strainer cloth was used as a top to retain the larvae within the trays. Each tray was lined with wax paper and contained about 130 apples. About 600 eggs, on pieces of wax paper, were placed in each tray and the tray was covered and placed in a glass-topped sleeve cage. The cages were then placed in a constant temperature-humidity room maintained at 84°F and 35% RH. Larvae completed feeding in about 18 days. Mature larvae spun cocoons in strips of corrugated paper used as partitions in and around the apples. When pupation was complete, the tops of the trays were removed, and the moths emerged into the sleeve cages. It took about 28 days to complete rearing from moth to moth.

This procedure averaged about 60 moths per tray of 130 apples and 600 eggs. About 60% of the eggs produced were viable. Increasing the humidity during hatching produced more entries but increased loss of fruit by fungus and consequently gave lower yields. Dusting green apples with sulfur prior to storage helped prevent their breakdown.

This method has been used by several laboratories in the United States; with certain modifications, it is still relied on as one of the principal methods for rearing codling moths. Bailey and Madsen (1964) suggest creasing the wax paper liner used in the oviposition cage at ¼-inch intervals. Female moths then lay their eggs in rows down the creases rather than scattering them and overlapping them in masses on the paper. This permits the clipping off of a single egg or a number of eggs more readily.

Changes in the method which we used at Vincennes, Indiana, included larger trays (12 × 18 × 4 inches) for retaining apples and placing freshly hatched larvae rather than eggs on the apples. Trays without covers were placed in a well-lighted rearing room. Larvae pupated in corrugated cardboard strips placed in the trays and tacked to shelves holding the trays. Newly emerged moths were attracted to fluorescent lights (80 watts) on the front and screened side of the room, where they were collected daily and placed in oviposition tubes. The lights also prevented the occurrence of diapause. Methods for handling eggs and larvae also differed and will be described later.

We found it difficult to locate green apples for storage free of insecticides that were not severely infected with apple scab, *Venturia inequalis* (Cke.) Wint., or injured by plum curculio, *Conotrachelus nenuphar* (Herbst) and codling moth. Attempts to reduce DDT, azinphosethyl, or carbaryl residues from sprayed fruit by washing were not successful. Residue-free apples were obtained by spraying trees with fungicides and three applications of malathion, and allowing the spray deposits to weather 3 to 4 weeks prior to picking. Storage at temperatures between 36° and 38°F was required for apples needed from July to the following June. Green apples kept best when stored in bushel or half bushel lots within a plastic film bag or liner within the container. Golden Delicious apples were the preferred variety. *Drosophila* and fungus-feeding insects became numerous in the constant temperature-humidity rooms where codling moths were reared, and mold was sometimes a problem. The mold was transmitted into the oviposition tubes in the incubator. Consequently, research that resulted in the development of a semi-synthetic diet for rearing codling moth larvae was started in 1958.

IV. MASS REARING

At Yakima, Washington, 10,000 codling moths were reared each day during the summer of 1965 for a sterile male release program and for the extraction of female sex attractant. The techniques, described by Dickson *et al.* (1952), were modified for our rearing program.

The oviposition cage used was a cylindrical plastic cage 11 inches long and 5 inches in diameter with an accordion-pleated waxed paper liner inserted against the inside wall of the cage. Moths were anesthetized with CO_2 and measured volumetrically; 8 cc of anesthetized moths usually equaled 100 to 125 males and females in equal numbers. This was the most desirable number of moths for each oviposition cage. The wax paper liner in the oviposition cages was changed once a day. Egg sheets and oviposition cages were surface-sterilized by dipping in a 0.1% sodium hypochlorite solution for 2 minutes and air-dried to prevent disease. The oviposition room was held under constant light, about 7 ft-c, at 60–70% RH, and 80° ± 2 F. Female moths laid about 80 eggs during the first 5 days of their lives, after which they were discarded. Giving the moths food and water to prolong their lives did not increase egg production enough to warrant the extra work.

The wax paper sheets on which the moths deposited their eggs were cut into strips and then into ½-inch squares. Care was taken to avoid injury to the numerous eggs laid in the creases. Between 1500 and 1800 eggs were placed in a quart carton. Three-day-old eggs

FIG. 2. Box with blowers used to distribute moth eggs on apples. (From Entomology Research Division, Agricultural Research Service, U. S. Department of Agriculture, Yakima, Washington.)

were placed on the green apples used as food for the larvae. About 400 apples were placed in a 24 × 24 × 4-inch wooden tray. A 23¼ × 22¾ × 17½-inch box with two air blowers was used to distribute codling moth eggs in these rearing trays (Fig. 2). Trays containing apples were passed under the box on a roller conveyor. The squares of wax paper containing codling moth eggs were fed into an opening in the top of the box and the circulating air distributed the paper squares over the apples. Several corrugated cardboard strips ¾ inch wide were stapled to the inside wall of the tray. Several more strips were laid in the center of the tray on top of the apples. These corrugations provided pupation sites for the larvae. Lids for the trays were made of 1 × 2-inch wood strips with 32-mesh saran cloth stapled to the wood frame. At the end of the roller conveyor the trays were removed and placed in racks. The racks were wheeled into rearing rooms made of polyethylene. Most of the eggs hatched in 5 days. Temperatures of the rearing rooms were maintained at 82°–86°F and 60–70% RH. A 16-hour photoperiod was provided by Gro-Lux fluorescent lights hung above a clear plastic ceiling. Larvae developed in 14 days and the pupae in 8 days.

Three weeks after the apples were infested, the corrugated pupation strips were removed. These strips were placed in 24 × 24 × 4-inch covered trays (Fig. 3). When the moths emerged they were

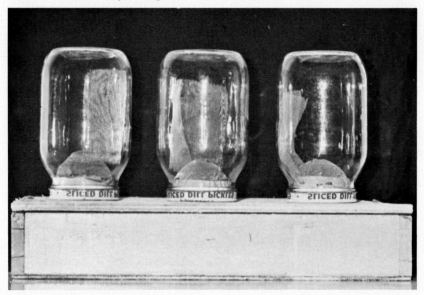

FIG. 3. Gallon glass jars on emergence boxes used to collect moths. (From Entomology Research Division, Agricultural Research Service, U. S. Department of Agriculture, Yakima, Washington.)

attracted by the light upward out of the boxes and were collected in gallon glass jars fitted with screen cones. This method of collection was much faster than using a modified vacuum cleaner. The collection bottle also contained a 5×7-inch wire screen for moths to rest on, which reduced injury to adults. Moths were immobilized by placing the bottles in a cooler at temperatures between 35° and 40°F. The moths were removed from the cooler, placed in cartons and anesthetized with CO_2, and separated with Schuco-Vac vacuum tweezers.[*] An X2 Dazor[†] magnifier and a fluorescent fixture were used to distinguish the moth sexes. An experienced person can separate 1000 male and female moths per hour.

The most desirable apples used as food were the Winesap and Red or standard Delicious varieties, since they keep well in storage. Apples were purchased from orchardists at thinning season and were stored in bulk bins that held 30,000–35,000 1- to 1½-inch apples per bin. Large perforated polyethylene bags were used to line the bins and prevent desiccation of the apples. Apples kept up to 1 year at 34°F had about 10% loss due to rot.

Bailey and Madsen (1964) described the method used to prepare fruit to be infested. This method consisted of sorting the thinning apples from the field, washing them in a trisodium phosphate solution to remove spray residues, then rinsing them in clean water, and air-drying them. The fruit was packaged in polyethylene bags that were perforated to provide ventilation. This same method, modified to include dipping the fruit in a 0.5% sodium hypochlorite solution following the clean water rinse, then dried and placed into the polyethylene-lined bins for storage, was used at Yakima.

The rearing racks, trays, and lids were washed with water and steam cleaned, then immersed in a 1% solution of sodium hypochlorite for 1 hour to prevent disease from infecting the moth culture. Rearing rooms were scrubbed with soap and water, and sprayed with a 0.5% sodium hypochlorite solution each week.

V. SEMISYNTHETIC DIETS FOR COLONIZING CODLING MOTHS

Theron (1947) succeeded in rearing codling moths on a medium based on corn meal, but yields were not satisfactory. He had difficulty with diapause. The report by Redfern (1964), based on the

[*] Schuco Scientific, A Division of Schueler & Company, 250 W. 18 Street, New York, New York.

[†] Dazor Floating Fixture Model M-270, Dazor Mfg. Corp., St. Louis, Missouri.

studies at Vincennes, Indiana, was the first report of successful semisynthetic diet for rearing codling moths. Hamilton (unpublished data) discussed modifications for the Redfern diet in 1964.

Our Vincennes method for handling eggs and larvae of the codling moth differs extensively from that described by Dickson *et al.* (1952). Research on the method extends back to the investigations described by Sazama (1932) and Steiner (1939). We modified their methods to fit improved techniques. The oviposition tube consisted of a fiber-board cylinder (a 1-lb salt box, for example), about 3 inches in diameter and 6 inches long, capped at each end (Fig. 4). A 1-inch hole was drilled near one end of each tube and a 1 × 2½-inch glass vial was inserted into this hole. The vial was filled with water and tightly plugged at the end with sterile cotton, which was kept damp by the water and allowed moths in the tube to drink. The water also helped keep a high humidity within the oviposition tube. Three small branches of pear wood, about 5 cm thick and 70 cm long, were placed in each tube. This has always increased egg laying. Reasons for this are not known; other smooth woods or smooth inert objects have not yielded comparable results. A very light coating of paraffin was placed on the inside of the tubes by carefully dipping and rolling them in hot melted paraffin. Only a light coating of paraffin should be applied, as heavy coatings seem to inhibit oviposition. Approximately 100 moths of mixed sexes were placed in each tube. The cap on one end of the tube was then replaced with a piece of cheesecloth that was held in place with a rubber band. The tubes were then placed in a constant temperature cabinet at 82°F for 5 days. Light in the oviposition cabinet was dim, about 3 ft-c. Eggs were laid on the inside of the tube (Fig. 5) and on the pieces of pear wood. After 5 days, some of the older eggs had developed to the black-head stage and began to hatch within 1 to 4 additional hours when left at temperatures of 82°F.

Next, adult moths were removed from the tube, a fresh vial of water and cotton plug was placed in the 1-inch hole, the cheesecloth was replaced with the cardboard cap, and the tubes were stored in a refrigerator at 50°F until needed for an experiment. When larvae were needed for infesting a batch of diet or any other study, tubes containing eggs were removed from the refrigerator and placed in a constant temperature-humidity room at 82°F and 45% RH. The vial of water was replaced with a dry vial and the tube placed near a bright light. Codling moth larvae are positively phototropic and upon hatching immediately travel toward the light transmitted through the 1-inch hole. They collected in the glass vial (Fig. 6) from which

FIG. 4. Codling moth oviposition tube. (From Entomology Research Division, Agricultural Research Service, U. S. Department of Agriculture, Vincennes, Indiana.)

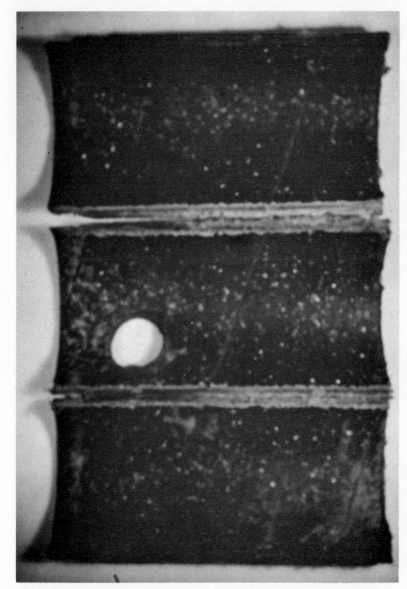

FIG. 5. Oviposition tube cut open to show codling moth eggs. (From Entomology Research Division, Agricultural Research Service, U. S. Department of Agriculture, Vincennes, Indiana.)

FIG. 6. Newly hatched larvae in vial on oviposition tube, and dish of semisynthetic diet. (From Entomology Research Division, Agricultural Research Service, U. S. Department of Agriculture, Vincennes, Indiana.)

they were removed with a small camel's hair brush and placed on green apples, semisynthetic diet, or insecticide-treated apples that were being utilized in experiments.

When sexed adults were needed for experiments, males and females were separated in the larval stage and reared in separate cages. The male gonads can be readily seen externally. They appear as two elongated black spots on the dorsum. When moths were allowed to emerge in small screened cages, i.e., 1 to 2 ft square by 18 to 24 inches high, that had glass slide panels for doors, they were readily collected by turning the back of the cage toward the light so that all the moths congregated near the rear of the cage. The breeze from a 10- to 16-inch electric fan was then directed toward the moths. The glass panel was removed and the moths were picked up in vials, by tweezers or with vacuum apparatus. Adults will stay perfectly still when in the draft of a fan.

The larval diet we first used at Vincennes, Indiana, was modified from the one used by Vanderzant and Davich (1958) for rearing boll weevil, *Anthonomus grandis* Boheman. Many modifications were tried before the yield of normal codling moth adults was considered satisfactory. At first, numerous larvae had elongated mandibles and the pupal caps stuck to the adults. Many pupae had weakened areas at the forefront of the abdomen. The occurrence of mold on the diet also created a problem. The use of ascorbic acid in the diet increased the yield of normal adults to a satisfactory level.

Later, data obtained by the Yakima, Washington, Laboratory indicated that codling moths could be reared on a medium modified from one developed for the cabbage looper, *Trichoplusia ni* (Hubner), by Ignoffo (1963). The Washington diet, with certain changes, was found to be equal in efficiency to the diet that originated in Vincennes. One of the principal changes made was in the mold inhibitor, as the one used by Ignoffo did not satisfactorily prevent mold in the codling moth diet.

By July 1, 1964, we had continuously reared codling moth larvae on semisynthetic diets for more than 3 years—through 35 generations. All codling moths used at Vincennes between December 10, 1963, and July 1, 1964, were reared on semisynthetic diets. More than 37,000 adults were reared in the 7-month period; this included 4 generations of larvae. About 60% of the larvae placed on the diet emerged as normal adults in the later tests. The two formulas found most satisfactory are listed in Table I.

The vitamin solution developed by Vanderzant and Davich (1958), which contained niacinamide (nicatinamide), 0.5 gm; thiamine

TABLE I
FORMULAS FOR SEMISYNTHETIC DIETS

Ingredient	Formula No. 1	Formula No. 2
Distilled water	1100 ml	1100 ml
Whole apple seeds	3/each cup	—
Wheat germ	—	45 gm
Ground apple seeds	30 gm	—
Dried apple	60 gm	60 gm
Sucrose	60 gm	60 gm
Casein	—	60 gm
Soybean protein	60 gm	—
Wesson salts	12.5 gm	12.5 gm
Yeast	12.5 gm	12.5 gm
Glycine	1.25 gm	1.25 gm
Cysteine	0.625 gm	0.625 gm
Cholesterol	0.625 gm	0.625 gm
α-Cellulose	30 gm	30 gm
Ascorbic acid	10 gm	10 gm
Linseed oil	10 ml	10 ml
Agar	20 gm	20 gm
Vitamin solution (V and D)	12.5 ml	12.5 ml
Potassium hydroxide (10%)	37.5 ml	37.5 ml
Mold inhibitor (V and D)	22.5 ml	22.5 ml

hydrochloride, 0.125 gm; folic acid, 0.125 gm; calcium pantothenate, 0.5 gm; B_{12} in mannitol, 1.0 gm; riboflavin, 0.25 gm; pyridoxine hydrochloride, 0.125 gm; choline chloride, 25 gm; and distilled water, 427.4 ml, was the most satisfactory of several we tested.

The mold inhibitor used also originated with Vanderzant and Davich (1958). It was composed of 20 gm sorbic acid, 15 gm methyl parasept (methyl p-hydroxybenzoate) and 170 ml of ethyl alcohol.

The diet was prepared by (1) weighing the dried apple (and apple seeds when used) into container No. 1; (2) weighing sucrose and soybean protein or casein and wheat germ, Wesson's salt "W," yeast, glyceine, cysteine, and cholesterol into container No. 2; (3) weighing ascorbic acid into container No. 3 and dissolving with cold water; (4) weighing α-cellulose into container No. 4; (5) weighing agar into container No. 5; (6) heating 220 ml water to boiling. While water was heating, placing ingredients of container No. 1 in a 1-gallon (Waring) blendor and measuring out remaining liquid ingredients into container No. 6; (7) after the water began to boil, measuring 120 ml into the blendor, activating blendor, and cutting ingredients into a paste consistency, dissolving agar from container

No. 5 in rest of boiling water and adding it to blendor, adding liquid ingredients from container No. 6 and ingredients of container No. 2 and blending thoroughly. Adding α-cellulose from container No. 4, mixing and cooling to 140°F, and adding ascorbic acid from container No. 3.

The blended diet was dispensed into ⅝-oz jelly cups[*] with a plastic squeeze bottle, using 5 to 7 ml per cup. When used, 3 whole apple seeds were placed in each cup before the diet solidified. The bottoms of the seeds were solid in the diet (Fig. 6). The diet was allowed to cool about 12 hours before it was infested with larvae.

Two larvae were placed in each cup. Since codling moth larvae are cannibalistic and tend to feed on each other, additional larvae will not increase moth yields. The cardboard caps were applied to the cups (Fig. 6) and the cups were placed in a constant temperature-humidity room at 82°F and 65% RH for adult emergence.

Adults emerged 29 to 54 days after the medium was infested. The larval period averaged 34 days for the Indiana tests. The larvae pupated in the capped cups. We uncapped the cups immediately prior to the period adults began to emerge. Emerging adults were attracted to a glass panel covering a 2-tube 80 watt white fluorescent lamp that was mounted on the front of the rearing cage, so that the shelves where the infested diet was stored were lighted at all times. This prevented larvae from going into diapause. Dickson *et al.* (1952) found that at least 15 hours of light per day was needed to prevent diapause. The screened cage used for rearing in the constant temperature-humidity room was 5 × 7 ft by 8 ft high. We reared more than 48,000 codling moth adults in a 3-year period during the development of these diets.

REFERENCES

Bailey, J. B., and Madsen, H. F. (1964). A laboratory study of three strains of codling moth, *Carpocapsa pomonella* (Linnaeus), exhibiting tolerance to DDT in the field. *Hilgardia* **35**, 185–210.

Dickson, R. C. (1949). Factors governing the induction of diapause in the oriental fruit moth. *Ann. Entomol. Soc. Am.* **42**, 511–537.

Dickson, R. C., Barnes, M. M., and Turzan, C. L. (1952). Continuous rearing of the codling moth. *J. Econ. Entomol.* **45**, 66–68.

Eide, P. M. (1936). Oviposition cage for obtaining large quantities of codling moth eggs. *U. S. Dept. Agr., Bur. Entomol. Plant Quarantine*, E.T. **ET73**.

Farrar, M. D., and Flint, W. P. (1930). Rearing codling moth larvae throughout the year (*Carpocapsa pomonella*). *J. Econ. Entomol.* **23**, 41–44.

[*] Premium Plastics, Chicago, Illinois (⅝-oz jelly cup No. 6916).

Harris, L. P., and Waters, H. A. (1943). Codling moth laboratory procedures in the studies of the chemical control of insects. *In* "Rearing Insects that Attack Plants," Publ. No. 20, p. 96. Am. Assoc. Advance. Sci., Washington, D. C.

Ignoffo, C. M. (1963). A successful technique for massrearing cabbage loopers on a semisynthetic diet. *Ann. Entomol. Soc. Am.* **56**(2), 178–82.

Redfern, R. E. (1964). Concentrate medium for rearing the codling moth. *J. Econ. Entomol.* **57**, 607–608.

Sazama, R. F. (1932). An improved oviposition cage for the codling moth. *J. Econ. Entomol.* **25**, 140–141.

Smith, R. H. (1926). The efficacy of lead arsenate in controlling the codling moth. *Hilgardia* **1**, 403–453.

Steiner, L. F. (1939). The laboratory-field method for testing codling moth insecticides. *U. S. Dept. Agr., Bur. Entomol. Plant Quarantine, E.T.* **88**, 1–10.

Theron, P. P. Q. (1947). Studies on the provision of hosts for the mass-rearing of codling moth parasites. *Union S. Africa, Dept. Agr., Sci. Bull.* **262**, 1–45.

Vanderzant, E. S., and Davich, T. B. (1958). Laboratory rearing of the boll weevil: A satisfactory larval diet and oviposition studies. *J. Econ. Entomol.* **51**, 288–291.

Waters, H. A. (1937). Methods and equipment for laboratory studies of insecticides. *J. Econ. Entomol.* **30**, 179–203.

Chapter 23

Pink Bollworms

DIAL F. MARTIN

Cotton Insect Research Branch,
Entomology Research Division,
Agricultural Research Service,
U. S. Department of Agriculture,
Beltsville, Maryland

I. GENERAL BIOLOGY

The pink bollworm, *Pectinophora gossypiella* (Saunders), is a lepidopterous insect which feeds within the fruiting parts of malvaceous plants. Host plants include more than 45 species, of which cotton is the most important. Larvae of the pink bollworm enter the fruit of the cotton plant and feed on the contents of the bolls or fruiting buds (squares). Owen and Calhoun (1932) determined under field conditions that most of the eggs hatched 4.5 days after deposition at a mean temperature of 83.04°F. They found that the total length of the developmental period for nondiapause larvae from egg deposition to moth emergence averaged 26.6 and 32.92 days for those reared from squares and bolls, respectively. Lukefahr and Griffin (1961) found that the rate of larval development was faster in squares than in bolls. They also found that as the age of squares and bolls increased, larval development was faster. Lukefahr and Griffin (1957) determined that copulation in this species occurred between the hours of 2 and 5 A.M., with the peak of mating occurring about 3:30 A.M. The peak of egg deposition occurred on the third night after emergence, with more than 50% of the eggs laid between 8 and 10 P.M. A light intensity of 0.02 ft-c or below appeared optimum for moth activity and oviposition; however, these activities were sharply reduced at temperatures below 70°F.

II. REVIEW OF LITERATURE ON
ARTIFICIAL DIETS

Rearing of pink bollworms on chemically defined media was first attempted by Beckman et al. (1953). These researchers used a modified chick ration with egg albumin as the protein constituent, crystalline vitamins, and dextrose. The ration was almost completely water-soluble. Heating the ingredients in boiling water coagulated the albumin and formed a homogeneous solid. After many modifications of the diet and many experiments, several insects were reared to the adult stage.

Later, Vanderzant and Reiser (1956a), working in the same laboratory used by Beckman et al., reported on certain modifications of the diet and introduced aseptic rearing techniques. Using data presented by Bailey (1948), they reared 259 adults, many of which deposited fertile eggs, on media prepared to contain nutrients in the same proportions as in bolls of different ages. Three generations of pink bollworms were reared in media devoid of any plant extracts. The effects of different protein-carbohydrate-fat ratios in the medium on size and growth of the pink bollworm were studied. Vanderzant and Reiser (1956b) also reported results of studies on the nutrition of the pink bollworm in which purified casein was substituted for the albumin and agar used to form a gel on which the larvae could feed. They prepared pure casein medium on which the pink bollworm developed in the normal period of time and produced moths which deposited fertile eggs. This development led to a study of the effects of modifications of the ingredients in the diet and addition or elimination of certain nutrients on larval size, growth, and pupation rates.

Vanderzant et al. (1956) demonstrated the feasibility of mass rearing pink bollworm larvae on immature or sprouted seeds of beans and peas under aseptic conditions and sprouted cottonseed under conditions that permitted a minimum of interference by contaminating microorganisms. They stated that rearing larvae on sprouted peas was the preferred aseptic method for rearing small numbers of larvae for laboratory studies, but pointed out that with improvements the cottonseed method should give better yields. Vanderzant (1957) determined the requirements for individual amino acids and was able to prepare a medium in which the nutritive constituents were chemically defined except for corn oil which could be replaced by linoleic acid. The investigator stated: "It is believed that this is the first insect to be perpetuated on a chemically defined diet." Vanderzant (1958) reported further on the amino acid requirements of the pink bollworm.

The role of dietary fatty acids in the development of the pink bollworm was determined by Vanderzant et al. (1957). B-vitamin requirements were reported by Ouye and Vanderzant (1964). Clark et al. (1961), in search of a suitable medium prepared from commercially obtainable plant products, screened natural foods such as cottonseed, okra, and seeds of other host plants and plant products such as cottonseed meal. They were able to rear larvae on two media consisting of cottonseed meal or peanut flour in combination with other constituents, but experienced trouble with fungus growths which were overcome to a certain extent by inclusion of combinations of antimicrobial agents. They also had trouble with cannibalism. Cannibalism was partially eliminated by furnishing large areas of medium per larva, and/or segregating the larvae by subdividing the total mass of medium with physical barriers.

Probably the most satisfactory diet was a wheat germ medium developed by Adkisson et al. (1960). This medium had wheat germ as the primary ingredient but also contained vitamin-free casein, sucrose, Wesson's salts, choline chloride, agar, sodium alginate, vitamins, and water.

Larvae were commonly reared with 1 larva per vial using aseptic conditions, but this procedure was too costly and tedious. Vanderzant et al. (1956) and Clark et al. (1961) had limited success by infesting natural foods with large numbers of larvae under aseptic or near aseptic conditions with antimicrobial agents included in the diets. Ouye (1962) reported on the effects of antimicrobial agents on the development of microorganisms and pink bollworm. Using a wheat germ diet similar to that of Adkisson et al. (1960), he was able to obtain larval development equal to that in cotton squares with a minimum of contamination when the proper kind and amount of antimicrobial agents were used in conjunction with good sanitary procedures.

Condensation of moisture, cannibalism, and a general tendency of the larvae to wander away from the food were common factors contributing to poor results in many of the early experiments. Richmond and Ignoffo (1964), by using the diet of Ouye (1962) and providing physical barriers between ¼-inch cubes of the medium, were able to rear pink bollworms in mass. Pink bollworms are now mass reared in 9-oz waxed paper cups with ¼-inch cubes of medium scattered between layers of nonabsorbent cotton.

III. MASS REARING PROCEDURE

A. SEMISYNTHETIC DIET

The composition of the semisynthetic diet used for rearing pink bollworm larvae is presented in Table I. This diet is basically the pink bollworm diet devised by Vanderzant and Reiser (1956a,b) and later modified by Adkisson *et al.* (1960) and Ouye (1962). The ingredients specified in Table I will make approximately 1 gallon of finished medium. Smaller batches may be prepared, if desired, but the ratio of the ingredients as given in the table should be maintained.

TABLE I

COMPOSITION OF MEDIUM USED FOR REARING PINK BOLLWORMS

Constituents	Amount
Methyl *p*-hydroxybenzoate (15% w/v in 95% ethyl alcohol)	36 ml
Choline chloride (0.1 gm/ml water)	36 ml
Potassium hydroxide (4 *M*)	18 ml
Formaldehyde (0.1/ml water)	13 ml
Vitamin stock[a]	6 ml
Casein (vitamin-free)	126 gm
Sucrose	126 gm
Wheat germ	108 gm
Salts, Wesson's	36 gm
α-Cellulose	18 gm
Agar	90 gm
Distilled water	3100 ml

[a] The vitamin stock contains 300 mg riboflavin, 150 mg pyridoxine, 150 mg thiamine, 150 mg folic acid, 600 mg niacin, 600 mg calcium pantothenate, 12 mg biotin, and 1.2 mg of vitamin B_{12} in 100 ml of water.

In preparing a batch of the size indicated in Table I, dissolve the agar in about 2200 ml of boiling water. The casein is blended in 900 ml of water and 18 ml of potassium hydroxide in a 1-gallon capacity commercial Waring Blendor. All solids are then added and blended into a homogeneous mixture. The choline chloride, formaldehyde, methyl *p*-hydroxybenzoate and vitamin solution are successively added with continuous blending. The dissolved agar is added and the entire mixture blended for about 2 minutes or until a homogeneous color is obtained.

After blending, the hot mixture is poured into mustard- or catsup-type plastic "squeeze" bottles for dispensing the medium into vials used for rearing single larvae or the hot liquid medium may be poured into $14 \times 18 \times \frac{3}{4}$ inch sterilized serving trays and allowed to solidify before use. Soon after the hot medium is poured into the serving trays, it is covered with brown wrapping paper to prevent contamination with airborne microorganisms and to allow the medium to solidify and excessive moisture to evaporate. The solidified medium is cut into cubes about ¼ inch in size. The cutting is accomplished by pressing the solidified medium through a cutter constructed from ¼-inch mesh hardware cloth mounted on a wooden rectangular frame. Several trays of medium may be cut and stored in sterile cloth bags, but the cubed medium should be used within several hours after being cut.

B. EQUIPMENT AND REARING PROCEDURE

1. *Oviposition Cage, Egg Collecting, and Adult Handling*

A culture of the pink bollworm may be started from adults emerged from material containing diapausing larvae or adults emerged from green cotton bolls collected during the growing season. The oviposition cage consists of a cylindrical 1 quart ice-cream container treated inside with melted paraffin to eliminate egg-laying sites (Fig. 1). The paper lid of the ice-cream container is replaced with a screen wire cover which fits snugly against the lips of the container and prevents escape of the moths. The screen used to construct the cover should be about 14×18 (or similar) mesh screen wire. A screen wire disc of similar mesh 2 to 3 inches in diameter is placed upon the screen cover, followed by an egg-laying pad. The egg-laying pads should be about the size of the screen wire disc and cut from milk strainer filters or filter paper. Almost any kind of material will serve as an egg-laying pad. The egg-laying pad is held in place with a stiff cardboard disc and weighted down to en-

FIG. 1. Oviposition cage showing container, screen wire cover, screen wire disc, egg-laying pad and cardboard paper cover with weight.

sure even contact over the entire surface of the egg-laying pad. A small rock or similar object will serve as a weight. Egg-laying pads are placed on the oviposition cages in the late afternoon (about 5 P.M.) and removed in the morning. Pads from several cages are placed in a 250-cc Erlenmeyer flask stoppered with cotton and held at 80°–85°F. Hatching of the eggs occurs in about 4 days. Newly hatched larvae are attracted to the light; thus, by proper exposure to a 40- or 60-watt light bulb, the larvae can be caused to migrate to the lip of the flask where they may be removed with a camel's hair brush or small tuft of cotton for use in infesting larval rearing cups or vials.

An oviposition cage of the size given above will accommodate about 50 pairs of moths. This is a convenient number of moths for handling but larger numbers and larger cages may be used if desired. The screen and card discs are replaced during the day with a tuft of cotton about 1 inch in diameter, saturated with a 5% sugar solution that serves as food for the adults. A squeeze bottle as shown in Fig. 1 may be used to apply fresh solution when needed throughout the day to maintain a moist condition. Other types of feeders may be used if preferred. Adults should be held at about 80°F. The peak of egg laying will be reached in 5 to 7 days. By the tenth day, most egg deposition will be completed.

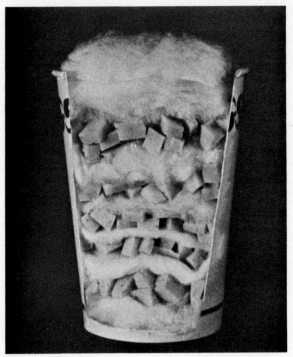

FIG. 2. Cross section of rearing cup showing layers of medium and cotton.

2. Larval Rearing

Several kinds of containers have been used successfully to rear pink bollworm larvae, varying in size from shell vials which hold single individuals to larger containers which will accommodate several hundred larvae. Two common rearing containers used at the U. S. Department of Agriculture Brownsville Laboratory have been 2-dram shell vials and 9-oz waxed paper cups.

a. Shell Vials. Where insects of exact known age and stage of development are desired, 2-dram, patent-lip, shell vials are used. The medium while still hot is poured at the rate of 3 ml per vial into the vials with a mustard squeeze jar. The vials are stoppered with absorbent cotton and held for 24 hours at room temperature before use to permit evaporation of condensed water. A camel's hair brush is used to transfer a single larvae to each vial. The vial is stoppered with a cotton plug and held at 80°–85°F.

b. Waxed Paper Cups. Where large numbers of larvae or adults are needed, the 9-oz waxed paper cup or similar container may be used (Fig. 2). A thin layer of sterile plucked cotton is placed in the bottom of the container followed with a layer of medium (about 25 ¼-inch cubes). About 25 newly hatched larvae are placed on the medium with a tuft of cotton or camel's hair brush. Then a thin layer of plucked cotton, which serves as a barrier, is placed on the medium followed with a layer of medium to which about 25 larvae are added. Alternate layers of cotton and medium with larvae are made until the container is filled; 4 to 5 layers of medium are generally used per cup. A layer of cotton is applied to the top layer of medium and a plastic snap-on lid placed on the cup. The cups are stored in an upside-down position in a dark room at 80°–85°F for several days to allow the larvae to settle down and start feeding. The larvae by nature do considerable moving about after hatching and will become isolated from the medium and die unless the cotton barriers and the plastic lid are used as outlined above. The snap-on plastic lids are removed after several days and the cups placed in emergence cans. Waxed paper cups are used to prevent excessive drying out of the medium.

3. Adult Collecting

a. Emergence Cans. A convenient and inexpensive container used for collecting emerging adults consists of a 50-lb shortening can equipped with a friction top (Fig. 3). These containers are washed and heat-sterilized to kill mites and other contaminants from time to time. A large hole is cut in the friction top and fitted with an inverted funnel-shaped screen wire cover. The screen cover or cone is soldered to the lid to ensure a moth-tight fit and allows light to enter the can, which attracts the adults. A metal screw-type lid that fits an 8-oz wide-mouth specimen jar is inverted and soldered onto the apex of the funnel or cone-shaped screen cover to serve as a holder for a wide-mouth glass jar or moth trap. This type of holder is convenient for installing and removing the moth trap. The emergence can holds about 18 of the waxed paper cups. A wire rack about 1 to 2 inches high and slightly smaller than the diameter of the can is placed in the bottom of the can. Shredded paper is distributed underneath the rack and serves as material in which the larvae that leave the cups can pupate. Full-grown larvae normally will cut small holes in the side of the cup and drop below. Many will pupate in the top layer of cotton on each cup. When the snap-on plastic lids are removed from the waxed paper cups, the cups are placed in the large emergence can. The cans are held in continuous light until the larvae are full grown as the light repels the older larvae and causes them to remain in the rearing cup until

FIG. 3. Emergence cans showing screen wire funnel with moth trap.

ready to pupate. The temperature should be held at 80°–85°F. About 14 days after the cups are infested, the cans should be covered with the lids, moth traps put in place, and the emergence can transferred to a holding room equipped with black lights. As the adults emerge they will be lured upward into the moth trap by the light.

b. Moth Traps. The moth trap consists of an 8-oz wide-mouth specimen jar fitted with a bronze screen wire cone (Fig. 4), that serves to trap newly emerged moths when they enter the jars. The cone of the moth trap should have a small hole provided in the apex to allow moths to pass into the glass jar but prevent the moths from returning to the emergence can. A piece of paper toweling folded into corrugations is placed in each jar to serve as a resting place for the newly emerged adults. This toweling prevents excessive

Fig. 4. Moth trap showing wide-mouth glass jar, corrugated paper toweling, and bronze screen wire cone.

activity and crowding of the adults and helps to preserve the scales and general good condition of the adults. The screen wire cone in the jar should fit tightly enough so that it remains in place when the jars are removed from the holder on the emergence can, thus preventing the escape of moths. A new jar should be screwed into place on the emergence can. Emergence may continue for several weeks. Carbon dioxide is used to anesthetize the moths for counting, sexing, pairing, etc. It may be necessary to remove moths from the jar traps several times each day, especially near the peak of emergence when large numbers of moths are emerging.

C. Problems in Rearing

1. Sanitation

Molds, bacteria, and yeast are constant problems in the rearing medium but can be held to a minimum if good sanitation is maintained throughout the rearing operation. The antimicrobial agents used in the medium inhibit the growth of most of these contaminants sufficiently to allow the larvae to make normal growth if the contamination is held to a minimum. All utensils used in the preparation of the medium should be washed, wrapped, and autoclaved after each operation. All table surfaces in the working area should be disinfected by wiping with a suitable germicidal agent frequently during the day to hold down contamination. Sodium hypochlorite (Chlorox) is good for this purpose. Personnel doing the rearing should be instructed in and required to maintain sterile procedures at all times. There will be some contaminants in ingredients used in the medium; however, the most important source of contamination is in the laboratory from air, tables, equipment, and personnel. Larval rearing containers with spent medium and cotton should be burned. Emergence cans should be washed with soap and water and heat-sterilized. The 8-oz moth traps should be washed and sterilized after each use.

The medium should be prepared in a laboratory other than the room used to infest the cups and rear larvae. The rearing facilities should be so arranged that spent materials and rearing containers can be disposed of without moving them through the medium preparation room.

Air-borne spores are one of the most common sources of contamination; therefore, the medium should not be exposed any more than necessary. Air movement should be held to a minimum but where air-borne contamination is a problem, air filters that retain bacteria, mold and yeast spores should be used.

When unusually persistent contaminants appear, the selection of an effective antimicrobial agent may be accomplished by running tests with antibiotic sulfonamide Uni-discs or similar techniques. Any new inhibitor should be tested to determine whether it is toxic to any stage of the larvae.

2. Diseases of the Pink Bollworm

In recent months, a cytoplasmic polyhedrosis virus has caused some sporadic trouble in the pink bollworm mass rearing program resulting in larval mortality, death of adult moths before they enter the traps on emergence cans, and reduced fecundity of the survivors. Surviving adults are reduced in size and the development period of larvae is increased. Little is known about the disease and proper measures for reducing or eliminating the infection from the culture has not been determined. This disease appeared after some 4 to 5 years of culturing. To combat this disease, the infected culture has been discarded and a new disease-free culture started.

IV. AUTOMATION AND MASS REARING

The rearing technique outlined in this paper involves a considerable number of hand operations which must be eliminated when daily demands require millions of insects. Available information indicates that the rearing operation may be completely automated with the possible exception of the handling of the egg-laying culture. Once eggs are obtained on egg-laying pads, removing, sterilizing, and dispensing them in the medium may be done mechanically. The mixing, cutting, and placing the medium in the cups or other type of containers can be done mechanically as well. Better control of contaminants and diseases should be possible when mechanical operations are instituted.

REFERENCES

Adkisson, P. L., Vanderzant, E. S., Bull, D. L., and Allison, W. E. (1960). A wheat germ medium for rearing of the pink bollworm. *J. Econ. Entomol.* **53**, 759–762.

Bailey, A. E. (1948). "Cottonseed and Cottonseed Products." Wiley (Interscience), New York.

Beckman, H. F., Bruckart, S. M., and Reiser, R. (1953). Laboratory culture of the pink bollworm on chemically defined media. *J. Econ. Entomol.* **46**, 627–630.

Clark, E. W., Richmond, C. A., and McGough, J. M. (1961). Artificial media and rearing techniques of the pink bollworm. *J. Econ. Entomol.* **54**, 4–9.

Lukefahr, M. J., and Griffin, J. A. (1957). Mating and oviposition habits of the pink bollworm moth. *J. Econ. Entomol.* **50**, 487–490.

Lukefahr, M. J., and Griffin, J. A. (1961). Pink bollworm development in relation to age of squares and bolls with notes on biology. *J. Econ. Entomol.* **55**, 158–159.

Ouye, M. T. (1962). Effects of antimicrobial agents on microorganisms and pink bollworm development. *J. Econ. Entomol.* **55**, 854–857.

Ouye, M. T., and Vanderzant, E. S. (1964). B-Vitamin requirements of the pink bollworm. *J. Econ. Entomol.* **57**, 427–430.

Owen, W. L., and Calhoun, S. L. (1932). Biology of the pink bollworm at Presidio, Texas. *J. Econ. Entomol.* **25**, 746–751.

Richmond, C. A., and Ignoffo, C. (1964). Mass rearing pink bollworm. *J. Econ. Entomol.* **57**, 503–505.

Vanderzant, E. S. (1957). Growth and reproduction of the pink bollworm on an amino acid medium. *J. Econ. Entomol.* **50**, 219–221.

Vanderzant, E. S. (1958). The amino acid requirements of the pink bollworm. *J. Econ. Entomol.* **51**, 309–311.

Vanderzant, E. S., and Reiser, R. (1956a). Aseptic rearing of the pink bollworm on synthetic media. *J. Econ. Entomol.* **49**, 7–10.

Vanderzant, E. S., and Reiser, R. (1956b). Studies of the nutrition of the pink bollworm using purified casein media. *J. Econ. Entomol.* **49**, 454–458.

Vanderzant, E. S., Reiser, R., and Ivy, E. E. (1956). Methods for the mass rearing of the pink bollworm. *J. Econ. Entomol.* **49**, 559–560.

Vanderzant, E. S., Kerur, D., and Reiser, R. (1957). The role of dietary fatty acids in the development of the pink bollworm. *J. Econ. Entomol.* **50**, 606–608.

Chapter 24

Corn Rootworms

W. L. HOWE AND B. W. GEORGE

Northern Grain Insects Research Laboratory,
Entomology Research Division,
Agricultural Research Service,
U. S. Department of Agriculture,
Brookings, South Dakota

I. INTRODUCTION

The recent increase in damage inflicted by corn rootworms (*Diabrotica* spp.) to corn and peanuts in areas of the United States where these crops are important has accelerated the research being conducted on this group of insects. All three of the North American rootworm species have developed resistance to the cyclodiene chlorinated insecticides, according to Ball and Weekman (1963), Burkhardt (1963), Boush and Alexander (1964), Blair *et al.* (1963),

Bigger (1963), Boush *et al.* (1963), and Hamilton (1965). The problem has also been amplified by the rapid spread of the resistant western corn rootworm into major corn growing areas of Nebraska, Iowa, Missouri, Kansas, South Dakota, and Minnesota.

A great need exists for basic investigations of the biology, behavior, and control of corn rootworms. A prerequisite of the success of such investigations is a satisfactory method for mass rearing. Rearing methods for *Diabrotica* species have been developed, but they have not been adequate for mass colonization.

Corn rootworms, according to the concept currently accepted in the United States, belong to the genus *Diabrotica* (Chrysomelidae) and comprise a group of three species: the northern corn rootworm [*D. longicornis* (Say)] (NCR), the western corn rootworm (*D. virgifera* LeConte) (WCR), and the southern corn rootworm (*D. undecimpunctata howardi* Barber) (SCR). The SCR is also known as the spotted cucumber beetle. The larvae of each species attack the underground portions of the corn plant. The adults of all three species feed on a wide range of plants, but WCR and NCR larvae appear to be monophagous under field conditions, since they feed only on corn roots. SCR larvae are polyphagous and feed on roots of cucurbits, corn, and other crops.

Other *Diabrotica* and related genera of the Chrysomelidae with subterranean feeding habits are known to feed on the roots of corn and certain other plants. In the United States these include the western spotted cucumber beetle (*Diabrotica undecimpunctata* Mannerheim), the banded cucumber beetle (*Diabrotica balteata* LeConte), and the striped cucumber beetle [*Acalymma vittata* (F.)] Rearing methods described for these species by other workers were utilized in developing the mass rearing techniques described below. Other species of *Diabrotica* are known to attack corn in subtropical and tropical areas of the Western Hemisphere. A complete review cannot be presented here; but in Guatemala alone, Melhus *et al.* (1954) observed 12 *Diabrotica* species that fed on the aerial portions of the corn plant. Six species injured roots and completed their development on the corn root system. It is thus apparent that corn rootworms, in the broad sense, include many species.

Information about rearing rootworms, particularly NCR and WCR, is indeed meager when compared with what we know about rearing other grain pests, such as the European corn borer [*Ostrinia nubilalis* (Hübner)]. No published reports on the nutritional requirements of any *Diabrotica* species have been found. So far as we know, many of the techniques reported herein constitute a pioneering effort with corn rootworms.

In certain ways rearing holometabolous soil insects is complicated. The larval habitat hinders our observations of how the insect is attracted by food, how and in what direction it migrates, and what its actual rate of growth and development is. There are greater problems in reproducing the field soil environment under artificial conditions. The abundant faunal-floral complex in soil as it occurs in the field may be upset under laboratory or greenhouse conditions and entomogenous pathogens may increase mortality.

Procedures for rearing SCR will be treated separately from those for NCR and WCR. A natural separation, due to differences in adult feeding habits, overwintering habits, and egg diapause, has led to variation in methods of rearing. Information given will stress the mass rearing techniques developed at the Northern Grain Insects Research Laboratory at Brookings, South Dakota.

II. REARING THE SOUTHERN CORN ROOTWORM

A. INTRODUCTION

For many years SCR has attracted greater research effort than any other *Diabrotica* species in the United States, probably because of its damage to numerous crops over a wide geographical area, its multiple seasonal generations, and its vector relationships with bacterial wilt. Numerous aspects of the biology, ecology, and control of SCR have been published, including rearing procedures by several researchers. These procedures generally involved small numbers of insects with considerable hand manipulation of various stages. Nonetheless, these reports provided information on food plants and feeding habits and served as a basis for expansion of colonization under artificial conditions. Unfortunately, many of the reports on rearing do not involve cyclic rearing in consecutive generations.

Rearing SCR at the Northern Grain Insects Research Laboratory was conducted in controlled temperature rooms with a refrigeration cooling unit to compensate for heat output from fluorescent lamps. Temperature was maintained at $80° \pm 4°F$. Double-shelf units on wheels, as shown in Fig. 1, were equipped with three 8-ft fluorescent lamps. These were installed with timers to control the light period,

FIG. 1. Movable double-shelf units for holding rearing equipment. Triple- and single-unit oviposition cages on lower shelf. Larval rearing trays with varied stages of corn growth on upper shelf.

which ranged from 8 to 16 hours per day. The optimum light period has not yet been determined. Final larval development, pupation, and adult emergence phases were carried out in a greenhouse at a temperature of about 75°–80°F.

B. CULTURE ESTABLISHMENT

Cultures of the SCR were started from field-collected adult females by confining them to oviposition cages, described in Section I,C. Adults may be collected on many plants over a large portion of the United States east of the Rocky Mountains. Cucurbits, corn, alfalfa, beans, and peanuts are but a few hosts harboring adults. Newly laid eggs from established cultures can be shipped, with proper permits, on moist filter paper in closed containers, but travel time should not exceed the incubation period of about 7 days.

A rapid build-up of cultures is possible with only a few females if disease problems can be avoided. In establishing colonies of the SCR at this laboratory, a few beetles collected in the fall were offered broad beans and fed upon the foliage voraciously at room temperature. These adults provided 168 eggs, which were transferred to the root zone of corn seedlings growing in vermiculite in a greenhouse pot. These eggs yielded 28 females and 10 males between December 7 and 14. Oviposition from these females began December 17; by January 14, 37 days after first adult emergence, over 6000 eggs had been collected. These eggs provided ample source material for rearing trials.

C. Adult Feeding and Oviposition

1. *Food Plants*

The polyphagous feeding habits of the SCR adult indicated that a satisfactory adult food could be found easily and grown continuously in the greenhouse. Mendoza and Peters (1963) used lettuce and fresh corn silks; Arant (1929) fed beans, cucurbits, and tomato leaves; Isely (1929), flowers and leaves of squash and cow peas; Sweetman (1926), cucurbit leaves and stems; Wray (1937), young corn leaves or clover leaves; Robinson and Arant (1931), beans, cucurbits, tomatoes, and other plants; and Bigger and March (1943) used soy bean leaves. Arant (1929) observed that candy tuft, *Umbellata* sp., was a highly attractive adult host under field conditions. Rimando *et al.* (1966) successfully colonized the closely related western spotted cucumber beetle on broad beans, *Vicia fabae*. The immediate acceptability of broad beans to SCR adults and the prolific fertile egg production precluded further search for a satisfactory food plant.

Continuous rearing of the SCR can best be carried out through the use of a cage devoted entirely to adult feeding and egg collection. The choice of cage should be determined by the number of eggs desired and the period for continuity of production. Several types were satisfactory for culture maintenance but not efficient for mass production. A simple pot cage, placed over broad bean plants used in culture build-up, was satisfactory for obtaining initially thousands of eggs. However, egg collection and adult transfer were inconvenient and time-consuming with this cage. A 1-ft³ cage used by George and Ortman (1965) (Fig. 1) was adapted for adult feeding and oviposition of SCR. The oviposition substratum consisted of a tray or Petri dishes of sifted soil, which were placed in the bottom of the cage. Wooden slats spaced over the base provided shading for the soil surface and supported the excised broad bean foliage. Sufficient shading was also obtained by placing adult food directly on the soil.

A third type of cage (Fig. 1) expedited adult manipulation, feeding, and cage cleaning. It consisted of three adjacent 1-ft^3 compartments, with each compartment separated from the next by sliding Plexiglas® partitions. The cage permitted alternate use of two units, leaving one always available for cleaning and rearing preparation. The base of each compartment was fitted with a removable ½-inch deep metal drawer or tray for holding oviposition substrates. Shading the oviposition soil was accomplished as above or a sliding galvanized metal sheet with access holes was provided in the base frame, as shown in Fig. 2. Further flexibility in the triple-unit cage was pro-

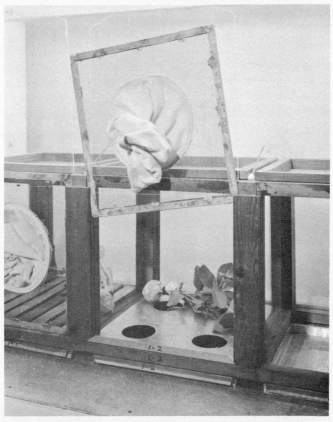

FIG. 2. Triple-unit adult cage showing slat and metal covering for oviposition soil. Portion of tray for holding soil visible on right unit.

vided by using a double panel in the front. The inner panel was a Plexiglas front for maintaining higher humidity levels. The outer panel consisted of a screen front with sleeve, which was put in place prior to removal of the Plexiglas, thus preventing beetle escape when supplying fresh food. Adult transfer to an adjacent unit with fresh food and oviposition soil involved partition removal, and darkening the occupied cage. The beetles moved to fresh food and light and thus the number of beetles requiring manual transfer was reduced. Beetles lagging behind were aspirated and moved to the desired compartment.

2. Adult Feeding

Pot-grown broad beans were supplied in bundles, as first suggested by Rimando et al. (1966). Several plants were removed from the pots and washed to clean the root system. The roots were then enclosed in a small polyethylene bag or sheet held in place by a rubber band wrapped around both the bag and stem bases. Broad bean foliage maintained sufficient turgidity without the addition of extra water. Young corn plants were handled similarly to supply food to the WCR. The number of adults introduced per section varied, depending upon the supply of eggs desired. Theoretically, 100 actively ovipositing females would provide 10,000 eggs daily over a period of maximum oviposition of 20 days. Male to female ratio in reared generations approximated 1:1. Therefore, equal numbers of males and females should probably be introduced to insure maximum fertility. The actual sex ratio required for maximum fertility has not yet been determined.

3. Egg Collection and Isolation

The previously mentioned soil or sand substrata were prepared by sifting loam top soil or plasterer's sand through a 60-mesh sloping screen mounted on a mechanical shaker. The fraction collected had a particle size smaller than the egg. Matteson (1966) used a fine sand fraction to facilitate separation of eggs of a false wireworm [*Eleodes suturalis* (Say)]. The entire tray or individual Petri dishes were filled about ⅜ inch deep with sifted soil or sand. Fine sprays were applied as needed to maintain a moist surface. Tests thus far have indicated that the SCR prefers to oviposit in the soil, which retains moisture better than sand. Adults tend to oviposit around the edges of the containers.

Egg separation was accomplished by placing the soil-egg mixture on a V-shaped 60-mesh screen, shown in Fig. 3. A fine tap water

FIG. 3. Washing fine sifted soil from rootworm eggs by using V-shaped screen filter. The 60-mesh screen allows soil to pass through and retains the eggs for transfer to beaker.

spray removed the soil, leaving the eggs on the screen surface. The eggs were washed directly into a beaker of water through the narrow open end of the screen and then into a Büchner funnel containing filter paper marked with a grid to facilitate counts. Gentle washing with the fine spray diminished damage to the eggs. Occasionally eggs may be laid on the foliage or plant stems, but they may be washed into a beaker and isolated as previously described. If counts of the eggs are not necessary, the eggs may be held in the oviposition soil for incubation or storage. Eggs incubated at 80°F commence hatching on the seventh day; however, our results indicated that the eggs may be stored up to 30 days at 40°F on moist filter paper in closed containers. A gradual loss in viability occurred; hence extended storage is not practicable.

D. LARVAL REARING

1. *Food Plants*

Numerous larval rearing techniques have been tried with different degrees of success. Robinson and Arant (1931) reviewed most of the early rearing procedures [including those of Marsh (1912), Garman (1891), Arant (1929), Searls (1928), and Sweetman (1926)]. These authors reared the larvae of the SCR on foods such as tender corn stalks, sorghum cane, and corn sprouts. Wray (1937) used tender corn stalks. Robinson and Arant (1931) reported that stems of squashes, cucumbers, cantaloupes, watermelons, and roots of hairy vetch and Austrian peas were unsatisfactory for rearing larvae. These two workers finally concluded that sprouting corn in layers of paper towels was best for larval food.

Bigger and March (1943) fed larvae on seedling roots growing in sterile agar and used the amount of feeding as an estimate of resistance to SCR. Employing this method, Hamilton (1964) attempted mass rearing but found it too time-consuming and also subject to excessive losses from entomogenous diseases. Mendoza and Peters (1963) successfully reared nearly 500 adults by using a technique involving small containers and feeding the larvae on corn stems. Stems were replaced by the more satisfactory newly silked corn ears, when available.

At our laboratory we too concluded that young corn roots were the most promising food source for mass colonization. The techniques of the above-cited authors involved excessive manual manipulation; therefore, we sought to develop methods by which large numbers of larvae could be fed on corn roots with minimal handling.

Pitre and Kantack (1962) reared larvae of the banded cucumber beetle on corn seedlings growing in vermiculite. In a single plastic rearing tray 12 inches long by 5 inches wide by 2½ inches deep as many as 300 larvae completed their development, pupated, and transformed to adults.

In a manner similar to the method previously described by Pitre and Kantack (1962), Rimando *et al.* (1966) also successfully produced cyclic generations of the western spotted cucumber beetle in pans of vermiculite containing germinating field corn. Rimando's method required one transfer of larvae to fresh food. The success of other workers who reared *Diabrotica* spp. on corn roots growing en masse in trays or flats prompted us to continue experimentation with this method for the SCR and other rootworms.

2. *Tray or Pan Method*

A successful method for growing larvae that involved using rust-proof trays of germinating corn was developed. The trays, shown in Fig. 4, were 1 inch deep, 11 inches wide, and 15 inches long. The

FIG. 4. View of dense root mat which develops on surface of cloth in bottom of tray and serves as larval food.

tray bottom consisted of a 9-mesh heavy gauge wire screen, welded completely around the rectangular tray frame. Trays may be constructed from heavy gauge galvanized sheet metal with a similar heavy gauge screen bottom welded on the base.

The tray was prepared for sprouting corn by first covering the screen and edges with 70-70 mesh synthetic fiber cloth to prevent escape of larvae. Field corn seed treated with thiram (Arasan®) was spread evenly over the surface of the fine cloth. The seeds, placed about ½ inch apart, were covered with a 1:1 vermiculite-potting soil mixture. This mixture was then moistened to its full depth but not saturated. Corn germination was facilitated by placing the entire tray in a plastic bag to prevent evaporation. The plastic bag, however, should be removed immediately when the tips of the corn plant appear. When the seedlings reached a height of 2 or 3 inches, a thick root mat had formed on the tray bottom, as shown in Fig. 4.

Incubated eggs or newly hatched larvae were transferred to the root mat in several ways. Eggs separated from the oviposition substratum were moved on the filter paper to the underside of the root mat, above the 70-70 mesh cloth. When eggs were incubated in the soil or soil and sand mixture on which they were laid, the mixture was sprinkled around the base of the corn seedlings. Newly hatched larvae were usually transferred directly from the egg-incubation filter paper to the root mat with a sable brush. Larval development could be observed by lifting the mat and probing the roots.

At this point rearing procedure varied, depending upon the developmental form desired. If larvae were required, the fine-mesh cloth was removed from the mat and the foliage clipped away. The mat was then replaced on the screen bottom of the tray. The trays were placed on a rack assembly with 100-watt incandescent lamps above each tray to hasten drying and larval drop. An enamel pan with moistened Cellucotton® placed beneath the tray served to hold larvae as they dropped through the coarse-mesh screen. The procedure developed for the western spotted cucumber beetle by Rimando *et al.* (1966) involved teasing the vermiculite and larvae from the root system and placing both in a standard Berlese funnel with a 9-mesh screen bottom. Larvae were captured in a jar placed below the funnel. This procedure would probably serve as well for the SCR.

E. PUPATION AND ADULT COLLECTION

The mature larvae appeared to prefer potting soil to the root mat mixture for preparation of pupal cells. Therefore, after 9–12 days of larval development, it appeared most efficacious to transfer the entire infested root mat to a wooden flat 15 inches × 23 inches × 4 inches, filled 2½ inches deep with lightly moistened potting soil mixture. The fine-mesh cloth was removed and the root mat buried slightly. Two to three weeks before use, the unused margins of the flat were planted with broad beans and corn. Otherwise, it was necessary to transplant broad bean plants or to provide excised foliage for emerging adults. Preplanted corn served as a supplemental food for larvae.

Just prior to adult emergence, a screen cage was placed over the flat. A centered hole was cut in a removable top and fitted with a sliding closure. In order to remove adults a small, inverted-cone "fly-trap" cage was placed over the hole. The cage was then darkened by covering it with a black cloth upon which most beetles migrated to the lighted trap cage. This trap unit simplified collection and eliminated the need for aspirating most adults. Captured beetles were then transferred to fresh oviposition cages. Because the preoviposition period of the beetle averages about 10 days, beetles should be moved prior to the end of that time to avoid oviposition in the emergence cage. Adult recovery averaged about 50% from colonies initiated with 200 to 500 newly hatched larvae.

F. Conclusions

At this writing we have reared five generations of the SCR. The period required for a complete generation ranged from 35 to 45 days, depending upon rearing room and greenhouse temperatures. The procedures and equipment may be improved to increase the number produced, and to decrease the labor cost. However, our basic procedures appear satisfactory. With changes in egg handling and food, the methodology used for the SCR can be adapted to other rootworm species.

III. REARING THE WESTERN AND NORTHERN CORN ROOTWORM

A. Introduction

Because the economic importance of these two species of rootworms has increased very recently, development of rearing methods is a current research program at several institutions. However, work has been hampered by a dearth of detailed information of the biology of these insects. Gillette (1912) and Ball (1957) discussed some aspects of the biology of the WCR; and the 10th, 11th, and 18th *Reports of the Illinois State Entomologist* (Thomas, 1881; French, 1882; Forbes, 1891–1892) contained many observations of the NCR. Prior to the paper on WCR by George and Ortman (1965), little had been published on methods of colonizing either species. The methods given below were drawn from the experience of several workers. They have not been in use long enough to have reached the desired degree of perfection; however, results thus far warrant their inclusion in this chapter.

B. Culture Establishment

Our colonies were established from field collections of adults. Methods for making large collections are described by Weekman and Ball (1963) and George and Ortman (1965). The choice of method depends on the weather and development of available corn plants. In fair weather, when beetles are plentiful, the simplest method is to sweep them from corn and grass in the field. A generator-powered vacuum collector works well during inclement weather when adults congregate behind leaf sheaths and in the silks. During silking, beetles can be tapped from the silks into a funnel soldered on the lid of a mason jar, or they may be captured in a plastic bag by placing a tassel in the bag and shaking them off into the bottom, a method used for NCR by Dicke (1964). Late in the season, beetles can be collected from clover and alfalfa fields and numerous flowering plants. Any of the cages described for the SCR are satisfactory for the WCR. Screen of slightly less than 16 mesh must be used for the NCR because of their smaller size.

C. Adult Feeding and Oviposition

The adults of the NCR and WCR are both most commonly observed feeding on the silks and tassels of corn. The WCR was reported by Brisley (1926) as feeding on the petals and pollen of wild gourd, as well as on the leaves, stems, petals, and pollen of watermelons, squash, lettuce, cucumbers, muskmelons, and beans. In the 10th, 11th, and 18th *Reports of the Illinois State Entomologist* (Thomas, 1881; French, 1882; Forbes, 1891–1892), the NCR was recorded as feeding on the pollen of various Compositae such as ragweed, thistles, squash, and red clover; on the vines of cucumbers and squash; and on other plants blooming in the corn field.

Caged insects were fed on a wide variety of plant parts, such as fruits of Hubbard squash, heads of lettuce, seedlings of corn, and silks and immature ears of sweet corn. George and Ortman (1965) used immature ears of corn because this food resulted in beetles that were long lived and had a high level of fecundity, and because it was convenient. A feeding arrestant that Derr *et al.* (1964) found to be concentrated in the kernels probably accounts for the voracious feeding on immature ears.

D. Egg Collection and Storage

How and when the eggs will be used determines the choice of collection method. The oviposition site of finely sifted soil or sand, previously described for the SCR, works equally well for the WCR. The eggs may be washed from the soil or left in the soil and stored during the cold period necessary to break diapause. Gustin (1965) held adults in a caged flat containing sweet corn seedlings. The soil was removed from the flat at the end of the oviposition period, enclosed in a plastic bag, and stored at 4°C to break the diapause of the eggs. The soil was then added to the potting mixture in flats of corn seedlings. This method seems useful to reduce the handling of eggs; however, the number of eggs must be established with a reliable sampling technique.

A method for holding eggs on Cellucotton is described by George and Ortman (1965). Pads of lightly moistened Cellucotton were placed beneath the screened floor of the cage underneath the immature ears used for food. The beetles laid their eggs on or in the pad of Cellucotton. These barely moist pads were then held in polyethylene bags for subsequent treatment.

E. Breaking Diapause

Both the WCR and NCR diapause in the egg stage. George and Ortman (1965) and Cunningham and Peters (1964) indicated that it is not a severe diapause. Eggs hatch without special treatment after a period of continuous incubation; however, time to first hatch and the duration of the hatching period are greatly reduced by exposure to cold. The most satisfactory cold treatment of WCR entails 2 weeks at room temperature, 17 weeks at +4°C, and incubation below 30°C. Eggs commence hatching at 14–24 days and hatching is complete in 40 days. Cunningham and Peters (1964) used a variety of chemicals on the NCR, but no treatment they tried offered any marked improvement on a cold treatment. Ortman (1965) found that a small percentage of WCR eggs would hatch only when exposed a second time to cold.

F. Larval Feeding and Rearing

Mass rearing WCR larvae, and probably those of the NCR, is possible by using the root mat method devised and previously described for the SCR. In a preliminary test, newly hatched larvae were placed on root mats and held at 80°F for 3 weeks. The mats were transferred to flats in the greenhouse, and adults started emerging after 24 days. Gustin (1965) placed known numbers of eggs on roots of seedling corn growing in vermiculite. At an average air temperature of 75°F, the eggs hatched; larvae developed to maturity and started to emerge in 55 days.

Howe and Matteson (1964) planted corn in flats of field soil heavily infested with NCR eggs. Starting on November 8 soil was brought in at weekly intervals and mixed 1:1 with a standard potting mixture. Samples of soil from the early collections were exposed only to temperatures that were above freezing, but 29 days after being brought to warm temperatures larvae were found. About 1700 larvae and adults were collected from 20 flats of soil. This method might provide a modest supply of larvae and adults early in the winter without any need for investing in a rearing program.

G. PUPATION AND ADULT EMERGENCE

Pupation usually takes place in a small cell formed in the soil by the prepupal larva. If larvae are placed in a dish containing agar in which corn has been allowed to germinate, this pupal cell may be observed. Larvae pupated readily in the flats of soil used in the root mat method developed for the SCR or in the pots of vermiculite. Emerging adults were collected from cages placed over the flats or pots. Sufficient corn was planted in the flats or pots to feed the adults until they were collected from the cage.

H. CONCLUSIONS

Mass colonization of the WCR and NCR is still in early stages of development. However, the methods described yielded groups of hundreds of beetles with only a modest investment in labor and materials. Further accumulation of information on the biology of these species and modifications of methodology should yield more efficient production techniques and make mass rearing possible.

REFERENCES

Arant, F. S. (1929). Biology and control of the southern corn rootworm. *Alabama Polytech. Inst., Agr. Expt. Sta., Bull.* **230**, 13.

Ball, H. J. (1957). On the biology and egg-laying habits of the western corn rootworm. *J. Econ. Entomol.* **50**, 126–128.

Ball, H. J., and Weekman, G. T. (1963). Resistance of corn rootworms to insecticides in Nebraska and adjoining states. *Proc. North Central Branch Entomol. Soc. Am.* **18**, 82 (abstr.).

Bigger, J. H. (1963). Corn rootworm resistance to chlorinated hydrocarbon insecticides in Illinois. *J. Econ. Entomol.* **56**, 118–119.

Bigger, J. H., and March, R. B. (1943). Rearing southern corn rootworms on seedling corn plants. *J. Econ. Entomol.* **36**, 349–350.

Blair, B. D., Triplehorn, C. A., and Ware, G. W. (1963). Aldrin resistance in northern corn rootworm adults in Ohio. *J. Econ. Entomol.* **56**, 894.

Boush, G. M., and Alexander, M. W. (1964). Evaluation of soil insecticide treatments for control of Cyclodiene-resistant southern corn rootworms. *J. Econ. Entomol.* **57**, 465–468.

Boush, G. M., Alexander, M. W., and Powell, W. L. (1963). Field tests with new insecticides for control of the southern corn rootworm attacking peanuts in Virginia. *J. Econ. Entomol.* **56**, 15–18.

Brisley, H. R. (1926). Notes on the Chrysomelidae (Coleoptera) of Arizona. *Trans. Am. Entomol. Soc.* **51**, 167–182.

Burkhardt, C. C. (1963). Corn rootworm resistance and damage in Kansas. *Proc. North Central Branch Entomol. Soc. Am.* **18**, 82–83 (abstr.).

Cunningham, V. D., and Peters, D. C. (1964). The effect of physio-chemical treatments on diapausing eggs of northern corn rootworm, *Diabrotica longicornis. J. Econ. Entomol.* **57**, 436–438.

Derr, R. F., Randall, D. D., and Kieckhefer, R. W. (1964). Feeding stimulant for western and northern corn rootworm adults. J. Econ. Entomol. **57**, 963–965.

Dicke, F. F. (1964). Unpublished communication. Pioneer Hi-Bred Seed Company, Johnstown, Iowa.

Forbes, S. A. (1891–1892). The northern corn rootworm (*Diabrotica longicornis* Say). *18th Rept. Illinois State Entomologist Noxious Beneficial Insects State of Illinois* pp. 135–145.

French, G. H. (1882). The corn rootworm (*Diabrotica longicornis* Say). *11th Rept. Illinois State Entomologist Noxious Beneficial Insects State Illinois* pp. 65–72.

Garman, H. (1891). On the life history of *Diabrotica 12-punctata. Psyche* **6**, 26–30 and 44–49.

George, B. W., and Ortman, E. E. (1965). Rearing the western corn rootworm in the laboratory. *J. Econ. Entomol.* **58**, 375–377.

Gillette, C. P. (1912). *Diabrotica virgifera* LeC. as a corn rootworm. *J. Econ. Entomol.* **5**, 364–366.

Gustin, R. D. (1965). Unpublished communication. Northern Grain Insects Research Laboratory, USDA-ARS-ENT, University Station, Brookings, South Dakota.

Hamilton, E. W. (1964). Unpublished report. Northern Grain Insects Research Laboratory, USDA-ARS-ENT, University Station, Brookings, South Dakota.

Hamilton, E. W. (1965). Aldrin resistance in corn rootworm beetles. *J. Econ. Entomol.* **58**, 296–300.

Howe, W. L., and Matteson, J. W. (1964). Unpublished report. Addresses: Northern Grain Insects Research Laboratory, USDA-ARS-ENT, University Station, Brookings, South Dakota, and Insecticide Chemicals Development Department, Monsanto, Company, 800 N. Lindbergh Blvd, St. Louis, Missouri.

Isely, D. (1929). The southern corn rootworm. *Arkansas, Univ. (Fayetteville), Agr. Expt. Sta., Bull.* **232**, 13.

Marsh, H. O. (1912). Biological notes on the species of *Diabrotica* in southern Texas. *U. S. Dept. Agr., Bur. Entomol., Bull.* **82**, Part 6, 76–84.

Matteson, J. W. (1966). Colonization and mass production of the false wireworm, *Eleodes suturalis* (Tenebrionidae). *J. Econ. Entomol.* **59**, 26–27.

Melhus, I. E., Painter, R. H., and Smith, F. O. (1954). A search for resistance to the injury caused by species of *Diabrotica* in the corns of Guatemala. *Iowa State Coll. J. Sci.* **29**, 75–94.

Mendoza, C. E., and Peters, D. C. (1963). Mass rearing southern corn rootworms. *Proc. North Central Branch Entomol. Soc. Am.* **18**, 92–93 (abstr.).

Ortman, E. E. (1964). Developments in corn rootworm research. *Proc. 19th Ann. Res. Conf. Hybrid Corn Ind.* **19**, 43. Am. Seed Trade Assoc., Washington, D. C.

Pitre, H. N., Jr., and Kantack, E. J. (1962). Biology of the banded cucumber beetle, *Diabrotica balteata*, in Louisiana. *J. Econ. Entomol.* **55**, 904–906.

Rimando, L. C., Corey, R. A., and Sun, Yun-Pei (1966). Mass rearing of the western spotted cucumber beetle. *J. Econ. Entomol.* **59**, 230–231.

Robinson, J. M., and Arant, F. S. (1931). Methods of rearing *Diabrotica. J. Econ. Entomol.* **24**, 835–843.

Searls, E. M. (1928). A simple method for life-history studies of root-feeding arthropods. *J. Agr. Res.* **36,** 639–645.

Sweetman, H. L. (1926). Results of life-history studies of *Diabrotica 12-punctata*. *J. Econ. Entomol.* **19,** 484.

Thomas, C. (1881). New corn insect (*Diabrotica longicornis* Say). *10th Rept. Illinois State Entomologist Noxious Beneficial Insects State Illinois* pp. 44–46.

Weekman, G. T., and Ball, H. J. (1963). A portable electrically operated collecting device. *J. Econ. Entomol.* **56,** 708–709.

Wray, D. L. (1937). Method of rearing *Diabrotica duodecimpunctata*, the southern corn rootworm. *In* "Culture Methods for Invertebrate Animals" (P. S. Goltsoff *et al.*, eds.), p. 477. Cornell Univ. Press (Comstock), Ithaca, New York.

Chapter 25

False Wireworms

JOHN W. MATTESON[*]

Northern Grain Insects Laboratory,
Entomology Research Division,
Agricultural Research Service,
U. S. Department of Agriculture,
Brookings, South Dakota

I. INTRODUCTION

The false wireworms (Tenebrionidae) have not been considered serious pests in recent years; however, according to several authors a few genera have caused economic losses to small grain crops in the semiarid areas of midwestern and western United States. Research on the biology (including some rearing efforts), morphology, distribution, and economic importance of several false wireworms includes that of Wade and St. George (1923) (*Eleodes suturalis* Say), McColloch (1918, 1919) (*Eleodes opacus* Say and *Eleodes*

[*] *Present address:* Monsanto Company, Agricultural Division, Insecticide Chemicals Development Department, St. Louis, Missouri.

tricostata Say), Wakeland (1926) (*Eleodes hispilabris* Say), and Wade (1921) (*Embaphion muricatum* Say).

The widespread occurrence of species of *Eleodes* and *Embaphion* in South Dakota prompted research at the Northern Grain Insects Research Laboratory, Entomology Research Division, Agricultural Research Service, U. S. Department of Agriculture, in Brookings, South Dakota, involving distribution, biology, physiology, and mass rearing studies. Major effort devoted to *Eleodes suturalis* resulted in a preliminary publication on colonization (Matteson, 1966). The information in this chapter was derived primarily from the latter publication and from unpublished data accumulated at the Northern Grain Insects Research Laboratory.

II. REARING OF *ELEODES SUTURALIS*

A. ESTABLISHMENT OF COLONY

Adult *E. suturalis* used in establishing a colony were collected throughout South Dakota using pitfall traps consisting of widemouth canning jars with funnels substituted for the lids (Fig. 1).

FIG. 1. Pitfall traps utilized in capturing adults of false wireworms.

Drainage holes were cut in the bottoms of the jars with a brass tubetype glass drill and carborundum powder, and aluminum screen was placed over the holes to retain insects. Traps were buried to the rim in or adjacent to small grain fields. Adults were collected during late spring, summer, and early fall. Those collected in the spring or early summer probably overwintered; therefore, their life expectancy was relatively short and egg-laying potential low. Adults collected later in the growing season provided the best source for colony establishment.

B. ADULT MAINTENANCE AND OVIPOSITION

1. *Food*

Normally adults and larvae of *E. suturalis* are phytophagous; however, according to Wade and St. George (1923), they will also feed on living and dead animal tissue. Webster (1912) observed an adult devouring chinch bugs. Wade and St. George (1923) state that native grasses, wheat, oats, corn, rye, millet, alfalfa, kafir, sugar beets, beans, potatoes, and several garden crops are food sources for larvae or adults or both.

2. *Holding and Oviposition*

The field-collected adults, in a ratio of 5 females to 1 male, were placed in covered containers with about ⅛ inch of slightly moistened sand previously sifted to provide a particle size smaller

FIG. 2. Enameled oviposition pan containing adults of *Eleodes suturalis*.

than the eggs. Several oviposition containers have been used including various sized enameled pans (Fig. 2) and aluminum pans with dimensions of 4 × 6 × 3 inches. The oviposition containers were covered to eliminate light and reduce desiccation of eggs. Enough beetles to cover one third of the bottom was a satisfactory number per oviposition container. These containers were held at 90–100% relative humidity (RH) and 75°–80°F. Whole grains of wheat in a ratio of about 2 grains/adult/day were provided as adult food. The beetles were confined in these containers for 1 to 3 days for oviposition without changing the sand. Less frequent removal of the egg-infested sand significantly decreased egg hatch.

3. Egg Collection, Fecundity, and Incubation

Eggs were separated from the sand by washing through a U. S. Standard Sieve Series sieve No. 35 (500 μ). The eggs collected were 1.2–1.37 mm in length and 0.63–0.77 mm in width. Wade and St. George (1923) indicate a larger size with an average length of 1.5–2 mm and a width of 1 mm.

Eggs were washed from the sieve onto a filter paper in a Büchner funnel. They were then brushed from the filter paper into Petri dishes which were placed in a container with a relative humidity of 90–100% and a temperature of 75°–80°F for incubation. A single female laid a maximum of 300 viable eggs in a 24-hour period on one occasion. The numbers of eggs laid normally averaged 14 to 20/day/female over a period of several months. Wade and St. George (1923) state that the average number of eggs laid by 100 females was 108, with a maximum of 335. Some field-collected individuals laid eggs in the laboratory for approximately 1 year; however, their rate of oviposition was relatively low for the last few months. In the mass rearing program beetles for oviposition ranged in age from 1 to 5 months. The eggs were incubated in Petri dishes. because placement of eggs directly on the larval medium reduced egg hatch.

A colony can be maintained by placing the beetles directly on the larval rearing medium for oviposition; however, considerable reduction in hatch occurs. Population density is also more difficult to control.

C. LARVAL HANDLING AND DEVELOPMENT

1. Rearing Containers and Medium

The newly hatched larvae and remaining eggs were transferred from the Petri dishes to the larval rearing containers (Fig. 3). These containers were constructed of galvanized sheet metal and were $12 \times 11 \times 6$ inches and were filled about three-quarters full with slightly moist sandy soil. Coarsely ground wheat distributed in the upper inch of soil provided larval food. The eggs and newly hatched larvae were scattered uniformly on the soil surface. Up

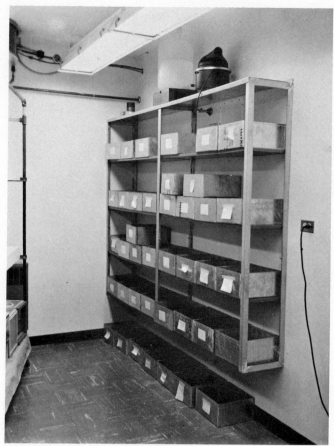

FIG. 3. Rearing pans for false wireworms in constant temperature and humidity room.

to 2000 larvae were reared to maturity in a pan without appreciable stunting or mortality; however, the normal number was 1000–1500 per pan. First-instar larvae were found to be quite susceptible to desiccation while the moisture requirements of later instars were considerably lower.

When larvae reached the fourth instar (about ½ inch long) they were fed whole grains of wheat which were spread generously on the surface of the soil. As long as wheat was visible on the soil surface, food supply was considered adequate. The soil was never allowed to dry to the point of being dusty. When soil near the surface felt dry to the touch, water was sprinkled in the pan; too much water, however, drove the larvae to the soil surface. Proper soil moisture can be more easily maintained under high humidity conditions.

Wade and St. George (1923) experienced considerable trouble in colonizing *E. suturalis* and eventually succeeded in rearing them individually in tin salve boxes containing ¼-inch layer of plaster of Paris, covered by a thick coating of India ink, and a small disc of colored blotting paper. Cannibalism was common when numerous larvae were maintained in a common container under these conditions. The author has experienced no serious problem with cannibalism; normally, only weakened or dead larvae are attacked.

2. *Number of Instars*

It was determined, through close observation and the application of Dyar's rule (Dyar, 1890) that there were normally 11 instars (Table I). These results differ considerably from those of Wade and St. George (1923), who experienced some difficulty in determining the number of instars and concluded that there were 6.

TABLE I

AVERAGE HEAD CAPSULE MEASUREMENTS AND GROWTH RATIOS OF
LARVAE OF *Eleodes suturalis*

Instar	No. measured	Average head capsule width (mm)	Growth ratio
1	24	0.40	1.15
2	51	0.46	1.33
3	39	0.61	1.39
4	60	0.85	1.35
5	72	1.15	1.33
6	40	1.53	1.35
7	78	2.07	1.31
8	36	2.73	1.18
9	36	3.23	1.15
10	34	3.71	1.15
11	20	4.28	—

D. PUPAE AND ADULTS

1. *Pupation*

The larvae reached the tenth instar (about 3.7 mm head capsule width and 1½ inches long) after 40–50 days at 80°F and their food requirements decreased rapidly. Further growth was rare without an exposure to a lower temperature; in the field larvae also overwintered in this instar. After nearly all the larvae in a rearing pan reached the tenth instar, the pan was transferred to a temperature of 40°–45°F and held for at least 2, or preferably 3 months to break the obligatory diapause. They were then transferred to an 80°F room where pupation began in about 2 months. Wheat grains were supplied in limited quantity.

The larvae formed pupation cells in the soil which were disturbed if populations of active larvae were high. Reduction of their numbers to about 200 alleviated this potential damage to pupae.

2. Emergence and Maintenance of Adults

Emergence of adults started 2 to 3 weeks after pupation. After their exoskeletons were thoroughly hardened, the adults were placed in oviposition chambers where they fed upon grain, and mated shortly thereafter. The adults produced enough eggs after a month to assure adequate numbers of larvae for a rearing program. The first generation of adults derived from the field-collected specimens provided the necessary larval population for productive colonization. Rearing of subsequent generations required an expansion of facilities; however, the rearing technique was the same.

E. Parasites and Diseases

Adults collected from the field were observed carefully for the emergence of braconid parasites of the genus *Perilitus*. Elimination of these parasites as they appeared protected the colony from further parasitization.

Occasionally populations of soil-inhabiting mites became a nuisance to other insect cultures in the rearing room, although apparently they did not adversely affect the false wireworms. It has been demonstrated that *E. suturalis* has a high tolerance for Kelthane (Hamilton and Matteson, 1966). Therefore, an application of Kelthane® [1,1-bis(*p*-chlorophenyl)-2,2,2-trichloroethanol] to the shelves and exterior of the rearing pans reduced the mite problem satisfactorily. The less organic matter in the medium, the less are the chances of a serious mite infestation.

Occasionally larvae became infected with a disease, the first indication of which was a small reddish-brown spot. This was apparently the same unidentified bacterial disease described by Wade and St. George (1923). They also mention two fungi, *Sporotrichium globuliferum* Speg. and *Metarrhizium anisoplae* Metschn., which occasionally attack larvae under laboratory conditions. As yet these diseases have not been serious problems in the mass rearing of *Eleodes suturalis*.

III. REARING OF OTHER FALSE WIREWORMS

A. ESTABLISHMENT OF COLONY

The adults of all species of false wireworms can be captured with pitfall traps described previously. The traps should be placed adjacent to, or in, small grain fields, pastures, or other types of grasslands. *Eleodes opacus, E. hispilabris, E. tricostata, Embaphion muricatum, Eleodes obsoleta* (Say), *Eleodes extricata* (Say), and *Asidopsis opaca* (Say) have been collected with ease in South Dakota with this method. Unlike the other species, *E. opacus* does not overwinter in the adult stage; therefore they are not available for trapping until late May or June. The adults of this species are more fragile than the others and are apt to be damaged by larger insects when confined in the traps for too long.

B. ADULT MAINTENANCE AND OVIPOSITION

1. *Food*

Adult false wireworms are phytophagous; however, it has been observed that they will feed on dead insects and other organic material. According to McColloch (1918), adults of *Eleodes tricostata* feed on germinating wheat, corn, and native prairie grasses. Swenk (1923) states that adults of *E. opacus* are known to feed on leaves of wheat, corn, alfalfa, Russian thistle, evening primrose, and smartweed, plus the kernels and chaff of grains, as well as manure and dead insects. *Eleodes hispilabris* feeds on many kinds of organic matter, but prefers bits of wheat kernels and chaff (Wakeland, 1926). The adults of *Embaphion muricatum* are known to feed on wheat grains and other seeds (Wade, 1921).

2. *Holding and Oviposition*

The adults of all the species mentioned previously can be maintained and the eggs collected by the same techniques that were described for *E. suturalis*. Information concerning holding of adults is meager; however, McColloch (1918, 1919) and Wakeland (1926) held adults of *E. opacus, E. tricostata,* and *E. hispilabris* in fruit jars containing an inch of soil and some bran for food.

3. *Egg Collection and Incubation*

The techniques described for *E. suturalis* for the collection and incubation of eggs apply to these other species of false wireworms. Wakeland (1926) is the only other author who described a method for the removal of eggs from soil. His method involved shaking the soil until the eggs of *E. hispilabris* appeared at the surface, where they were removed with small, moist brushes. He did not remove all the eggs, but took those he needed. These eggs were placed in shell vials and surrounded with a small amount of slightly moist soil, and the vial was then corked securely. McColloch (1918, 1919) incubated the eggs of *E. opacus* and *E. tricostata* in small vials closed with cotton plugs and kept in a field insectary under outdoor conditions.

C. LARVAL HANDLING

1. *Food*

The larvae of false wireworms, as in the case of adults, are essentially phytophagous. Swenk (1923) and McColloch (1919) report that larvae of *E. opacus* feed on the roots of such plants as native grasses, weeds, wheat, oats, barley, corn, and sorghum. McColloch (1918) states that larvae of *E. tricostata* have been known to feed on cabbage, native grasses, weeds, wheat, and corn. *Eleodes hispilabris* larvae feed on wheat (Wakeland, 1926) and *Embaphion muricatum* larvae feed on roots of native grasses, wheat, and corn (Wade, 1921). Larvae of these insects will also feed on cast skins and dead larvae. In rearing programs ground wheat for small larvae and whole wheat grains for larger larvae are satisfactory as larval food.

2. *Rearing Containers and Medium*

The species of *Eleodes* and *Embaphion* mentioned thus far have been reared according to the methods described previously, but not in as great numbers as *Eleodes suturalis* because of a lack of space and labor. Past efforts on the rearing of false wireworms have involved the use of individual containers for larvae (McColloch, 1918, 1919). These containers were usually tin salve boxes for larger larvae and vials for small ones. The medium was always soil with some bran or split wheat as food for the smaller larvae and whole wheat grains for the larger larvae. Attempts were made to duplicate the temperatures to which larvae were subjected in the field, including cold, wintertime temperatures. As a result, only one generation per year was reared and no mention was made about diapause breakage. The larvae consistently overwintered in the next to last instar which, according to Wakeland (1926) and McColloch (1918), was the tenth instar for *E. hispilabris* and *E. opacus,* respectively.

These studies revealed no obligatory diapause for *E. opacus,* *E. extricata,* or *Embaphium* sp. *Eleodes hispilabris* seems to have a partial diapause, because all larvae do not need a cold treatment previous to pupation.

D. PUPAE AND ADULT EMERGENCE

Other false wireworm species pupated in earthen cells; therefore, as with *E. suturalis,* it was advantageous not to overcrowd pupating larvae. Other workers have allowed pupation to take place in the individual containers used for larval rearing. The pupal stage may average from 14.1 days for *E. opacus* (McColloch, 1918) to as long as 33.6 days for *E. hispilabris* (Wakeland, 1926). Upon emergence, adults should be allowed to harden before they are placed in oviposition containers.

E. PARASITES AND DISEASES

The braconid parasite, *Perilitus eleodis* Viereck, attacks all of the false wireworms discussed in this chapter. It need not be a problem in a rearing program if field-collected beetles are isolated and observed for emerging parasite larvae. According to Wade (1921), *Embaphion muricatum* is attacked by the bacterial disease discussed previously as well as the fungus *Metarrhizium anisoplae.* Swenk (1923) reported the bacterial disease as well as two fungi, *M. anisoplae* and *Sporotrichium globuliferum,* attacking *E. opaca.*

F. DISCUSSION

There are many factors that qualify false wireworms as excellent organisms for mass rearing. These species can also be utilized for experimental purposes along with commonly used insects such as the cockroaches, house flies, and stored grain insects. The adults are easily trapped, they do not fly, they are reasonably large and resistant to damage by handling, and most of them are long lived. No special diet or equipment is necessary for adult maintenance or oviposition. Eggs are easily procured and are reasonably large. The larvae require no special diet or elaborate equipment and can be reared en masse in a common container with a minimum of disease or cannibalism problems.

Thus far the size of the colony of *Eleodes suturalis* has been limited only by the number of adults involved in egg production, the space devoted to larval rearing, and the laboratory's need for larvae. Ten hours of a technician's time per week maintained a colony of 40,000 to 50,000 larvae for nearly a year.

False wireworms have several characteristics that would appeal to the basic researcher in endocrinology or physiology. The endocrinologist could utilize these insects in studies involving molting or diapause hormones. Observations of adults of *E. suturalis* indicate the presence of a chemical sex attractant. Males were observed to attempt to copulate with males that had recently mated, indicating possible transference of chemical from female to male. Males also became agitated in the presence of females without actual contact with them. In preliminary tests, larvae given a choice between sand through which was passed moist air from flasks with and without germinating wheat, chose the sand with moist air from wheat. This indicated an olfactory response to airborne chemicals or a general chemical sense response to chemicals dissolved in moisture on the sand.

Adults and larvae of most wireworms secrete an oily, offensive liquid as a defensive mechanism when disturbed; thus an opportunity for research on repellents exists. Larvae develop normally on a diet of ground wheat in an atmosphere with high humidity; hence, the use of aseptic nutrition experiments with chemically defined solid diets appears feasible.

REFERENCES

Dyar, H. G. (1890). The number of molts of lepidopterous larvae. *Psyche* **5**, 420–422.

Hamilton, E. W., and Matteson, J. W. (1966). Laboratory studies on the control of the false wireworm *Eleodes suturalis* Say (Tenebrionidae). *J. Econ. Entomol.* **59**(1), 24–25.

McColloch, J. W. (1918). Notes on false wireworms with special reference to *Eleodes tricostata* Say. *J. Econ. Entomol.* **11**, 212–224.

McColloch, J. W. (1919). *Eleodes opaca* Say, an important enemy of wheat in the Great Plains area. *J. Econ. Entomol.* **12**, 183–194.

Matteson, J. W. (1966). Colonization and mass production of the false wireworm *Eleodes suturalis* Say (Tenebrionidae). *J. Econ. Entomol.* **59**(1), 26–27.

Swenk, M. H. (1923). The plains false wireworm and its control. *Nebraska Univ., Agr. Expt. Sta., Circ.* **20**, 1–11

Wade, J. S. (1921). Biology of *Embaphion muricatum*. *J. Agr. Res.* **22**, 323–334.

Wade, J. S., and St. George, R. A. (1923). Biology of the false wireworm, *Eleodes suturalis* Say. *J. Agr. Res.* **26**, 547–566.

Wakeland, C. (1926). False wireworms injurious to dry-farmed wheat and a method of combatting them. *Idaho, Univ., Agr. Expt. Sta., Res. Bull.* **6**, 1–52.

Webster, F. M. (1912). Preliminary report on the alfalfa weevil. *U. S. Dept. Agr., Bur. Entomol., Bull.* **112**, 1–47.

Chapter 26

Aegeriidae, with Special Reference to the Peach Tree Borer

EDWARD H. SMITH

Department of Entomology,
North Carolina State University,
Raleigh, North Carolina

I. BIOLOGICAL CHARACTERISTICS OF THE FAMILY

The family Aegeriidae, the clearwing moths, is represented in North America by 26 genera and some 120 species. A comprehensive taxonomic monograph of the family, together with biological notes, has been provided by Engelhardt (1946).

The species of this family share a number of biological features which have made them of special interest aside from their importance as economic pests.

397

All of the larvae of the Aegeriidae are borers in the trunk, bark, stem, or roots of trees, shrubs, vines, and herbaceous plants. Most species have long life cycles of 1, 2, or 3 years, with 2 years being most common. Diapause occurs in the larval stage.

The sexes are in some cases strikingly dimorphic. Some members of the family mimic Hymenoptera in both form and behavior. Moth emergence generally occurs in the morning hours before noon with mating taking place an hour or so after emergence, usually on the host plant near the point of emergence. Males are attracted to the females by a sex attractant. It appears that only virgin females emit sex attractant and that the females mate only once. In the case of the peach tree borer, males can be attracted to extracts taken from the tips of the abdomens of virgin females. Moth flight occurs generally under conditions of bright sunlight. Eggs are deposited on the host plant close to the site of larval entry.

Another feature of the family that has created interest is their exquisite beauty.

II. ECONOMIC IMPORTANCE OF THE FAMILY

The economic status of Aegeriidae is due to the larval feeding habits as borers in living plants. The relatively large size of the larvae and their extended period of larval development make them capable of causing severe damage or death of the host plant. The species which are commonly considered economic species are those which attack plants under commercial production, but as the host plants of the Aegeriidae include approximately 100 species of plants, it is likely that the real economic significance of the family is not fully recognized.

The species commonly considered as economic pests are listed in Table I.

The best known of the economic species is the peach tree borer whose original host plants were varieties of native *Prunus*. The cultivated peach has been under severe attack since its introduction in colonial times.

III. PROBLEMS IN COLONIZATION

A. DURATION OF LIFE CYCLE

A number of features of the group account for difficulty in colonization, their long life cycle being one. They are at best single brooded

TABLE I

ECONOMIC PEST SPECIES OF AEGERIIDAE

Common name	Species
Peach tree borer	*Sanninoidea exitiosa* (Say)
Lesser peach tree borer	*Synanthedon pictipes* (Grote and Robinson)
Squash vine borer	*Melittia cucurbitae* (Harris)
Currant borer	*Ramosia tipuliformis* (Clerck)
Strawberry crown moth	*Ramosia bibionipennis* (Boisduval)
Grape root borer	*Vitacea polistiformis* (Harris)
Lilac borer	*Podosesia syringae syringae* (Harris)
Apple bark borer	*Thamnosphecia pyri* (Harris)
Dogwood borer	*Thamnosphecia scitula* (Harris)
Persimmon borer	*Sannia uroceriformis* Walker
Maple callus borer	*Sylvora acerni* (Clemens)
Ash borer	*Podosesia syringae fraxini* (Lugger)
Hornet moth	*Aegeria apiformis* (Clerck)

in nature, with extended periods of larval development and diapause occurring in the larval stage.

B. COLLECTING

The life history stages are difficult to collect. The larvae are in most cases rather inaccessible in the burrows of the host plant, often subterranean, and they are easily injured. The moths are not easily captured in nature, although limited success can be had in collecting them from host plants during the morning hours when emergence and mating occur.

Limited numbers of eggs can be collected from host plants. The stage which lends itself best to collecting is the pupal stage. In some species the mature larvae desert the burrows in the host plant and construct cocoons in the soil and debris nearby.

C. FOOD

Providing satisfactory food for rearing poses a problem. In a number of cases the larvae do not feed satisfactorily on excised tissue of the host plant. Despite the marked host specificity of the two species attacking peach trees, both feed satisfactorily on immature apples. The larvae of these species also readily feed on the cankers caused by the black knot organism *Dibotryon morbosum* (Sch.) Theissen and Sydow. Howe (1950) has reported success in rearing larvae of the squash vine borer on excised cubes of squash fruit, although the vines of the plant are the most common feeding site. While all the species of Aegeriids are rather host-specific, it may be that this is due chiefly to the oviposition site selected by the female rather than to specific requirements of the larvae. This question provides an intriguing point for investigation.

The rearing of larvae on artificial media has not been fully investigated, although preliminary tests with the peach tree borer have been encouraging.

D. BEHAVIOR

There appear to be no behavioral features of the Aegeriidae which preclude colonization. Several species, such as the peach-tree borer, currant borer (Taschenberg, 1965), and squash vine borer (Howe, 1950) oviposit readily under laboratory conditions. By contrast, very limited success has been had in obtaining eggs of the lesser peach tree borer under laboratory conditions. Females of this species can be induced to oviposit on host plants by caging in mass, as reported by Armstrong (1943).

For a time, continuous rearing of the peach tree borer was limited by inability to induce mating under laboratory conditions, but this problem has been overcome, as will be reported.

IV. COLONIZATION OF THE PEACH TREE BORER

It is only recently that techniques for continuous rearing of the peach tree borer have been developed. Details of the method and biological notes have been reported by Smith (1965). While the peach tree borer is the only aegeriid which has been reared continuously, it seems likely that the techniques employed might be applicable to other species as well. A number of features of the rearing method are in need of further refinement and study, particularly the regulation of diapause.

A. FOOD FOR LARVAE AND ADULTS

The chief limiting factor in colonization of the peach tree borer has been the availability of a satisfactory food for larvae. The larvae do not feed satisfactorily on excised tissue of the host plant, and continuous production on growing host plants proved impractical. The larvae readily feed on immature peach or apple fruits, but because of their superior keeping qualities, immature apples approximately 1½ inches in diameter were employed for routine rearing.

These foods are also acceptable to larvae of the lesser peach tree borer. It is not known whether other species of the family will also accept these foods.

Immature apples can be obtained from commercial orchards when the trees are being thinned. If apples are to be stored for later use, care should be exercised to avoid bruising. The immature fruits should be stored under conditions favorable to storage of mature apples. Care should be taken to avoid apples bearing heavy insecticide residues.

Drosophila readily infests apples being held for larval feeding unless measures are taken to exclude the flies. They also increase the problem of rot in apples infested with larvae. General sanitation in disposal of abandoned fruits and cleaning of container is required to reduce the incidence of rot.

Food for moths is not necessary, although Armstrong (1940) has reported an increase in longevity and oviposition when moths were fed a solution of cane sugar.

B. Obtaining Moths for Establishment of a Culture

Moths may be reared from field-collected pupae. Care must be taken to avoid injury to pupae in collecting. The cocoons in which larvae have pupated can be dug from the soil around the base of host trees. Cocoons are then placed, apical end up, in cells about 1 inch deep, formed with the point of a pencil in moist sand held in plastic trays. Upon emergence the moths remain on the cocoon until their wings are fully spread. The sex of pupae can be determined by the rows of spines on the seventh abdominal segment, the male having two as compared to one in the female. These characters have been illustrated by Peterson (1923).

The moths generally emerge between 8:00 and 11:00 AM. For an hour or so after emergence the females are docile and can be enticed to crawl up onto the inside wall of a vial for transfer to a mating cage.

C. Mating

The females can be mated indoors with captive males or outdoors with males lured by sex attractant. For mating indoors the moths are placed in a cage constructed of saran cloth on a wooden frame (30 × 30 × 30 inches). The cage is illuminated by outside fluorescent lights directed against the side opposite the door. The females, being attracted to light, move to the lighted wall and extend the genitalia in the characteristic position assumed when emitting the sex attractant. The males, which are more active than the females, hover about the brightly lighted screen on which the females have congregated and make occasional strikes until successful in coupling. The features which are favorable to mating are illumination of at least 200 ft-c, high temperature (80°–85°F) and high humidity (80–90% RH), and minimum distractions of sound and movement. The pairs in copulation usually fall to the floor of the cage where they remain for half an hour to an hour until copulation is completed. The mated females are then transferred to oviposition cages.

For mating outdoors the females are transferred to a cylindrical screen cage (12 inches high, 8 inches in diameter) supported on a board. The cage containing a virgin moth is placed outdoors to await the arrival of males attracted to the female. Males quickly appear at the cage, although there may be no known host plants in the immediate vicinity. As males hover about, the cage is raised to allow a male to enter and mate. Only virgin females emit sex attractant, and the females mate only once.

D. OVIPOSITION

Mated females are confined individually or in groups beneath inverted funnels (4 inches in diameter) on filter paper held in a Petri dish. The females begin oviposition shortly after mating and deposit their eggs on the filter paper, which can be replaced at intervals as eggs are needed. The females average about 500 eggs each; over 60% is produced on the first day. The moths rarely live more than 4 days, although, as indicated earlier, longevity might be increased by feeding. The conditions for oviposition are not critical and no component from the host plant is required, although light seems favorable.

The eggs can be handled on the filter papers or removed by soaking in water and recovered by straining the water through a screen. The period of incubation is approximately 8 days at 80°F. Fertility of eggs is high, generally being 97% or higher.

E. ESTABLISHING AND FEEDING LARVAE

Under natural conditions the most critical stage in survival is the newly hatched larva which is exposed to desiccation and predation in moving from the site of hatch to the point of establishment on the host plant. These hazards are almost completely eliminated under laboratory conditions.

The apples to be infested with newly hatched larvae are sliced almost through in ¼-inch slices with a slight margin of cut surface exposed for ready access to the larvae. Apples are provided at the rate of 1/100 eggs. The papers bearing eggs are placed on top of the sliced apples which are arranged one layer deep in a plastic tray. The newly hatched larvae are strongly geotropic and heliophobic.

After several days of feeding, the apple slices are separated and dispersed among uncut apples to ensure adequate food. The larvae are not cannibalistic, even under conditions of acute food shortage. The larvae will abandon fruits when the food supply is exhausted and enter new ones, after which the abandoned fruits can be removed.

TABLE II

THE INSTAR AND SIZE OF PEACH TREE BORER LARVAE REARED ON
IMMATURE APPLE FRUITS AT 80°F[a]

| Instar | Age (days) | Average size (mm) | |
		Head capsule	Body length
1	—	0.23	2.3
2	6	0.38	3.6
3	9	0.66	6.3
4	14	0.96	8.6
5	30	1.49	16.1
6	50	2.20	22.2

[a] From Smith (1965).

There are seven larval instars with diapause generally occurring in the sixth. The rate of larval development and size of instars are broadly indicated in Table II. The rate of development is quite uniform in the early instars. Development may continue for 30 to 50 days before the onset of diapause. Diapause may be broken by exposing the larvae in infested fruits to low temperature (40°F) for a period of 30 days or more. The factors controlling diapause are not known. Larvae which pupate without entering diapause produce adults which are below normal size. These will mate and produce fertile eggs, although the number produced is subnormal.

Feeding is resumed following diapause and larvae reach maturity after feeding for about 10 days. Pupation and emergence follow in about 20 days. Thus, the period from egg to adult is about 110 days allowing for a 30-day minimal period of diapause.

Disease and predation have not been observed in laboratory culture although both are common under natural conditions.

REFERENCES

Armstrong, T. (1940). The life history of the peach tree borer, *Synanthedon exitiosa* Say in Ontario. *Sci. Agr.* **20**, 557–565.

Armstrong, T. (1943). Notes on the lesser peach tree borer, *Synanthedon pictipes* G and R, in Ontario. *Ann. Rept. Entomol. Soc. Ontario* **73**, 52–57.

Engelhardt, G. P. (1946). The North American clear-wing moths of the family Aegeriidae. *U. S. Natl. Museum, Bull.* **190**, 222 pp.

Howe, W. L. (1950). Biology and host relationships of the squash vine borer. *J. Econ. Entomol.* **43**, 480–483.

Peterson, A. (1923). The peach tree borer in New Jersey. *New Jersey Agr. Expt. Sta., Bull.* **391**, 129.

Smith, E. H. (1965). Laboratory rearing of the peach tree borer and notes on its biology. *J. Econ. Entomol.* **58**, 228–236.

Taschenberg, E. F. (1965). Private communication.

Chapter 27

Boll Weevils

R. T. GAST AND T. B. DAVICH

Boll Weevil Research Laboratory,
Entomology Research Division,
Agricultural Research Service,
U. S. Department of Agriculture,
State College, Mississippi

The boll weevil, *Anthonomus grandis* Boheman, has been a major pest of cotton for nearly half a century. Studies on this insect were limited to field-reared weevils until 1957, when Vanderzant and Davich (1958) first developed an artificial larval diet. Since then, progress in laboratory rearing of the boll weevil has reached a point where it is possible to produce the millions of weevils needed for a sterile male release eradication program if and when such a program becomes feasible.

Mass production methods must be mechanized and often are not suitable for small cultures or for specific experiments, especially when it is desirable to obtain the highest possible yield of adults from a given number of eggs. It is possible to obtain yields of 75 to 80% by use of hand methods, while with efficient mechanical methods yields may be as low as 10 to 15%. The cost of rearing weevils by hand methods, however, may be over $120.00 per thousand weevils while that of mechanical methods may be as low as $3.00 per thousand. Both types of rearing methods are necessary for studies of the boll weevil and both methods will be described in this chapter.

I. EGG PRODUCTION

A. PARENT STOCK

It is possible to start a culture from a single gravid female; however, 25 to 50 pairs of weevils generally have been used to initiate laboratory cultures. The best place to obtain the parent stock is from a well-established, disease-free laboratory culture. If a wild strain is required, it is best to gather infested squares and allow the adults to emerge. This will ensure young healthy weevils capable of maximum egg production.

B. OVIPOSITION CAGES

For small cultures, one of the most satisfactory cages is a wide-mouth glass canning jar in which the solid metal disc of the lid is replaced with screen wire. The ½-pint size is satisfactory for holding up to 30 weevils each; the 1-pint size will hold 50 to 60. The jars can be cleaned and sterilized easily. Some laboratories prefer 6-inch cubical cages covered with screen. Such cages can hold up to 200 weevils each, but they are expensive to build and difficult to clean.

For large cultures, it has been the experience of the authors that stainless-steel cages are the most satisfactory. If a shop is available, such cages can be constructed for about $5.00 each and are no more expensive than wooden cages of the same size. These cages consist of a stainless-steel box 13 inches square and 3 inches high. The bottom is made of 14-mesh stainless-steel wire and the top is a sliding stainless-steel door. The cages are placed on a rack so that all light is reflected into the screen bottom of the cage. The adult weevils are attracted to light and remain on the screen near the food, while in cages with screen tops and sides a large portion of the weevils are on the screen some distance from the food. Weevils in the screen bottom cages, when fed on artificial diet pellets, produce about 30% more eggs than those in cages with screen tops and sides. Approximately 2500 weevils are held in each cage.

To facilitate changing the adult food, a wire basket made of ¼-inch mesh stainless-steel screen, 10 inches square with 1-inch sides, is used as a food container. Dimples pressed into the bottom of the basket serve as legs to keep the underside of the basket ¼ inch above the screen bottom of the cage; thus the weevils can feed on all sides of the food. To change the food, the basket is held above the open cage and shaken vigorously. The weevils fall through the basket while the food is retained.

C. OVIPOSITION DIETS

For small cultures or experiments where maximum egg production is desired, cotton squares (flower buds) provide the best food and oviposition sites. As many as 25 eggs per day can be obtained from a single female, but the average is 10 to 12; however, it is necessary to provide at least 1 square per weevil per day to obtain this number. It is also necessary to keep the individual pairs of weevils in separate cages. Egg production per female will decrease as the number of weevils per cage is increased, even though adequate food is provided. If more than one pair of weevils are allowed to feed on each square, the egg production per female will drop considerably until it virtually ceases at 8 weevils per square.

Small bolls are more desirable than squares as food for small cultures when maximum egg production per female is not required. As many as 12 weevils can be fed on a single boll ½ to ¾ inch in diameter. The egg production per female will be less than that of square-fed weevils but should average from 6 to 8 eggs per female. Since the number of fruiting bodies produced by greenhouse grown cotton will be the limiting factor in egg production, the use of small bolls will produce about 4 times as many eggs as the equivalent number of squares.

For mass rearing it is not practical to depend on fresh bolls or squares for food and oviposition sites. Two thousand square feet of greenhouse planted in cotton will supply enough bolls to obtain only ten thousand eggs per day. The use of artificial media is much more economical even though the number of eggs produced per female may be only ⅓ that of females fed on bolls. Vanderzant and Davich (1961) developed a satisfactory adult medium utilizing enzymatic hydrolyzate of casein and germinated cotton seed as the main dietary constituents. Although this medium is satisfactory for laboratory rearing, it tends to putrify rapidly. The substitution of soy bean protein and acetone-extracted square powder for the enzymatic hydrolyzate of casein helps to minimize this problem.

The adult medium used in the mass rearing facilities at the Boll Weevil Research Laboratory is shown in Table I.

TABLE I
ADULT MEDIUM USED IN MASS REARING

Ingredient	Amount
Acetone-extracted cotton squares	4.00 gm
Soy bean protein	4.00 gm
Sucrose	4.00 gm
Agar	3.00 gm
Wesson's salts	0.75 gm
Ascorbic acid	0.40 gm
Cholesterol	0.05 gm
Germinated cotton seed	10.00 gm
Water	100.00 gm
B-vitamin mixture	1.00 ml
Niacinamide	1.00 gm
Calcium panothenate	1.00 gm
Thiamine HCl	0.25 gm
Riboflavin	0.50 gm
Pyridoxine HCl	0.25 gm
Folic acid	0.25 gm
Biotin	0.02 gm
B_{12}	0.002 gm
Choline chloride	120.00 gm
Water	1000.00 ml

Most of the ingredients may be purchased from biological supply houses; however there is no commercial source for the germinated cottonseed or the acetone-extracted square powder. Acid-delinted cottonseed having 85 to 90% germination should be used. The seeds are soaked for 24 hours and the water changed at least twice during this time. Small amounts of seed may be placed on wet paper toweling and covered with a wet cloth. When 50 or more pounds of seed is processed, it is better to place the soaked seeds on screen bottom trays not more than ½ inch deep. The trays should be stacked so that air can circulate around the seed, and then covered with a plastic sheet to keep the relative humidity near saturation. At 85°F the seed should have a root 1 inch long within 24 hours.

The germinated seeds are autoclaved for 3 minutes at 20 lb pressure. The roots, which are slightly toxic to the weevils, are removed by placing the autoclaved seeds on a 6-mesh screen and washing the roots away with a strong jet of water. The paste-like pulp is removed from the seed hulls by means of two 6-inch diameter rollers (Fig. 1). The pulp sticks to the surface of the rollers and is scraped off while the hull pieces are discarded. This paste is then frozen until needed.

FIG. 1 Six-inch steel rollers used to remove pulp from germinated cottonseed.

The square powder is prepared by grinding fresh cotton squares in acetone. At least 1 gallon of acetone is required for each 5 lb of squares. The slurry is drained in a muslin sac and the residue pressed to remove any remaining liquid. The residue is ground in fresh acetone and pressed again. This process is continued until the acetone remains colorless after draining. The finished square powder is light tan in color, has the consistency of coarse flour, and is kept under refrigeration until used.

The adult medium is made by mixing all the ingredients, with the exception of the ascorbic acid and vitamin solution, in a blender, and heating the mixture in an autoclave to 240°F. After cooling to 200°F, the vitamins and ascorbic acid are added, and the hot liquid is poured into a mold to harden.

The shape of the hardened medium influences the number of eggs laid. The most satisfactory shape is a short cylinder, ¼ to ⅜ inch in diameter. Weevils will lay only a few eggs on a flat surface. Gast (1965) described a method whereby pellets 5/16 inch in diameter and ½-inch long could be mass produced. A stack of ½-inch thick aluminum plates with 5/16-inch holes drilled in them are used as the mold.

It is necessary to coat the medium pellets with wax to prevent desiccation. Parraffin may be used but is quite brittle after cooling and tends to crack off the medium. A mixture of 50% paraffin and 50%

Fig. 2. Plate with retractable needles used to hold medium pellets while they are being dipped into hot wax.

beeswax is superior to either wax by itself. Small numbers of medium pellets may be dipped in hot wax by impaling each pellet on a tooth pick. For waxing large numbers of pellets a plate with retractable needles is used (Fig. 2).

D. MANAGEMENT OF OVIPOSITION CAGES

Female weevils will lay eggs for 30 to 40 days, and for small cultures it may be desirable to keep the oviposition stock for this length of time. In mass cultures more efficient use of adult diet and space will be realized if the adult weevils are discarded after 14 to 16 days. Maximum egg production occurs 7 to 8 days after the adults emerge and then drops off to a lower level for 3 to 4 weeks. Nearly 25% more eggs can be obtained from the same amount of medium and the same number of cages if the adults are renewed every 2 weeks instead of holding them 3 to 4 weeks.

Providing fresh medium twice daily will increase egg production by nearly 50% over a single changing. This probably is due to spoilage and desiccation of the medium after 12 to 15 hours in the cages.

The most satisfactory temperature for ovipositing weevils is between 85° and 87°F. Cooler temperatures result in lower egg production while temperatures higher than 93°F may cause egg production to cease entirely.

Humidity control is important in keeping the food fresh and acceptable. If small bolls are used as food, it is possible to keep the relative humidity (RH) between 30 and 40%. Artificial medium pellets and squares will require 50 to 60% relative humidity to prevent excessive drying. Relative humidities greater than 60% result in a rapid growth of bacteria and yeast on the food making it unfit for the weevils.

E. EXTRACTING EGGS FROM FOOD

For small cultures, or where knowledge of the exact number of eggs laid is required, hand extraction is the best method. The eggs are dissected from the medium plug or boll by means of a sharp scalpel. An experienced technician can extract about 200 eggs per hour. If fresh bolls are used as the oviposition site, the eggs are usually free of surface contamination and may be transferred directly to the larval medium. This procedure should yield 80% adult weevils.

Mass rearing requires more rapid extraction methods even though a large number of eggs is destroyed in the process. By mechanical methods, one technician can extract over a quarter million eggs in half an hour.

The wax coating on the medium pellets may be removed by hand if only a few pellets are involved; however, for large amounts of medium a mechanical method is required. The use of a blender is not desirable because a high percentage of the eggs is destroyed and many of the pellets remain intact. The utilization of a simple dewaxing machine ensures that the wax will be removed from every pellet with minimum damage to the eggs.

Two 12-inch diameter aluminum plates with concave surfaces are fixed so that one plate is stationary and the other plate revolves (Fig. 3). The concave surfaces face each other. The resulting cavity is ¾-inch wide at the center and tapers gradually toward the periphery where a 3/16-inch space is maintained between the edges of the plates. Medium pellets entering through a hole in the center of the stationary plate are gently broken as the outer plate is revolved. A stream of water is used to wash the medium pieces and wax from the cavity. The water is caught in a container where the wax floats to the surface and is skimmed off.

The broken pieces of diet are washed through a 20-mesh screen and trapped on a 45-mesh screen. After the water has drained from the particles, the residue is transferred to a separatory funnel containing a saturated solution of sodium chloride. The eggs float to the surface and the particles settle and are discarded. Several more

FIG. 3. Medium dewaxer showing wax-covered pellets being washed into cavity between stationary and revolving plates.

extractions with saturated salt solutions remove nearly all of the trash. When fresh water is added to the separatory funnel, the eggs sink rapidly while the remaining trash will stay suspended in the water. Eggs recovered in this manner are completely free of trash particles.

The question of injury to the egg by saturated salt water may be raised; however, our tests have shown that the egg of the boll weevil can remain in saturated salt water for 48 hours and hatch normally.

F. SURFACE STERILIZATION OF EGGS

Except for eggs hand extracted from fresh bolls, all other eggs must be surface-sterilized to minimize contamination of the larval medium. Several choices of chemicals exist, but formaldehyde is preferred by the authors. Boll weevil eggs are relatively resistant to formaldehyde and can withstand 4% actual formalin in water for periods up to 1 hour. Soaking the eggs for 2 hours in 0.75% formaldehyde and planting them from a 0.2% formaldehyde solution eliminates surface microorganisms and is useful in control of certain egg-transmitted diseases of the weevil (Section III, B).

Other materials used to surface sterilize the eggs are 0.02% mercuric chloride in an aqueous solution of 33% ethanol; sodium hypochlorite at 0.1%; and an aqueous solution of copper sulfate. The egg may be soaked in the mercuric chloride solution for 20 minutes without harm, but they must be rinsed in sterile water before implanting in the larval diet. Sodium hypochlorite has the disadvantage of causing partial dechorionation of the egg, thus making it susceptible to mechanical injury during the implanting process.

II. LARVAL DIETS AND REARING

A. LARVAL DIETS

1. *Natural Diets*

The cotton square is the natural food of the boll weevil larva, and to date it has not been possible to produce an artificial diet that is equal to it. The use of cotton squares as larval food may be desirable for certain experiments. For this purpose large squares are picked in a manner to leave a short length of stem attached. Eight to ten such squares, with the stems imbedded in moist sand, are placed in a cage with one pair of weevils. Squares are replaced daily with fresh ones; those showing oviposition punctures are kept in moist sand for 1 week. Then they are placed on a moist paper towel and held at 80% RH until the adult weevils emerge. The use of fresh squares necessitates an ample source of growing cotton plants. One large plant under ideal greenhouse conditions produces 10 to 15 squares per week.

To avoid maintaining cotton plants during the winter months, large quantities of squares can be collected during the summer growing season and processed for storage. After the leaf bracts are mechanically removed (Gast, 1961), the debracted squares are ground with a small amount of water and freeze-dried (Jenkins *et al.*, 1964). The resulting powder is stored in a freezer. When needed, sterile water is used to reconstitute the powder and the resulting paste provides a larval medium quite similar to that of fresh squares. Unless aseptic conditions are maintained, it is necessary to add inhibitors to the medium to prevent contamination by microorganisms.

2. *Artificial Larval Diets*

The use of artificial larval media is the most practical means for mass rearing of the boll weevil. A number of such media have been developed, all based on the original work of Vanderzant and Davich

(1958). The main difference among the different media is the protein source. Vanderzant and Davich used soy bean protein; more recently we have added oven-dried cotton leaves. Earle *et al.* (1959) introduced the use of acetone-extracted cotton square powder and the senior author has used solvent-extracted cottonseed meal. The medium used in the mass rearing program at the Boll Weevil Research Laboratory is listed in Table II.

TABLE II
ARTIFICIAL LARVAL MEDIUM USED IN MASS REARING

Ingredient	Amount
Water	350 ml
Sucrose	7.0 gm
Agar	10.5 gm
Brewer's yeast	3.5 gm
Wesson's salt	1.0 gm
Soy bean protein	10.5 gm
Acetone-extracted square powder[a]	17.5 gm
Solvent extracted cottonseed meal	5.0 gm
B-vitamin mixture[a]	3.5 ml
Choline chloride	0.25 gm
Cholesterol	0.3 gm
Methyl p-hydroxybenzoate	0.3 gm
Potassium sorbate	0.4 gm

[a] See Section I, C.

Solvent-extracted cottonseed meal can be substituted for the square powder but the larval period will be extended for about 5 days. Weevils reared on the above medium have an average weight of 14.6 mg at the time of emergence.

All the dry ingredients, with the exception of the cholesterol and the two mold inhibitors, are added to boiling water in a blender. The cholesterol, dissolved in hot ethanol, is added to the mixture and the medium is autoclaved for 10 minutes at 20 lb pressure. The potassium sorbate is dissolved in 20 ml of sterile water and the methyl p-hydroxybenzoate is dissolved in 10 ml of ethanol. The two inhibitors plus the B-vitamin mixture are added to the autoclaved medium, which is poured into sterile vials or Petri dishes and allowed to solidify.

B. PLANTING EGGS IN MEDIUM

Hand planting eggs in individual 2-dram vials gives the highest per cent yield of adult weevils from eggs. A fine sable hair brush is used to transfer the surface-sterilized eggs to a hole punched in 1 ml of medium in the vial; the vial is then capped with aluminum foil. Should a vial become contaminated with bacteria or yeast, the loss is limited to a single egg. A technician can emplant from 200 to 400 eggs per hour and yields should average between 70 and 80%.

The use of larger containers such as 9-cm Petri dishes greatly increases the speed of planting the eggs. The surface of the larval medium, ¼-inch deep in the bottom half of the Petri dish, is punched full of small holes. The punch is covered with 50 to 60 1/16-inch needles and only a single stroke is required per Petri dish. A technician can transfer between 600 and 700 eggs per hour to these dishes and yields should average between 40 and 60%.

Mechanical methods of planting eggs are required for large-scale rearing. Although the per cent yield of adult weevils from mechanically planted eggs may be only one quarter that of hand-planted eggs, a technician can plant over a quarter million eggs per hour. Surface-sterilized eggs are suspended in a sterile solution of 20 gm sucrose, 2 gm cornstarch, 100 ml water, and 0.5 ml of 40% formaldehyde. The concentration of eggs is adjusted to 100 per ml and 1 ml of the suspension is sprayed onto the roughened surface of medium in each Petri dish. The spray method of planting eggs is useful in planting large trays of medium adaptable to a conveyor belt operation.

It is necessary to remove free water from the surface of the larval medium after the eggs are planted. This is accomplished by replacing the Petri dish top with a desiccator lid (a metal ring with a thick porous paper in it) for 24 hours. A more rapid method is to place the open dishes in a current of air from which all microorganisms have been filtered.

The larvae are kept in a room maintained at 85°F and 50 to 60% RH during the developmental period. Relative humidities greater than 60% increase the problem of contamination by microorganisms; below 50% the larval diet dries excessively, resulting in reduced yields.

C. ADULT EMERGENCE

Adult weevils start to emerge from the medium 13 to 14 days after the eggs are planted. For small cultures the adult weevils are picked from the surface of the larval medium with a pair of forceps, but for larger cultures an emergence box is necessary. The emergence box (Fig. 4) is a large, shallow, light-tight box with several screen containers at one end. The larval dishes are opened and placed in the box. The adult weevils will crawl to the screen traps where they are

FIG. 4. Emergence boxes with screen traps on front of box. Weevils are being removed from one of the screen traps.

easily removed. Five to six days are required for the majority of adults to emerge. The boxes are steam-sterilized between loadings.

Frequently it is necessary to maintain large populations of adult weevils with no interest in obtaining eggs from them. Artificial adult medium is expensive to make and the following more economical materials may be used to maintain adult weevils for periods of 1 to 3 weeks: 10% sucrose solution on absorbant paper or cotton pads; sliced apples, provided they are changed daily; cotton seedlings 2–3 inches high; whole small bolls; or sliced large bolls before the lint has matured.

III. PROBLEMS IN MASS REARING

A. MEDIUM CONTAMINATION BY MICROORGANISMS

One of the main problems encountered in mass rearing the boll weevil is contamination of the larval medium by yeasts, molds, and bacteria. Of these, the yeasts are the most difficult to control. The most widely used inhibitors in the larval medium are methyl *p*-hydroxybenzoate and either sorbic acid or potassium sorbate. The amount needed to control the yeasts is quite close to the tolerance limits of the weevil larvae. Potassium sorbate is slightly less effective against the contaminants than sorbic acid but is much less toxic to the weevil larvae and eggs.

Aside from the use of inhibitors, the most effective means of controlling contamination is cleanliness in the rearing facilities. Floors and work surfaces should be washed daily with a germicidal agent. Air-borne spores are the most common source of contamination. If possible, the medium plates should never be opened except in sterile air. The use of a small hood or dry box is helpful to exclude air-borne spores when the plates are open for planting eggs. A better method is the use of a hood having a current of sterile filtered air passing out the front opening. There are numerous high-volume air filters available that retain virtually all bacteria, mold, and yeast spores.

B. DISEASES OF THE BOLL WEEVIL IN CULTURES

Until a protozoan disease destroyed the mass culture at the Boll Weevil Laboratory, there was no record of any disease of the boll weevil. Since then several highly contagious diseases have been found in laboratory cultures. Recognition of an unknown disease is difficult and the first indication of trouble generally is excessive mortality in the breeding stock, or an unexplained drop in egg production. Normal mortality among adult weevils is 10–15% during the first 3 weeks; the presence of a disease should be suspected if greater mortality is experienced, especially during the first week. Extreme temperatures, improper nutrition, and toxic materials in the medium are the usual causes of high mortality, but any sick or abnormal weevil should be examined for the presence of pathogens.

Of the four diseases found in the mass culture by the authors, all were capable of transmission in or on the egg and could not be controlled by surface sterilization of the egg. The diseases also were spread by ingestion of the pathogens by larvae and adult weevils. When a diseased weevil dies and breaks up in an oviposition cage, the liberated pathogens are ingested by healthy weevils and the disease spreads rapidly throughout the entire colony.

The most effective control of a disease, obviously, is preventing its introduction into the culture. Start with disease-free weevils and make certain that no wild types are introduced in infested squares or bolls. Any new culture of weevils should be quarantined for 4 to 6 months before being brought into the main rearing facility.

The most effective means of eliminating a disease is to destroy the culture and decontaminate the rearing facility. Months of time can be wasted in trying to eliminate the disease from the culture; it is much easier to obtain clean stock and start again.

REFERENCES

Earle, N. W., Gaines, R. C., and Roussel, J. S. (1959). A larval diet for boll weevils containing an acetone powder of cotton squares. *J. Econ. Entomol.* **52**, 710–712.

Gast, R. T. (1961). Some shortcuts in laboratory rearing of boll weevils. *J. Econ. Entomol.* **54**, 395–396.

Gast, R. T. (1965). Methods for mass production of diet pellets for adult boll weevils. *J. Econ. Entomol.* **58**, 1024–1025.

Jenkins, J. N., Maxwell, F. G., and Parrott, W. L. (1964). A technique for measuring certain aspects of antibiosis in cotton to the boll weevil. *J. Econ. Entomol.* **57**, 679–681.

Vanderzant, E. S., and Davich, T. B. (1958). Laboratory rearing of the boll weevil: A satisfactory larval diet and oviposition studies. *J. Econ. Entomol.* **51**, 288–291.

Vanderzant, E. S., and Davich, T. B. (1961). Artificial diets for the adult boll weevil and techniques for obtaining eggs. *J. Econ. Entomol.* **54**, 923–928.

Chapter 28
Wheat Stem Sawflies

LEW E. WALLACE

Wheat Stem Sawfly Investigations,
Agricultural Research Service,
U. S. Department of Agriculture,
Bozeman, Montana

I. REARING WHEAT STEM SAWFLY LARVAE ON ARTIFICIAL MEDIA

Rearing of larvae of the wheat stem sawfly (*Cephus cinctus* Nort.) on artificial media is in the experimental stage. The sawfly poses different and perhaps more difficult problems than other insects reared in this fashion. It requires a specialized environment for oviposition and larval development. To illustrate this point, a brief synopsis of the life cycle is presented.

The female sawfly oviposits in the lumen of various grass stems, wheat included. The eggs hatch in the stem and the larvae begin feeding on the stem parenchyma. They continue to feed up and down the stem, tunneling the nodes as they feed. Ultimately they make their way to the base of the plant, cut the stem about 1 inch above the ground, and form a cocoon in the stub for overwintering and transformation to adults.

A. Essential Environmental Requirements of the Sawfly

The essential requirements pertinent to rearing deal with the females and larvae. The female requires a suitable plant stem in which to oviposit. The legless larvae require a confined area to aid in movement, an environment of high humidity during development, and a gradually drier environment as they reach maturity. As Salt (1947) has pointed out, the larvae also need a cold period of 10°C for 90 days to break the obligatory diapause and allow them to transform into pupae and adults.

B. Experimental Rearing of Larvae on Artificial Media

Interest in the nutritional requirements of the larvae led to attempts to rear them on a defined medium. Two Canadians, Kasting and McGinnis (1958; McGinnis and Kasting, 1962a) began the study. They worked together testing rearing chambers and several media.

1. *Selection of a Suitable Rearing Chamber*

Several chambers were tried including soda straws, to select a suitable rearing container. These workers settled on a polymethyl methacrylate block with several 3/32-inch square grooves as the base. A block of wood was then used to cover the grooves. This made a series of chambers in each plastic block which were easy to provision with food and larvae.

To provide the humidity necessary, the wood was soaked in water before it was placed on the provisioned and inhabited grooves.

2. *Manipulation of the Larvae*

Wheat stems were used to induce oviposition and the infested stems were cut open to obtain the developing larvae. Larvae were used because they are much easier to handle than the fragile eggs. In fact, difficulty in survival was encountered with small larvae (McGinnis and Kasting, 1962a). Only larvae of at least 5 mg in weight had a high survival ability.

The larvae were carefully lifted from the wheat stems and placed in a hollow space in the provisioned grooves. Care was taken to place one larva only in each groove as they are cannibalistic. When all the provisioned grooves of a plastic block were inhabited, the wet wooden block was placed over the grooves and held in place with clamps or rubber bands. Both ends of the grooves were then plugged with cotton.

In spite of the wet wood block, the Canadian workers found it was necessary to transfer the larvae daily to freshly provisioned grooves to maintain the humidity necessary for larval development.

3. *Composition of the Medium Used*

McGinnis and Kasting used a medium of casein, 29.4%; yeast extract, 2.9%; cellulose powder, 1.0%; water, 66.7%; and trace amounts of anhydrous lanolin, NaCl, CaCl, $NaLiCo_3$, $NaH_2PO_4H_2O$, and K_2HPO_4. Lyophilized wheat plants added to the diet invariably caused larval mortality.

McGinnis and Kasting believed there was some toxic substance in the plant that was released when it was crushed. This was also indicated in a study they made (1962b) on the pale western cutworm. Ether extracts of wheat pith were toxic to the small larvae of this organism.

4. *Present State of Larval Rearing on Artificial Media*

To date no adults have been reared from larvae fed on the artificial media used, even though they reached maturity and formed the overwintering cocoon. There also exists the inability to culture the very young larvae. Whether these failures are due to missing nutrients in the diet or contamination with disease during handling is not known.

C. THE VALUE OF THIS REARING METHOD

At best, rearing the wheat stem sawfly larvae on artificial media is a tedious process and does not lend itself to mass rearing. It does, however, offer a valuable tool for a better understanding of larval nutrition and the nature of plant resistance to the larvae.

II. REARING ADULTS FROM INFESTED STUBBLE

By far the most effective and simple method of obtaining adult sawflies is the collection of overwintering larvae in the infested wheat stubble. These larvae are manipulated to induce transformation to adults.

A. COLLECTION OF INFESTED MATERIAL

Collection of the infested stubble is easiest in cultivated fields of wheat even though wild grasses are also infested. Observations of the grain fields just before harvest reveals the number of sawfly-cut stems and allows one to choose fields with heavy infestations.

After harvest in the fall, the stubble containing the larvae can be collected.

If the ground is moist from rainfall, the stubble can easily be pulled by hand. If the ground is hard and dry, this method of collection often leaves the cut stubs containing the larvae in the ground. In that case the ground must be cultivated before the stubble is collected. A single-row cultivator can be used, but there is little loss of larvae by using heavy farm equipment.

The cultivation should be just below the stem end. If done properly, a rake can be used to gather the stubble into a pile for collection.

The stubble is placed in a watertight container and carried to a convenient storage place. Dry stubble should be moistened, using 1 quart of water per cubic foot of stubble. The containers are then covered and stored.

B. HOLDING THE COLLECTED MATERIAL

The storage facilities are maintained at 10°C for 90 days to break the diapause. In Montana, outside unheated storage will break the diapause by the first of January.

After diapause has been broken, the stubble can be held at 10°C until needed. It is possible to hold the material through one summer and still get a fair yield of adults. Storage for two summers, however, reduces the yield to almost zero.

C. INCUBATION OF INFESTED MATERIAL AND COLLECTION OF ADULTS

The stored material is brought into the laboratory for rearing. It is again moistened if it is dry, placed in a closed, light-tight box, and held at approximately 22°C. The box should be of a shallow depth to avoid piling the stubble too deep as this makes it difficult for the sawflies to get out. The box is also fitted with openings near the top on one side to allow light to enter the box. These openings are covered with glass jars for collecting the adults. The stubble must be held in this incubator for 2 to 3 weeks to allow pupation and transformation to adults.

The adults should be taken from the collection jars daily. If they are to be held in the laboratory they should be placed in a cage of at least 1 yd^3 per 1000 adults.

Cool temperature, between 13°C and 16°C, and the addition of a 10% sugar solution and water in covered containers with wick feeders will aid in prolonging the life of the sawflies. Even with these precautions, holding the adults beyond 5 days will result in some loss.

D. The Value of Collection Rearing

Collection rearing of adults is a means of obtaining large numbers for use in greenhouse studies, irradiation studies, oviposition studies, and so on. It is a necessary adjunct to the larval rearing studies.

REFERENCES

Kasting, R., and McGinnis, A. J. (1958). Note on a method of artificially sustaining larvae of the wheat stem sawfly *Cephus cinctus* Norton (Hymenoptera: Cephidae). *Can. Entomologist* **90,** 63–64.

McGinnis, A. J., and Kasting, R. (1962a). A method of rearing larvae of the wheat stem sawfly (Hymenoptera: Cephidae) under artificial conditions. *Can. Entomologist* **94,** 573–574.

McGinnis, A. J., and Kasting, R. (1962b). Comparison of tissues from hollow- and solid-stemmed spring wheats during growth III an ether-soluble substance toxic to larvae of the pale western cut worm *Agrotis orthogona* Morr. (Lepidoptera: Noctuidae). *Entomol. Exptl. Appl.* **5,** 313–321.

Salt, R. W. (1947). Some effects of temperature on the production and elimination of diapause in the wheat stem sawfly (*Cephus cinctus* Norton). *Can. J. Res.* **D25,** 66–86.

Chapter 29

Lygus Bugs

G. T. Bottger

Entomology Research Division,
Agricultural Research Service,
U. S. Department of Agriculture,
Tucson, Arizona

Controlled experiments for determining relative varietal resistance of host plants and effectiveness of insecticides require test insects with a minimum of variability, so that only naturally acquired levels of resistance or susceptibility are measured. Laboratory colonization accomplishes this by providing test insects of uniform age and nutrition.

The rearing method described here was first tried at the Tucson Cotton Insect Laboratory early in 1959 and has been in continuous use since then. A satisfactory laboratory method for rearing lygus bugs on green beans has been used at the U. S. Department of Agriculture Cotton Insect Laboratory during the past 6 years where 47 successive generations have been reared. The method was developed primarily for rearing *Lygus hesperus* Knight, but *Lygus lineolarus* (P. de B.) and *Lygus elisus* Vanduzee have also been reared successfully. A similar method was reported by Beards and Leigh (1960).

I. FOOD AND OVIPOSITION MEDIUM

Fresh green pole-type beans (*Phaseolus vulgaris*) provide food and a suitable medium for oviposition. Green beans are usually available in grocery stores throughout the year, but better quality and prices can be had by going directly to the produce terminal. In some localities it may be practical to grow the beans. Beans from commercial sources may be contaminated with an insecticide or, if they have been harvested for some time, they may be of poor quality, which sometimes results in early molding. Known insecticide contamination has occurred only once in 5 years at the Tucson Laboratory and beans of poor quality can usually be avoided by careful selection.

II. COLLECTION AND MAINTENANCE OF CULTURES

Parent cultures of *Lygus* can readily be collected from alfalfa hay fields, other legumes, or certain weed hosts with either a hand sweep net or mechanized vacuum insect net. The lygus bugs can usually be separated from other insects and trash by aspirating them directly into vials from the sweep or vacuum net.

The bugs suffer the least mortality when handled with an aspirator, although CO_2 can be used satisfactorily if overexposure is avoided.

Oviposition cages are $8 \times 8 \times 12$ inch wood frames covered with a 30-mesh saran screen on three sides and a piece of glass on the fourth which serves as a sliding door. Seventy-five to one hundred bugs of each sex with 5 to 10 green beans, depending on size, per cage result in the best production. The use of this type of cage in several tests resulted in a greater number of eggs per female than when the insects were confined in glass jars.

After the green beans have been exposed to oviposition for 1 or 2 days, they should be transferred to 1-gallon glass jars. Each jar should be dated and set on the shelf in the rearing room for incubation, which, when the temperature is near 78°F, requires 6 days. A day or two before the eggs are due to hatch, fresh beans should be added to provide food for the young nymphs. Under the conditions described above, nymphal development requires 15 to 18 days. Fresh beans should be added every 2 days. The old feeding beans should be removed at that time, but the beans containing eggs are left for 14 days. The nymphs should be shaken from the old beans into the bottom of the jar when fresh beans are added. The preoviposition period for laboratory-reared bugs is from 6 to 7 days. The longer periods occur in the winter. Egg laying usually lasts about 2 weeks.

Best results have been obtained when rearing is conducted in a room where the temperature is maintained at approximately 78°F with the relative humidity near 60%, and 12 to 13 light-hours provided per day.

Disease has not been a problem in *Lygus* rearing when the following precautions are practiced: After use, the jars and cages are washed with soap and water; the jars are rinsed with acetone and the cages with water. They are placed on metal racks outdoors where they are exposed to the sun until they are reused, usually one to several days.

REFERENCE

Beards, G. W., and Leigh, T. F. (1960). A laboratory rearing method for *Lygus hesperus* Knight. *J. Econ. Entomol.* **53**, 327–328.

Chapter 30

Aphids

F. H. HARRIES*

Entomology Research Division,
Agricultural Research Service,
U. S. Department of Agriculture,
and Washington State University,
Pullman, Washington

I. INTRODUCTION

The aphids are one of the largest and most successful families of insects and have some of the most interesting adaptations found in nature. They are perhaps the most prolific insects, due to their rapid growth and telescoping of generations rather than to the number of young or eggs per female. There are many exceptions in the different species, but in general the aphids overwinter in the egg stage, and the hatching nymphs become stem mothers which produce living young in succeeding generations during the summer.

* *Present address:* Tree Fruit Research Center, Wenatchee, Washington.

These may be both wingless or winged agamic viviparous forms. In the fall winged males may appear which mate with the females to complete the cycle. In warmer climates the sexual part of the cycle may be entirely eliminated.

The aphids are generally restricted to one or several related host plants, although many species, such as the bean aphid or the green peach aphid, may affect a wide variety of plants. Not all of the plants on which the aphids are found are good food plants for growing colonies. Patch (1938) has given a food plant catalog of the aphids of the world, and Averill (1945) an index to the genera and species of the food plants of aphids. Lists of host plants of most of the common species of aphids are given by Essig (1926) and others.

II. GENERAL BIOLOGY AND METHODS

A. METHODS

In most biological and insecticide work with aphids it is desirable to have a vigorous and biologically uniform supply of the species concerned. During the growing season these may often be found in the field, but to have a dependable. supply it is usually necessary to grow the insects in an insectary, greenhouse, or indoor culture room. Most aphids can be grown easily through most of the year in a greenhouse under favorable temperatures and with some supplemental lighting. In cloudy weather artificial lighting to maintain healthy plants and a photoperiod of 12 hours or more to prevent excessive production of the winged form may be necessary. In hot weather it is often difficult to keep the greenhouse cool enough for good production of aphids, and it may be advantageous to use an indoor room where temperature, humidity, and light can be controlled consistently at favorable levels. A basement room with temperature control and artificial lighting such as described by Waters (1937) may be useful.

In an extensive book on culture methods for invertebrate animals (Galtsoff et al., 1937) methods were discussed for growing the bean aphid, *Aphis fabae* Scopuli, the greenbug, *Schizaphis graminum* (Rondani), the apple grain aphid, *Rhopalosiphum fitchii* (Sanderson), the pea aphid, *Acyrthosiphon pisum* (Harris), the melon aphid, *Aphis gossypii* Glover, the corn leaf aphid, *Rhopalosiphum maidis* (Fitch), the corn root aphid, *Anuraphis maidiradicis* (Forbes), and the potato aphid, *Macrosiphum euphorbiae* (Thomas). Waters (1937), has discussed methods and equipment for laboratory studies of insecticides and Waters (1943), and Peterson (1953) have discussed methods of rearing insects that attack plants.

Soft-bodied insects such as aphids should be handled as gently as possible when transferred from one plant to another with a camel's hair brush. This is especially important when the insects are to be used in tests and the best possible techniques should be worked out carefully. In some cases infested plants were cut and allowed to wilt slightly (Waters, 1943) so that the aphids would remove their mouth parts from the plant and wander about so that they could be handled with less injury than would occur if they were handled when feeding. The adults may be handled with a camel's hair brush or a No. 00 artist's brush, but probably a better way is to use a glass tube with a suitably small opening so that they can be lifted and moved by applying the tube with suction to the insect's back. A similar device operated by a small electric vacuum pump and equipped with metal tubes of various sizes for handling insects is commercially available. A portable electrically powered aspirator useful for aphids was described by Shanks and Gans (1963).

Uniformity in pretreatment conditions is desirable to avoid variability in the test insects. The growth rate, rate of reproduction, and susceptibility to insecticides has been shown to differ between the winged and wingless forms of the same species (Wadley, 1931). Crowding on the plants or poorer nutrition has been found to influence size in the chrysanthemum aphid, *Macrosiphoniella sanborni* (Gillette), and the tolerance to phosphorous insecticides (Johansen, 1952). Pea aphids raised on broad beans were less susceptible to rotenone than those raised on *Trifolium praetense* (Potter and Gillham, 1957) and green peach aphids raised on turnips or lettuce were about three times more resistant to nicotine than those raised on nasturtium (Richardson and Casanges, 1942). Sun (1960) mentioned some other examples of pretest influences. Some of the pretest conditions to be considered are temperature, light, photoperiod, nutrition and food plants, overpopulation, and cages. This seems to be especially important in aphids, where development of the young begins before the mother's birth, or in the grandmother's body. It has also been supposed that colonies raised under controlled conditions and originating from a single female may have less inherent variability than a colony collected in the field. In colonizing aphids special care should be taken to avoid the introduction of hymenopterous parasites and fungus diseases that may infect them.

Aphids are most productive during the early adult stage and usually there is a postreproductive period. Regular replacement of plants for the stock colonies helps prevent overcrowding of the aphids and further reduces feeding injury to the plants by eliminating the spent or nonproductive adults.

Waters (1937, 1943), in a general discussion of plant-feeding insects, has given many useful ideas on cages, watering of the plants with wicks, and other methods of colonizing aphids. He also recommended the use of vigorous growing plants and the avoidance of overcrowding to prevent the production of smaller and weaker aphids and the production of winged forms.

For use in raising lady beetles at other times during the year, Haug (1938) described methods of collecting and freezing large quantities of aphids when these are abundant in the field. Species frozen were the turnip aphid, the pea aphid, the bean aphid, and some others. These were packed in air-tight containers and frozen at −21°–25°C. Cellucotton saturated with water was placed in the tops of the containers to increase the humidity before freezing.

B. Feeding and Nutrition

It is evident that a great number of species of aphids can be raised in the greenhouse or laboratory, but those that can be easily grown on the more common vegetable and garden flower plants have been favored for testing insecticides. Among these Shull (Galtsoff et al., 1937) recommended beans, peas, radishes, cabbage, tomatoes, nasturtiums, calendulas, asters, wheat, oats, and potatoes. Some species such as the bean aphid and the green peach aphid may be grown on a wide variety of plants.

The feeding and nutrition of aphids has been given much study and Auclair (1963) has given an extensive review of the subject. This includes discussion of the mouth parts, methods of feeding, physiology and biochemistry, honeydew production and composition, and possible nutritional role of the symbiotes. Feeding and nutrition were discussed by Kennedy and Stroyan (1959) in an extensive review of the biology of aphids. Lipke and Fraenkel (1956) also discussed the feeding of aphids in a general review of insect nutrition and Friend (1958) discussed the nutritional requirements of insects.

The mouth parts of aphids are specialized for the ingestion of a liquid diet; aphids have been known as sucking insects. The two maxillary stylets in opposition form two channels, the salivary canal and the food tube. There is a salivary syringe that injects fluids into the plant and a food pump that must be under sensory control. Most species evidently depend to considerable extent on the translocatory mechanism of the plants or sap pressure in feeding. It has been found that when the rostra of feeding aphids are cut the sap continues to exude at a rate similar to that of honeydew from feeding aphids (Mittler, 1957). This may not be as marked in aphids that feed on herbaceous plants as in those that feed on tree stems, but it is evident that many aphids take advantage of turgor pressure so that they are fed both chemically and physically. Carter (1962) stated that, although it is reasonable to assume that turgor pressure is an aid in feeding, it may not be a necessity. Evidently there is some sensory control of the sap intake since aphids do not always feed at the maximum rate. This may be regulated by the food pump and the esophageal valve may prevent the backflow of juices and so aid in the posterior movement through the intestines. This wasteful feeding mechanism is puzzling since most of the sugars and much of the nitrogen of the sap are excreted. A review of information on the composition of the saliva and of honeydew is given by Auclair (1963).

Probably it is the feeding adaptations to the plants that make it difficult to devise good artificial feeding techniques for aphids. Considerable progress in the artificial feeding of aphids has been made by Hamilton (1935), Pletsch (1937), Maltais (1959), Mittler and Dadd (1962), and others, but methods of colonizing aphids in abundance on artificial media are not available.

Saliva is injected during penetration which gels to form a sheath that remains in the plant when the stylets are withdrawn. It is believed that there are two kinds of saliva, a watery fluid and a more viscous material that forms the sheath.

The symbiotes, or bacteroides or yeast-like hereditary microorganisms present in special structures or mycetomes in aphids, are believed to have an important function in nutrition. This may be that of converting the nitrogen from the plant into the usable form for the aphids, or the organisms may synthesize vitamins or some other metabolic essentials. The question of possible nitrogen fixation from the atmosphere has not been settled. From analyses of the sieve-tube sap and the honeydew, Michel (1942) concluded that the aphids obtained more protein than was available to them in the sap, indicating that this was provided by their symbiotes. Other discussion of the question may be found in a review by Lipke and Fraenkel (1956). Work on symbiosis and the symbiotes of insects has been extensive and has been covered by Buchner (1953) in his classic monograph on this subject. Steinhaus (1949) discussed the intracellular microbiota of insects and the more recent studies of internal symbiosis in insects has been reviewed by Richards and Brooks (1958), who list 83 references.

C. FORM DETERMINATION

Another problem in colonizing aphids is control of the production of the wingless form, which is usually preferred in testing insecticides. Temperatures of 70° to 75°F, adequate lighting to maintain healthy host plants, and a photoperiod of 12 hours or more are usually favorable for production of vigorous colonies of aphids with a minimum of alates. Many early studies showed that lower temperatures and decrease in the daylight period influenced wing production and the appearance of the sexual forms. Later studies on effects of the photoperiod were made by White (1946), Bonnemaison (1951), and Bodenheimer and Swirski (1957).

There is some tendency for the winged and wingless forms to alternate in successive generations so that the apterae produce a higher proportion of alatae and vice versa. Wadley (1931) found that progeny of the wingless form were more influenced in wing form by environmental conditions than were offspring of the winged form. Some genetic factors seem to be involved, making it very difficult to raise a high proportion of apterae in some species. Brittain (1921), Reinhard (1927), Lal (1952, 1955), and Lees (1961) have emphasized that overcrowding may increase the proportion of winged forms. Studies of polymorphism in aphids have been extensively reviewed by Hille Ris Lambers (1966).

D. GROWTH AND REPRODUCTION

The individual fecundity of most kinds of aphids seems modest, since different studies have shown only an average of about 4 per day under favorable conditions and usually a total production of less than 100 nymphs. It is the short developmental period and the compounding or number of generations a year that give the aphids their enormous rates of multiplication in which the theoretical progeny from 1 female in 1 year may be many billions.

In many species the reproductive period is more than twice as long as the maturation period. The rate of reproduction increases to a maximum and then declines, and in most species a definite postreproduction period has been found (Wadley, 1931; MacGillivray and Anderson, 1958b). In studies of four species of aphids, MacGillivray and Anderson (1958a) found that the reproductive period was about twice as long as the maturation period and that the greatest reproduction occurred between the fifth and tenth days. They observed a maximum of 81 young per female and as many as 10 nymphs per day by 1 female. The apterae matured in about 9 days and survived for 41 to 44 days. Overcrowding did not increase the number of alates. In the clover aphid, *Anuraphis bakeri* Cowen, Davis (1908) reported a daily reproduction of 2 to 3 young per female and a maximum of 7 young per female in 1 day. In the same species Smith (1923) found an average total reproduction of 105 young per female and a daily production of 3 to 5 nymphs per female. For apple aphid, *Aphis pomi* DeGeer, Gillette and Taylor (1908) reported 3 to 4 nymphs per day per female and maxima of 10 to 12. Wadley (1931) in the greenbug reported a maximum of 10 offspring in 1 day from 1 female.

III. COLONIZING SOME COMMON SPECIES

A. THE BEAN APHID, *Aphis fabae* SCOPOLI

This species has been widely used in insecticide work. It is easily grown on a variety of plants in the greenhouse or laboratory; nasturtium plants or the broad bean have been favored as host plants (Waters, 1943). The aphids are black and show up well which makes counting easier and more accurate; being short-legged, they are probably less likely to be injured in handling (Shepard, in Galtsoff *et al.*, 1937). Seeds of the dwarf nasturtium or the broad bean should be soaked in warm water for an hour or so and planted at weekly intervals in rich black loam or a potting mixture of silt, sand, and peat moss. It may be convenient to grow the plants in 4-inch pots set in sand or soil on a greenhouse bench. It is well to plant new seeds frequently and eliminate the older colonies as fast as possible to prevent parasitization and production of the winged forms.

In winter in the north it is usually necessary to use supplemental lighting to keep the plants in good condition and to increase the photoperiod for the aphids by using a bank of fluorescent lights above the plants. The lights should be operated by an electric time switch and photoperiods of 12 to 18 hours may be advantageous. Some workers have used undisturbed colonies on nasturtium plants in insecticide tests and others have used fixed numbers of the wingless adults. In some cases infested plants were cut and allowed to wilt slightly so that the aphids would remove their mouth parts and move about so that they could be handled more easily and with less injury by a camel's hair brush (Waters, 1943). In raising the aphid in the greenhouse during the winter Davidson (1924) found that increasing the photoperiod with artificial lights stopped the production of sexual forms.

Staub (1957) described methods of raising large numbers of the aphids at any time during the year in the laboratory as food for predators. Seeds of the broad bean were soaked in water and then germinated in damp vermiculite. Two or three of the sprouts were then placed with the roots in narrow-necked bottles and held in place by wadding. The shoots were infested with 150 to 250 aphids and the whole was covered with a plastic bag. Illumination was provided by fluorescent lights for 12 hours daily at about 65°F and 40 to 80% relative humidity (RH). The colonies developed rapidly and reached a maximum in about 2 weeks. Waters (1943) said that the dwarf nasturtium was the best host for rearing this species indoors. Plantings of nasturtiums were made at weekly intervals to ensure a continual supply of new plants and supplemental lighting was used in the greenhouse during cloudy weather. Other host plants are beets, spinach, and a number of weeds and ornamental plants.

B. The Potato Aphid, *Macrosiphum euphorbiae* (Thomas)

In studies in eastern Canada, MacGillivray (1955) and Mac-Gillivray and Anderson (1958a) grew the aphids on Katahdin potatoes in copper screen cages in the greenhouse. Fluorescent lights above the plants were operated for 18 hours daily to supplement natural light. In biological studies the aphids were raised individually on excised potato leaves. Alates and apterae produced about the same number of progeny, but the apterous aphids usually were more numerous. The aphids matured in about 9 days and the reproductive period was more than twice this long with the peak of reproduction occurring in 5 to 10 days. In each case there was a definite postreproductive period which was significantly longer in the wingless form although the length of life was about the same for both forms. In further studies MacGillivray and Anderson (1958b) found that although wingless and winged forms produced about the same proportion of wingless progeny, winged sister aphids produced a higher percentage of wingless progeny than did their wingless sisters.

The potato aphid also thrives on tomato and cucurbit plants. Waters (1943) preferred small Blue Hubbard squash plants since these could be easily grown in quantity in a short time. A temperature of 77°F was satisfactory and fluctuations to lower temperatures were favorable. The aphids were raised continuously in the laboratory under a 200-watt Mazda lamp, but stronger lights above a water heat screen were more favorable for the plants. The aphids withdraw the mouth parts and drop to the soil when disturbed.

C. THE PEA APHID, *Acyrthosiphon pisum* (HARRIS)

These aphids can easily be produced in large numbers on potted broad beans (*Vicia faba* L.) in the greenhouse or under fluorescent lights in the laboratory. For some reason the aphids thrive better with less light on broad beans than on peas (Waters, 1943). In sunny climates supplemental greenhouse lighting may not be necessary to obtain a good production of apterae, but under cloudy conditions some artificial lighting may be necessary during the day and to extend the photoperiod. The apterous aphids readily drop to the soil if disturbed; this is probably the best way to obtain them for use in tests, since the mouth parts are so easily injured if the insects are removed directly from the plants. Aphids of uniform age for use in tests may be obtained by removing all adults from the plants each day (Harries, 1956). The aphids may be handled with a No. 00 artist's brush, but probably a better way is to use a small suction tube applied to the insect's back.

For greater uniformity of test plants in biological and insecticide studies, Stone (1940) used Perfection peas grown in quartz sand in No. 2 tin cans and watered with a complete nutrient solution. In studies of the pea aphid on Perfection peas under controlled temperature and humidity conditions, a photoperiod of 12 hours with a high light intensity was necessary for more normal survival of the adults. In some work it was necessary to use a 500-watt Mazda lamp in the top of each air-conditioned cabinet and over glass-bottomed trays of running water to reduce the heat as much as possible (Waters, 1943; Harries, 1956). Where cages are used these should be designed to admit as much light as possible. Strong fluorescent lights mounted as close to the plants as possible without creating excessive heat may be used under some conditions.

In some experiments moisture to simulate dew was applied by rotating potted pea plants in a fine mist made by directing a jet of distilled water against a suitable baffle. The moisture was then held on the plants during the night (12 hours) by placing them in 1-gallon waxed paper cartons lined with wet blotting paper, and sealing the lids with decorator's tape. Occurrence of moisture on the plants made derris residues more effective against the aphids

but only while the residues were wet. Thus, wetting and drying of
the residues on the plants would explain the extreme variation in
effectiveness of derris dusts in the field. Humidity did not have
any effect on the aphids and 75°F or temperatures fluctuating moderately above and below this level were best for raising the aphids
(Harries, 1956).

Mittler and Sylvester (1961) raised the pea aphid on alfalfa plants
in screened cages in the greenhouse. The insect transfers were
made with a camel's hair brush or with a micropipette applied to
the insect's back.

Cartier (1960) raised the pea aphid on Perfection peas at about
69°F, 50% RH, and a photoperiod of 16 hours. The apterous adults
produced an average of 106 nymphs in a 20-day period of reproduction. During the first 8 days the daily reproduction of nymphs
was about equal to 24% of the weight of the female. There was a
definite postreproduction period of about 10 days. In nutrition
tests, Maltais (1959) raised the pea aphid on Perfection peas grown
in the greenhouse and on cuttings of peas grown in nutrient solutions in a plant-growth cabinet at 70°F and 45% RH. A light intensity of 1000 ft-c for 18 hours daily was used. In all experiments the
aphids required 6 days at this temperature to develop through the
fourth instar. On some nutrient solutions, obtained through the
pea cuttings, the aphids were heavier than in the controls. Growth
of the aphid evidently was favored by asparagine and glutamine
taken up from the solutions by the plants. Maxwell and Harwood
(1960) found increased reproduction of the aphid on broad beans
treated with 2,4-D.

D. THE GREEN PEACH APHID, *Myzus persicae* (SULZER)

This aphid has a wide host range and is easily raised on a number of
common vegetables in the greenhouse or laboratory. Smooth leaf cabbage [*Brassica juncea* (Coss.)] has been used by a number of workers
(Sylvester, 1954, 1956, 1964; Cook and Sylvester, 1961; Toba, 1964).
Sugar beets are a good host and these may easily be grown in flats
in a mixture of silt, sand, and peat moss, and then transplanted into
clay pots. Medium-sized sugar beets stored in a suitable cool place
in the fall may also be useful for raising colonies of the aphid during
the winter. Rutabagas or turnips may be stored for use during the
winter months or they can usually be bought in the grocery store
when needed. The smaller roots are satisfactory and soon produce
vigorous plants when set in pots of soil in the greenhouse. Rutabagas may be preferable to turnips since when potted in the green-

house they seem less likely to rot during the development of new foliage (Harries and Mattson, 1963). Shirck (1960) used large broccoli plants in 1-gallon cans for growing colonies of the aphids and seedling broccoli plants wrapped with cellulose tissue to keep them upright in shell vials were used in the insecticide tests. Finney *et al.* (1960) raised the aphids on Irish potato plants grown in 6-inch pots of vermiculite and under fluorescent lights. Broad beans and spinach are also excellent for growing stock colonies of the aphids. The ground cherry, *Physalis floridana,* is a fair host plant and has been used to obtain smooth succulent leaf discs for use in special cages to confine the aphids in screening tests of insecticides and studies of chemosterilants (Harries and Mattson, 1963).

Sylvester (1956) raised the green peach aphid on sugar beets and on smooth leaf mustard and found that most of the young of the apterae were produced in the first 2 weeks, although most of the adults lived for about 4 weeks and showed a definite postreproductive period. Females that survived for 20 or more days produced a total of about 80 young or an average of about 4 nymphs per day during the period. The results were almost the same on leaf discs as on attached leaves. Night and day reproduction were about the same.

In the writer's experience a considerable proportion of the winged forms always occurs and adequate lighting and photoperiod and the prevention of overcrowding favor production of the wingless form. Temperatures of 70° to 75°F seem most favorable. When the green peach aphid is raised in the same area with other aphids, such as the cabbage aphid or the turnip aphid, care should be taken to prevent it from mixing with the other species or these may be largely eliminated by the competition.

MacGillivray and Anderson (1958b) found that the apterae matured in about 9 days and survived for 41 to 44 days. A maximum of 103 nymphs and an average of 75 per female were observed. There was an average postreproduction period of about 14 days. The greatest production of young occurred between the fifth and seventh days. The aphids molted four times. An average of 5 young per day per female were produced between the fifth and tenth days. The aphids were grown on potato plants and overcrowding seemed to cause the production of more alates.

E. THE GREENBUG, *Schizaphis graminum* (RONDANI)

Wadley (1923, 1931) has reported extensively on the biology, ecology, and colonization of this species. The aphids were produced abundantly on oats under conditions favorable for the plants and it was possible to raise a high proportion of the wingless form. Poor nutrition, lower temperatures, and shorter photoperiod increased the number of winged aphids. Differences in relative humidity seemed to have little or no effect and moderate temperatures were more favorable. The winged form tended to produce more of the wingless form under most conditions, but the wingless form produced a high proportion either of the alatae or the apterae according to the environmental conditions. Reproduction was most rapid at about 73°F. The wingless adults produced an average of about 3.5 young per day at this temperature and on some days as many as 10 nymphs per female. The winged females were slightly less prolific. There was a definite postreproductive period. In both forms the rate of egg laying from the minimum to the maximum was an exponential function of the temperature (Harries, 1939).

F. The Woolly Apple Aphid, *Eriosoma lanigerum* (Hausmann)

Hoyt and Madsen (1960) obtained a constant supply of these aphids by infesting potted apple seedlings in the greenhouse. An initial group of seedlings was infested by putting about 100 field-collected, first-instar nymphs on the leaves at the top of the trees. Another group of trees was similarly infested every 2 weeks with first-instar nymphs from the trees previously infested. The nymphs were collected by holding an infested tree horizontally over a piece of paper and striking it sharply to dislodge the aphids, which were picked up in the desired numbers by an aspirator. Movements of the aphids on the plants and the course of the infestations were followed by placing cellophane tape bands on the trees. A thin strip of polybutene material was put in the center of the band to trap the aphids that came into contact with it. By infesting a tree with a single aphid, the course of the subsequent infestation could be followed. The plants were watered in saucers from the bottom to prevent the soil from becoming too damp and the colonies from forming on the roots.

G. The Chrysanthemum Aphid, *Macrosiphoniella sanborni* (Gill.)

The chrysanthemum aphid has been used extensively in screening and testing insecticides. Johansen (1952) raised the aphid on rooted chrysanthemum cuttings and found that temperatures between 75° and 60°F did not appreciably affect the size of the aphids or their susceptibility to phosphorous insecticides. The wingless aphids produced about 2 young per day and the alates about the same number. Succeeding generations on the same plant became smaller and less tolerant to the insecticides. Presumably, this was due to crowding and poorer nutrition. Patch (1938) lists five species of chrysanthemum as hosts and no other plants.

H. THE SPOTTED ALFALFA APHID, *Therioaphis maculata* (BUCKTON)

Finney *et al.* (1960) raised this aphid on pruned alfalfa plants 6 to 8 inches high that were cultured in 6-inch pots of vermiculite and watered with dilute Hoaglund's solution. Paschke and Sylvester (1957) used test plants of alfalfa seedlings that were grown in sterile sand and then transplanted into 3-inch clay pots of sterile soil and watered with half-strength Hoaglund's solution. Mittler and Sylvester (1961) maintained colonies on older alfalfa plants in screened cages in the greenhouse and transfers were made either with a fine camel's hair brush or with a micropipette applied to the insect's back.

I. OTHER SPECIES

The green chrysanthemum aphid, *Capitophorus rosarum* (Kltb.), has also been used in screening and testing insecticides and may be raised on chrysanthemum plants in the greenhouse or laboratory.

The corn root aphid, *Anuraphis maidiradicis* (Forbes), has been raised on corn sprouts in glass vials plugged with cotton, the aphids being transferred with a camel's hair brush. It has also been reared on bundles of small wheat plants placed in wide-mouth bottles of nutrient solution (Galtsoff *et al.*, 1937).

The melon aphid, *Aphid gossypii* Glover, was raised by Bergamin (1954) on various plants in nutrient solution. Squash was most suitable of the plants tested. Other cucurbits and also cotton plants are good hosts. Small Blue Hubbard squash plants were recommended by Waters (1943) for growing the aphids in the greenhouse or under special lights in the laboratory.

The spirea aphid, *Aphis spiraecola* Patch, has been used in insecticide testing. It may often be found on the tender terminal shoots of *Spirea, Viburnum,* or some other ornamental shrubs or trees on college campuses where it is conveniently obtained for indoor rearing. The infested shoots from outdoors may also be placed in vials of water and used in insecticide tests (Darley, 1931).

The apple aphid, *Aphis pomi* DeGeer, can be raised in the greenhouse on the tender terminal shoots of potted apple seedlings. It also thrives on the tender terminals of young, potted pear seedlings. A No. 00 artist's brush was used in moving the aphids (Harries and Mattson, 1963).

The cabbage aphid, *Brevicoryne brassicae* (L.), and the turnip aphid, *Rhopalosiphum pseudobrassicae* (Davis), were raised by the writer during the winter in the laboratory on turnip and ruta-baga plants. These were grown as needed from the stored roots which were set in soil in 4-inch pots or in No. 2 tin cans of quartz sand and watered with a complete nutrient solution. Fluorescent lights were used about 12 inches above the tops of the plants and were operated about 16 hours daily by an electric time switch. Temperature was held at about 72°F and relative humidity at 50%. A high proportion of wingless forms of both species was obtained under these conditions. The adult aphids were handled with a small artist's brush or with a glass suction tube applied to the insect's back.

REFERENCES

Auclair, J. L. (1963). Aphid feeding and nutrition. *Ann. Rev. Entomol.* **8**, 439–490.

Averill, A. W. (1945). Index to genera and species of food plants. *Maine Agr. Expt. Sta., Bull.* **393-S**.

Bergamin, J. (1954). Utilization of hydroponics in ecological studies of the cotton aphid. *Pan-Pacific Entomologist* **30**, 251–257.

Bodenheimer, F. S., and Swirski, E. (1957). "Aphoidea of the Middle East," 378 pp. Weismann Scientific Press, Jerusalem, Israel.

Bonnemaison, L. (1951). Contribution à l'étude des facteurs provoquant l'apparition des formes ailées et sexuées chez les Aphidinae. *Ann. Inst. Natl. Recherche Agron. Ann. Epiphyties* **C2**, 1–380.

Brittain, W. H. (1921). Some factors influencing the occurrence of alate forms in certain Aphididae. *Acadian Entomol. Soc. Proc.* **7**.

Buchner, P. (1953). "Endosymbiose der Tiere mit pflanzen Mikroorganismen." Birkhäuser, Basel.

Carter, W. (1962). "Insects in Relation to Plant Disease." Wiley, New York.

Cartier, J. J. (1960). Growth, reproduction, and longevity in one bio-type of the pea aphid, *Acyrthosiphon pisum* (Harris). *Can. Entomologist* **92**, 762–764.

Cook, P. P., and Sylvester, E. S. (1961). Influence of caging and transferring techniques on aphid mortality and virus transmission. *J. Econ. Entomol.* **54**, 101–103.

Darley, M. M. (1931). Some comparative tests with rotenone, nicotine, and pyrethrum. *J. Econ. Entomol.* **24**, 111–115.

Davidson, J. (1924). Factors which influence the appearance of sexes in plant lice. *Science* **59**, 364.

Davis, J. J. (1908). Studies on aphididae. *Ann. Entomol. Soc. Am.* **1**, 251–264.

Essig, E. O. (1926). "Insects of Western North America." Macmillan, New York.

Finney, G. L., Puttler, B., and Dawson, L. (1960). Rearing of three spotted alfalfa aphid parasites for mass release. *J. Econ. Entomol.* **53**, 655–659.

Friend, W. G. (1958). Nutritional requirements of phytophagous insects. *Ann. Rev. Entomol.* **3**, 57–74.

Galtsoff, P. S. (1937) *et al.* "Culture Methods for Invertebrate Animals." Cornell Univ. Press (Comstock), Ithaca, New York.

Gillette, C. P., and Taylor, E. P. (1908). A few orchard plant lice. *Colo. Agr. Expt. Sta., Bull.* **133.**

Hamilton, M. A. (1935). Further experiments on the artificial feeding of *Myzus persicae* (Sulzer). *Ann. Appl. Biol.* **22,** 243–258.

Harries, F. H. (1939). Some temperqture coefficients for insect oviposition. *Ann. Entomol. Soc. Am.* **32,** 758–776.

Harries, F. H. (1956). Variation in effectiveness of derris dusts against the pea aphid. *J. Econ. Entomol.* **49,** 363–367.

Harries, F. H., and Mattson, V. J. (1963). Effects of some antibiotics on three aphid species. *J. Econ. Entomol.* **56,** 412–414.

Haug, G. W. (1938). Rearing the coccinellid *Hippodamia convergens* Guer. on frozen aphids. *Ann. Entomol. Soc. Am.* **31,** 240–248.

Hille Ris Lambers, D. (1966). Polymorphism in Aphididae. *Ann. Rev. Entomol.* **11,** 47–78.

Hoyt, S. C., and Madsen, H. F. (1960). Dispersal behavior of the first instar nymphs of the woolly apple aphid. *Hilgardia* **30,** 267–299.

Johansen, C. A. (1952). Ph.D. Thesis, Cornell University, Ithaca, New York.

Kennedy, J. S., and Stroyan, H. L. G. (1959). Biology of aphids. *Ann. Rev. Entomol.* **4,** 139–160.

Lees, A. D. (1961). Clonal polymorphism in aphids. *Symp., Roy. Entomol. Soc. London,* **1,** 68–79.

Lal, R. (1952). Effect of malnutrition due to crowding and starvation of alate parents on the production of alate offspring among aphids. *Indian J. Entomol.* **24,** 11–19.

Lal, R. (1955). Effect of water content of aphids and their host plants on the appearance of alatae. *Indian J. Entomol.* **27,** 52–62.

Lipke, H., and Fraenkel, G. (1956). Insect nutrition. *Ann. Rev. Entomol.* **1,** 17–44.

MacGillivray, M. E. (1955). A method of rearing potato-infesting aphids throughout the year in the greenhouse. *Am. Potato J.* **32,** 67–68.

MacGillivray, M. E., and Anderson, G. B. (1957). Three useful insect cages. *Can. Entomologist* **89,** 43–46.

MacGillivray, M. E., and Anderson, G. B. (1958a). Development of four species of aphids (Homoptera) on potato. *Can. Entomologist* **90,** 148–155.

MacGillivray, M. E., and Anderson, G. B. (1958b). Production of apterous and alate viviparae of *Macrosiphum solanifolii* (Ashm.) (Homoptera: Aphididae). *Can. Entomologist* **90,** 241–245.

Maltais, J. B. (1959). Feeding the pea aphid, *Acyrthosiphum pisum* (Harris) (Homoptera: Aphididae), on plant cuttings in organic nutrient solutions. *Can. Entomologist* **41,** 336–340.

Maxwell, R. C., and Harwood, R. F. (1960). Increased reproduction of pea aphids on broad beans treated with 2,4-D. *Ann. Entomol. Soc. Am.* **53,** 199–205.

Michel, E. (1942). Beiträge zur Kenntnis von *Lachnus roboris* L., einer wichtigen Honigtauerzeugerin an der Eiche. *Z. Angew. Entomol.* **29,** 243–281.

Mittler, T. E. (1957). Studies on the feeding and nutrition of *Tuberolachnus salignus* (Gmelin) (Homoptera: Aphididae) 1. The uptake of phloem sap. *J. Exptl. Biol.* **34,** 334–341.

Mittler, T. E., and Dadd, R. H. (1962). Artificial feeding and rearing of the aphid, *Myzus persicae* (Sulzer) on a completely defined diet. *Nature* **195,** 404.

Mittler, T. E., and Sylvester, E. S. (1961). A comparison of the injury to alfalfa by the aphids, *Therioaphis maculata* and *Macrosiphum pisi. J. Econ. Entomol.* **54**, 615–621.

Patch, E. M. (1938). Food plant catalogue of the aphids of the world. *Maine Agr. Expt. Sta., Bull.* **393**.

Paschke, J. D., and Sylvester, E. S. (1957). Laboratory studies on the toxic effects of *Therioaphis maculata* (Buckton). *J. Econ. Entomol.* **50**, 742–748.

Peterson, A. (1953). "A Manual of Entomological Techniques." Edwards, Ann Arbor, Michigan.

Pletsch, D. J. (1937). An improved device for artificial feeding of aphids. *J. Econ. Entomol.* **30**, 211–212.

Potter, C., and Gillham, E. M. (1957). Effect of host plant on the resistance of *Acyrthosiphon pisum* (Harris) to insecticides. *Bull. Entomol. Res.* **48**, 317–322.

Reinhard, H. J. (1927). The influence of parentage, nutrition, temperature, and crowding on wing production in *Aphis gossypii* Glover. *Texas Agr. Expt. Sta., Bull.* **353**.

Richards, G. A., and Brooks, M. A. (1958). Internal symbiosis in insects. *Ann. Rev. Entomol.* **3**, 37–56.

Richardson, H. H., and Casanges, A. H. (1942). Studies of nicotine as an insect fumigant. *J. Econ. Entomol.* **35**, 242–246.

Shanks, C. H., and Gans, G. (1963). A portable electrically powered aspirator. *J. Econ. Entomol.* **56**, 237–238.

Shirck, F. H. (1960). Response of different strains of the green peach aphid to malathion. *J. Econ. Entomol.* **53**, 85–88.

Smith, R. H. (1923). The clover aphis: Biology, economic relationships, and control. *Idaho, Univ., Expt. Sta., Res. Bull.* **3**.

Staub, A. (1957). Eine Methode zur Zucht der Bohnenblattlaus, *Aphis fabae*, unter Laboratoriumbedingungen. *Mitt. Schweiz. Entomol. Ges.* **30**, 313–316.

Steinhaus, E. A. (1949). Principles of Insect Pathology. McGraw-Hill, New York.

Stone, P. V. (1940). Technique employed in producing uniform pea aphid stock. *U. S. Dept. Agr., Bur. Entomol. Plant Quarantine, E.T.* **170**.

Sun, Yun-Pei. (1960). "Methods of Testing Chemicals on Insects, " Vol. 2. Burgess, Minneapolis, Minnesota.

Sylvester, E. S. (1954). Insectary life history and apterous instar morphology of *Myzus persicae* (Sulzer). *Ann. Entomol. Soc. Am.* **47**, 397–406.

Sylvester, E. S. (1956). Beet yellows transmission by the green peach aphid. *J. Econ. Entomol.* **49**, 789–780.

Sylvester, E. S. (1964). Some effects of temperature on the transmission of cabbage mosaic virus by *Myzus persicae. J. Econ. Entomol.* **57**, 538–544.

Toba, H. H. (1964). Life-history studies of *Myzus persicae* in Hawaii. *J. Econ. Entomol.* **57**, 290–291.

Wadley, F. M. (1923). Factors affecting the proportion of alate and apterous forms of aphids. *Ann. Entomol. Soc. Am.* **16**, 279–303.

Wadley, F. M. (1931). Ecology of *Toxoptera graminum*, especially as to factors affecting importance in the northern United States. *Ann. Entomol. Soc. Am.* **24**, 325–395.

Waters, H. A. (1937). Methods and equipment for laboratory studies of insecticides. *J. Econ. Entomol.* **30**, 179–203.

Waters, H. A. (1943). In "Rearing Insects that Attack Plants," Publ. No. 20, Am. Assoc. Advanc. Sci., Washington, D. C.

White, W. S. (1946). The environmental conditions affecting the genetic mechanism of wing development in the chrysanthemum aphid. *Am. Naturalist* **80**, 245–270.

Chapter 31

Phytophagous Mites

STANLEY W. JACKLIN AND FLOYD F. SMITH

Entomology Research Division,
Agricultural Research Service,
U. S. Department of Agriculture,
Beltsville, Maryland

I. INTRODUCTION

Mites of the family Tetranychidae are among the most important agricultural pests. The common green two-spotted spider mite, *Tetranychus urticae* Koch (= *telarius*), has been especially important in our experience; consequently this chapter deals with that species almost exclusively.

Two-spotted mites have been studied from several different aspects. Because of their economic importance, control has received much attention (Smith, 1952). The advent of organophosphorus acaricides in 1947 was soon followed by the appearance of resistant strains (Smith and Fulton, 1951; Dittrich, 1963b). The mechanism of this resistance (Voss and Matsumura, 1964; Matsumura and Voss, 1964) and the genetics of resistance have been studied extensively (Taylor and Smith, 1956; Van Zon *et al.*, 1964; Dittrich, 1963a,b; Boudreaux, 1963). Spider mite nutrition and fecundity or susceptibility, especially as affected by host plant nutrition (Henneberry, 1962, 1964; Rodriguez, 1963) and other aspects of physiology (Mehrotra, 1961a,b; McEnroe, 1961; Polcik *et al.*, 1964), have also been studied.

II. ESTABLISHING THE COLONY

In the simplest sense, a colony is established by placing some mites, which may be offspring of a single virgin female, on a host plant. In this section we shall discuss methods of providing a clean food supply and some of the problems of maintaining isolated colonies.

A. Choosing the Food Plant

Lima bean (*Phaseolus limensis*) is probably the most popular food plant used in maintaining laboratory spider mite colonies. Snap bean (Black Valentine variety of *Phaseolus vulgaris*) was tried at Beltsville but discontinued because of being mildew-susceptible and having sharp, hooked hairs upon which the mites became impaled and died. From the lima bean varieties we chose Henderson's bush lima because its leaves are small enough to be used handily in leaf dip tests. They are also free of hooked hairs and are not subject to mildew infection under most conditions.

B. The Rooting Medium

We have discontinued growing our lima bean food plants in soil because of its weight, problems with uneven germination, with damping-off infection, and the need for sterilization. Most of these problems have been overcome by changing to the artificial rooting medium known as the Cornell Mixture. The batch recipe which we mix in a concrete mixer is as follows:

> 1 bushel finely broken sphagnum peat moss
> 1 bushel horticultural grade vermiculite
> ¼ lb 5-10-5 fertilizer
> ½ lb ground limestone (52% CaO, 2% MgO)
> 1 gm chelated iron

This medium is light in weight and its use results in better germination; there is little or no damping off as long as pots are sterilized before reusing. At one time we started quantities of seeds in sand under mist and transplanted them to soil in 4-inch pots, but we now plant directly in the pots, which is a saving in both seed and labor.

C. Growing the Food Plants

We plant beans on a weekly schedule. Five fungicide-treated bean seeds are planted per pot of rooting mixture. The plants emerge in about a week and are ready for feeding mites in another 2 to 3 weeks. The pots are watered daily and on one day every week, a commercial 15-15-15 soluble fertilizer is mixed with the water at 1.5 gm per gallon. About 200 pots per week are required to maintain and carry on the testing work associated with the five spider mite strains with which we work.

D. Clean Food Plants and Colony Isolation

Clean food plants cannot be grown on open greenhouse benches when spider mite colonies are kept under the same roof because the mites move about themselves, also they are easily carried on air currents and are transported on tools and on people's arms and clothing. It does little good to keep a small stock colony of a given mite strain well isolated if some of the fresh food plants placed in the colony harbor mites from another strain.

We are gradually shifting to a method of rearing mites that involves two levels of isolation security. The more secure isolation is reserved for the stock or nucleus colony of each strain. These colonies are not only well isolated themselves but the food plants for them are grown in isolation to ensure a mite-free supply. Mites for use in experiments are raised as a larger, satellite colony in a cloth-covered cage set over a water moat which has been started from the nucleus colony. The satellite colonies are not as positively isolated and they are fed with plants grown on open greenhouse benches. These mites are never returned to the nucleus colony.

The food plants for the maximum isolation nucleus colonies are grown in a tightly sealed greenhouse-like cage which is built on a bench in a closed-off compartment of the greenhouse. The cage is 4 × 10 ft, has an "A" roof, and is 38 inches high from the bench to the eaves. It is covered with transparent cellulose nitrate except for the front wall, which is made from two sliding storm windows that move horizontally. The natural light is supplemented by fluorescent and incandescent lights controlled by a time clock. Constant internal air movement is provided by a Variac-controlled circulating fan. A thermostatically controlled exhaust fan at one end of the cage works with a Fiberglas intake filter at the other end to bring the temperature within the cage near that of the greenhouse compartment which is heated in the winter and can be cooled in the summer.

The pots within the cage are watered automatically and it is not necessary to open the cage except to remove and replace pots.

The nucleus colony of each strain is held in a sealed plywood cabinet 32 × 32 inches and 42 inches high. Each cabinet is placed over a water moat on a bench, each in a separate closed-off greenhouse compartment. Each colony is constantly lighted by a bank of 4 fluorescent tubes 24 inches long suspended from the ceiling within the cabinet. Air intakes covered with fine mesh screen are cut into each cabinet near its lower edge and a constantly operating exhaust fan is located in the ceiling. Just as in the method for rearing food plants in isolation, the cabinet assumes the room temperature, the pots are watered automatically by a time switch and a solenoid valve which controls the flow of water through small plastic tubes leading to each pot in the cabinet. Entry into the cabinet is not required frequently. The pan for the water moat and the plywood cabinet with equipment for ventilating, lighting, and watering the plants costs approximately $150.

E. OTHER METHODS OF REARING

The methods as outlined are necessary for maintaining several strains of mites in greenhouses where other projects are underway. It is possible, however, to grow large numbers of mites at a very reasonable cost. Naegele and McEnroe (1963) have reported on mass producing spider mites for a little over $.01 per hundred mites.

Artificial diets have not yet proved practical for rearing spider mites even though considerable progress has been made (Rodriguez, 1963).

REFERENCES

Boudreaux, H. B. (1963). Acarine genetics. *Proc. 1st Intern. Congr. Acarology, Fort Collins, Colorado, 1962* pp. 284–287.

Dittrich, V. (1963a). Genetics and dynamics of organophosphate-resistance in strains of *Tetranychus urticae* K. (= *telarius*). *In* "Recent Advances in Acarology" Vol. I, pp. 239–247. Cornell Univ. Press, Ithaca, New York.

Dittrich, V. (1963b). Investigation on OP resistance of two genetically differing populations of *Tetranychus urticae* K. *Entomol. Exptl. Appl.* **6**, 10–20.

Henneberry, T. J. (1962). The effect of host-plant nitrogen supply and age of leaf tissue on the fecundity of the two-spotted spider mite. *J. Econ. Entomol.* **55**, 617–618.

Henneberry, T. J. (1964). Effect of host plant nutrition on susceptibility to malathion of two strains of two-spotted spider mites. *J. Econ. Entomol.* **57**, 813–815.

McEnroe, W. D. (1961). Control of water loss by the two-spotted spider mite (*Tetranychus telarius*). *Ann. Entomol. Soc. Am.* **54**, 833–887.

Matsumura, F., and Voss, G. (1964). Mechanism of malathion and parathion resistance in the two-spotted spider mite *Tetranychus urticae. J. Econ. Entomol.* **57,** 911–917.

Mehrotra, K. N. (1961a). Carbohydrate metabolism in the two-spotted spider mite, *Tetranychus telarius* L. I. Hexose monophosphate cycle. *Comp. Biochem. Physiol.* **3,** 184–198.

Mehrotra, K. N. (1961b). The occurrence of acetylcholine in the two-spotted mite, *Tetranychus telarius* L. *J. Insect Physiol.* **6,** 180–184.

Naegele, J. A., and McEnroe, W. D. (1963). Mass rearing of the two-spotted spider mite (*Tetranychus telarius* L.). *In* "Recent Advances in Acarology" (J. A. Naegele, ed.), Vol. I, pp. 191–192. Cornell Univ. Press, Ithaca, New York.

Polcik, B., Nowosielski, J., and Naegele, J. A. (1964). Daily sensitivity rhythm of the two-spotted spider mite, *Tetranychus urticae,* to DDVP. *Science* **145,** 405–406.

Rodriguez, J. G. (1963). Nutritional studies in the Acarina. *Proc. 1st Intern. Congr. Acarology, Fort Collins, Colorado, 1962* pp. 324–337.

Smith, F. F. (1952). Spider mites and resistance. Insects. *Yearbook Agr. (U. S. Dept. Agr.)* pp. 652–656.

Smith, F. F., and Fulton, R. A. (1951). Two-spotted spider mite resistance to aerosols. *J. Econ. Entomol.* **44,** 229–233.

Taylor, E. A., and Smith, F. F. (1956). Transmission of resistance between strains of two-spotted spider mites. *J. Econ. Entomol.* **49,** 858–859.

Van Zon, A. Q., Overmeer, W. P. J., and Helle, W. (1964). Resistance to Tedion in haploid and diploid offspring of *Tetranychus urticae* Koch. *Entomol. Exptl. Appl.* **7,** 270–276.

Voss, G., and Matsumura, F. (1964). Resistance to organophosphorus compounds in the two-spotted spider mite: Two different mechanisms of resistance. *Nature* **202,** 319–320.

Chapter 32

Coneworms

EDWARD P. MERKEL AND CARL W. FATZINGER

Southeastern Forest Experiment Station,
Forest Service,
U. S. Department of Agriculture,
Olustee, Florida

The larvae of *Dioryctria abietella* (D. and S.) and *Dioryctria amatella* (Hulst) feed destructively on the flowers, shoots, and cones of slash pine, *Pinus elliottii* Engelm., and longleaf pine, *P. palustris* Mill., in the coastal plain region of the southeastern United States.

Continuous cultures of *D. abietella* have been maintained at the U. S. Forest Service, Naval Stores and Timber Production Laboratory at Olustee, Florida, by a rearing method developed by Ebel (1959). In 1963, a method of rearing *D. amatella* was developed at this same laboratory. Although the present rearing methods are essentially the same as those described by Ebel (1959), the authors have included additions and innovations which have increased the efficiency and success of rearing.

I. REARING METHOD FOR *DIORYCTRIA ABIETELLA*

The original culture of *D. abietella* was started with moths obtained by storing slash pine cones infested with the larvae until the moths emerged. The larvae are mainly found in May within diseased [*Cronartium strobilinum* (Arth.) Hedgc. and Hahn] first-

451

A

FIG. 1A. For legend see opposite page.

year cones, and from July through August in nearly mature cones in northeast Florida.

Moths are mated in copper or aluminum screen cages (Fig. 1) 1 ft wide by 1 ft high by 1 ft long. Usually about 30 male and 30 female moths are placed in a cage. Sugar water must be provided if the females are to lay viable eggs. The sugar water is prepared by diluting 1 part of saturated sucrose-water solution with 1 part distilled water. The sugar water is placed in a shell vial and a wick made of twisted cheesecloth is inserted into the vial so that it projects slightly above the top of the vial and forms a moist feeding pad (Fig. 1). Mating is assured if the males and females are left in the breeding cage for 2 days. Females are removed from the breed-

B

FIG. 1. Two types of mating cages: (A) with sliding glass door and (B) with sliding galvanized iron door. Note glass vials containing sugar water for moth feeding. Cage, as in (A) above, is also used to hold cocoons for moth emergence.

ing cage on the third day and isolated for oviposition. The oviposition container consists of a half-pint Mason jar (Fig. 2). A 9-cm filter paper disc is placed in the bottom of the jar and is moistened with water. Next, a 1- by 3-inch strip of 32-mesh Saran plastic screen is placed with one narrow edge resting on the bottom center of the jar and the other end resting against the side of the jar. The egg strip is not changed during the oviposition period. Two female moths are isolated in each jar and a disc of 32-mesh Saran fabric, held in place by a screw-on Mason jar lid, is used to cover the jar. Egg laying begins during the first day of isolation and is completed within 7 days. Room temperature is maintained between 21° and 24°C during mating and oviposition.

If the eggs are fertile, they will turn from a pale yellow color to a bright orange color within 24 hours after deposition when reared at 21°C. The plastic screen strips with the fertile eggs are transferred from the oviposition jars to covered Petri dishes, where they are placed on moist filter paper. Hatching occurs from 3 to 5 days after deposition at a constant temperature of 21°C. One egg strip,

FIG. 2. Egg-laying jar with isolated female ovipositing on plastic screen or cheese-cloth strip. Eggs are also laid commonly on plastic screen jar cover.

containing 50 to 100 eggs, is placed in each hatching dish to facilitate later transfer of larvae to their food. To prevent the newly emerged larvae from wandering in search of food, individual scales from first-year cones are scattered sparsely over the egg strip in the hatching dishes.

The first-instar larvae are now ready to be transferred to more permanent food for development. The most suitable natural larval food has been first-year slash and longleaf pine cones collected from April to December and young second-year cones collected from January to March in northeast Florida. Larvae can be reared on the larger second-year cones collected in March and April, but these cones are more cumbersome to handle and desiccate more rapidly than the first-year cones. The conelets are gathered from

Fig. 3. Laboratory stock colony of *Dioryctria abietella* larvae are reared in Petri dishes. Larvae form cocoons from brown frass pellets expelled from hollowed-out cone.

recently felled trees in timber harvest areas. A portion of one side of each conelet is sliced superficially to provide a flat surface upon which the conelet can rest. Then the cones are dipped in melted paraffin. The waxed cones will remain suitable for food up to 3 months if refrigerated at 5°C.

Four waxed conelets or cone halves are placed on moist filter paper in a covered Petri dish (Fig. 3). A shallow slice is made through the paraffin coating on the flat surface of the cone. The newly hatched larvae are then transferred from the hatching dishes to the rearing dishes with a small moistened sable brush. One larva is placed on each cone. Larval entry into the cone is facilitated by the slit cut into the underside of the cone. Cannibalism among larvae has not been observed when each larva is placed with its own cone.

After 10 to 12 days the cones are usually completely hollowed out and a fresh waxed cone is placed beside each hollowed-out cone. Two first-year cones are sufficient food for each larva to complete development. The filter paper discs in the rearing dishes are usually moistened at 5- or 7-day intervals until the larvae leave the cones and construct frass-covered pupal chambers.

Saprophytic fungi and molds may develop on the cones, particularly if the filter papers are moistened too frequently. Excessive contamination by these organisms lowers the larval survival and causes variation in the size of different larvae of the same age. Thorough washing and dry-heat sterilization of the rearing dishes, prior to the rearing of new colonies, increase the survival from first-instar larvae to adults.

Standard procedure has been to maintain a stock culture of 200 or 300 larvae in the individual Petri dish rearing containers. This practice reduces the chances of a harmful organism from destroying the culture completely since the organism would be confined to the Petri dish in which it became established.

When large numbers of larvae or adults are needed for experimental purposes, the larvae can be reared in large, rectangular, glass baking dishes (Fig. 4) with dimensions 13 inches wide by 9 inches long by 2 inches high. From 25 to 50 larvae can be reared per dish. Paper toweling is used in place of filter paper to cover the bottom of the baking dishes. Cones and larvae are then added as in the case of the Petri dishes. The baking dishes are then covered with a pane of window glass which has been cut to project about 1 inch beyond the sides of the dish.

Larvae of D. abietella invariably leave their food to pupate. The frass-covered cocoons are formed either under the hollowed out cones or adjacent to them. When most of the larvae have spun cocoons, the filter papers, with the cocoons adhering to them, are transferred to wire screen cages (Fig. 1) for moth emergence. When moths begin to emerge they are removed daily from the emergence cages and transferred to the mating cages. Both the moth emergence and mating cages have glass or metal doors which slide vertically in lateral grooves. To prevent the moths from escaping while the cage door is raised, during the transfer of moths, a small white fluorescent lamp is held against the end of the cage opposite the door in a dark room. The moths will remain quietly clinging to the sides of the cage and can easily be caught individually in small vials for transfer either to the mating cage or to the oviposition jars.

Merkel (1962) found that larvae of D. abietella, reared in the laboratory, as described above, had five instars based on width of head capsules.

As with most insects, temperature was found to have a pronounced effect on the rate of development of D. abietella. Two series of larvae were reared in separate constant temperature cabinets: one at 20°–

FIG. 4. Colonies of *Dioryctria abietella* larvae, for insecticide tests and other research, are reared in larger glass baking dishes, 50 larvae per dish.

21°C, the other at 29°–30°C. The rearing containers were covered
Petri dishes and larval food was first-year slash pine cones. Relative humidity was uncontrolled but ranged between 50 and 80%
within the cabinets. The total developmental time from hatching to
moth emergence averaged 49 days at 20°–21°C and averaged 24
days at 29°–30°C.

When larvae were reared in an outdoor, screened insectary,
subject to normal fluctuating temperature, humidity, and light,
the average duration from hatching to moth emergence was as
follows: July–August, 33 days; August–September, 37 days; September–November, 57 days; and December–April, 137 days.

TABLE I

SUMMARY OF *Dioryctria abietella* SURVIVAL FROM FIRST-INSTAR LARVA TO
ADULT UNDER DIFFERENT REARING CONDITIONS AT
OLUSTEE, FLORIDA—1958 TO 1964

	Rearing location			
	Incubator (20°–21°C, constant)		Laboratory (20°–30°C, variable)	
Sterile treatment	Petri dish (%)	Baking dish (%)	Petri dish (%)	Baking dish (%)
Sterilized[a]	66.3	59.2	63.4	60.3
Not sterilized	41.9	44.5	42.8	40.0
Average	49.3	50.4	58.9	57.7

[a] Dishes placed in dry-heat oven at 80°C for 1 hour.

Eighty-six consecutive generations of *D. abietella* were reared
from November 1958 to November 1964. Survival from first-instar
larvae to adults depended on where the colonies were reared, i.e.,
in incubator or laboratory room, and whether or not the glass rearing
containers were dry-heat sterilized (Table I). The differences in
survival between rearing in Petri dishes (Fig. 3) and baking dishes
(Fig. 4) were not significant for a given rearing location. However,
survival in sterilized dishes averaged 15 to 20% higher than in non-
sterilized dishes, irrespective of the rearing location or type of
rearing dish.

II. REARING METHOD FOR *DIORYCTRIA AMATELLA*

Dioryctria amatella can be reared by a method somewhat analogous to the rearing method for *D. abietella*. However, in labora-

tory rearings, the fecundity of this moth is much lower than that of *D. abietella*.

The larvae are collected from infested fusiform rust [*Cronartium fusiforme* (A. and K.) Hedgc. and Hunt] cankers in young slash pine plantations in northern Florida by cutting into their galleries and removing them with a small brush. Suitable rearing food for the larvae is provided by first- and second-year slash pine or longleaf pine cones which are prepared and placed in Petri dishes with the larvae in the same manner as described above for *D. abietella*. If the cones collected for rearing are too large to be placed in Petri dishes, ½-pint Mason jars may be substituted for the Petri dish bottom, using a Petri dish top for a lid.

The development time for the larvae varies greatly from culture to culture when the larvae are obtained fresh from the field. Some of these larvae may appear to be in a state of aestivation while others feed continuously and pupate within a relatively short time. However, after an even-aged culture is obtained from eggs deposited by wild moths, the larval stage persists for approximately 35 days at room temperature during which time some larvae pass through five instars and others through six instars.

Under field conditions pupation generally occurs within the infested material. However, in laboratory rearings the majority of the larvae leave the food material and pupate within silken cocoons covered with brown frass. These pupae are then collected and placed on moist vermiculite in the bottom half of a Petri dish. The Petri dish is then placed within a screen cage 1 ft wide by 1 ft high by 1 ft deep to await emergence. The pupal period lasts for about 6 days at room temperature.

Upon emergence of the first moth, a second Petri dish bottom containing absorbent cotton is placed in the cage. The cotton is kept saturated with a sugar-water solution by means of a glass tube extending to the cotton from outside the cage. This prevents undue disturbance of the moths while replenishing the solution each day. For egg deposition, a newly cut piece of a slash pine branch (6 inches long and approximately 2 inches in diameter) containing a small fusiform rust canker is placed on the floor of the cage.

The cage is then placed in a constant temperature cabinet maintained at 25°C for 7 days. During this time, the emerging moths are given a light period of 11½ hours per day, using a 15-watt Gro-Lux fluorescent lamp, and water is sprayed into the cage with a hand atomizer (connected to a compressed air supply) for approximately 2 minutes every 2 hours from 8:00 A.M. to 4:00 P.M. each day.

As the moths emerge, they feed on the sugar water, mate, and the females deposit their eggs on the freshly cut surface and under the bark scales of the slash pine branch. Approximately 30 eggs are deposited by each female. A 2-inch by 8-inch by ½-inch balsa wood slab with overlapping pieces of green blotter paper stapled to the top surface may be substituted for the slash pine branch canker, but the egg recovery is reduced to approximately 6 eggs per female. The eggs are deposited under the edges of the blotter paper.

At the end of the 7-day period, the branch is removed from the cage and is placed within a white, 1-quart, cylindrical paper container. After 2 or 3 days, the hatched larvae can be found crawling on the inner walls of the container and are removed daily with a small artist's brush.

The newly emerged larvae are then placed in new rearing containers and the rearing method is continued for the next generation.

REFERENCES

Ebel, B. H. (1959). Laboratory rearing of a pine cone insect, *Dioryctria abietella* (D. & S.). *J. Econ. Entomol.* **52**, 561–564.

Merkel, E. P. (1962). The number of larval instars of *Dioryctria abietella* (D. and S.) (Lepidoptera: Phycitidae) in Florida. *Can. Entomologist* **94**, 1005–1007.

Chapter 33

Cabbage Loopers

T. J. Henneberry and A. N. Kishaba

Entomology Research Division,
Agricultural Research Service,
U. S. Department of Agriculture,
Riverside, California

I. INTRODUCTION

Laboratory rearing of insects is an integral part of most entomological programs. A continuous supply of insects for experimentation facilitates progress in many research areas and is essential in some applied studies, such as those concerned with sterility approaches to insect control, and the production of insect pathogens, parasites, and predators. With increased interest in these areas of entomological study, the need for efficient insect-rearing procedures has become apparent. Recent advances in the field of insect nutrition have provided the basic essentials for the formulation of artificial diets for many phytophagous insect species heretofore difficult to maintain in artificial culture.

The cabbage looper, *Trichoplusia ni* (Hübner), has been consistently rated as one of the most important economic insect pests in various parts of the United States. Little was known of the basic

TABLE I

DEVELOPMENTAL PERIODS OF VARIOUS STAGES OF THE CABBAGE LOOPER UNDER
LABORATORY CONDITIONS AS REPORTED BY DIFFERENT AUTHORS

Data extracted from	Rearing temperature (°C)	Larval diet	Sex	Number of days as				Pupal weight
				Egg	Larva	Prepupa	Pupa	
McEwen and Hervey (1960)	24	Broccoli	♂[a]	3.0	9–11.0	—	8.0	233.0
			♀					217.0
Atkins (1960)	27	Citrus	[a]	4.0	14.0	—	7.6	—
Shorey et al. (1962)	14	Bean	♂	11.7	44.0	2.9	36.4	286.0
			♀	—	42.8	3.0	34.0	268.0
	23	Bean	♂	4.8	17.5	0.8	8.8	263.0
			♀	—	16.9	0.9	7.6	215.0
		Cabbage	♂	—	19.3	0.6	9.0	228.0
			♀	—	20.0	0.8	8.9	184.0
	32	Bean	♂	2.3	15.1	0.3	6.1	201.0
			♀	—	14.6	0.4	5.4	208.0
Shorey (1963b)	27	Artificial bean diet	♂[a]	—	14.9	—	7.2	224.0
			♀					206.0
Shorey and Hale (1965)	27	Modified artificial bean diet	♂	3.2	14.8	—	8.9	229.0
			♀	—	14.3	—	8.3	212.0
Getzin (1962)	25	Artificial diet	[a]	3.0	12.0	—	8.0	220.0
Ignoffo (1963)	29	Artificial diet	♂[a]	2.3	8.1	1.1	7.6	243.6
			♀					235.0
Henneberry and Kishaba (1966)	24	Ignoffo's modified diet	♂[a]	3.0	9.0	—	7.0	266.0
			♀					251.0

[a] Sex not designated or only for pupal weight.

biology of the species until the development of laboratory rearing methods. Early attempts to rear the cabbage looper were unsuccessful due to the repeated occurrence of disease epizootics. McEwen and Hervey (1960) overcame the problem by isolation, careful temperature control, rearing small numbers of insects per unit, proper sanitation, and the liberal use of antimicrobial agents. Subsequent to these developments, the amount of pertinent biological information concerning the cabbage looper has increased (Table I).

The most significant recent advance in cabbage looper rearing was the development of satisfactory artificial rearing media (Getzin, 1962; Ignoffo, 1963; Shorey, 1963b; Shorey and Hale, 1965). The use of these diets facilitates larval rearing by (1) reducing the probability of disease contamination; (2) dietary standardization; (3) continuous production, independent of season, geographical location, or the insect's natural food source; and (4) reduced space requirements.

The cabbage looper rearing methods presented herein are a compilation of techniques and methods developed by a number of investigators and supplemented by the authors.

II. LABORATORY SANITATION

The occurrence of disease is the most serious obstacle to continuous laboratory rearing of the cabbage looper. In many research programs combined laboratory and field activities increase the number of potential sources of contamination. Where possible, rearing facilities should be isolated from other work areas, and all laboratory work benches should be surface-sterilized routinely with a germicidal solution before and after use. The authors find 0.5% sodium hypochlorite, as recommended by Ignoffo and Dutky (1963), excellent for this purpose. Effective decontamination of equipment that cannot be autoclaved can be accomplished by immersion in sodium hypochlorite (McEwen and Hervey, 1960). Sterilization of all rearing equipment to prevent contamination is essential.

III. FACTORS AFFECTING OVIPOSITION

Large numbers of cabbage looper eggs are relatively easy to obtain. Each mated female, under the proper environmental conditions, can produce 600 to 800 eggs during her life. Egg viability from mated females ranges from 60 to 95% and averages about 80%. Moth longevity and female fecundity and oviposition may be influenced by diet, temperature and humidity conditions, mating, and moth density in oviposition cages.

A. MOTH DIET

Adult food is necessary for maximum cabbage looper longevity and reproduction. Moths fed a diet of water alone may live 6 to 8 days but mated females lay few viable eggs. Moths have been maintained successfully on water solutions containing various concentrations of sucrose or honey. The authors have found 10% sucrose solution an adequate diet, resulting in mean male and female longevities of 15 and 11 days, respectively. Females produced an average of 731 eggs and 92% were viable. A combination of 5% each of sugar and honey is also acceptable. Sucrose solutions of 4 to 5% or less generally result in reduced oviposition and longevity of females (Shorey, 1963a) and males.

B. TEMPERATURE AND HUMIDITY CONDITIONS

High oviposition rates have been obtained at temperatures of 24° to 29°C (McEwen and Hervey, 1960; Getzin, 1962; Shorey *et al.,* 1962; Shorey, 1963a, 1964a) and 30 to 50% relative humidity (Shorey, 1964a). The precise minimum or maximum temperatures at which cabbage looper oviposition occurs are not known. However, reduced oviposition occurs at temperatures of 19°C and below or when temperatures of 35°C or higher exist in the laboratory for extended periods.

High humidity conditions enhance oviposition and apparently account for the suitability of moist substrates for oviposition sites simply because of the moist environment around them (Shorey, 1964a).

C. MATING AND SEX RATIO

Equal numbers of males and females in cages result in excellent mating and oviposition, but mating can be increased by increasing the male to female ratio (Table II). The majority of females mate the first time on nights 2 and 3 of adult life. In laboratory cultures females may mate from 0 to 6 times but normally average 2 matings during their lives. Increases in oviposition occur with increased mating frequency (Shorey, 1963a). Cabbage looper mating conditions are easier to obtain in the laboratory than is the case for some other noctuid moths (Callahan, 1962). Successful copulation will occur in cages with only 35 cc of available volume per moth; visual or auditory stimuli do not appear necessary (Shorey, 1964b).

TABLE II

PERCENT OF CABBAGE LOOPER FEMALES MATING IN 48 OR 72 HOURS WITH
VARIOUS MALE TO FEMALE RATIOS

Male to female ratio	Female mating (%)	
	48 hours	72 hours
0.25:1	35	35
0.5:1	37	41
1:1	52	74
2:1	85	89
4:1	83	100

Males, except for the first night of adult life, will successfully transfer a spermatophore each night if a receptive female is available (Shorey, 1964b).

D. OVIPOSITION CAGE

Efficient cabbage looper oviposition cages eliminating natural plant material and thereby excluding a potential source of disease contamination were designed by Ignoffo (1963, 1964). The cages, with the exception of the floors and tops, were covered with potential oviposition substrate that was readily accessible for egg collection without handling the insects.

The component parts of a cage similar to that designed by Ignoffo (1963) are shown in Fig. 1. The cylindrical body of the cage (a), constructed of ¼-inch hardware cloth, is 6 inches in diameter by 11 inches high. The top of the cage (b) is a circular piece of 16-mesh wire screen, 6 inches in diameter, which is soldered to the cylindrical cage body. A hole in the center of the top, large enough to accommodate a No. 5 rubber stopper, provides for the introduction of moths. The open bottom of the cage sets on an 8-inch diameter cake pan (c) with a 4-inch diameter hole cut out in the center. A 1-pint Mason jar top (d), with insert removed, is soldered along the periphery of the hole to the bottom surface of the cake pan. A Mason jar (e) filled with sucrose solution and equipped with a Cellucotton wick supported on an 8-inch high cylinder of ¼-inch hardware cloth (f) is screwed into place to provide adult food and high humidity conditions within the cage. These feeders require little attention and have been more efficient than other types. Moths appear to accept food more readily from this feeder than they do from absorbent material wetted with sucrose solution and placed on top of the cage. The cage body is held in place on the cake pan with two 4-inch wire springs (g).

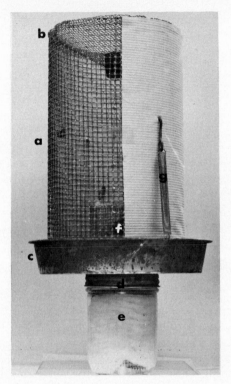

FIG. 1. Oviposition cage.

1. Oviposition Substrate

Cabbage looper females oviposit on substrates of leaf tissue, paper toweling, filter paper, wax paper (Callahan, 1962; Ignoffo, 1963; Shorey, 1964a), and a variety of other materials. Mated females, as in the case of 14 other noctuid species studied by Callahan (1962), lay their eggs under minimum required environmental conditions, once the inherent physiological conditions leading to oviposition reach a maximum. Oviposition may be inhibited for extended periods, but is rarely prevented under laboratory conditions once mating has occurred.

Paper toweling is well suited as an oviposition substrate for the requirements of the oviposition cage described. It is economical, easy to handle, and possesses a high degree of wet strength, an important feature in subsequent handling procedures. Other substrates, such as sheet plastic and wax paper, are inferior toweling for the present requirements. The toweling is wrapped around the cage, held in place with Scotch tape, and wetted to ensure close contact with the cage on drying (Ignoffo, 1963). If given a choice, females deposit more eggs on yellow than on oviposition substrates of other colors, and the preferred surface texture may vary under different humidity conditions (Shorey, 1964a). With no choice, yellow, white or blue paper toweling has been used without apparent effect on oviposition.

The substrate is not replaced until the third or fourth day and daily thereafter for the collection of eggs. Peak egg production normally occurs between days 3 and 6. Most of the egg production occurs within the first 8 to 10 days. No advantage is gained by holding moths in an oviposition cage for longer periods.

Good results are obtained when cages are stocked with 1- to 2-day-old moths. The moths are removed and the cage restocked at weekly intervals. Before reuse the cages are surface sterilized in 0.5% sodium hypochlorite for 1 hour or autoclaved.

2. Adult Density

The number of adult moths per oviposition cage of the dimensions described should not exceed 24 to 30 pairs. This allows 85 to 100 cc of volume per moth. Crowding reduces oviposition and increases mortality. As much as 8,000 to 10,000 eggs are recovered per week from 24 pairs. When the moth density is increased to 48 pairs per cage, fewer eggs per female are produced, and moth mortality is increased. The number of moths per cage does not affect mating or egg viability.

E. OTHER OVIPOSITION CAGES

Cardboard or plastic cartons lined with paper toweling (Ignoffo, (1963) or blotting paper (Shorey and Hale, 1965) have also been used successfully as cabbage looper oviposition cages. Shorey and Hale (1965) find that good results are obtained with approximately 10 pairs of moths in 1-gal cylindrical cardboard cartons equipped with a screen top and a 4-ounce bottle containing a paper-towel wick in 8% sucrose solution. The inside walls of the container and the feeding bottle are covered with blotting paper as an oviposition substrate. This method has been used to collect eggs from at least eight noctuid species in addition to the cabbage looper. The oviposition cartons can be discarded after use, eliminating a possible source of disease contamination and the cost of maintenance. However, the oviposition substrate is less accessible than that from the screen-type cages for recovery of eggs without handling or inactivating the moths.

Wooden frame cages covered with 14- to 16-mesh wire screen have proved efficient when eggs are collected on natural leaf oviposition substrates. Cages from 12 (Shorey, 1963a) to 15 inches (McEwen and Hervey, 1960) in all dimensions to 16 inches square by 19 (Getzin, 1962) or 30 inches long (Shorey et al., 1962) have been used. These may be equipped with a hinged door or muslin sleeve for easy access to the interior; a removable bottom may have some advantage in cleaning and maintenance (McEwen and Hervey, 1960).

Excised plant leaves with petioles set in water-filled containers, or small potted plants of a suitable type, are placed in the cage for egg collection. Leaves of broccoli (McEwen and Hervey, 1960; Getzin, 1962), young cabbage (Shorey et al., 1962), Brussels sprout (Paschke, 1964), lima bean, and cotton (Shorey, 1964a) plants have proved acceptable to cabbage looper females for oviposition.

IV. HANDLING EGGS

Cabbage looper eggs hatch in 2 to 3 days at temperatures of 24° to 29°C. Frequently it is advantageous to stockpile a number of eggs to supplement current production and facilitate the regulation of rearing schedules. Eggs 1 to 2 days old may be stored for up to 1 week at 10°C without adverse effects on egg hatch, larval survival, pupal yields, or subsequent adult mating and oviposition. Lower temperatures or longer storage periods may result in reduced egg hatch. Development at 10°C is suppressed but not completely stopped. Three-day-old eggs stored at 10°C will hatch at that temperature within 7 days. Eggs that are 1 or 2 days old when stored do not hatch during the 7-day storage period, but between days 7 and 14 the developing larvae can be observed within the chorion.

A. Egg Sterilization

Sterilization of eggs is recommended as a routine part of any cabbage looper rearing procedure. Several investigators (Getzin, 1962; Ignoffo, 1963, 1964; Paschke, 1964) have regarded this step as one of the most important in preventing or reducing the incidence of nuclear polyhedrosis in laboratory cultures of the cabbage looper.

1. Sodium Hypochlorite Methods

Two effective methods of sterilizing cabbage looper eggs with sodium hypochlorite are available. The first (Getzin, 1962), consists of washing eggs in 0.05% sodium hypochlorite containing 0.02% Triton X-100 for 1 hour. The eggs are then placed on a Büchner funnel, washed with water, and incubated to hatching at 25°C in a Petri dish on moist filter paper. The second method (Ignoffo, 1963; Ignoffo and Dutky, 1963) consists of soaking the eggs in 0.3% sodium hypochlorite for 5 minutes, followed by rinses with sodium thiosulfite and sterile distilled water. The eggs are incubated in a Petri dish on moist filter paper to hatching at 29°C.

Both sodium hypochlorite methods result in partial or total removal of the chorion from the eggs. These are subsequently subject to dessication and care must be taken to assure high humidity and careful temperature control during embryonic development if large numbers of larvae are to be recovered.

2. *Formaldehyde Method*

Sterilization of eggs in formaldehyde also effectively reduces the occurrence of disease. Eggs are left intact, no special care during embryonic development is necessary, and larval rearing containers can be infested with eggs. This saves considerable time and eliminates possible contamination in handling larvae.

Formaldehyde sterilization is accomplished as follows: The toweling oviposition substrate with eggs is removed from the cage and placed for 45 minutes in a $10 \times 18 \times 4$ inch porcelain tray containing 10% formaldehyde. The time has been varied up to 1 hour without adverse effects. The formaldehyde is poured from the tray and replaced with tap water. A small diameter hose attached to a water faucet is placed in the water-filled tray, which is set in a sink, and water is allowed to run slowly for 1 hour. If many egg sheets are handled, a photographic print washer may facilitate rinsing. The toweling with eggs is then removed and allowed to air-dry.

The value of the formaldehyde treatment in preventing disease was determined by dipping cabbage looper eggs in a virus suspension containing 10^6 polyhedra per ml and sterilizing with formaldehyde as described. Checks were dipped in the virus suspension but not sterilized. No diseased larvae developed from eggs sterilized in formaldehyde, as compared to 99% diseased larvae when eggs were not sterilized. The larvae from formaldehyde-sterilized eggs developed normally and no effect on pupation or subsequent adult oviposition occurred.

V. LARVAL REARING

Before the development of egg sterilization techniques high larval mortality resulting from disease severely limited rearing. With the use of egg sterilization methods very low larval mortality occurs. Prevention of disease contamination, however, remains a serious consideration in the rearing technique. Contaminated larvae may transmit the virus to healthy larvae in numerous ways and the probability of disease transmission is greater with increased larval density (Jaques, 1962). One of the most successful methods to protect against complete loss of laboratory cultures from disease has been the use of small rearing units with relatively few insects per unit. In most instances of disease contamination, a few individual containers with diseased insects are discarded without significantly affecting the rearing program.

In spite of elaborate precautions and under the most extreme sanitary measures, occasional disease contamination may occur. For continued rearing it is essential that immediate action be taken. A method of reducing disease in these instances which has given good results is as follows: Individual moth pairs are isolated in 1-pint ice cream carton oviposition cages lined with blotting paper and equipped with sterile 1-dram vial feeders containing sterile sucrose solution. All eggs obtained on blotters are surface-sterilized with 10% formaldehyde as described above. The larval rearing containers are appropriately marked to identify the eggs obtained from each isolated pair.

With the occurrence of disease in any rearing container, all larvae from a given pair can be discarded. On at least two occasions this method has eliminated or reduced the incidence of disease to extremely low levels in one generation. This method may also be useful in establishing a colony from wild moths collected from the field.

A. Artificial Diets

Several artificial diets have been developed for continuous cabbage looper rearing (Getzin, 1962; Ignoffo, 1963; Shorey, 1963b; Shorey and Hale, 1965). The ingredients in each of these diets are shown in Table III. The reader is urged to consult the original publications for the specific details of preparation and use.

The authors of the present paper use the diet formulated by Ignoffo (1963) with minor changes. These are (1) substitution of alfalfa leaf meal for cotton leaf stock, (2) the use of methyl p-hydroxybenzoate and sorbic acid as mold inhibitors, (3) the use of crude casein, and (4) the use of twice as much vitamin mixture. The ingredients, the amounts necessary, and method of preparing approximately 10 gallons of this medium are listed below.

TABLE III

WEIGHTS OF INGREDIENTS USED IN THE FORMULATION OF 100 MILLILITERS OF
ARTIFICIAL CABBAGE LOOPER LARVAL DIETS

Ingredient	Diet[a] formulated by			
	Getzin (1962)	Ignoffo (1963)	Shorey (1963b)	Shorey and Hale (1965)
Agar	2.47	2.37	1.27	1.41
Cabbage tissue	1.78[b]	—	—	—
Cotton leaf stock	—	1.43	—	—
Lima beans	—	—	11.39[b]	—
Pinto beans	—	—	—	8.47[b]
Water	81.68	81.00	83.54	85.67
Casein	3.46	3.32	—	—
Sucrose	3.46	3.32	—	—
Wheat germ	2.96	2.85	—	—
Wesson's salts	0.98	0.95	—	—
Alphacel	—	0.43	—	—
Sodium alginate	0.02	—	—	—
Potassium hydroxide	—	0.10	—	—
Ascorbic acid	0.49	0.39	0.32	0.35
Brewer's yeast	—	—	3.16	3.50
Choline chloride	0.10	0.10	—	—
Cholesterol	0.29	—	—	—
Inositol	0.02	—	—	—
Methyl p-hydroxybenzoate	—	0.13	0.32	0.22
Sorbic acid	0.11	—	—	0.11
Formaldehyde	—	0.04	—	0.09
Aureomycin	—	0.013	—	—
Vitamin mixture[c]				
Niacinamide	1.00	—	—	—
Niacin	—	1.00	—	—
Calcium pantothenate	1.00	1.00	—	—
Riboflavin	0.50	0.50	—	—
Thiamine (HCl)	0.25	0.25	—	—
Folic acid	0.25	0.25	—	—
Pyridoxine	0.25	0.25	—	—
Biotin	0.02	0.02	—	—
Vitamin B_{12}	0.002	0.002	—	—
Inositol	20.00	—	—	—

[a] Grams per 100 ml of medium.

[b] Corrected for water content, which is added to total water content of the medium.

[c] Milligrams per 100 ml of medium.

1. *Preparation*

The diet is prepared in a 60-gal, steam-jacketed, stainless-steel container (Legion Utensil Co., Contract No. DA 11009 Q M, New York, N. Y.). The agar, 900 gm, is dissolved in 22,200 ml of water in the kettle and the steam shut off. The remaining ingredients are added under continuous mixing with a ¼ horsepower Lightning mixer (Mixing Equipment Inc., Rochester, New York): casein, 1260 gm; alfalfa meal, 540 gm (Nutrilite Corp., Hemet, Calif.); and 4 M potassium hydroxide solution, 180 ml, are mixed in 8500 ml of water and added to the contents of the kettle. This is followed by a dry-mix of sucrose, 1260 gm; wheat germ, 1080 gm; Wesson's salts, 360 gm; and alphacel, 180 gm. Choline chloride (10% aqueous), 360 ml; formaldehyde (10% aqueous), 150 ml; vitamin stock, 120 ml; and 180 ml each of 38% solutions of sorbic acid and methyl *p*-hydroxybenzoate in 95% ethanol are added individually. The final ingredients, 150 gm of ascorbic acid and 5 gm of Aureomycin, are added suspended in 300 ml of water when the temperature of the kettle contents drops below 70°C.

The vitamin stock contains 600 mg each of niacin and calcium pantothenate, 300 mg riboflavin, 150 mg each of thiamine, pyridoxine, and folic acid, 12 mg biotin, and 1.2 mg vitamin B_{12} in 100 ml of water.

2. *Mold Inhibitors*

At least four microbial contaminants have been observed developing on the larval diet described. Pupal yields are reduced in contaminated rearing containers, perhaps due to physical interference with larval feeding or a low level of microbial pathogenicity. Such contaminants may become increasingly more of a problem. Shorey and Hale (1965) have reported the apparent adaptation of unidentified mold species to antimicrobial chemicals or concentrations thereof which had previously inhibited growth in their diet.

Sorbic acid and methyl *p*-hydroxybenzoate, in the amounts shown, have given excellent results without adverse effects on larval development, pupal yields, or adult oviposition, longevity, and mating. The concentration of sorbic acid should not be increased above 4000 ppm if eggs are used to infest larval rearing containers. In some cases high egg mortality has resulted. Methyl *p*-hydroxybenzoate alone has been used in the medium in concentrations up to 8000 ppm without adverse effects. In combination with 2000 ppm of sorbic acid, methyl *p*-hydroxybenzoate can be reduced to 500 ppm with excellent mold inhibition. However, to consistently obtain 95% of the rearing cartons mold-free, it has been necessary to incorporate 1800 to 2000 ppm of both sorbic acid and methyl p-hydroxybenzoate.

Formaldehyde alone, under our rearing conditions, does not notably inhibit mold development. It appears helpful in reducing the incidence of disease when the egg method of infesting larval rearing units is used.

3. Rearing Containers

The hot medium is poured into 6-ounce paraffin-coated Lily cups (6-s Lily cup, Lid No. 526-A, Lily-Tulip Corporation, New York, New York) and allowed to cool; 70 to 80 ml of the medium is required in each rearing container. This is approximately one-third more than the minimum required for the development of 22–24 larvae. Under the present rearing conditions the excess is necessary to prevent desiccation. With 10 to 15 ml of medium per container, larvae can develop on 1.7 to 2.5 ml of the medium per larva, with resulting pupal weights ranging from 254 to 281 mg for males and 229 to 253 mg for females (Table IV).

TABLE IV

MEAN[a] YIELDS AND WEIGHTS OF CABBAGE LOOPER PUPAE FROM LARVAE REARED ON DIFFERENT AMOUNTS OF ARTIFICIAL MEDIUM

Ml of medium/container	Yield (%)	Pupal weight (mg)	
		Males	Females
Two larvae/container			
5	76 c[b]	176 d	166 e
10	95 d	295 a	285 a
15	97 d	274 ab	281 ab
Four larvae/container			
5	63 c[b]	174 d	169 e
10	96 d	281 ab	253 bc
15	98 d	279 ab	273 ab
Six larvae/container			
5	49 b[b]	153 d	135 f
10	98 d	257 bc	238 cd
15	96 d	265 abc	244 c
Eight larvae/container			
5	24 a[b]	117 e	119 f
10	91 d	234 c	212 d
15	95 d	254 bc	229 cd

[a] Means in the same column not followed by a common letter are significantly different.

[b] Medium dried.

The air-dried toweling with formaldehyde-sterilized eggs is cut into strips, each containing approximately 30 eggs. One strip is stapled to a rearing carton lid. The lid is set in place and rearing is accomplished at 27°C.

a. Larval Density. Crowding in the larval rearing containers should be avoided. As many as 24 larvae can be reared to pupation in either 6- or 8-ounce cups of the type described. If larval densities higher than this are attempted, resulting pupal weights are decreased (Fig. 2). Subsequent oviposition of emerged adults, mating, or longevity does not appear to be affected.

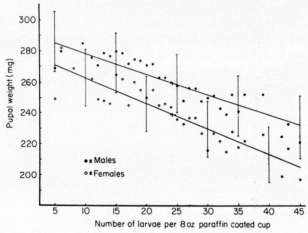

FIG. 2. Effect of larval density in rearing containers on cabbage looper pupal weights.

Pupal yields from the rearing containers infested with eggs average 75 to 80%. Over 90% of the larvae that hatch from eggs develop to the pupal stage and less than 5% of the pupae fail to produce adult moths. On the average, 20 to 22 adult moths are ultimately obtained from each individual larval rearing unit. Pupal weights average 266 mg for males and 251 mg for females.

B. NATURAL DIETS

Cabbage looper larvae can be reared on leaves of broccoli (McEwen and Hervey, 1960), citrus (Atkins, 1960), cabbage (Shorey *et al.*, 1962), Brussels sprouts (Paschke, 1964), lima beans (Shorey, 1963a), and cotyledons of germinated lima bean seeds (Shorey, 1963a).

Following the methods of McEwen and Hervey, 10 to 15 larvae

are placed on a broccoli or cabbage leaf in a 5¼ × 7⅜ × 3¾ inch plastic container lined with paper towels. Ventilation is provided through a 1-inch diameter screen-covered hole in the top of the container lid. Cylindrical, 1-gal cardboard cartons, fitted with hardware-cloth false bottoms, are also suitable larval rearing containers which can be discarded after use (Paschke, 1964). A small hole is cut in the top of the carton to permit ventilation.

A single leaf provides adequate food for 2 to 3 days. Thereafter food can be supplied daily or as needed. At 24°C, larvae develop in 10 to 12 days. These should be moved to clean, sterile containers with fresh food and crumpled paper toweling for pupation sites if plastic containers are used.

It is advisable to sterilize cabbage leaves with 0.5% sodium hypochlorite before feeding to larvae. Paschke (1964) sterilized cabbage looper eggs on Brussels sprout plants in 10% formalin; this may also be a satisfactory method for sterilization of larval food.

Shorey *et al.* (1962) reared 15 to 20 cabbage looper larvae on lima bean plants in 8-inch-square flats, transferring the last instar larvae to a fresh flat of beans in a 12-inch-square, 14-mesh wire screen cage equipped with a muslin sleeve. They harvested pupae from the sides of the screen cage. Shorey (1963a) also reared 10 larvae in 1-pint Mason jars from the first instar to pupation on the cotyledons of 40 to 50 germinated bush lima bean seeds. The inserts of the screw-cap jar tops were replaced with 9-cm filter paper discs. He germinated the bean seed in a mixture of 100 ml of vermiculite and 0.078% sodium hypochlorite, with enough vermiculite on top of the seeds to adsorb all free water. Pupae were harvested in 12 to 18 days when rearing was accomplished at 27°C.

VI. HANDLING PUPAE AND IMAGOS

Most of the larvae pupate in silken cocoons on the top and sides of the larval rearing cartons. After being removed from the cartons, pupae are placed in a container of 1 to 1.5% sodium hypochlorite for approximately 10 to 15 minutes to remove the silk (Table V). The naked pupae are subsequently rinsed several times in tap water and placed on paper toweling to dry.

Thereafter, the pupae are sexed and placed in emergence cages made from 1-gal cylindrical cardboard containers (Fig. 3A). Lids of the containers are inverted and stapled in each corner of a 14-inch square of ⅜-inch plywood. The gallon container (*a*) with bottom removed fits snugly into the lid stapled on the plywood. The nylon

TABLE V

EFFICIENCY OF SODIUM HYPOCHLORITE IN
REMOVING SILK FROM CABBAGE LOOPER PUPAE

Sodium hypochlorite concentration	Silk-free pupae (%) after		
	5 min	15 min	30 min
0.26	2	20	24
0.53	14	42	72
1.05	56	88	100
2.10	80	98	100
3.10	74	100	94
5.30	96	98	100
Water alone	0	2	0

cloth top (*b*) of the emergence container is held in place with a lid (*c*), insert removed, of a second gallon container. Four such emergence cages to a plywood piece are convenient and easy to handle.

The emergence containers with pupae are held at 24°C. On emergence adults crawl up the sides of the containers while the wing pads expand and dry. The emergence cages, when handled carefully, can be removed without disturbing the adults. Moths are anesthetized with carbon dioxide by setting the emergence cage

FIG. 3. Adult emergence cages (A) and method of anesthetizing moths with carbon dioxide (B).

into a cardboard cylinder (Fig. 3B) approximately 8 inches in diameter by 14 inches high, fitted with a false bottom perforated with holes. Carbon dioxide is introduced through the bottom of the cardboard cylinder. Anesthetized moths can be easily handled for experimental purposes or placed in oviposition cages. However, mating may be decreased within the first 24 to 48 hours after anesthetization if moths are exposed continuously to carbon dioxide for longer than 15 minutes.

VII. PRODUCTION COSTS

Using the larval diet described, 9,000 to 10,000 cabbage looper adults can be produced per week in less than 24 ft^3 of rearing space with approximately 14 to 16 man-hours of labor.

The cost of the medium, larval rearing container, and labor in preparation is approximately $.36 per pupa. Of this cost 31% is incurred in medium ingredients, 24% in the rearing container, and 45% in labor. During a 4-month period in 1965 approximately 320,000 to 350,000 adult cabbage looper moths were produced for experimental purposes.

ACKNOWLEDGMENTS

The authors are grateful for the constructive criticisms of H. H. Shorey, University of California, Riverside, California, and C. M. Ignoffo, U. S. Department of Agriculture, Entomology Research Division, Brownsville, Texas.

REFERENCES

Atkins, E. L., Jr. (1960). Cabbage looper on citrus. *Calif. Citrograph* **45**, 154–156.
Callahan, P. S. (1962). Techniques for rearing the corn earworm, *Heliothis zea. J. Econ. Entomol.* **55**, 453–457.
Getzin, L. W. (1962). Mass rearing of virus-free cabbage loopers on an artificial diet. *J. Insect Pathol.* **4**, 486–488.
Henneberry, T. J., and Kishaba, A. N. (1966). Pupal size and mortality and reproduction of cabbage loopers reared at several densities. *J. Econ. Entomol.* (In press.)
Ignoffo, C. M. (1963). A successful technique for mass-rearing cabbage loopers on a semisynthetic diet. *Ann. Entomol. Soc. Am.* **56**, 178–182.
Ignoffo, C. M. (1964). Production and virulence of a nuclear-polyhedrosis virus from larvae of *Trichoplusia ni* (Hübner) reared on a semisynthetic diet. *J. Insect Pathol.* **6**, 318–326.
Ignoffo, C. M., and Dutky, S. R. (1963). The effect of sodium hypochlorite on the viability and infectivity of *Bacillus* and *Beauveria* spores and cabbage looper nuclear-polyhedrosis virus. *J. Insect Pathol.* **5**, 422–426.
Jaques, R. P. (1962). The transmission of nuclear-polyhedrosis virus in laboratory populations of *Trichoplusia ni* (Hübner). *J. Insect Pathol.* **4**, 433–445.

McEwen, F. L., and Hervey, G. E. R. (1960). Mass rearing the cabbage looper, *Trichoplusia ni*, with notes on its biology in the laboratory. *Ann. Entomol. Soc. Am.* **53**, 229–234.

Paschke, J. D. (1964). Disposable containers for rearing loopers. *J. Insect Pathol.* **6**, 248–251.

Shorey, H. H. (1963a). The biology of *Trichoplusia ni* (Lepidoptera: Noctuidae). II. Factors affecting adult fecundity and longevity. *Ann. Entomol. Soc. Am.* **56**, 476–480.

Shorey, H. H. (1963b). A simple artificial rearing medium for the cabbage looper. *J. Econ. Entomol.* **56**, 536–537.

Shorey, H. H. (1964a). The biology of *Trichoplusia ni* (Lepidoptera: Noctuidae). III. Response to oviposition substrate. *Ann. Entomol. Soc. Am.* **57**, 165–170.

Shorey, H. H. (1964b). Sex pheromones of Noctuid moths. II. Mating behavior of *Trichoplusia ni* (Lepidoptera: Noctuidae) with special reference to the role of the sex pheromone. *Ann. Entomol. Soc. Am.* **57**, 371–377.

Shorey, H. H., and Hale, R. L. (1965). Mass-rearing of the larvae of nine noctuid species on a simple artificial medium. *J. Econ. Entomol.* **58**, 522–524.

Shorey, H. H., Andres, L. A., and Hale, R. L., Jr. (1962). The biology of *Trichoplusia ni* (Lepidoptera:Noctuidae). I. Life history and behavior. *Ann. Entomol. Soc. Am.* **55**, 591–597.

Chapter 34

Tobacco Hornworms

J. David Hoffman, F. R. Lawson,* and
Robert Yamamoto†

Entomology Research Division,
Agricultural Research Service,
U. S. Department of Agriculture,
Oxford, North Carolina
and † Department of Entomology,
North Carolina State University,
Raleigh, North Carolina

I. INTRODUCTION

The tobacco hornworm, *Manduca sexta* (Johannson), is a serious pest of tobacco in the United States. This species and its subspecies inhabit South and Central America, Mexico, the West Indies, and the United States northward into southern Canada. The principal host plants are members of the solanaceous family.

The literature on this insect describes a number of techniques for small-scale rearing of hornworms (Yamamoto, 1957; Waldbauer *et al.*, 1964; Madden and Chamberlin, 1945). Svec (1964) described a technique for laboratory rearing of the tomato hornworm, *Manduca*

* *Present address:* Entomology Research Division, Agricultural Research Division, U. S. Department of Agriculture, Columbia, Missouri.

quinquemaculata (Haworth). A preliminary study on mass rearing of the tobacco hornworm was published by Hoffman and Lawson (1964).

Four attempts, thus far, have been made to mass rear this insect on tobacco in the field. Field rearing depends upon a favorable combination of weather, vigorous plants, and low parasite and predator populations, and is restricted to the plant-growing season.

From the foregoing considerations it is evident that a controlled environment must be provided if predictable results are to be obtained.

Studies are now being conducted to mechanize the rearing of the larval stage on artificial diets and to accommodate all other phases of the rearing program indoors so that rearing of the insect could be maintained on a continuous basis. The procedures, equipments, and accounts of the behavior presented in this paper are therefore preliminary in nature and do not reflect the ultimate potential for mass rearing.

II. MATING AND OVIPOSITION

A. Mating

The adults are large insects, about 2½ inches long from head to wing tips and weighing about 2 gm each. Almost all activities—feeding, oviposition, and orientation of the males to the females—are performed during flight; therefore the cages must be large enough to accommodate them. The smallest cage in which consistent matings occurred was $3 \times 4 \times 4$ ft. Such a cage, however, limited the number of moths to only 6 pairs. A large outdoor cage, 20 ft square and 9 ft high, and shaped like a Quonset hut, accommodated 200 pairs of moths. The percentage of matings that occurred in the large cages was no different from that in the smaller cages housing only 6 pairs. Cages of this size, however, were limited to outdoor and seasonal use only.

The frames of the large cages were constructed of ½-inch steel conduit pipes and covered with tobacco shading cloth having 12×12 meshes per square inch, which provided a soft surface that did not injure moths that landed on it or struck it in flight. All cages were placed under trees to prevent desiccation of the moths during the heat of the day.

Hornworm moths are nocturnal, and mating usually occurs between 9:00 PM and 2:00 AM (Allen and Hodge, 1955). A sex pheromone is produced by the females which attract and orient the males to them (Allen *et al.*, 1962). Copulation usually occurs on a vertical surface and lasts from 1 to 3 hours. During this period the insects face in opposite directions with the female positioned above the male.

B. OVIPOSITION

With adequate intake of sugar solutions, the life span of the moths in confinement is about 10 days. Oviposition begins about the 3rd night after emergence and reaches a maximum during the 4th and 5th nights. For mass-rearing purposes, moths need not be kept beyond 6 days.

The average number of eggs deposited per female over a 9-day period was approximately 200, whether the females were confined in a large or small cage. In an experimental cage covering ¼ acre and containing 300 females, each female produced approximately 70 eggs over a 3-day period.

The moths are host-specific and require a host plant, usually tobacco, as an oviposition site. One tobacco plant, about 12 inches high, provided adequate foliage for oviposition in a small cage, whereas in the large Quonset-type cage, 4 plants about 4 ft high were required. The exact period when the majority of eggs were laid was not known; however, observations indicate that there were two brief flurries of activity, one during dusk and the other during dawn. The moths did not appear to be active all night. The environmental requirements for maximal oviposition are not known.

Efforts to obtain indoor mating and oviposition activity comparable to those obtained in cages outside have not been consistently satisfactory. Studies are continuing at the Oxford Tobacco Research Laboratory, Oxford, North Carolina, to determine the optimum indoor conditions for mating and egg production. Recent studies indicate that a strong contrast between daylight and the light level at dusk is required for mating and oviposition. Complete darkness and bright light inhibit moth activities. A low light intensity is required during the oviposition and mating periods. A relative humidity of 80% at 75°F resulted in good mating and egg production.

III. FEEDING REQUIREMENTS

A. ADULT FEEDING

Moths in the small cages fed erratically or not at all from containers filled with a 10% sucrose solution. Poor feeding by the moths resulted in early mortality and low egg production. When

fed individually, using a hypodermic syringe filled with a 10%
sucrose solution, oviposition and longevity were about the same
as in the larger cages where moths fed freely from artificial blossoms
filled with a sucrose solution.

Artificial blossoms in the large cages were made from plastic
containers 2 inches in diameter by 2 inches high. The "corolla"
was made by fastening strips of stiff, light-colored paper around
the rims of the containers. To avoid fermentation, the artificial
blossoms were refilled daily with a 10% sucrose solution. A synthetic attractant (isoamyl salicylate) was painted on the blossoms
for added attraction.

The flowers of the tobacco plant, growing in clusters at the tip
of the plant, were more attractive to feeding moths than were the
artificial blossoms. However, tobacco flowers do not provide sufficient nectar to sustain a large number of moths. Even though the
tobacco flowers were depleted of nectar, moths continued feeding
attempts and ignored the artificial blossoms.

B. LARVAL FEEDING ON TOBACCO

Hoffman and Lawson (1964) described the first attempt to mass
rear tobacco hornworms. Three hundred mated females were released into a cloth-covered, ¼-acre tobacco field. An estimated
21,000 eggs (10 per plant) were laid in a 3-day period. When the
eggs were deposited the plants were 20 inches high; they were
4 ft high by the time the larvae had reached the fifth instar. Throughout this period of growth the larvae ate very little; approximately
90% of their total food was consumed during the fifth instar. One
tobacco plant 4 ft high was sufficient food for 10 larvae. The food
cost was estimated at $1.00 per 1000 larvae.

C. LARVAL FEEDING ON ARTIFICIAL DIET

The artificial diet for the tobacco hornworm was fashioned after
the diets developed for other lepidopterous insects—for example,
the pink bollworm (Adkisson et al., 1960) and the cabbage looper
(Ignoffo, 1963). It has been used in one modification or another
to rear approximately 15,000 larvae over 8 generations and appears
to be quite satisfactory for rearing the hornworm on a large scale.
The ingredients are given in Table I.

The dry ingredients, except for agar, are ball-milled together
in bulk for 12 hours, and the resulting homogeneous and finely
ground mixture is transferred to large Mason jars and stored in the

TABLE I

ARTIFICIAL DIET FOR TOBACCO HORNWORM LARVAE[a]

Ingredient	Amount (gm)
Wheat germ	50.00
Sucrose	30.00
Casein, high nitrogen	35.00
Torula or brewer's yeast	15.00
Wesson's salt mixture	10.00
Ascorbic acid	4.00
Cholesterol	1.00
Sorbic acid	1.50
Methyl-p-hydroxybenzoate	1.00
Streptomycin sulfate	0.20
Aureomycin	0.10
Agar	2.00
Vitamin solution[b]	5.0 ml
Water (for agar)	600.0 ml
Water (for dietary mixture)	250.0 ml

[a] Ingredients and amounts used for preparing approximately 1 liter of diet.

[b] The vitamin solution consists of the following: nicotinic acid, 300 mg; calcium pantothenate, 300 mg; riboflavin, 150 mg; thiamine, 75 mg; pyridoxine, 75 mg; folic acid, 75 mg; biotin, 6 mg; and choline chloride, 20 gm; in 200 ml of water.

refrigerator or freezer. In preparing the diet, the requisite amount of the mixture is weighed out and suspended in a large, stainless-steel beaker containing the lesser amount of water (see Table I). The vitamin solution is pipetted into the mixture. The agar is brought to a boil in the rest of the water and poured into the beaker containing the suspended nutrient mixture. The entire diet is then thoroughly mixed with a thick glass stirring rod or a wooden spatula. As the diet begins to thicken, it is poured into glass or enamel trays, and the trays are stored in a refrigerator for use as needed.

The diet does not contain any host plant extractives or leaf powder. The tobacco hornworm adapts well to this diet and comparative dietary tests indicate that only slight advantages are gained by adding plant adjuvants. This is not the case with the tomato hornworm M. quinquemaculata), a related species which also feeds on tobacco. For this species, 2% tobacco leaf powder or a water extract of tobacco leaves is necessary before feeding and establishment on the diet occurs. One hundred larvae can be reared on 3.5 liters of the diet. At a temperature of 80°F, 80% of the larvae complete development in 14–17 days. Research at mechanizing the rearing of the larvae on the diet is now being conducted.

IV. COLLECTION OF LARVAE, PUPATION, STORAGE OF PUPAE, EMERGENCE

A. COLLECTION OF LARVAE

Fifth-instar larvae were collected from the tobacco plants and placed on tables designed to prevent escape (Hoffman and Lawson, 1964). The larvae quickly established themselves on freshly cut tobacco plants suspended above, and touching, the table surfaces.

When the larvae entered the prepupal stage they crawled from the plants and wandered about, eventually dropping into a box at one end of the table. The top of the box was covered with ½-inch mesh hardware cloth through which only those larvae in the pre-pupal stage passed. Immature larvae did not attempt to pass through the hardware cloth but crawled back onto the table.

B. PUPATION

Each prepupa was placed in a wooden cell, 1 × 1 × 4 inches, the ends of which were covered with ¼-inch mesh hardware cloth

FIG. 1. Wood cells in which prepupae were placed.

(Fig. 1). The cells were placed horizontally in an incubation chamber at 75°F and 90–100% relative humidity.

C. STORAGE OF PUPAE

After 7 days the pupae were removed from the cells, sexed, and placed in a single layer on a wooden tray. Allen and Hodge (1955) describes a method used in determining sex of pupae. Nondiapausing pupae obtained from larvae reared during the long daylight periods (14 hours minimum) of early and mid-summer were stored at 75°F until emergence. Larvae reared during the shorter daylight period (12 hours or less) of late summer produced diapausing pupae which were stored at 55°F (Rabb, 1965). Storing the pupae at 55°F for 90 days disrupted diapause, allowing development to the adult stage when incubated at 75°F.

D. EMERGENCE

Upon emerging from the pupal case, the wings of the moth are abbreviated, pad-like structures, which must be inflated and allowed to harden within a few minutes following emergence. Wing deformity results if the moths cannot suspend themselves in a position that allows the wings to hang freely. Since flight is necessary for feeding, deformed wings result in failure to feed and mate.

To provide proper conditions for emergence and wing development, pupae were allowed to emerge in screen wire cages (2 × 2 × 1 ft), the sides of which sloped inward at the top. Not more than 200 pupae were placed in each emergence cage, in order to provide sufficient surface area during the period of wing inflation.

Newly emerged moths were disturbed by the movement of other moths left in the emergence cages from the previous day. Wing damage also resulted when the flying moths came into frequent contact with the sides of the small emergence cages. Daily collection of the moths from the emergence cages was necessary, therefore, to obtain vigorous adults.

V. CONCLUSION

Mass rearing of the tobacco hornworm, in desired numbers of insects and under controlled conditions of production, has not been attained as yet. Mass-rearing efforts in the field have indicated many undesirable features: rearing is dependent upon the vagaries of the weather; the larvae are subjected to parasites and diseases; and the cost of labor is high. Rearing the insects on artificial diets, under controlled conditions of photoperiod, temperature, and humidity, holds much promise despite the size and space requirements of the insect. All other phases, including adult requirements for optimal survival and oviposition, pupation, and storage, need considerable research, and attention is now being directed toward meeting these needs.

REFERENCES

Adkisson, P. L., Vanderzant, E. S., Bull, D. L., and Allison, W. E. (1960). A wheat germ medium for rearing the pink bollworm. *J. Econ. Entomol.* **55**, 759–762.

Allen, N., and Hodge, C. R. (1955). Mating habits of the tobacco hornworm. *J. Econ. Entomol.* **48**, 526–528.

Allen, N., Kinard, W. S., and Jacobson, M. (1962). Procedure used to recover a sex attractant for the male tobacco hornworm. *J. Econ. Entomol.* **55**, 347–351.

Hoffman, J. D., and Lawson, F. R. (1964). Preliminary studies on mass-rearing of the tobacco hornworm. *J. Econ. Entomol.* **57**, 354–355.

Ignoffo, C. M. (1963). A successful technique for mass rearing cabbage loopers on a semisynthetic diet. *Ann. Entomol. Soc. Am.* **56**, 178–182.

Madden, A. H., and Chamberlin, F. S. (1945). Biology of the tobacco hornworm in the southern cigar-tobacco district. *U. S. Dept. Agr., Tech. Bull.* **896**, 1–51.

Rabb, R. L. (1965). Diapause in *Protoparce sexta* (Lepidoptera: Sphingidae). Unpublished data.

Svec, H. J. (1964). Laboratory rearing of the tomato hornworm, *Protoparce quinquemaculata* (Haworth). *Can. J. Zool.* **42**, 717.

Waldbauer, G. P., Yamamoto, R. T., and Bowers, W. S. (1964). Laboratory rearing of tobacco hornworm, *Protoparce sexta* (Lepidoptera: Sphingidae). *J. Econ. Entomol.* **57**, 93–95.

Yamamoto, R. T. (1957). The specificity of the tobacco hornworm, *Protoparce sexta* (Johan.) to solanaceous plants. Thesis, Univ. of Illinois, Urbana, Illinois, pp. 1–60.

Section D

Insect Parasites, Predators, and Pathogens

Chapter 35

Insect Parasites and Predators

F. J. SIMMONDS

Commonwealth Institute of Biological Control,
Gordon Street, Curepe,
Trinidad, West Indies

I. INTRODUCTION

The mass production of insect parasites and predators may be necessary or desirable in biological control work for several reasons; in this connection we may perhaps first consider two general methods of biological control. The first is that in which an exotic natural enemy is introduced against a pest into an area where it does not already occur naturally with the object of establishment and the subsequent development of its population at the expense of that of its host; the second method is that in which a natural enemy, exotic or native, is liberated in very large numbers against a pest in a limited area with a view to reducing the incidence of the pest in that particular or the subsequent generation by sheer weight of numbers of the beneficial species released.

While these two methods of utilizing parasites and predators have the same ultimate objective, the control of the pest, the mode of achievement is rather different in each. The former method, which may be termed that of "classic" biological control, endeavors to achieve permanent control of the pest; the second method is designed to give only temporary control, and necessitates periodic

releases of large numbers of suitable parasites or predators season-
ally or annually. Obviously, for a given degree of control obtained,
this is not as economical or as desirable as the former method. However, since it entails for its utilization production of very large numbers of predators or parasites it will be dealt with first.

II. MASS LIBERATIONS

The object of the method of mass releases of parasites or predators is to inject into the population of a pest species a sufficient
number of a suitable natural enemy such that these will virtually
eliminate the host species present at that time and thus prevent
further damage. It is obviously an advantage to select a parasite
or predator which will destroy the pest before any damage is done;
for this reason egg parasites have, where possible, been utilized
where it is the larval stage which causes damage, since it is of little
use destroying the pest after, say, a tree has been defoliated. In
this method natural enemies are being used virtually as a self-
propagating and self-dispersing insecticide which is able actively
to search out and kill the pest. They develop at the expense of one
generation of the pest and their progeny are then very often able
to attack members of the subsequent generation of the pest species
which may still exist in that locality. It is necessary to time the liberations of parasites and predators very carefully, ensuring that
they are made at the exact time when the pest population is in a
suitable stage for attack, and preferably when this population is
also low, so that the maximum effect may be derived from the numbers liberated. Liberations should also be made, too, when natural
parasitism or predatism is low. Thus, in all sound endeavors to use
this method a considerable amount of accurate information is required as to the exact state of pest population, its stage of development, degree of parasitism, and presence of predators, before releases
are made in any one area. This clearly entails a very efficient detailed
organization, since the exact situation may vary from field to field
or orchard to orchard with consequent differences in the optimal
release dates. The dates of releases also govern any mass-breeding
program for parasites and predators, and this program is therefore
dependent on data obtained. In former efforts with the use of this
method such detailed knowledge was often not available and mass-
production programs and releases were made at a "generally suitable" time of the seasonal cycle of the pest, e.g., in connection with
mass releases of *Trichogramma minutum* Riley in Barbados (see

Tucker, 1935) and in British Guiana (see Cleare, 1934) against the sugar-cane moth borers *Diatraea* spp.

However, it is with this type of operation that really large-scale mass production of parasites and predators is absolutely necessary, and it has to date particularly involved the use of the egg parasites *Trichogramma* spp. in many parts of the world against sugar-cane borers, corn borers, codling moth, cotton bollworm, and lepidop-terous pests of sugar beet, and parasites of scale insects and mealy bugs in various parts of the world, particularly California (DeBach and White, 1960; Flanders, 1942, 1943, 1951), and to a lesser extent larval parasites, e.g., the use of *Lixophaga diatraeae* Townsend against the sugar-cane borer *Diatraea saccharalis* (Fabricius) in Cuba (Scaramuzza, 1930, 1958) and Antigua (Box, 1937). *Eurygaster integriceps* Puton, a serious cereal pest in the eastern Mediterranean and other areas, has a number of egg parasites with some of which the same type of method is being tried. In all these the same basic principles apply—the release in the field at a critical period in the seasonal life cycle of the pest, when few other natural enemies are present, of sufficient numbers of parasites or predators either to reduce the pest population immediately to a low level or to pro-vide nucleus populations which will develop and accomplish this before the crop is seriously damaged. By its very nature such an operation must be seasonal and may have to be carried out more than once during the year. Hence large-scale breeding plants have to be kept in operation, involving annually recurrent effort and costs.

This method has been the subject of, to a certain extent acri-monious, discussion between its protagonists and antagonists. It is obvious that in some instances, for example, the use of some parasites and predators against some citrus scales in California, there is no doubt that successful control is often obtained. With the use of *Trichogramma* against *Diatraea saccharalis* (and other species) in British Guiana, Barbados, and Louisiana (Jaynes and Bynum, 1941), the method was abandoned eventually (although recently revived in Louisiana).

In Ceylon in recent years the method has been used against the coconut defoliator *Nephantis serinopa* Meyrick, but the numbers of parasites liberated could seem to have little impact when con-sidered against the population of both host and other naturally occurring parasites.

The main difficulty in these operations is that of having imme-diately available large numbers—astronomical numbers, one might say—of the required parasite or predator at exactly the right time to have the maximum effect on the pest population; on reflection it can be seen that, both technically from the point of view of breeding, and because of often considerable seasonal variations in pest development, which necessitates altered dates of liberations and hence breeding schedules, the difficulties here are great, if such releases are to be really effective. In certain instances it would appear at first sight that this method has considerable possibilities, but in most cases the processes involved and the difficulties in assessing exactly the right time for liberation make the chances of full effectiveness of this method rather slim.

It would be interesting to make a thorough survey of all the instances where this method has been tried, with as detailed an appraisal as possible of the effectiveness, and costs. It would also be interesting to carry out further large-scale experimental projects using this method, since it does seem that this method could be effective if we had really adequate information as to the exact biology of the pest and its natural enemies, its response to different weather conditions with regard to dates of emergence, and its general population dynamics. The mass production of any individual species of natural enemies, particularly if they are to be available in adequate numbers at certain definite and limited periods (which vary from season to season), is a matter of detailed organization and of developing suitable techniques—as has already been done with some species.

III. ESTABLISHMENT OF EXOTIC SPECIES

The second, and more desirable, procedure is to establish a suitable exotic parasite or predator against a pest, such that it will thrive in the new environment and reduce the population of the pest indefinitely without further effort being required. This has, of course, been accomplished very satisfactorily on very many occasions, but we are still very far from knowing *why* certain species of entomophages become very quickly acclimatized to a new area and control the pest, while others, apparently as suitable or possibly even more so, fail completely. Obviously, environmental conditions are the important factor, but these are so complex that it is only recently that we have begun to determine some of them with any degree of certainty. Often, when an apparently promising entomophage does not become established, it is assumed that insufficient numbers were liberated, and an attempt is made to mass produce the species to ensure liberations of sufficient size—although the question as to "adequate" numbers in such liberations is always only a matter of conjecture, and is usually determined by the availability of material. We have come to the point where it is apparent that mass production of parasites and predators is more often than not an integral part of any biological control problem, whether it be "classic" biological control, or the more recent developments in this general field (sterile-male releases, or the release of genetically incompatible material), for although these individuals are not parasites and predators they act in a very similar way.

IV. METHODS OF MASS PRODUCTION

In many cases the mass production in the sense of having large numbers of a desired species available is accomplished most easily and cheaply by field collections, of some stage of the host in case of parasites, and of the insect itself in the case of predators. Following this collection the material is brought into the laboratory, and fed (if in the form of a host larva or predator larva) until pupation or its equivalent; the material is kept for emergence of adult entomophages (which may follow shortly or may occur only after a prolonged period of storage, possibly cold storage). Difficulties of feeding are here similar to those of actual laboratory breeding, although usually not as great, and if cocoon material of parasitized host or adult predators can be collected this feeding is eliminated. However, there is with field-collected material the question of undesirable secondary parasites emerging from hosts, and with predators the possibility of adult parasites (as in coccinellids) or undesirable diseases, none of which should be allowed to enter the new area where biological control of the pest is desired.

While field collection is in a number of instances an excellent way of producing large numbers of entomophages for biological control work, it is more usual that a comparatively small stock of the desired species is obtained from the field and is then brought into the laboratory, not only for further propagation, but in the first instance to study its biology.

Laboratory propagation and mass production have the advantage that hyperparasites, diseases, etc., may usually be eliminated, and hence all material produced may be liberated in the field. However, the propagation of any entomophage in the laboratory is a particular and specific operation in which optimum conditions of environment, cage size and shape, feeding, illumination, host preferences, etc., have to be worked out afresh for each species. There are virtually no "rules" to indicate how best to tackle any individual species. Any really mass-production scheme must be based on a technique developed in the laboratory and then modified for cheap, large-scale production. Once we arrive at this point there are, however, a number of general aspects to be considered, quite apart from the fact that special techniques have to be developed in connection with every individual problem.

In many cases it may be necessary or desirable to provide very large numbers of the host species (or a closely allied one) as food for the entomophage. It may be possible to collect sufficient material in the field, possibly storing it in some convenient way. For example, pine sawfly cocoons collected in the field in Canada were used for very large-scale production of the parasite *Dahlbominus* (*Microplectron*) *fuscipennis* (Zetterstedt), and field-collected larvae have been used almost exclusively in the mass production of larval parasites of *Diatraea* spp. However, such large-scale field collections may be impossible or impracticable. Then efforts are made to propagate the host in the laboratory. Numerous species of lepidopterous hosts have been produced in this way, often on a continuous basis in heated insectaries throughout the year, for example, *Loxostege sticticalis* (Linnaeus), the beet webworm, where adult material was forced out from larvae in diapause, eggs obtained, and larvae fed during the winter in Canada on commercial spinach purchased locally and probably grown in Florida. This host material was then used to propagate several larval parasites. *Diatraea saccharalis* has been mass produced in the laboratory on a continuous basis for parasite breeding, using green corncobs as food plant. Great care must be taken in such cases to adjust environmental conditions so that normal, healthy individuals are produced, since such bred material may often prove to be rather susceptible to disease. It is also often necessary to ensure that cannibalism of larvae does not occur.

Normal host plants may be unavailable or difficult to handle under laboratory or mass-culture conditions. It may then be possible to find another plant acceptable to the host insect as food which is more amenable to mass culture in the laboratory. The use of sprouting potatoes as the host for mealy bugs [*Planococcus citri* (Risso)] in mass production of some coccinellids, for example, *Cryptolaemus montrouzieri* Mulsant, is a good example of this. Others are the use of several types of squash and pumpkin as hosts for California red scale, *Aonidiella aurantii* (Maskell), in mass production of several parasites; and the use of potatoes as hosts for the scale *Pseudaulacaspis pentagona* (Targioni-Tozzetti) in mass production of both parasites and predators.

Along similar lines is the use of an artificial, not necessarily synthetic, diet on which the host may develop satisfactorily. The simplest example of this is perhaps the large-scale production of *Drosophila* spp., on media consisting of bananas or tomatoes, corn meal plus yeast (with very many modifications), large-scale production of house flies and blow flies on different nutrient media, Tephritid fruit flies on media based on pulverized carrots—all in connection with parasite breeding programs. Some of the most successful mass-production methods have been evolved along these lines. Production of screw-worms for use with the sterile-male techniques has been developed with this method.

A variation of this method is when the normal host cannot be produced in adequate numbers, but when a suitable, not necessarily related, alternative host can be found on which the entomophage can develop and which can be produced easily in large numbers. Examples of this may be seen in the use of the stages of various stored-product insects in mass production of some parasites. For example, *Trichogramma* spp. are often bred in large numbers using eggs of the Angoumois grain moth, *Sitatroga cerealella* (Olivier), which can be produced in very large numbers by sieving flour in which moths have oviposited. The eggs of the Mediterranean flour moth *Anagasta* (*Ephestia*) *kühniella* (Zeller) have also been successfully used in the mass production of *Chelonus texanus* Cresson, an egg-larval parasite of *Loxostege sticticalis*, and *C. annulipes* Wesmael, a parasite of the European corn borer, *Pyrausta* (*Ostrinia*) *nubilalis* (Hübner). The larvae of the greater wax moth, *Galleria mellonella* (Linnaeus), and those of the stored-produce pest, *Brachmia modicella* (Christoph), have been used as readily obtainable hosts for the mass breeding of *Lixophaga diatraeae*. A further development along these lines is the "conditioning" of an easily bred host which is suitable for the development of the larvae of a given parasite, but in which the adult parasite will not normally oviposit. It was found, for example, that female *Meteorus loxostegei* Viereck would not normally attack and oviposit in larvae of *Anagasta kühniella* but that if these larvae were covered with an extract of *Loxostege* larvae, then they were attacked and progeny could be successfully reared from *Anagasta*.

There are undoubtedly a large number of techniques of this type which could be developed in connection with different problems to facilitate mass production of entomophages.

The logical development from this has been research into the possibilities of producing purely synthetic diets for either host or entomophage. While some progress along these lines has been made in that it has been possible to breed several insects on purely synthetic media (e.g., *Pyrausta, Ostrinia, Heliothis, Diatraea,* and even a parasite, *Sarcophaga*), it is usually found more practical to have as a basis of such a medium, when mass production is required, some naturally derived material—flour, alfalfa meal, liver, etc. The rearing of several species of predacious coccinellids on diets consisting of pollen with various additives might be mentioned here. This is a promising field of research in the development of techniques for mass production of entomophagous species which should certainly be investigated further.

The use of hosts other than the normal, natural ones may, though certainly not necessarily, produce peculiarities in the parasite or predator progeny reared such as to affect their usefulness as biological control agents. For example, it has been found that the *Diatraea* parasite *Lixophaga*, when reared in *Brachmia* is not as large as, and the females produce fewer larvae (the species is ovo-larviparous) than, those from normal hosts. Other differences in reproductive potentialities may also occur when unnatural hosts are used in parasite and predator production. A related factor, of importance in mass production, is that of the food of the adult parasites and predators used for breeding. In order to obtain maximum production careful investigation should be made of the exact requirements in each case such that the maximum reproductive rate, both total eggs and high fertility, is obtained. In coccinellids, for example, it has been shown that adults of a single species preying on scale insects may possibly feed on a wide range of hosts, and keep themselves alive. However, when only some species of these hosts are used as food no eggs are laid, with other hosts only few eggs with low fertility are obtained, while with others, which we may consider the normal hosts, normal egg laying occurs with virtually 100% fertility. The quality of adult food is obviously most important here. With adult ichneumonids it has been found that the quality and quantity both of the host used as larval food and of the food consumed by the adult female have an effect on the length of adult life and on the number of eggs laid, their fertility, and the proportion of progeny which enter diapause in the late larval state.

It has been suggested, in connection with the use of any but the normal natural host of an entomophagous species, that substitution of alternate abnormal hosts might alter the host preferences of the progeny and hence render them less useful or useless in biological control work. Several investigations have been made on this point, and while there is some evidence for a certain amount of preimaginal conditioning of progeny reared in this way with some species, it is certainly insufficient to mitigate against the use of alternate or synthetic host materials in mass-production techniques. It does, however, indicate a factor which may possibly be of some importance in certain instances and which should be borne in mind.

The genetic aspect of mass production, and of even laboratory breeding, of entomophagous parasites and predators is important. In most instances a comparatively small quantity of material is collected in the field and from this a laboratory culture of a particular entomophagous species may be obtained. This stock may be kept in the laboratory for a number of generations, possibly with considerable inbreeding, and at times numbers may sink to a very low level. From such a laboratory stock individuals may be taken to develop a mass-production unit from which very large numbers may be produced for field release. It is obvious that during the course of such a procedure genetic variability must have been reduced, possibly considerably, even from that existing in the small quantity of original field material. However, in connection with mass production of parasites and predators for release in connection with biological control programs, it is essential that every effort should be made to ensure that material thus produced has as great a genetic variability as possible, in order that it may be as adaptable as possible to differing environmental conditions.

Problems of obtaining mating of insects may arise, and, as with other factors, the conditions necessary to obtain adequate mating to provide maximum progeny with an adequate sex ratio may vary with each species. It is often best to keep males and females separated in different cages for most of the day. When they are then placed together mating may often occur readily, whereas if on emergence they are left constantly together there appears often to be no adequate stimulation by the presence of the other sex.

In mass production of parasites and predators it is usually simple to eliminate hyperparasites in the case of the former, and parasites in the case of the latter; diseases and mites, however, often cause considerable losses and are more difficult to deal with. The crowded conditions of hosts, such as may often occur with mass production, render them more susceptible to disease (close contact, conditions of stress, etc.) and in cases where this occurs rearing conditions have to be suitably altered.

Some diseases are transmitted by the females through the eggs; then extreme care, with every sanitary precaution, has to be exerted to obtain from field-collected material a disease-free stock, and to maintain this condition. A case in point is that of the moth *Tyria jacobaeae* Linnaeus used in the biological control of the weed ragwort, where the production of a disease-free line has been a long and tedious procedure.

For examples of types of units used in various mass-production programs and the method in which difficulties have been overcome in individual cases reference should be made to the appropriate sections of the recent book "Biological Control of Insect Pests and Weeds," edited by DeBach (1964). It is pointless to list techniques employed with individual insect species, and it appeared more appropriate to deal with general principles, although as I have stressed this is difficult to do in any detail since each problem is different from any other—involving different species, with different behaviors and host-parasite or host-predator relationships, and consequent differing requirements regarding the equipment and organization for mass production. There is also the question as to the number of parasites or predators required in connection with each problem, and hence the degree of mass production. In the more satisfactory method of biological control, involving the successful introduction and establishment of exotic entomophages into an area followed by their natural increase and spread, the need for prolonged mass production is often limited, or in many of the most successful examples, this may have been actually unnecessary. With control problems where periodic releases of large numbers of entomophages are to be made the necessity for inexpensive mass production is obvious, but with the attempted introduction and establishment of an exotic species into an area the extent to which mass production is necessary depends on the availability of the entomophage in the field in its country of origin, the numbers considered desirable or necessary to obtain establishment of the species in a suitable area of the pest population, and finally the dispersive powers of the entomophage. If these are low and the area covered by the pest is large, then many foci of establishment may be desirable, and hence mass production of the species will be necessary.

In considering the final results of any mass production and release of an entomophage the actual diminution of the damage caused by the pest should be carefully investigated, as should the actual fate of the entomophages released. While it is certainly true that in many examples production of extremely large numbers is necessary, it is, unfortunately, too often the case that with problems where mass production for release of entomophages is developed, a form of megalomania is also entailed, and there is a tendency to consider the ever-increasing numbers of entomophages released the sole object of the operation. This is obviously quite ridiculous, but unfortunately it is true that administrative bodies can often be rather easily impressed by large numbers quoted in reports, and this does tend to foster this quite unscientific obsession.

REFERENCES

Box, H. E. (1937). Report on the *Lixophaga* campaign for 1936 and the status of the parasite in Antigua at the end of the year. *Colonial Develop. Fund, Antigua* 3.

Cleare, L. D. (1934). Sugar-cane moth-borer investigations in British Guiana: The present position. *Agr. J. Brit. Guiana* 5, 13–21.

DeBach, P., ed. (1964). "Biological Control of Insect Pests and Weeds." Chapman & Hall, London.

DeBach, P., and White, E. B. (1960). Commercial mass culture of the California red scale parasite *Aphytis lingnanensis. Calif., Univ., Agr. Expt. Sta., Bull.* **770.**

Flanders, S. E. (1942). Propagation of black scale on potato sprouts. *J. Econ. Entomol.* **35,** 687–689.

Flanders, S. E. (1943). Mass production of the California red scale and its parasite *Comperiella bifasciata. J. Econ. Entomol.* **36,** 802–803.

Flanders, S. E. (1951). Mass culture of California red scale and its golden chalcid parasites. *Hilgardia* **21,** 1–42.

Jaynes, H. A., and Bynum, E. K. (1941). Experiments with *Trichogramma minutum* Riley as a control of the sugar-cane borer in Louisiana. *U. S. Dept. Agr., Tech. Bull.* **743.**

Scaramuzza, L. C. (1930). Preliminary report on a study of the biology of *Lixophaga diatraeae* Tns. *J. Econ. Entomol.* **23,** 999–1004.

Scaramuzza, L. C. (1958). Achievements on the biological control of the sugar-cane borers (*Diatraea* spp.) (Lepidoptera: Pyralidae) in the Americas. *Proc. 10th Intern. Congr. Entomol., Montreal, 1956* Vol. 4, pp. 845–850. Intern. Congr. Entomol., Ottawa, Canada.

Tucker, R. W. E. (1935). A review of control work on *Diatraea saccharalis* F. in Barbados. *Proc. Intern. Soc. Sugar-Cane Technologists* **5,** 386–397.

Chapter 36

Insect Viruses

CARLO M. IGNOFFO[*]

International Minerals and Chemical Corporation,
Bioferm Division,
Wasco, California

I. INTRODUCTION

Man has always dreamed of using naturally occurring pathogens to control insect pests. The potentials inherent in their use are dramatically demonstrated by the occurrence of natural epizootics which may completely decimate field populations of these pests.

[*] Formerly Agricultural Research Service, Entomology Research Division, U. S. Department of Agriculture, Brownsville, Texas.

TABLE I

REPORTED NATURAL VIRUS ASSOCIATIONS OF INSECTS AND SPIDER MITES[a]

Order	Virus types[b]					
	NP	CP	PI	G	NI	Total
Lepidoptera	100	83	1	35	2	221
Hymenoptera	12	12	—	—	2	26
Acarina	—	—	—	—	3	3
Neuroptera	—	2	—	—	—	2
Diptera	3	—	—	—	3	6
Coleoptera	—	—	—	—	1	1
	115	97	1	35	11	259

[a] Listings of Bergold (1963), Smith (1963), and Huger (1963), and recent reports of 18 new virus associations.

[b] NP: nuclear polyhedroses; CP: cytoplasmic polyhedroses; PI: polymorphic inclusion; G: granuloses; NI: noninclusions.

Unfortunately, the natural development and spread of diseases lag behind the injurious insect populations and therefore most of the crop damage is done before an epizootic occurs. This lag may be minimized if early "artificial" epizootics can be induced.

Over 250 natural virus associations with insects are now described (Table I). Less than 10% of these viruses have been used to control insect pests, although the reported uses of insect viruses are, for the most part, successful and in some instances spectacular (Balch and Bird, 1944; Balch, 1946). If the use of viruses offers such promise and is so graphically demonstrated in the past, why are not viruses more widely used today? The answer is obvious! Viruses are not being used because they are not available. Availability depends on an efficient method of production. Up to now, only bacteria and fungi have been commercially produced and made available as microbial insecticides (Briggs, 1963). Bacteria can be grown in large capacity (30,000–40,000 liter) fermentators. In contrast, the production of insect viruses is presently limited to *"crawling fermentators"* of less than ½ ml capacity.

The purpose and scope of this paper is to demonstrate how and what insect viruses can or may be produced and *ipso facto* become available. Of course, it is impossible to present detailed production techniques for every insect virus or, for that matter, each of the major types of insect viruses (Fig. 1). Therefore, the details of virus production will largely pertain to the nuclear polyhedroses

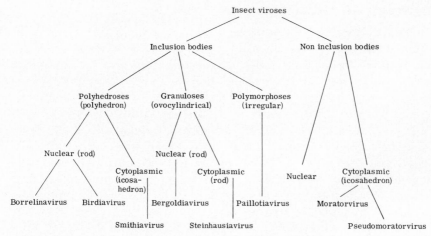

FIG. 1. Generic types of insect viruses classified on basis of size and shape of inclusion bodies, virus particles, and site of virus multiplication.

of the cabbage looper, *Trichoplusia ni* (Hübner), and the bollworm, *Heliothis zea* (Boddie). The selection of these insects is based upon the demonstrable effectiveness of their viruses, the availability of semisynthetic diets and rearing protocols, the importance of these insects as major pests of food and fiber crops, and their reported resistance to chemical insecticides.

Innately associated with insect virus production are subsequent identification and standardization of viral preparations. The reader is referred to a previous review which covers past studies, inherent problems, and possible future approaches to virus identification and standardization (Ignoffo, 1966d).

II. POSSIBLE METHODS OF INSECT VIRUS PRODUCTION

A. PREFATORY

Theoretically, insect viruses can be propagated on either living or nonliving media. The nonliving media may be chemically defined, chemically undefined, or have various combinations of these alternatives. The living media may be embryonated eggs, cultures of whole organs, tissues, animal or plant cells, or the insect itself. Each type of medium, as it applies to the possible production of insect viruses, will be briefly discussed and evaluated. The various methods of insect virus production are summarized by Martignoni (1964a) and Vasiljevic (1964).

B. Nonliving Media

The cultivation of an insect virus on a nonliving, chemically defined medium is the acme of a program to develop insect virus production. Production under these conditions can be controlled with the greatest flexibility and thereby ensure continuous production of a quality product. The advantages of using nonliving media were recognized early in the historical development of production techniques for insect pathogens (Metchnikoff, 1880; Krassilstschik, 1888; Giard, 1892; Forbes, 1895); however, cultivation of insect viruses on nonliving media has not been achieved and remains only a theoretical possibility. As our knowledge of the biological requirements for virus duplication and development increases, cultivation of insect viruses on nonliving media may become a reality (Ham, 1965; Haruna and Spiegelman, 1965). At present, only living cells may be used for mass propagation of insect viruses.

C. Living Media

1. *Fertilized Egg Technique*

Some early attempts to produce insect viruses, using sources other than the insect itself, employed embryonated hen's eggs. Eggs are successfully employed to culture vertebrate viruses and rickettsia; therefore, they offered a possible approach to production of insect viruses.

Steinhaus (1951) inoculated embryonated eggs with crude and raw preparations of six different insect viruses [nuclear polyhedrosis viruses of *Colias philodice eurytheme* Bvd., *Spodoptera exigua* (Hbn.), *Phryganidia californica* Pack., *Bombyx mori* (L.); the granulosis viruses of *Peridroma margaritosa* (Haw.), and *Junonia coenia* (Hbn.)] with no detectable evidence of virus propagation. Aizawa (1961) renewed attempts with the nuclear polyhedrosis virus of the silkworm. Over 1500 embryos were inoculated without any discernible production, but Aizawa did report changes in the shape of inclusion bodies which may indicate some virus propagation. Future experiments with embryonated hen's eggs or any fertilized egg may be more successful when applied to the noninclusion viruses or freed virus particles of the inclusion viruses.

2. *Tissue-Cell Culture Technique*

Insect viruses, and indeed all viruses, are intimately associated with and dependent upon living cells. Therefore, any attempt to mass produce insect viruses must first solve the extremely difficult problem of mass producing insect tissue cells. The demonstrations that (1) insect viruses will develop in tissue cultures (Trager, 1935; Vago and Chastang, 1958; Grace, 1958, 1962b; Medvedeva, 1959; Aizawa and Vago, 1959a; Martignoni and Scallion, 1961; Vaughn and Faulkner, 1963), (2) that insect cell strains can be subcultured and grown *in vitro* (Aizawa and Vago, 1959b; Grace, 1959a,b, 1962a; Day and Grace, 1959), and (3) that mammalian tissue cells can be mass cultured in large, stainless-steel fermentors (Ziegler *et al.*, 1958; Harris, 1964; Gori, 1965) support the feasibility of the tissue-cell approach to production of insect viruses. Actual commercial production, however, awaits (1) the isolation of cell strains which divide rapidly and can be repeatedly subcultured, and (2) development of a culturing medium and production-line techniques. These problems are mainly of a technical nature and hence surmountable. The future outlook for the tissue-cell approach to mass production of insect viruses is promising. Research on a scope equivalent to that provided for studies of mammalian viruses could make mass production of insect viruses from tissue-cell cultures a commercial reality within a decade. Our present tissue-cell techniques, however, cannot provide the quantity and diversity of viruses that are available utilizing the living whole insect.

3. *Living Insect Techniques*

Most viruses are produced in living insects, usually in developing larvae. Viruses can also be propagated in pupae (Vago, 1957), injected into mature larvae, and harvested from pupae (Vago and Atger, 1961), or propagated in adults (Martignoni, 1964b). Adults and/or pupae may be used in future programs, but for the present, the larva is the best stage on which to propagate viruses. Virus for field tests is obtained from diseased larvae collected from (1) epizootics, (2) fields that are selectively treated with virus in order to obtain a maximum yield of larvae, and (3) laboratory or field-reared larvae fed on natural or semisynthetic diets, and then subsequently infected with the virus. Rearing insects on natural foliage places dependence on the periodic presence of either the insect and/or its natural food. It also decreases the opportunity for continuous virus production. In spite of these difficulties the technique is used extensively to produce insect viruses (Table II). Only viruses of the nuclear polyhedroses and granuloses have been widely field tested. The reader is referred to the reviews of Steinhaus (1949, 1951), Hughes (1957), Dutky (1959), Tanada (1959), Gershenson

TABLE II

Virus types	Insect species	References
Nuclear polyhedroses	*Choristoneura fumiferana* (Clem.)	Stairs and Bird (1966)
	Colias philodice eurytheme Bvd.	Steinhaus and Thompson (1949); Thompson and Steinhaus (1950)
	Diprion hercyniae (Htg.)	Balch and Bird (1944); Balch (1946); Bird and Burk (1961)
	Heliothis zea (Boddie)	Chamberlin and Dutky (1958); Tanada and Reiner (1962); Ignoffo (1965); Ignoffo et al. (1966)
	Kotochalia junodi (Heyl.)	Ossowski (1957, 1959)
	Malacosoma fragile Stretch	Clark and Thompson (1954)
	Neodiprion sertifer (Geoff.)	Breny (1951); Bird (1953, 1955, 1962); Dowden and Girth (1953); Franz and Niklas (1954); Benjamin et al. (1955); Schuder (1957); Lewis (1960); Rivers (1964)
	Neodiprion swainei Midd.	Smirnoff (1961, 1964)
	Plusia gamma (L.)	Vago and Cayrol (1955)
	Prodenia litura (F.)	Abul-Nasr (1959)
	Thaumetopoea pityocampa Schiff.	Grison et al. (1959); Martouret and Dusaussoy (1959); Grison (1960); Biliotti et al. (1956b, 1959)
	Trichoplusia ni. (Hbn.)	Hall (1957); McEwen and Hervey (1958); Genung (1959, 1960); Elmore (1961); Hofmaster and Ditman (1961); Semel (1961); Getzin (1962b); Ignoffo (1964b)
Granuloses	*Argyrotaenia velutinana* (Wlk.)	Glass (1958)
	Choristoneura fumiferana (Clem.)	Stairs and Bird (1966)
	Eucosma griseana (Hbn.)	Martignoni and Auer (1957)
	Pieris brassicae (L.)	Biliotti et al. (1956a); Smith and Rivers (1956)
	Pieris rapae (L.)	Tanada (1953, 1956); Kelsey (1957); McEwen and Hervey (1959); Smith (1959); Wilson (1960)

(1960), Martignoni and Langston (1960), Franz (1961), Krieg (1961), Bird (1962), Bergold (1963), Hall (1963), Heimpel (1963), Huger (1963), and Smith (1963) for additional examples and listings of viruses reported from arthropods. Although the use of natural foliage for rearing insects has served us well, semisynthetic diets are currently available that permit sustained rearing of insects. The cabbage looper, bollworm, and their respective nuclear polyhedroses were selected as models in pilot programs which explored and established protocols for mass producing insect viruses from larvae reared and infected on semisynthetic diets.

The cabbage looper feeds gregariously and is relatively easy and inexpensive to rear en masse. The bollworm, in contrast, is cannibalistic and therefore difficult and expensive to mass rear. If virus production can be demonstrated with these species, which are probably examples of extreme cases, then production of any insect virus is a possibility. Assuming, of course, that the insect can be reared on a semisynthetic diet and has or can be infected with viroses. Artificial diets and rearing protocols are presently our best approach to production of a viral product which meets the prerequisites imposed upon microbial insecticides.

III. SEMISYNTHETIC DIET USED TO REAR *HELIOTHIS* AND *TRICHOPLUSIA*

A. Prefatory

The semisynthetic diet for *Heliothis* spp. and *Trichoplusia ni* is basically that developed by Vanderzant et al. (1962a,b) and subsequently modified by Berger (1963), Getzin (1962a), and Ignoffo (1963a, 1964b, 1965b). The same or slightly modified diet also can be used to rear several other insects (Vanderzant et al., 1962a; Vanderzant and Richardson, 1963; Adkisson et al., 1960; Ignoffo, 1965a).

B. Diet Ingredients and Its Preparation

The ingredients shown in Table III make about 3.8 liters of the finished diet. The following procedure is used: Dissolve granulated agar in 2200 ml of boiling water; mix casein with 880 ml of water and 18 ml of potassium hydroxide in a 1-gal capacity commercial blender (Fig. 2A); add all solids, except ascorbic acid and the antibiotic, and blend for 2–3 minutes; add solutions, blend, then add dissolved agar; add ascorbic acid and antibiotic (chlorotetracycline); blend entire mixture for 2 minutes. Vitamin stock contains 600 mg niacin, 600 mg calcium pantothenate, 300 mg ribo-

TABLE III

BASIC INGREDIENTS OF THE SEMISYNTHETIC DIET USED TO REAR
Heliothis AND *Trichoplusia*

Ingredient	Quantity
Distilled water	3100 ml
Methyl-*p*-hydroxybenzoate	
(15% w/v in 95% ethyl alcohol)	36 ml
Choline chloride (0.1 gm/ml water)	36 ml
Potassium hydroxide, 4 *M*	18 ml
Formalin (0.1 gm/ml)	15 ml
Vitamin stock	6 ml
Casein	126 gm
Sucrose	126 gm
Wheat germ	108 gm
Leafmeal*a*	54 gm
Agar	90 gm
Wesson's salts	36 gm
Alphacel	18 gm
Ascorbic acid	15 gm
Antibiotic	0.5 gm

a Used only in *Trichoplusia* diet.

flavin, 150 mg each of thiamine, pyridoxine, and folic acid, 12 mg biotin, and 1.2 mg of vitamin B_{12} in 100 ml distilled water. A commercial, dry, vitamin-dextrose mixture can be substituted (36 gm) for the vitamin stock and choline chloride. If the vitamin-dextrose is used the sucrose should be reduced from 126 to 96 gm.

The hot liquid diet is dispensed into the appropriate rearing containers and allowed to solidify prior to infesting with either larvae or eggs. The costs and sources of ingredients used in the *Heliothis* and *Trichoplusia* diets are listed in the appendix.

IV. MICROBIAL CONTAMINATION

An important phase of insect rearing is cleanliness. No known antimicrobial substance, at a concentration which will permit insect development, can completely nullify the activities of a careless insect rearer, or eliminate the reappearance of contamination problems. The use of a standard, systematic, clean, rearing procedure can help to eliminate or solve contamination problems once they occur. The most recurring problem in rearing *Heliothis* and *Trichoplusia* is contamination of the diet by *Aspergillus flavus* Link and *Aspergillus niger* van Tieghan. Contamination by *Aspergillus* usually occurs late (12–14 days at 30°C), mainly on feces, and therefore has

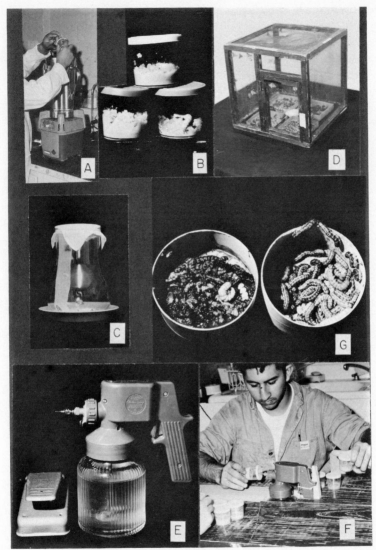

FIG. 2. Apparatus and techniques used in *Heliothis* program. A, preparation of semisynthetic diet; B, rearing cups; C, mating-oviposition cage; D, adult emergence cage; E, inoculator; F, inoculating cups and larvae with virus; G, diseased dead and living larvae.

little or no effect on larval development or pupation. However, it becomes a serious problem when it occurs during early stages of larval development.

If possible, antibiotics should be avoided. Sources of contamination should be traced and eliminated by exclusion, disinfection,

510   CARLO M. IGNOFFO

or sterilization. If antibiotics are necessary, their selection should be based on tests conducted against the particular contaminant and the insect concerned. Even the diet ingredients should be considered as possible sources of contamination. After experiencing some difficulty in rearing pink bollworms, I have traced sources of diet contamination to vitamin stock, wheat germ, casein, and water, but not to potassium hydroxide, methyl-p-hydroxybenzoate, choline chloride, formalin, alphacel, agar, sucrose, and Wesson's salts.

Antimicrobial substances, i.e., formalin, methyl-p-hydroxybenzo-ate, butyl-p-hydroxybenzoate, dichlorophene, pimaracin, chlorotetra-cycline, kanamycin, dihydrostreptomycin sulfate and sodium pro-pionate are added to the basic diet to inhibit the growth of fungi, yeast, or bacteria (Ouye, 1962; Berger, 1963; Ignoffo, 1963a,b). Kana-mycin, chlorotetracycline, dihydrostreptomycin, and sodium pro-pionate added to the diet at 0.13 mg/ml and formalin at 0.4 mg/ml do not affect larval development, pupation, or adult emergence. Formalin at or above 1.0 mg/ml of diet does affect larval survival, development, and subsequent pupation (Table IV). Penicillin, streptomycin, tetracycline, and oxytetracycline will not prevent viral infections (Bergold, 1953; Aizawa, 1954a; Krieg, 1957) but grasseriomycin may increase the incubation period of viral infec-tions (Ueda *et al.*, 1955).

TABLE IV

Per Cent Pupation, Average Days to Pupation, and Pupal Weights of *Trichoplusia* Reared on Diets Containing Various Concentrations of Formalin[a]

Formalin (mg/ml)	Pupation (%)	Average days to pupation	Pupal weight (mg)
0.4	100	10.2a[b]	284.0a
0.8	100	10.7a	273.6a
1.0	95	12.1b	262.3b
2.0	43	24.1c	233.3c
5.0	0	—	—

[a] Seven individually reared larvae/treatment, 3 replicates.
[b] Values with different letters are significantly different at 5% level.

Sodium hypochlorite (commercial household bleach) at 0.5% (about 1 part bleach to 9 parts water) is suggested as an ideal gen-eral laboratory disinfectant. It has excellent microbiocidal activity, good stability and solubility, low mammalian toxicity, and is inex-pensive. In addition, available chlorine can be easily determined by an acid-KL, colorimetric reaction, and its activity can be stopped with sodium thiosulfate (Ignoffo and Dutky, 1963).

V. PRODUCTION OF THE NUCLEAR POLYHEDROSIS VIRUS OF *HELIOTHIS*

A. REARING EQUIPMENT AND PROCEDURES

The following descriptions of the *Heliothis* rearing apparatus and procedures are taken from the studies of Berger (1963) and Ignoffo (1965b). The hot liquid diet (Fig. 2A) after mixing, is poured into 16-ounce polyethylene bottles and then squeezed into rearing cups. *Heliothis* larvae are individually reared in plastic cups (Fig. 2B). Approximately 10 or 25 ml of the diet is used to rear larvae for virus propagation or stock, respectively. After diet solidification (about 15 minutes), the cups are stacked and infested with larvae within 4–6 hours.

First-instar larvae are obtained from eggs collected in the following manner. Newly emerged adults are collected daily, paired, then placed (10 pairs/cage) into a mating-oviposition cage (Fig. 2C). A large lantern globe is used to cage the adults. The bottom of the cage is a pie pan covered with an 8 × 8-inch cheesecloth. Adults are fed on a 5 or 10% sterile sugar solution from a cup placed in the center of the cage. A 3 × 12-inch gauze, draped inside the globe, serves as a resting ramp. The cage is topped with an 8 × 8-inch oviposition pad. The resting ramp and oviposition pad are secured with an inverted 6-inch Petri dish top. A wetted milk-filter disc, lining the inside of the Petri dish, is used to increase the humidity. The mating-oviposition cages are kept at 23°–25°C. Two cages are set up daily and taken down 8 days later. Maximum oviposition is obtained during this period. To ensure mating and deposition of fertile eggs, the temperature of the mating-oviposition room should not exceed 25°C and the relative humidity should be cycled between 30% and 90%. Oviposition pads are collected daily, placed in a porcelain pan containing 1000 ml of 0.2% sodium hypochlorite and soaked for 5–7 minutes. This treatment disinfects and frees the eggs from the oviposition pads. Hypochlorite treatment is an important phase in the rearing protocol. Pathogens, potential pathogens, and contaminants can be excluded or reduced with hypochlorite treatment (Ignoffo and Dutky, 1963). The excess hypochlorite is discarded after the eggs settle and the remaining hypochlorite neutralized with 10% sodium thiosulfate (1 ml thiosulfate will neutralize about

50 ml hypochlorite). The eggs are poured over the original oviposition pads (the free liquid is removed with vacuum filtration),
transferred to waxed paper cups, and incubated at 30°C. Hatching
occurs 3–4 days later. Two to three newly hatched larvae are transferred to each rearing cup with the aid of a fine pointed brush. Three
persons can infest 1500 to 2000 cups/hour. The cups are capped,
stacked in cartons, and stored at 30°C. After 14 days (90% pupation
level) pupae are removed, washed in 0.2% hypochlorite (15 minutes),
and then placed on vermiculite in shallow cardboard trays. A separate tray is used for each daily collection and may contain from
100–150 pupae. The trays are dated and placed in an adult-emergence cage kept at 24°–26°C (Fig. 2D). The cage is bottomless and
has swinging doors to facilitate collecting adults, which start emerging
7 days later.

Newly emerged females can be differentiated from males on the
basis of wing coloration, general size, and shape of the body and
abdomen. Females have tan wings with conspicuous brown markings, a robust body, a blunt-tipped abdomen, and average 249 mg.
Males have green-tinted wings with no conspicuous markings, a
slender body, a slim tapering abdomen, and average 208 mg. All
Heliothis rearing is conducted under continuous, low intensity,
fluorescent lighting.

B. Virus Inoculating Equipment and Procedures

Larvae of *H. zea* (179.4 ± 12.1 mg) and the tobacco budworm,
Heliothis virescens Fabricius, (153.7 ± 12.0 mg) reared at 30°C for
6 and 7 days, respectively, are used to propagate the virus. The
inoculating apparatus (Fig. 2E) is an electric hand sprayer (the
nozzle modified to accept a hypodermic needle) wired to a lever
rheostat (sewing-machine foot control). In operation the inoculator
is placed in a niche cut into the center of the infecting table. Each
cup is jammed on the hypodermic needle. A slight sideward knee
movement (against the control lever mounted under the table) activates the sprayer to release 0.2 ml of a virus suspension containing
1.8×10^7 polyhedral inclusion bodies (PIB)/ml of suspension (Fig.
2F). The available diet surface of a rearing cup is 1385 mm²; therefore a dose of 2598 PIB/mm² is provided. The virus dose and larval
age are standardized to attain maximum utilization of larval tissue
for virus propagation. Maximum utilization is not attained if younger
or older larvae are used (Table V).

Two persons, one operating the inoculator and a general helper,
can inoculate 2000 cups/hour. Cups and larvae thus treated are

TABLE V

AVERAGE PER CENT LARVAL MORTALITY (LM) AND LETHAL TIME IN DAYS FOR
50% LARVAL MORTALITY (LT$_{50}$) OF *H. zea* AND *H. virescens* LARVAE
CONTINUALLY EXPOSED TO DOSES OF 2598 AND 1247 PIB/MM^2 OF
DIET SURFACE, RESPECTIVELY[a]

Larval age (days)	*Heliothis zea*			*Heliothis virescens*		
	Number	LM	LT$_{50}$	Number	LM	LT$_{50}$
1	150	100.0	3.4	149	100.0	3.1
4	144	100.0	5.0	237	100.0	4.3
5	144	100.0	5.5	238	100.0	4.6
6	144	100.0	6.3	256	99.6	6.0
7	145	73.8	6.7	252	78.2	7.0
8	144	41.7	—	232	35.3	—

[a] LT$_{50}$ values were interpolated from time-mortality curves.

TABLE VI

MORTALITY OF 6-DAY-OLD *H. zea* AND *H. virescens* LARVAE CONTINUALLY
EXPOSED TO DIETS CONTAINING 2598 AND 1247 PIB/MM^2 OF
AVAILABLE DIET SURFACE, RESPECTIVELY[a]

Days after inoculating cups with virus	Larval mortality (%)	
	H. zea	*H. virescens*
3	1.4	0.0
4	4.2	1.6
5	11.1	55.6
6	33.3	86.7
7	73.6	93.4
8	87.5	96.5
9	97.9	98.4
10	100.0	99.6

[a] A total of 144 *H. zea* and 256 *H. virescens* larvae were used in these tests.

held at 24°C; 7 and 9 days later, approximately 75 and 95% of the
larvae are dead (Table VI). The larvae are manually collected between the 6th and 9th day, separated into dead or living larvae
(Fig. 2G), transferred to dated, 8-ounce cartons, and stored as whole
larvae at −20°C until processed for field and/or laboratory studies.

C. RESULTS OF PILOT PROGRAMS

The results of pilot programs (Table VII) demonstrated that the
Heliothis virus can be obtained in large quantities from larvae individually reared on semisynthetic diets and that the protocol and

TABLE VII

NUMBER AND ESTIMATED COST OF LARVAL PRODUCTION[a]

Insect species	No. of larvae produced		Cost/larva ($)
	Total	Av./week	
Trichoplusia ni	20,520	3,420	0.010
Heliothis zea	201,706	11,865	0.070
Heliothis virescens	14,645	861	0.070
	601[b]		0.028

[a] Pilot programs: T. ni, 6 weeks, 1962; Heliothis spp., 17 weeks, 1963.
[b] Four larvae/container.

costs were within the realm of commercial feasibility (Ignoffo, 1965a). More than 200,000 bollworms and over 15,000 budworms were produced during a 17-wk pilot program. Preliminary estimates were that 4000–5000 larvae would be needed daily in order to infest 2000 to 2500 cups. An average 12,762 Heliothis/week were produced (H. zea, 11,865; H. virescens, 897) or 2552 larvae/day. Approximately 95% of the total number reared can be used for virus propagation.

An increase of 2000- to 7000-fold over the number of PIB introduced was obtained from each last instar H. zea larva. An estimated 1.3 to 5.3 quadrillion PIB was produced in 17 weeks or enough virus to treat 2160 to 8380 acres at 100 larval equivalents/acre (Ignoffo, 1965; Ignoffo et al., 1965). A larval equivalent equals 6×10^9 PIB/larva, or the lowest value ever recorded from microscopic counts made on suspensions of 1000 last-instar larvae. The highest value was 24 billion PIB/larva. It is estimated that 1 billion PIB weighs 1 mg; therefore, each larva may yield 6–24 mg of pure inclusion bodies, which is about 1–4% of the average body weight of bollworms. The amount of available infective units, i.e., virus particles, may be increased by a factor of 20–200 if particles can be released from inclusion bodies without loss of activity and then stabilized.

Six persons were employed in the Heliothis virus program, four to rear Heliothis and two to propagate the virus. The estimated cost, excluding overhead, was $.07/larva. Labor, rearing cups, and diet accounted for 0.040, 0.025, and 0.005 of the total cost, respectively. This estimate reflected the high cost of an initial pilot program, and may be reduced through automation of the egg-collecting, larval-infesting, and virus-inoculating phases. Per-unit costs may also be further decreased with multiple-rearing containers, substi-

TABLE VIII

USE OF *H. virescens* AS A LESS CANNIBALISTIC, MULTIPLE-REARED, ALTERNATE
HOST FOR PRODUCTION OF THE NUCLEAR POLYHEDROSIS VIRUS OF *H. zea*[a]

No. of larvae			
Infested		Recovered	
Per cup	Total	Total	Per cup
1	150	146	1.0
3	450	397	2.6
5	750	601	4.0

[a] Larvae (6-day-old) exposed to 2288 PIB/mm² of diet surface.

tution of crude for chemically defined ingredients, and the use of
non- or less cannibalistic hosts (Table VIII).

VI. PRODUCTION OF THE NUCLEAR POLYHEDROSIS VIRUS OF *TRICHOPLUSIA NI*

A. REARING EQUIPMENT AND PROCEDURES

The diets and procedures used to rear cabbage loopers for over
75 generations were previously described (Ignoffo, 1963a, 1964a,b)
and are discussed further in another chapter (Chapter 32 of this
volume). Dried cotton leafmeal or alfalfa leafmeal is used to fortify
the basic diet (see Section III,B). Approximately 35 ml of the hot,
liquid diet is poured into rearing containers. The containers are
capped, tilted and twirled to distribute the diet over the inner surface, and placed on their sides until the diet solidifies. About 8
inch² of feeding surface is provided. The containers are stored cap-
side down at room temperature and used within a week. One diet
preparation will fill 100–200 containers, depending on whether
they are used for insect-stock or virus propagation. Females deposit
their eggs on paper toweling wrapped around cylindrical mating-
oviposition cages (Fig. 3A). Two cages, kept at 25°C and 30% relative humidity, provided all the eggs used in our program. A gravity
feeding device automatically drops 5 or 10% sugar solution (3–5
drops of solution/minute) on an absorbent-paper pad placed on top
of the cage (Fig. 3A). Adults feed on droplets formed in the mesh
under the paper pad.

Eggs are removed from the toweling, using essentially the technique previously described (see Section V,A). The eggs are con-

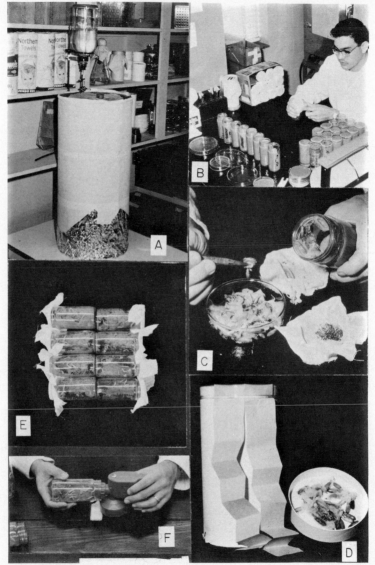

FIG. 3. Apparatus and techniques used in *Trichoplusia* program. A, mating-oviposition cage; B, infesting rearing jars with larvae; C, collecting pupae; D, adult emergence cage; E, larvae for virus propagation; F, inoculating jars and larvae with virus.

solidated by filtering, washed with 10% sodium thiosulfate, and rinsed with sterile, distilled water. They are then transferred to a Petri dish which is plugged with cotton batting. The eggs hatch within 2–3 days (30°C) and 10 newly hatched larvae are transferred

TABLE IX

AVERAGE WEIGHT OF MALE AND FEMALE *Trichoplusia* PUPAE REARED
FROM DISTURBED AND UNDISTURBED LARVAE[a]

| | Average pupal weight (mg) | |
Treatment	Male	Female
Individually reared, not disturbed	305.2 ± 4.5[b]	290.4 ± 4.2
Individually reared, disturbed daily	228.5 ± 7.9	215.2 ± 6.9
Group-reared, 10 larvae/jar	241.8 ± 2.8	231.7 ± 6.4

[a] Averages based upon 25 individuals/sex/treatment.
[b] $\pm$ standard error of the mean.

to each rearing container (Fig. 3B). The containers are capped with cheesecloth or punctured lids and placed at 30°C. Overcrowding or mishandling larvae may affect their development. Both male and female pupae from undisturbed larvae weigh significantly more than disturbed larvae (Table IX). About 98% pupation is reached 12 days later. The pupae are picked from the rearing containers and transferred to adult-emergence cages (Fig. 3C). Buffered hypochlorite (1 part 1% hypochlorite to 1 part 5% sodium carbonate) (Dutky *et al.*, 1962) will dissolve the loosely webbed cocoons in about 30 minutes and therefore may be used to collect pupae. It is advisable to use an emergence cage (Fig. 3D) for each collection of pupae. Adults begin emerging 7 days later and emergence is completed within another 7 days. Newly emerged adults are immobilized with carbon dioxide, then transferred to the mating-oviposition cage. Adults will live for 7–10 days in these cages. Dead adults are vacuumed off the bottom of the cage when necessary. Two cages containing 1000 adults each provide a daily collection of nearly 30,000 eggs/cage or approximately 60 times the number actually used in the virus program. Based upon a 7-day oviposition period, 50 eggs/day/female is a conservative estimate of the number of eggs that will be produced. The entire cage is autoclaved once every 2 months. All rearing is done under continuous fluorescent lighting.

B. VIRUS INOCULATING EQUIPMENT AND PROCEDURES

Larvae to be used for virus propagation are reared at 30°C for 6–7 days (Fig. 3E). Larvae 6–7 days old are in the late 4th to early 5th instar, have completed about 70% of their total developmental period, achieved about 63% of their total weight, and average 209 ± 15 mg. Normal larvae will consume about 75% of the total food eaten (2.16 ± 0.08 gm) within the remaining 2–3 days of development.

The use of late-instar larvae accomplishes several important objectives. The pickup of a lethal virus dose occurs within a short period, maximum utilization of larval tissue is obtained, and the phases of virus production, i.e., larval rearing, infecting, and harvesting, are easily systematized.

A hand atomizer was first used to inoculate the diet and larvae with the virus suspension. Later, an automatic inoculator (Section V,B) with the spray nozzle intact, was more effectively employed (Fig. 3F). The cap of each container is removed and the larvae, diet, and interior sprayed with 0.2 ml of a suspension containing 5×10^6 PIB/ml, or 200 PIB/mm^2 of available diet surface. The treated containers are recapped and placed at 23°C. The lower temperature (23°C) permits continual harvesting of intact larvae. The diseased larvae are manually harvested 4–5 days after inoculation with the virus, classified as living or dead, packed into dated 8-ounce cartons, and stored at −20°C.

C. RESULTS OF A PILOT PROGRAM

The results of a pilot program designed to determine the feasibility of producing the nuclear polyhedrosis virus of *Trichoplusia ni* from larvae reared on a semisynthetic diet are included in Table VII. A total of 20,520 loopers was reared in 2,904 containers or an average of 3,240 larvae/week (Ignoffo, 1964b). Observations made at the time of the program and subsequently reconfirmed indicate that 95% of the larvae can be used for virus propagation. Various types of disposable plastic and paper containers were tried. In general, larval yields from disposable containers were comparable to yields from glass jars, but many of the disposable containers became contaminated with *A. flavus* and *A. niger*. The use of inexpensive, disposable containers is preferred, since it eliminates glass washing and minimizes the hazards of recontamination.

The average yield was $12.6 \pm 0.7 \times 10^9$ PIB/larva. In contrast, the yields from field-collected larvae averaged $6.5 \pm 2.7 \times 10^9$ PIB/larva. These averages, based on microscopic counts made on only 10 larvae from each source, may indicate that the yields of laboratory-infected larvae are greater and less variable than that of field-diseased larvae. An estimated 10,000-fold increase in the number of PIB was obtained from each diseased, last-instar larvae. Assuming that 95% of the larvae is used for virus propagation and the average count is 12.6×10^9 PIB/larva, then a calculated 245 trillion PIB was produced. Using 10 larvae/acre (12.6×10^{10} PIB/acre) 245 trillion PIB could treat nearly 2000 acres.

VII. VIRUS PURIFICATION, STANDARDIZATION, AND STORAGE

Little has been done to develop an efficient method of preparing insect viruses for field use. This is quite surprising since the ultimate success or failure of field tests is directly related to virus virulence and stability. Viral preparations are probably most vulnerable during their collection, purification, and storage phases. Past methods of preparing insect viruses are as different as the number of persons preparing them. Diseased larvae are collected living and/or dead from field and/or laboratory populations; either bled, crushed, triturated, or blended with water; and either chemically treated, frozen, decomposed, filtered, sedimented, or centrifuged to concentrate the inclusion bodies. After purification, they have been stored as suspensions or dusts, at room, refrigerator, or freezing temperatures.

The factors affecting virulence or stability of viral preparations, and how these factors operate, have never been clearly described. Temperature, chemicals, pH, ultraviolet, and ultrasonic radiation are some factors known to affect viral preparations. Generalizations from past studies indicate that activity and stability decrease as temperature rises above 0°C (Bergold, 1943; Watanabe, 1951; Aizawa, 1953a,b, 1954a,b; Tanada, 1953, 1956; Steinhaus, 1954, 1960a; Glass, 1958; Kelsey, 1958; Rivers, 1959; Smith, 1959; Neilson and Elgee, 1960); at pH below 5 and above 8 (Hills and Smith, 1959; Bergold, 1958); and after exposure to either ultraviolet or ultrasonic radiation (Aizawa, 1955; Watanabe, 1951). Treatment with inorganic, organic, or biological materials may or may not affect the virulence of virus preparations (Bergold, 1948, 1953, 1959; Huger, 1963; Zalmanzon, 1949; Graffi and Krischke, 1960; Ivanicova, 1961; Tarassevitch *et al.*, 1964; Krieg, 1957; Aizawa, 1953c, 1954c; Ueda *et al.*, 1955; Speyer, 1925).

The method most often used to consolidate virus for field tests is to pulverize 1 part virus-diseased larvae with 3 parts water, allow the crushed insects to decompose, filter the resulting suspension through several layers and grades of cloths, and then concentrate the polyhedra by sedimentation.

Dried, refrigerated, or frozen viruses, with few microbial contaminants, are probably the most stable preparations. It is therefore suggested that only living or recently dead larva be used to prepare viruses. Diseased larvae could be washed under cold flowing water, blended (15–30 seconds) using 2–3 parts of ice water/larva, filtered through cheesecloth and/or nylon (1/10, 1/50, 1/100 mesh), and then centrifuged at 5,000–15,000g (0°C) for 15 minutes. Centrifugation should ensure a high level of recovery, but minimize packing of inclusion bodies. The lipids (top layer) and supernatant are discarded and the sediment immediately freeze-dried. The dried sediment is triturated, consolidated with other preparations, mixed, sieved, and remixed to obtain a homogeneous preparation. This preparation should be characterized on the basis of (1) infective units expressed in number or weight/unit weight or volume of preparation; (2) an assay of insecticidal activity (Vaughn and Faulkner, 1963; Ignoffo, 1964a, 1965c); (3) a determination of bacteria, i.e., differential plate counts for total bacteria, coliforms, and viables spores (Ignoffo and Heimpel, 1965). Information of this type will materially aid in determining optimum purification and storage conditions for viral preparations. Until these conditions are delineated it is suggested that a reference standard be sealed in glass under vacuum, and that this standard, as well as other preparations, be stored at subfreezing temperatures.

The following sources should be consulted for detailed information on methods used to release and purify insect viruses. Each of the major groups of insect viruses are represented in these references: nuclear polyhedroses (Brake, 1951; Bergold, 1959, 1963, 1964); cytoplasmic polyhedroses (Hills and Smith, 1959; Bird, 1952); granuloses (Huger, 1963); and the noninclusion viruses (Williams and Smith, 1957, 1958; Smith *et al.*, 1961; Plus, 1954, 1960; Krieg and Huger, 1960).

VIII. APPLICATION TO OTHER INSECT VIRUSES

Is the production of the nuclear polyhedroses of *Heliothis* and *Trichoplusia ni* an isolated example, or can these production methods be applied to other insects and their respective viruses? Only time can fully answer this question. The only way presently open to commercial production of insect viruses is by using nature's efficient "*crawling fermentators.*" The procedures and costs are both feasible and realistic. The applications are vast. Sixteen lepidopteran pests of field crops have at least one virus disease (the armyworm has four) and these species can also be reared on semisynthetic diets (Table X). If the viruses of *Heliothis* and *Trichoplusia* can be propagated, then why not the pathogens of other species. The time is opportune. Necessity has given impetus to search for other methods of insect control which will minimize the problems of chemical resistance and residues. Insect viruses offer an excellent alternative. Its application should be now.

TABLE X

Important Lepidopteran Pests of Field Crops Which Have a Virus
Disease and Can Also Be Reared on Semisynthetic Diets

Common name	Scientific name	Reported viruses
Alfalfa looper	*Autographa californica* (Speyer)	Nuclear polyhedrosis, granulosis
Armyworm	*Pseudaletia unipuncta* (Haw.)	Nuclear and cytoplasmic poly-hedrosis, granulosis, non-inclusion
Beet armyworm	*Spodoptera exigua* (Hbn.)	Nuclear polyhedrosis, granulosis
Bollworm	*Heliothis zea* (Boddie)	Nuclear and cytoplasmic poly-hedrosis
Cabbage looper	*Trichoplusia ni* (Hbn.)	Nuclear polyhedrosis, granulosis
Cotton leafworm	*Alabama argillacea* (Hbn.)	Nuclear polyhedrosis
Fall armyworm	*Laphygma frugiperda* (J. E. Smith)	Nuclear polyhedrosis and granulosis
Granulated cutworm	*Felitia subterranea* (F.)	Granulosis
Imported cabbage-worm	*Pieris rapae* L.	Nuclear and cytoplasmic poly-hedrosis, granulosis
Pink bollworm	*Pectinophora gossypiella* (Saund.)	Cytoplasmic polyhedrosis
Salt-marsh caterpillar	*Estigmene acrea* (Drury)	Nuclear and cytoplasmic poly-hedrosis, granulosis
Southern armyworm	*Prodenia eridania* (Cram.)	Nuclear polyhedrosis, granulosis
Tobacco budworm	*Heliothis virescens* (F.)	Nuclear polyhedrosis
Variegated cutworm	*Peridroma margaritosa* (Haw.)	Nuclear polyhedrosis, granulosis
Yellow-striped army-worm	*Prodenia ornithogalli* (Guen.)	Nuclear polyhedrosis
Western yellow-striped army-worm	*Prodenia praefica* (Grote)	Nuclear polyhedrosis

APPENDIX A

Costs and Sources of Diet Ingredients

Ingredients	Cost/unit ($)	Source
Ethyl alcohol, absolute, pure grain	1.25/liter	U. S. Industrial Chemicals[a]
Formaldehyde, reagent grade	1.66/liter	E. H. Sargent and Co.[b]
Potassium hydroxide, reagent grade	1.30/lb	E. H. Sargent and Co.
Methyl-p-hydroxybenzoate, Eastman	6.36/lb	E. H. Sargent and Co.
Casein, vitamin-free	1.94/lb	Nutritional Biochemicals[c]
Wesson's salt mixture	0.90/lb	Nutritional Biochemicals
Alphacel, non-nutritive, bulk	0.64/lb	Nutritional Biochemicals
Wheat germ	0.34/lb	Nutritional Biochemicals
Agar, granulated, USP	3.15/lb	Nutritional Biochemicals
Alfalfa leafmeal, entomological grade	0.75/lb	Nutrilite Products, Inc.[d]
Cotton leafmeal	1.00/lb	Prepared locally
Sucrose	0.10/lb	Purchased locally
Vitamin mixture	0.02/gm	Nutritional Biochemicals
Niacinamide	0.16/gm	Nutritional Biochemicals
D-Calcium pantothenate	0.09/gm	Nutritional Biochemicals
Riboflavin	0.07/gm	Nutritional Biochemicals
Choline chloride	0.07/gm	Nutritional Biochemicals
Pyridoxin hydrochloride	0.35/gm	Nutritional Biochemicals
Thiamine hydrochloride	0.10/gm	Nutritional Biochemicals
Folic acid, crystalline	1.03/gm	Nutritional Biochemicals
Biotin, crystalline	10.00/gm	Nutritional Biochemicals
B_{12}, crystalline	0.35/mg	Nutritional Biochemicals
Ascorbic acid	0.02/gm	Nutritional Biochemicals
Aureomycin (chlorotetracycline)	1.04/gm	Lederle Laboratories[e]
Kanamycin	1.28/gm	Bristol Laboratories[f]
Dihydrostreptomycin sulfate	0.10/gm	Nutritional Biochemicals

[a] 1959 W. 8th, Los Angeles, California.

[b] 4647 W. Foster Avenue, Chicago, Illinois.

[c] 21010 Miles Avenue, Cleveland, Ohio.

[d] Buena Park, California.

[e] Pearl River, New York.

[f] 6860 E. Asco, Los Angeles, California.

APPENDIX B
EQUIPMENT USED IN *Heliothis* PROGRAM

Item	Specifications	Source
Commercial blendor	Waring, gallon size	Any scientific supply house
Rearing cups	Two-ounce, transparent plastic, cylindrical, 1¾ × 1¾-inch; lid: flexible, polyethylene plastic	Massachusetts Plastic Co., Ludlow, Massachusetts
Oviposition-mating cage	Pioneer lantern globe, 11 × 6-inch, 6-inch diameter	R. E. Dietz, Box 1214, Syracuse, New York
Filter pad	Rapid-flow, milk filter, single gauge, 6½-inch diameter	Johnson and Johnson, Chicago, Illinois
Adult-emergence cage	Screen cage, square, 15 × 15 × 15-inch, 1/16-inch mesh	Locally constructed
Oviposition substrate	Bleached cheesecloth, 1/44-inch mesh	Purchased locally
Virus inoculator	Electric hand sprayer, 20-ounce capacity	Z and W Mfg. Co., Chicago, Illinois
Inoculator switch	Sewing-machine, foot-pedal control	Dayton Electric Mfg. Co., Chicago, Illinois
Virus storage cartons	Eight-ounce, liquid-tight food cartons	Sealright Co., Inc., Kansas City, Kansas

APPENDIX C
EQUIPMENT USED IN *Trichoplusia* PROGRAM

Item	Specifications	Source
Mating-oviposition cage	Cylindrical, screen cage, 15 × 30-inch, ¼-inch mesh	Locally constructed
Feeding bottle	Intravenous administration set	Will Ross, Inc., Milwaukee, Wisconsin
Rearing containers	Wide-mouth glass, plastic, or waxed jars, 6–8 ounce; lid: cloth or perforated plastic	Armstrong Glass Co., Lily-Tulip Corp., New York, New York
Adult-emergence cage	Cylindrical, 32-ounce, liquid-tight cartons	Sealright Co., Inc., Kansas City, Kansas
Oviposition substrate	Absorbent paper toweling, 11-inch width	Scott Paper Co., Everett, Washington
Virus inoculator	Electric hand sprayer, 20-ounce capacity	Z and W Mfg. Co., Chicago, Illinois

REFERENCES

Abul-Nasr, S. (1959). Further tests on the use of a polyhedrosis virus in the control of the cotton leafworm *Prodenia litura* Fabricus. *J. Insect Pathol.* **1,** 112–120.

Adkisson, D. L., Vanderzant, E. S., Bull, D. L., and Allison, W. E. (1960). A wheat germ medium for rearing the pink bollworm. *J. Econ. Entomol.* **53,** 759–762.

Aizawa, K. (1953a). Some methods of keeping the virus activity of the silkworm jaundice. *Sansi-Kenkyu* **3,** 75–77.

Aizawa, K. (1953b). On the inactivation of the silkworm jaundice virus. *Japan J. Appl. Zool.* **17,** 181–190 (in Japanese with English summary).

Aizawa, K. (1953c). On the dissolving curve of polyhedral bodies of the silkworm jaundice in Na_2CO_3 solution. *Japan. J. Appl. Zool.* **17,** 145–154.

Aizawa, K. (1954a). Immunological studies of the silkworm jaundice virus. III. Experiments on the defence of infection in the silkworm jaundice. *Virus* (Osaka) **4,** 245–248 (in Japanese with English summary).

Aizawa, K. (1954b). Immunological studies of the silkworm jaundice virus. I. Neutralization and adsorption test of the silkworm jaundice virus. *Virus* (Osaka) **4,** 238–240 (in Japanese with English summary).

Aizawa, K. (1954c). Dissolving curve and the virus activity of the polyhedral bodies of *Bombyx mori* L., obtained 37 years ago. *Sansi-Kenkyu* **8,** 52–54 (in Japanese with English summary).

Aizawa, K. (1955). Inactivation of the silkworm jaundice virus by the ultraviolet irradiation. *J. Sericult. Sci. Japan* **24,** 398–399 (in Japanese with English summary).

Aizawa, K. (1961). Change in the shape of silkworm polyhedra by means of passage through chick embryo. *Entomophaga* **6,** 197–201.

Aizawa, K., and Vago, C. (1959a). Sur l'infection a Borrelinarirus en culture de tissus d'insectes. *Ann. Inst. Pasteur* **96,** 455–460.

Aizawa, K., and Vago, C. (1959b). Culture *in vitro* de cellules separees de tissue d'Insectes. *Compt. Rend.* **249,** 928–930.

Balch, R. E. (1946). The disease of the European spruce sawfly. *Can. Dept. Agr., Bi-Monthly Progr. Rept.* **2,** 1.

Balch, R. E., and Bird, F. T. (1944). A disease of the European spruce sawfly, *Gilpinia hercyniae* (Htg.), and its place in natural control. *Sci. Agr.* **25,** 65–80.

Benjamin, D. M., Larson, J. D., and Drooz, A. T. (1955). The European sawfly on the Henderson State Forest, Illinois, with notes on its biology and control. *J. Forestry* **53,** 359–362.

Berger, R. S. (1963). Laboratory techniques for rearing *Heliothis* species on artificial medium. *U. S. Dept. Agr., ARS* ARS-33-84, 1–4.

Bergold, G. H. (1943). Über Polyeder-Krankheiten bei Inseken. *Biol. Zentr.* **63,** 1–55.

Bergold, G. (1948). Inaktivierung des Polyeder Virus durch Kollidon. *Z. Naturforsch.* **3b,** 300–301.

Bergold, G. H. (1953). Insect viruses. *Adv. Virus Res.* **1,** 91–139.

Bergold, G. H. (1958). Viruses of insects. *In* "Handbuch der Virusforschung" (K. F. Meyer and C. Hallauer, eds.), Vol. IV, Suppl. 3, pp. 60–142. Springer, Vienna.

Bergold, G. H. (1959). Purification of insect virus inclusion bodies with a fluoro-carbon. *J. Insect Pathol.* **1,** 96–97.

Bergold, G. H. (1963). The nature of the nuclear-polyhedrosis viruses. *In* "Insect Pathology" (E. A. Steinhaus, ed.), Vol. 1, pp. 413–456. Academic Press, New York.

Bergold, G. H. (1964). Insect viruses. *In* "Techniques in Experimental Virology"

(R. J. C. Harris, ed.), pp. 112–144. Academic Press, New York.

Biliotti, E., Grison, P., and Martouret, D. (1956a). L'utilisation d'une maladie à virus comme méthode de lutte biologique contre *Pieris brassicae* L. *Entomophaga* 1, 35–44.

Biliotti, E., Grison, P., and Vago, C. (1956b). Essai d'utilisation des polyèdres isolés de la processionnaire du pin, comme methode de lutte biologique. *Compt. Rend.* 243, 206–208.

Biliotti, E., Grison, P., Maury, R., and Vago, C. (1959). Emploi d'une poudre a base de virus specifique contre la chenille processionnaire du pin (*Thaumetopoea pityocampa*) dans le massif du Ventoux. *Compt. Rend. Acad. Agr. France* 45, 407–411.

Bird, F. T. (1952). On the multiplication of an insect virus. *Biochim. Biophys. Acta* 8, 360–368.

Bird, F. T. (1953). The use of a virus disease in the biological control of the European pine sawfly, *Neodiprion sertifer* (Geoffr.). *Can. Entomologist* 85, 437–446.

Bird, F. T. (1955). Virus diseases of sawflies. *Can. Entomologist* 87, 124–127.

Bird, F. T. (1962). The use of viruses in biological control. *Entomophaga Mem.* 2, 465–473.

Bird, F. T., and Burk, J. M. (1961). Artificially disseminated virus as a factor controlling the European spruce sawfly, *Diprion hercyniae* (Htg.), in the absence of introduced parasites. *Can. Entomologist* 93, 228–238.

Brake, M. K. (1951). Density gradient centrifugation: A new separation technique. *J. Am. Chem. Soc.* 73, 1847.

Breny, R. (1951). Polyedrofe chez *Neodiprion sertifer* (Geoffr.) *Parasitica* (*Gembloux*) 7, 118–124.

Briggs, J. D. (1963). Commercial production of insect pathogens. *In* "Insect Pathology" (E. A. Steinhaus, ed.), Vol. 2, pp. 519–548. Academic Press, New York.

Chamberlin, F. S., and Dutky, S. R. (1958). Tests of pathogens for the control of tobacco insects. *J. Econ. Entomol.* 51, 560.

Clark, E. C., and Thompson, C. G. (1954). The possible use of microorganisms in the control of the Great Basin tent caterpillar. *J. Econ. Entomol.* 47, 268–272.

Day, M. F., and Grace, T. D. C. (1959). Culture of insect tissues. *Ann. Rev. Entomol.* 4, 17–38.

Dowden, P. B., and Girth, H. B. (1953). Use of a virus disease to control European pine sawfly. *J. Econ. Entomol.* 46, 525–526.

Dutky, S. R. (1959). Insect microbiology. *Advan. Appl. Microbiol.* 1, 175–200.

Dutky, S. R., Thompson, J. V., and Cantwell, G. E. (1962). A technique for mass rearing the greater wax moth. (Lepidoptera: Galleridae). *Proc. Entomol. Soc. Wash.* 64, 56–58.

Elmore, J. C. (1961). Control of cabbage looper with a nuclear polyhedrosis virus disease. *J. Econ. Entomol.* 54, 47–50.

Forbes, S. A. (1895). On contagious disease in the chinch-bug (*Blissus leucopterus* Say). *19th Rept. Illinois State Entomologist* pp. 16–176.

Franz, J. M. (1961). Biological control of pest insects in Europe. *Ann. Rev. Entomol.* 6, 183–200.

Franz, J., and Niklas, O. F. (1954). Feldersuche zur Bekampfung der roten Kieferabuschnornblattweape (*Neodiprion sertifer* geoffr.) durch kunstliche Verbreitung einer Virrusseuche. *Nachrbl. Deut. Pflanzenschutzdienst.* (*Berlin*) [N.S.] 6, 131–134.

Genung, W. G. (1959). Observations on and preliminary experiments with a poly-hedrosis virus for control of cabbage looper, *Trichoplusia ni* (Hbn.). *Florida Entomologist* **42**, 99–104.

Genung, W. G. (1960). Comparison of insecticides, insect pathogens and insecticide-pathogen combinations for control of cabbage looper *Trichoplusia ni* (Hbn.). *Florida Entomologist* **43**, 65–68.

Gershenson, S. M. (1960). A bibliography of Soviet works on virus diseases of insects. *Entomol. Rev. (USSR) (English Transl.)* **39**, 334–340.

Getzin, L. (1962a). Mass rearing of virus-free cabbage loopers on an artificial diet. *J. Insect Pathol.* **4**, 486–488.

Getzin, L. W. (1962b). The effectiveness of the polyhedrosis virus for control of the cabbage looper, *Trichoplusia ni. J. Econ. Entomol.* **55**, 442–445.

Giard, A. (1892). *L'Isaria densa* (Link) Fries, champignon parasite du hanneton commun (*Melolontha vulgaris* L.). *Bull. Sci. France Belg.* **24**, 1–112.

Glass, E. H. (1958). Laboratory and field tests with the granulosis of the red-banded leaf roller. *J. Econ. Entomol.* **51**, 454–457.

Gori, Gio B. (1965). Continuous cultivation of virus in cell suspensions by use of the lysostat. *Appl. Microbiol.* **13**, 909–917.

Grace, T. D. C. (1958). Introduction of polyhedral bodies in ovarian tissues of the tussock moth *in vitro. Science* **28**, 249–250.

Grace, T. D. C. (1959a). Prolonged survival and growth of insect ovarian tissue under *in vitro* conditions. *Ann. N. Y. Acad. Sci.* **77**, 275–282.

Grace, T. D. C. (1959b). II. Tissue culture for arthropod viruses. *Trans. N. Y. Acad. Sci.* [2] **21**, 237–241.

Grace, T. D. C. (1962a). Establishment of four strains of cells from insect tissues grown *in vitro. Nature* **195**, 788–789.

Grace, T. D. C. (1962b). The development of a cytoplasmic polyhedrosis in insect cells grown *in vitro. Virology* **18**, 33–43.

Graffi, A., and Krischke, W. (1960). Über die Eignung von Fluorocarbon fur die An-reicherung des Virus der myeloischen Leukamie der Maus. *Acta Biol. Med. Ger.* **5**, 304–306.

Grison, P. (1960). Utilisation en foret d'une preparation a base de virus specifique contre *Thaumatopoea pityocampa* Schiff. *Z. Angew. Entomol.* **47**, 24–31.

Grison, P., Vago, C., and Maury, R. (1959). La lutte contre la processionnaire du pin "*Thaumetopoea pityocampa*" Schiff dans le massif du Ventoux; essai d'utilisa-tion practique d'un virus specifique. *Rev. Forestiere Franc.* **5**, 353–370.

Hall, I. M. (1957). Use of a polyhedrosis virus to control the cabbage looper on lettuce in California. *J. Econ. Entomol.* **50**, 551–553.

Hall, I. M. (1963). Microbial control. *In* "Insect Pathology" (E. A. Steinhaus, ed.), Vol. 2, pp. 477–517. Academic Press, New York.

Ham, R. G. (1965). Clonal growth of mammalian cells in a chemically defined syn-thetic medium. *Proc. Natl. Acad. Sci., U. S.* **53**, 288–293.

Harris, R. J. C., ed. (1964). "Techniques in Experimental Virology." Academic Press, New York.

Haruna, I., and Spiegelman, S. (1965). Autocatalytic synthesis of a viral RNA *in vitro. Science* **150**, 884–886.

Heimpel, A. M. (1963). Introductory remarks on microbial control. *Develop. Ind. Microbiol.* **4**, 131–136.

Hills, G. J., and Smith, K. M. (1959). Further studies on the isolation and crystalliza-tion of insect cytoplasmic viruses. *J. Insect Pathol.* **1**, 121–128.

Hofmaster, R. N., and Ditman, L. P. (1961). Utilization of a nuclear polyhedrosis virus to control the cabbage looper on cole crops in Virginia. *J. Econ. Entomol.* **54**, 921–923.

Huger, A. (1963). Granuloses of insects. *In* "Insect Pathology" (E. A. Steinhaus, ed.), Vol. 1, pp. 531–575. Academic Press, New York.

Hughes, K. M. (1957). An annotated list and bibliography of insects reported to have virus disease. *Hilgardia* **26**, 597–629.

Ignoffo, C. M. (1963a). A successful technique for mass rearing cabbage loopers on a semi-synthetic diet. *Ann. Entomol. Soc. Am.* **56**, 178–182.

Ignoffo, C. M. (1963b). Sensitivity spectrum of *Bacillus thuringiensis* var. *thuringiensis* Berliner to antibiotics, sulfonamides and other substances. *J. Insect Pathol.* **5**, 395–397.

Ignoffo, C. M. (1964a). Bioassay technique and pathogenicity of a nuclear polyhedrosis virus of the cabbage looper, *Trichoplusia ni* (Hubner). *J. Insect Pathol.* **6**, 237–245.

Ignoffo, C. M. (1964b). Production and virulence of a nuclear polyhedrosis virus from larvae of *Trichoplusia ni* (Hubner) reared on a semi-synthetic diet. *J. Insect Pathol.* **6**, 318–326.

Ignoffo, C. M. (1965). Evaluation of the polyhedrosis virus for Bollworm control. *Proc. Conf. Beltwide Cotton Prod. Mech., 1965* pp. 26–27.

Ignoffo, C. M. (1965a). The nuclear polyhedrosis virus of *Heliothis zea* (Boddie) and *Heliothis virescens* (F.). Part I. Virus propagation and its virulence. *J. Insect Pathol.* **7**, 209–216.

Ignoffo, C. M. (1965b). The nuclear polyhedrosis virus of *Heliothis zea* (Boddie) and *Heliothis virescens* (F.). Part II. Biology and propagation of diet reared *Heliothis*. *J. Insect Pathol.* **7**, 217–226.

Ignoffo, C. M. (1965c). The nuclear polyhedrosis virus of *Heliothis zea* (Boddie) and *Heliothis virescens* (F.). Part IV. Bioassay of virus activity. *J. Insect Pathol.* **7**, 315–319.

Ignoffo, C. M. (1965d). Production, identification and standardization of insect viral pathogens. *Entomophaga* **10**, 29–40.

Ignoffo, C. M., and Dutky, S. R. (1963). The effect of sodium hypochlorite on the viability and infectivity of *Bacillus* and *Beauveria* spores and cabbage looper nuclear polyhedrosis virus. *J. Insect Pathol.* **5**, 422–426.

Ignoffo, C. M., and Heimpel, A. M. (1965). The nuclear polyhedrosis virus of *Heliothis zea* (Boddie) and *Heliothis virescens* (F.). Part V. Toxicity-pathogenicity of virus to white mice and guinea pigs. *J. Insect Pathol.* **7**, 329–339.

Ignoffo, C. M., Chapman, A. J., and Martin, D. F. (1965). The nuclear polyhedrosis virus of *Heliothis zea* (Boddie) and *Heliothis virescens* (F.). Part III. Effectiveness of the virus against field populations of *Heliothis* on cotton, corn and grain sorghum. *J. Insect Pathol.* **7**, 227–235.

Ivanicova, S. (1961). Inactivation of Aujetzky disease (pseudorabies) by fluorocarbon. *Acta Virol. (Prague)* **5**, 328.

Kelsey, J. M. (1957). Virus sprays for control of *Pieris rapae* L. *New Zealand J. Sci. Technol.* **A38**, 644–646.

Kelsey, J. M. (1958). Control of *Pieris rapae* by granulosis viruses. *New Zealand J. Agr. Res.* **1**, 778–782.

Krassilstschik, I. M. (1888). La production industrielle des parasites vegetaux pour la destruction des insectes. *Bull. Sci. France Belg.* **19**, 461–472.

Krieg, A. (1957). "Toleranzphanomen" und Latenzproblem. *Arch. Ges. Virusforsch.* **7**, 212–219.

Krieg, A. (1961). "Grundlagen der Insektenpathologie," 304 pp. Steinkopff, Darmstadt.

Krieg, A., and Huger, A. (1960). A virus disease of coleopterous insects. *J. Insect Pathol.* **2**, 274–288.

Lewis, F. B. (1960). How to collect and process small polyhedral viruses of insects. *U. S. Dept. Agr. Forest Serv., Northeast. Forest Expt. Sta., Res. Note* **109**, 1–8.

McEwen, F. L., and Hervey, G. E. R. (1958). Control of the cabbage looper with a virus disease. *J. Econ. Entomol.* **51**, 626–631.

McEwen, F. L., and Hervey, G. E. R. (1959). Microbial control of two cabbage insects. *J. Insect Pathol.* **1**, 86–94.

Martignoni, M. E. (1964a). Mass-production of insect pathogens. *In* "Biological Control of Insect Pests and Weeds" (P. deBach, ed.), pp. 579–609. Reinhold, New York.

Martignoni, M. E. (1964b). Progressive nucleopolyhedrosis in adults of *Peridroma saucia* (Hubner). *J. Insect Pathol.* **6**, 368–372.

Martignoni, M. E., and Auer, C. (1957). Bekampfungsversuch gegen *Eucosma griseana* (Hubner) (Lepidoptera, Tortricidae) mit einem Granulosis-Virus. *Mitt. Schweiz. Zentanst. Forstl. Versuchsw.* **33**, 73–93.

Martignoni, M. E., and Langston, R. L. (1960). Supplement to an annotated list and bibliography of insects reported to have virus diseases. *Hilgardia* **30**, 1–40.

Martignoni, M. E., and Scallion, R. J. (1961). Multiplication *in vitro* of a nuclear polyhedrosis virus in insect amoebocytes. *Nature* **190**, 133–1134.

Martouret, D., and Dusaussoy, G. (1959). Multiplication et extraction des corps d'inclusion de la virose intestinale de *Thaumetopoea pityocampa*. Schiff. *Entomophaga* **4**, 253–259.

Medvedeva, N. B. (1959). Multiplication of polyhedral virus in cultures et insect tissue. *Vepr. Virusol.* **4**, 449–456.

Metchnikoff, E. (1880). Zur Lehre über Insectenkranheiten. *Zool. Anz.* **3**, 44–47.

Neilson, M. M., and Elgee, D. E. (1960). The effect of storage on the virulence of a polyhedrosis virus. *J. Insect Pathol.* **2**, 165–171.

Ossowski, L. L. J. (1957). The biological control of the wattle bagworm, *Kotochalia junodi* (Heyl.) by a virus disease. II. Large-scale experiments. *Ann. Appl. Biol.* **48**, 299–313.

Ossowski, L. L. J. (1959). The use of a nuclear virus disease for the control of the wattle bagworm, *Kotochalia junodi* (Heyl.) *Proc. 4th Intern. Congr. Crop Protect., Hamburg, 1957* Vol. 1, pp. 879–883. Bibliothek Biol. Bundesanstalt Land- Forstwirtsch., Messeweg, Brunswick.

Ouye, M. T. (1962). Effects of antimicrobial agents on micro-organisms and pink bollworm development. *J. Econ. Entomol.* **55**, 854–857.

Plus, N. (1954). Étude de la multiplication du virus de la sensibilité au gaz carbonique chez la Drosophile. *Bull. Biol. France Belg.* **88**, 248–293.

Plus, N. (1960). Utilisation des méthodes de séparation des organites cellulaires pour la purification du virus o de la Drosophile. *Compt. Rend.* **251**, 1685–1686.

Rivers, C. F. (1959). Virus resistance in larvae of *Pieris brassicae* (L.) *Trans. 1st Intern. Conf. Insect Pathol. Biol. Control, Praha, 1958* pp. 205–210.

Rivers, C. F. (1964). The use of a polyhedral virus disease in the control of the pine sawfly *Neodiprion sertifer* Geoffr. in Northwest Scotland. *Entomophaga Mem.* **2**, 477–480.

Schuder, D. L. (1957). A specific virus disease for control of the European pine sawfly, *Neodiprion sertifer* (Geoffr.). *Proc. Indiana Acad. Sci.* **66**, 101–102.

Semel, M. (1961). The efficiency of a polyhedrosis virus and *Bacillus thuringiensis* for control of the cabbage looper on cauliflower. *J. Econ. Entomol.* **54**, 698–701.

Smirnoff, W. A. (1961). A virus disease of *Neodiprion swainei* Middleton. *J. Insect Pathol.* **3**, 29–46.

Smirnoff, W. A. (1964). Preparation and application of viral material, in biological control of the jack pine sawfly. *Forestry Chron.* **40**, 187–194.

Smith, K. M. (1959). The insect viruses. *In* "The Viruses" (F. M. Burnet and W. M. Stanley, eds.), Vol. 3, pp. 369–392. Academic Press, New York.

Smith, K. M. (1963). The cytoplasmic virus diseases. *In* "Insect Pathology" (E. A. Steinhaus, ed.), Vol. 1, pp. 457–494. Academic Press, New York.

Smith, K. M., and Rivers, C. F. (1956). Some viruses affecting insects of economic importance. *Parasitology* **46**, 235–242.

Smith, K. M., Hills, G. J., and Rivers, C. F. (1961). Studies on the cross-inoculation of the Tipula iridescent virus. *Virology* **13**, 233–241.

Speyer, W. (1925). Beitrag zur Wirkung non Arsenverbindugen auf Lepidoptera. *Z. Angew. Entomol.* **11**, 395–399.

Stairs, G. R., and Bird, F. T. (1966). Dissemination of viruses against the spruce budworm, *Choristoneura fumiferana* (Clem.). *Can. Entomologist* (in press).

Steinhaus, E. A. (1949). "Principles of Insect Pathology," 757 pp. McGraw-Hill, New York.

Steinhaus, E. A. (1951). Report on diagnoses of diseased insects, 1944–1950. *Hilgardia* **20**, 629–678.

Steinhaus, E. A. (1954). Duration of infectivity of the virus of silkworm jaundice. *Science* **120**, 186–187.

Steinhaus, E. A. (1960a). The duration of viability and infectivity of certain insect pathogens. *J. Insect Pathol.* **2**, 225–229.

Steinhaus, E. A. (1960b). Notes on polyhedroses in *Peridroma, Prodenia, Colias, Heliothis*, and other Lepidoptera. *J. Insect Pathol.* **2**, 327–333.

Steinhaus, E. A., and Thompson, C. G. (1949). Preliminary field tests using a polyhedral virus to control the alfalfa caterpillar. *J. Econ. Entomol.* **42**, 301–305.

Tanada, Y. (1953). Description and characteristics of a granulosis virus of the imported cabbageworm. *Proc. Hawaiian Entomol. Soc.* **15**, 235–260.

Tanada, Y. (1956). Microbial control of imported cabbageworm. *Hawaii Farm Sci.* **4**, 6–7.

Tanada, Y. (1959). Microbial control of insect pests. *Ann. Rev. Entomol.* **4**, 277–302.

Tanada, Y., and Reiner, C. (1962). The use of pathogens in the control of the corn earworm, *Heliothis zea* (Boddie). *J. Insect Pathol.* **4**, 139–154.

Tarassevitch, L. M., Oulanova, E. F., and Terestchenko, N. S. (1964). Mecanisme de la stabilité des polyèdres. *Entomophaga Mem.* **2**, 397–401.

Thompson, C. G., and Steinhaus, E. A. (1950). Further tests using a polyhedrosis virus to control the alfalfa caterpillar. *Hilgardia* **19**, 411–445.

Trager, W. (1935). Cultivation of the virus of grasserie in silkworm tissue culture. *J. Exptl. Med.* **61**, 501–513.

Ueda, K., Okomoto, Y., Sakai, H., Arima, K., Yonchara, H., and Sakagami, Y. (1955). An antibiotic against silkworm jaundice virus, grasseriomycin, produced by *Streptomyces* species. *J. Antibiot. (Tokyo)* **A8**, 91–95.

Vago, C. (1957). Multiplication du virus *Borrelina bombycis* sur chrysalides de vers à soie. *Compt. Rend.* **245**, 2115–2117.

Vago, C., and Atger, P. (1961). Multiplication massive des virus d'insectes pendant la mue nymphale. *Entomophaga* **6**, 53–56.

Vago, C., and Cayrol, R. (1955). Une virose à polyèdres de la noctuelle gamma *Plusia gamma* L. (Lepidoptera). *Ann. Inst. Natl. Rech. Agron.* **C6**, 421–432.

Vago, C., and Chastang, S. (1958). Culture *in vitro* d'un tissu nymphal de lépidoptère. *Experientia* **14**, 426–427.

Vanderzant, E. S., and Richardson, C. D. (1963). Ascorbic acid in the nutrition of plant feeding insects. *Science* **140**, 989–991.

Vanderzant, E. S., Pool, M. C., and Richardson, C. D. (1962a). The role of ascorbic acid in the nutrition of three cotton insects. *J. Insect Physiol.* **8**, 287–297.

Vanderzant, E. S., Richardson, C. D., and Fort, S. W. (1962b). Rearing of the bollworm on artificial diets. *J. Econ. Entomol.* **55**, 140.

Vasiljevic, L. (1964). Multiplication des Virus. *Entomophaga Mem.* **2**, 407–416.

Vaughn, J. L., and Faulkner, P. (1963). Susceptibility of an insect tissue culture to infection by virus preparations of the nuclear polyhedrosis of the silkworm (*Bombyx mori* L.) *Virology* **20**, 484–489.

Watanabe, S. (1951). Studies on the grasserie virus of the silkworm, *Bombyx mori*. IV. Physical and chemical effects upon the virus. *Japan. J. Exptl. Med.* **21**, 299–313.

Wilson, F. (1960). The effectiveness of a granulosis virus applied to field populations of *Pieris rapae* (Lepidoptera). *Australian J. Agr. Res.* **2**, 485–497.

Williams, R. C., and Smith, K. M. (1957). A crystallizable insect virus. *Nature* **179**, 119–120.

Williams, R. C., and Smith, K. M. (1958). The polyhedral form of the *Tipula* iridescent virus. *Biochim. Biophys. Acta* **28**, 464–469.

Zalmanzon, E. S. (1949). Action of protease on nuclear inclusions in silkworm jaundice infection. *Microbiologiya* **18**, 361–365.

Ziegler, D. W., Davis, E. V., Thomas, W. J., and McLimans, W. F. (1958). The propagation of mammalian cells in a 20-liter stainless fermentor. *Appl. Microbiol.* **6**, 305–310.

Section E

Insects by the Million

Chapter 37

Screw-Worms

ALFRED H. BAUMHOVER,* CHESTER N. HUSMAN,† AND
ANDREW J. GRAHAM‡

Entomology Research Division,
U. S. Department of Agriculture,
Oxford, North Carolina;
Administrative Services,
U. S. Department of Agriculture,
Beltsville, Maryland; and
Animal Health Division,‡
U. S. Department of Agriculture,
Mission, Texas

* Formerly Entomologist in Charge of Screw-Worm Research, Entomology Research Division, U. S. Department of Agriculture, Mission, Texas.

† Formerly Supervisory Equipment Specialist, Animal Disease Eradication Division, U. S. Department of Agriculture, Mission, Texas.

‡ Formerly Animal Disease Eradication Division.

I. INTRODUCTION

Mass production and release of irradiated screw-worms [*Cochlyi-omia hominivorax* (Coquerel)—Diptera: Calliphoridae], represents the first attempt to utilize an insect for its own destruction. As early as 1937, Dr. E. F. Knipling (1955) proposed eradication or control of the screw-worm by rearing, sexually sterilizing, and releasing the flies in overwhelming numbers. Early attempts to sterilize the screw-worm with chemicals were unsuccessful; however, Bushland and Hopkins (1951, 1953) sterilized screw-worms successfully with X- and γ-radiation. These authors found that irradiated males in caged populations competed successfully with untreated males to reduce hatch of eggs from untreated females. Later, field tests in Florida demonstrated ability of the sterile males to compete in nature, and the feasibility of this technique was established through eradication of the screw-worm from the Island of Curacao, Netherlands Antilles (Baumhover *et al.*, 1955).

Mass production (Graham and Dudley, 1959), irradiation (Jefferson, 1960), release, and field evaluation (Baumhover *et al.*, 1959) procedures were developed, and in 1959 screw-worms were eradicated from southeastern United States in a joint state-federal program administered by the Florida Livestock Board and the USDA Animal Disease Eradication Division (Knipling, 1960). Program cost was $10 million, or half the annual loss to livestock owners from screw-worm infestations. Since 1958 southeastern ranchers have accrued $160 million in savings to their industry. In 1962 the USDA Animal Disease Eradication Division joined with the State of Texas' Animal Health Council and a rancher organization, the Southwest Animal Health Research Foundation, in implementing a screw-worm eradication program in southwestern United States. Included in addition to Texas were the states of Louisiana, Arkansas, Oklahoma, and New Mexico. In 1965 Arizona and California joined the effort to eliminate screw-worms from the entire United States. Through the cooperation and support of the Mexican government and Mexican ranchers, screw-worms are now being released in strategic areas in Mexico, 300 miles south of the international boundary, to prevent reinfestation from Mexico. The program, costing $5 million annually, is saving livestock owners in southwestern United States $50 to $100 million each year, and additional savings are being enjoyed by ranchers in northern Mexico. Using the higher figure, savings in the Southwest alone have totaled $375 million from 1962 through 1965. Eradication of the screw-worm throughout Mexico and Central America to the

Isthmus of Panama would reduce the size of the area presently being treated from 300,000 to only 30,000 mi^2.

II. DISTRIBUTION

Screw-worms, obligate parasites of warm-blooded animals, are indigenous to tropical and subtropical areas of North and South America. They sometimes attack man. In the United States, prior to the eradication program, screw-worms overwintered primarily in peninsular Florida and southern Texas. During the spring and summer they dispersed hundreds of miles northward and caused serious losses in much of southern United States. Movement of infested animals extended their range as far northward as Montana and Minnesota, and screw-worm infestations followed until cold weather eliminated the flies.

III. BIOLOGY

Screw-worm flies mate at the age of 2 to 3 days (80°F), and at age 6 days females may oviposit 200 to 500 eggs. Most frequent oviposition sites are the navels of newborn animals; however, breaks in the skin caused by barbed wire, vegetation, fighting, dehorning, castration, tick and mosquito bites, and other unhealthy conditions invite oviposition. Larvae hatch in 16 hours to feed near the surface of the skin on wound fluids; later they penetrate more deeply to devour muscular tissue. Growth is complete in 5 to 9 days, and the larvae then migrate from the wound to enter the soil where they pupate. Adults emerge in 8 days to complete the life cycle. Infestation increases the attractiveness of wounds to flies, and multiple oviposition may produce thousands of larvae, which can kill a full-grown bovine in 10 days if the wound is not treated. Smaller mammals such as rabbits may succumb from infestations of as few as 50 to 100 larvae.

IV. COLONIZATION OF WILD STRAINS

Colonies of screw-worms were first established at the USDA Laboratory in Menard, Texas, in the mid-thirties. Native collections were added periodically to the laboratory strain to maintain vigor and a broad genetic base; however, evaluation of these introductions was not made. This Texas strain was reared continuously for laboratory tests in Texas and was also used for field tests with irradiated males in Florida from 1951 to 1953. Attempts to establish a Curacao strain for the eradication test on this island in 1954 met with only limited success; since ecological conditions on Curacao were similar to those in Texas, the Texas strain was used. However, for the eradication program in the Southeast, screw-worms were collected in 12 locations throughout Florida and 1 in southern Georgia to obtain a broad genetic base representative of the area. Larvae near full size were removed from infested wounds of livestock and placed in jars of damp sand for pupation. Emergence and longevity of adults were excellent in the parental generation; however, the females failed to oviposit in the shell vials containing lean meat used in routine rearing of established colonies. After several unsuccessful attempts to obtain eggs on lean meat, 12-day-old females were placed on wounded animals. Only half the normal egg production was obtained, and only half of the eggs hatched. However, the F_1 larvae adapted well to the artificial medium, and fecundity improved in subsequent generations.

During the eradication program in the Southeast, screw-worms persisted in Broward County, Florida, several months longer than in other areas. One of the factors suspected of delaying success in eradication efforts was incompatibility of the native females with released males. To investigate the possibility of incompatibility, a Broward County strain was established. Laboratory tests failed to indicate incompatibility, and since the Broward County strain showed excellent vigor, it was introduced into the Florida rearing colony. Since a culture of the original Florida strain had earlier been shipped to Kerrville, Texas, to establish a standby colony should a disaster strike the Sebring, Florida, production facility, the present Florida strain now in use in the Southwest has not been modified by the Broward County introductions.

During 1960, colonies of screw-worms were established from collections made near Frio and Brady, Texas, to compare these strains with the Florida strain under simulated Florida and Texas humidity conditions. Repeated tests failed to show differences in survival of the various strains, and since the Southwest eradication program was initiated before the strains could be field tested, use of the Florida strain was continued. Egg mass hatching records in the eradication zone indicated that the Florida strain was competing effectively with local strains, and research efforts were devoted to more urgent problems.

V. GENETIC SELECTION

In the laboratory as well as in nature, selection for survival obviously continues, allowing only the better adapted individuals to survive. The drastic changes in environment and food under laboratory conditions, compared with the natural habitat, undoubtedly influence the characteristics of a culture. In fact, through our inability to duplicate natural conditions adequately, selection, intended or not, may effectively operate toward establishment of a vigorous colony. Planned or artificial selection offers intriguing possibilities for improving specific qualities which may better adapt the insect for man's intended use. Several genetic approaches have been followed to improve the colony used for the production of sterile males.

A. SELECTIONS FOR MAXIMUM LONGEVITY AND SEXUAL VIGOR

The Florida strain of screw-worms (see Section IV) was selected for maximum longevity and male sexual vigor by caging single males with 15 to 25 virgin females. Egg masses were collected from 12-day-old females, and progeny fathered by the most active males were pooled for increase. In 5 generations mean fertile matings per male increased from 5 to 17, and longevity greatly improved. Incidental selection by improving adaptation of the cultures to laboratory conditions likely played a role in this dramatic increase in longevity and male mating frequency. However, Bushland and Hopkins (1951) obtained only 5 matings from Texas strain males reared artificially and 11 from the same strain reared on live animals in the laboratory. F_6 progeny were pooled to establish the present Florida strain.

B. SELECTION FOR RESISTANCE TO STARVATION

Under the hot, dry conditions in the Southwest low survival of released screw-worm flies would be expected. To increase survival, Florida-strain screw-worms were selected for resistance to starvation by withholding food and water from adults until almost 90% were dead. In 12 generations 56-hour mortality decreased from 85 to 4% for males, and in F_{28} mortality was only 25% following 96 hours' starvation (Baumhover and Spates, 1965). Tolerance to starvation has continued to improve through F_{43} when male mortality was only 3% at 120 hours. Body weight increased 8–10% and fat body 75% over the unselected strain. Unfortunately, periodic checks after the 12th generation showed a decline in male sexual aggressiveness (Baumhover, 1965), and field releases under hot, dry conditions failed to show improved survival based on recapture of females. Low survival in the F_8 generation nearly interrupted the selection program, and excessive inbreeding may have contributed to a lack of vigor. However, selection for survival under starvation may be expected to produce a less active strain since inactivity would increase survival. Selection on a large scale to increase the genetic base and removal of males following the starvation period (since mating did occur under starvation) might prevent the loss in male vigor noted in this selection program.

C. Miscellaneous Selection Programs

Since screw-worm activity in nature declines during periods of extremes in temperature, release of a cold-hardy strain during the winter and heat-resistant strain during the summer would theoretically increase the efficiency of a sterile-male-release program. However, serious attempts to develop these strains have not been made. Florida strain screw-worms, although separated into 4-hour pupation groups, emerge over a 2- to 3-day period. Selection for uniform development to obtain eclosion in 1 day would simplify release and reduce losses from concussion if pupae are released, or adult losses from extended confinement if releases are delayed until the entire culture has emerged. A selection program in which early and late emerging flies were discarded failed to improve uniformity in development after 7 generations. An attempt was made to increase the spread between rate of development for males and females to discard the females for predominantly male releases. Although careful timing in separating emerged flies normally will provide a 3:1 male ratio in the younger groups, the proportion of males was not increased by selection.

D. Incidental Selection

Several examples of incidental selection under laboratory conditions have been apparent in colonizing screw-worms. Insects collected to establish the Florida strain (see Section IV) and recent Texas collections have shown greatly reduced fecundity in early generations. Flies failing to mate or oviposit under laboratory conditions fail to contribute to succeeding generations, and fecundity increases rapidly through selection of adaptable individuals. Oviposition response has been greatly altered in the Florida strain. Several oviposition stimulants, highly effective for this strain, have failed to induce oviposition by wild females even when the stimulant was placed on live animals. Colony flies for mass production are held in large $3 \times 6 \times 6$ ft cages to reduce labor demands. If lighting is uneven, the flies orient to the brightest light, and overcrowding results in tremendous losses. As a result the colony has been held in almost complete darkness since 1958, except during oviposition when a series of 7½-watt incandescent bulbs were used to attract flies to the oviposition vat. Success of the eradication program tends to rule out the possibility of a genetic shift which might decrease competitiveness in the field, but the effect of drastic changes in the laboratory environment may warrant periodic evaluation of the strain's adaptability in nature.

VI. DISEASES, PARASITES, AND PREDATORS

Occasional difficulties encountered in laboratory production of screw-worms have prompted concern regarding the role of disease, parasites, and predators. However, with few exceptions, production failures have been related to other factors such as temperature, humidity, and diet deficiencies. If the temperature of the larval medium is held as low as 85°F, growth rate, larval size, and survival are greatly reduced. There are obvious differences in the gross appearance and odor of the cool medium compared to medium held at the standard 95°F; however, the relative importance of the direct effect of reduced temperature and the indirect effect of changes in medium composition due to the influence of reduced temperature on bacterial growth have not been determined.

Full-grown larvae and prepupae are highly susceptible to desiccation. An exposure of 48 hours to 90°F and 40% relative humidity (RH) resulted in a weight loss of 53% and only 20% of the insects survived compared to a weight loss of 24% and survival of 94% for controls protected with a sand cover and held in room conditions of 85% RH (Baumhover, 1963a).

A small hymenoptera, *Nasonia vitripennis* (Walker), has occasionally parasitized screw-worm pupae at the USDA laboratory at Kerrville, Texas. However, since development of the parasite takes several days longer than its host, prompt disposal of nonemerged pupae will prevent establishment of this parasite.

Predators have not been a serious problem in mass production of screw-worms; however, ants and rodents will cause serious losses if not controlled. Various predators such as ants, birds, and lizards have been observed to congregate near ground release sites.

VII. MASS PRODUCTION, IRRADIATION, AND RELEASE PROCEDURES FOR THE SOUTHEASTERN AND SOUTHWESTERN (UNITED STATES) SCREW-WORM ERADICATION PROGRAMS

Screw-worms were first reared artificially (Melvin and Bushland, 1936) on a mixture of milk, blood, lean beef, and formaldehyde.

In later studies (Melvin and Bushland, 1940) milk was deleted and the following basic formula was derived:

Water	1000 cc
Formalin	6 cc
Citrated beef blood	500 cc
Lean ground meat	1000 gm

This formula, with minor modifications, has been used successfully from 1936 to the present, with no apparent change in the normal physiology and morphology of the insect. Prior to the development of an artificial medium, screw-worms were reared on living animals such as baby calves and rabbits. From the standpoint of humaneness, objectionable odors, and efficiency, the development of an artificial method for rearing screw-worms represented an important breakthrough in research to control and eradicate these insects.

Prior to development of the sterile male technique only a few thousand screw-worms were required weekly for biological studies and insecticide screening programs. These requirements were met readily with use of simple equipment such as shell vials, Petri dishes, small screened cages, and wash tubs. However, as weekly production requirements were projected to 50 million insects for the eradication program in southeastern United States, research and development were devoted to development of larger production units, cheaper diet materials, and automated handling to reduce production costs.

A. Fly Colony and Egg Production

For small-scale production 700 screw-worm flies of both sexes were allowed to emerge in a $12 \times 12 \times 20$ inch screened cage. Water, honey, and a mixture of honey and meat were provided in each cage. Eggs were obtained by capturing 10 to 15 flies with a small vial containing several grams of lean ground beef. Vials containing the flies were held 1 to 2 hours at 95°F to induce oviposition. Maximum egg production could be calculated at 60,000 per cage with 300 females averaging 200 eggs each; however, usually half this number was used in calculations of egg production to allow for variations in adult mortality, sex ratio, and fecundity. Egg production was greatly facilitated through the development of a large cage $3\frac{1}{2} \times 3\frac{1}{2} \times 6$ ft draped with paper toweling to provide adequate resting area for 50,000 flies (Fig. 1). The capacity of each cage was equivalent to 70 of the small cages; however, it has been necessary to hold the flies in the large cages in darkness since high mortality occurred when the

FIG. 1. Fly colony cage. Six liters of pupae are placed in this cage to produce approximately 50,000 adults. Four million or more eggs are produced by each cage of flies. Paper streamers are placed in the cage to provide resting space for the flies. Food consists of a honey-meat mixture, honey alone, and water. (U. S. Department of Agriculture photograph.)

flies crowded to the side of the cage nearest the highest light intensity (see Section V,D). Further research should be conducted with diffuse or indirect lighting to develop a normal photoperiod. Oviposition was induced by inserting into the cage a tray 5½ × 1 ft and 1½ inches deep containing a mixture of meat and an oviposition stimulant made by incubating meat juices or albumin from blood. This mixture was warmed to 95°F with a thermostatically controlled, soil-heating cable built into the base of the tray. A wooden grate placed over the tray provided the dry surface preferred for oviposition by the females. Flies were attracted to the oviposition tray with a series of 7½-watt incandescent lamps. After 4 hours, when oviposition was complete, the cage was transferred to a cold room held at 32°F to immobilize the flies and allow removal of the oviposition tray without escape of the flies. Escaped flies would create a hazard should they escape from the plant where they could cause screw-worm infestations in domestic animals or wildlife.

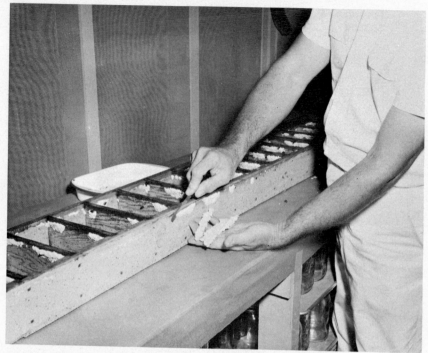

FIG. 2. Grid removed from oviposition tray for removal of screw-worm eggs. Eggs are weighed into 6-gm lots to provide 120,000 eggs for each starting tray. (U. S. Department of Agriculture photograph.)

Eggs, cemented tightly together, were readily removed from the tray and grid with a spatula (Fig. 2) and were weighed into 6-gm lots of 120,000 eggs. Each cage of flies produced 4 million or more eggs when an equal sex ratio was present. When the colony was selected from early maturing larvae to increase the female ratio, as many as 6 to 7 million eggs were obtained per cage.

B. LARVAL FEEDING

Egg hatching began 12 hours after the end of the 4-hour oviposition period, and the eggs and larvae were transferred to starting pans $26 \times 16 \times 4$ inches deep containing a ½-inch layer of medium (Fig. 3) which supported the larvae for 30 hours. Plasma was substituted for whole blood in the starting medium to improve growth and survival. During this critical period the young larvae were kept in a special chamber held near 100°F and 95% RH.

At 30 hours the larvae were transferred to 4×5 ft vats 1½ inches deep on the main rearing floor (Fig. 4). These vats, similar in design

FIG. 3. Transfer of hatched screw-worm larvae from Petri dish to starting tray. Larval medium consists of lean ground meat, bovine plasma, water, and formalin. The starting chamber is maintained near 100°F and 95% RH. (U. S. Department of Agriculture photograph.)

to the oviposition trays, were also held at 95°F. Racks containing the vats were supported on overhead, powered monorails. Contents of the starting tray were distributed evenly on opposite sides of the vat on narrow strips of fresh medium held in place by a plastic underlay supported by an aluminum retainer. When the larvae consumed the initial ration, the plastic underlay and aluminum dividers were removed and the entire vat was filled to a depth corresponding to the length of the larvae. Waste occurred when the medium was too deep since the larvae feed gregariously in a vertical position and must maintain their anal spiracles near the surface to obtain oxygen. Unless the medium became dry the larvae did not penetrate to the bottom of the vat to consume unused medium. As the larvae fed toward the center of the vat, waste medium was removed with a vacuum line into a storage tank. Since a few larvae might be withdrawn with the used medium, the material was heated to prevent escape of larvae

FIG. 4. Screw-worm rearing vats. After 30 hours in the starting chamber the larvae are transferred to vats on the main floor. Diet is similar to the starting medium except that whole bovine blood is substituted for plasma. At 4 days of age larvae reach the size shown, migrate from the vat, and are directed to the water conveyor beneath the grate. (U. S. Department of Agriculture photograph.)

when the waste was pumped to the sewage disposal area. The rearing medium was renewed with increased frequency as consumption increased with larval size.

Recently, a new method for rearing larvae has been under test at the Mission, Texas, plant. Dehydrated materials such as spray-dried blood, yeast, powdered milk, cottage cheese, and eggs, and fish flour mixed with water have been tested in various combinations. Since the diet is very fluid, a layer of cotton is placed at the bottom of the vat. The cotton fibers floating through the medium provide support for the larvae and prevent drowning. Medium from the entire vat is removed periodically with a screened vacuum device and replenished with fresh medium. With this new technique the number of larvae per vat can be doubled since larvae disperse throughout the vat instead of feeding in waves as in the semiliquid diet. Costly cold storage facilities are not required since the processed nutrients can be stored at room temperatures. However, the size of larvae and the competitiveness of the adult males produced has been substandard, and efforts are being continued to improve this new technique.

C. HANDLING OF PUPAE

At 4–6 days of age the larvae ceased feeding and crawled from the vats into huge funnels which directed them into sand pupation trays on the lower floor. These trays were moved beneath the funnels by means of a motor-driven endless belt; however, attendants placed and removed the trays manually. During periods of heavy flow of larvae from the funnels it was necessary for the attendant to redistribute them to other trays to prevent overcrowding. When the trays reached the discharge end of the belt they were transferred to racks supported on an overhead monorail timed to deliver the trays 8 hours later to the separator which removed the sand. Larvae and pupae remaining were transported to a large 8-mesh/inch endless screen belt through which the larvae crawled and later dropped into collection containers to be recycled on the pupation monorail. Pupae, collected at the far end of the separator, were measured into 2-liter lots and spread evenly over 18 × 26 inch screened trays. If pupae were more than ½ inch in depth, a rise in temperature caused uneven development; if several inches deep, lethal temperatures occurred at the center. The pupa storage trays were placed in racks also supported by an overhead monorail. The racks were filled in sequence for orderly irradiation at the scheduled age. The room where the pupae were stored was held at 80°F and 85% RH.

At the Mission, Texas, plant the large larval collection funnels have been eliminated through development of a water conveyor. Larvae are collected in trenches built into the concrete floor. Water flowing at the rate of 1¼ ft/sec transports the larvae to a sump from which they are pumped to a larva-water separator. Here the larvae are measured by the operator and placed into the pupation trays. Elimination of the collection funnels has greatly reduced the plant area since two stories are no longer required. Sawdust has replaced the sand as a pupation medium (Fig. 5) to improve ease of handling and to reduce costs through elimination of the washing and drying process required when sand was used. The sawdust is discarded and incinerated following its use. Furthermore, pupae remain beneath the surface of the sawdust in contrast to the sand in which the burrowing activity of the larvae tends to sift the pupae to the surface where they are subject to desiccation (Baumhover, 1963a). As a

FIG. 5. Sawdust separator. Larvae are collected at the larva-water separator (not shown) and placed in pupation trays containing sawdust; 16 hours later the sawdust is removed from the mixture of larvae and pupae to permit their separation (see Fig. 6). (U. S. Department of Agriculture photograph.)

further precaution against desiccation, pupation trays are transferred to chambers held at 80°F and 85% RH in contrast to the ambient conditions existing in the Sebring, Florida, plant. Larva-pupa separation is accomplished through use of a solid, ribbed, motor-driven belt (Fig. 6). Fluorescent lights above the belt cause the negatively phototropic larvae to crawl to either side where they fall into collection containers for recycling to the pupation chamber. As in the Sebring separator, pupae are collected at the end of the belt for storage. Use of the new larva-pupa separator has eliminated losses that occurred with use of the Sebring separator due to large larvae or small pupae becoming lodged in the wire mesh belt.

D. IRRADIATION

Early small-scale laboratory and field studies utilized a deep-therapy X-ray unit and various Co^{60} units. Six automatically controlled Co^{60} units were developed for the Southeastern Screw-Worm Eradica-

Fig. 6. Larva-pupa separator. The mixture of larvae and pupae is transported to a slowly moving endless belt. The negatively phototropic larvae crawl to the sides and drop into containers for recycling in the pupation chamber. Pupae, remaining on the belt, are collected at the opposite end for storage. (U. S. Department of Agriculture photograph.)

tion Program (Jefferson, 1960). These units, ranging from 450 to 660 curies each, contained a total of 3600 curies. Eight Co^{60} strips 2 inches wide, 1/8 inch thick, and 13 inches long were encapsulated in stainless steel and arranged in a cylinder within the lead shield to accommodate the 5-inch-diameter irradiation canister. The usable field ranged from 789 to 810 r/min at the time of installation. In order to completely sterilize the screw-worms 8000 r ± 10% were delivered to pupae at 5.2–5.7 days of age. The irradiation canisters were loaded with 2 liters of pupae (18,000 insects) and attached by the operator to a carriage which automatically inserted them into the irradiation chamber and removed them after the required treatment. The operator then placed the treated canisters of pupae on an endless belt which conveyed them to the packaging area. Precise time records were kept with each treated canister to intercept any that might inadvertently be transferred to the packaging area prior to irradiation. During the

FIG. 7. Co⁶⁰ irradiation unit. Screened canisters containing screw-worm pupae are attached to the carriage at the operator's position (not shown) and are automatically inserted into the radiation field, removed, and dropped onto the packaging room conveyor (foreground). (U. S. Department of Agriculture photograph.)

final phase of the program a chemical dosimeter was placed with each canister of pupae to verify treatment.

Several important changes have been made in irradiation procedures for the Mission, Texas, plant. During the final phases of the Southeastern Screw-Worm Eradication Program it was discovered that anoxia in the radiation canisters was responsible for failure to completely sterilize the females (Baumhover, 1963b). Anoxia is now being avoided through the use of screened canisters in contrast to the solid canisters used in the Sebring, Florida, plant and by allowing minimum delay between the time of loading the canisters and irradiating. At the Sebring, Florida, plant it was possible for the operator to place the loaded canister directly on the conveyor to the packaging room without irradiating the pupae. This possibility for error has been eliminated at the Mission, Texas, plant by modifying the irradiation carriage to automatically drop the treated canister, after irradiation, onto the packaging room conveyor (Fig. 7) which is inaccessible to the operator.

E. PACKAGING

During field trials on Sanibel Island, Florida, ground releases of screw-worms were made by suspending cartons of pupae from trees. Later, when male adults were released by airplane, flies were packaged in small drinking cups. For the Curacao trial, 1 lb Kraft bags were partially filled with excelsior to increase resting area. Because of the lightness of the filled bags and the strong trade winds, sand mixed with an adhesive was applied as a ballast to the bottom exterior to prevent excessive drift of the falling bags. During later field tests in Florida, frozen food cartons were used and for the Southeastern Screw-Worm Eradication Program a $5\frac{1}{2} \times 4\frac{1}{2} \times 2$ inch carton was developed in cooperation with Container Corporation of America. Perforations 5/64 inch in diameter provided aeration, and special flaps on the top and front secured the lid to the carton. Partitions were inserted manually in the carton to increase resting area for the flies. Considerable difficulty was experienced in developing a flyproof carton, since the flies are very pliable immediately after eclosion and they either escape or become entrapped if openings larger than 5/64 inch are present.

Commercial carton forming, filling and closing equipment (Fig. 8) was obtained to mechanize packaging. Up to 50 cartons, containing 440 pupae each, were packaged per minute. Cartons were placed manually on 26×18 inch trays, each holding 15 cartons, and trays were transferred to racks, each holding 18 trays.

At Mission, Texas, packaging has been further automated through the development of partitions which are formed and inserted mechanically. Although food was not provided in release cartons for the southeast program, a sugar solution is provided for flies released in the southwest program. The liquid is dispensed automatically into a paper cup containing a cotton ball; however, the cups are placed manually into the carton after it has been loaded with pupae.

F. RELEASE

Packaged screw-worm pupae were stored at 80°F and 85% RH for eclosion. However, if a delay in release was anticipated because of

Fig. 8. Packaging line. Operator on stool is emptying irradiated screw-worm pupae into an automatic filler which dispenses the pupae into the release cartons. Cartons are formed and closed mechanically at the rate of 50 per minute. (U. S. Department of Agriculture photograph.)

inclement weather or unavailability of aircraft, temperature was reduced to 55°–60°F to prevent emergence or to reduce mortality of adults already emerged. Although pupae were separated into 8-hour pupation groups, complete eclosion required 2 to 3 days, resulting in a compromise between loss of pupae at the time of release due to concussion or predation and loss of adults due to extended storage. However, with careful sampling and timing of releases these losses were less than 2% during the Southeast Screw-Worm Eradication Program.

Although survival of screw-worm adults following release in the Southeast was of limited concern owing to the abundance of water and flowering plants for food, further consideration was given to handling of screw-worms for release in the hot, semiarid areas of the Southwest and northern Mexico. Screw-worms normally emerge from daylight until noon and pupae failing to emerge the first morning will not emerge until the following morning. Survival of the early emerging flies can be increased by reducing the holding temperatures to 55°F for 12 hours without delaying emergence of the remaining pupae. Chilling within 15 minutes of emergence must be avoided since unfolding of the wings is interrupted and the flies are unable to resume this process later. Utilization of food reserves (fat body) by the adults continues at a rate independent of external sources of food. At 80°F adults placed on starvation at 4 days reach 50% mortality in 26–28 hours compared to 48–50 hours for those starved upon eclosion and at 1 day of age (Baumhover and Spates, 1965). Consequently, during periods of high temperature and scarce food supply in the release area, it is imperative that the flies be released as promptly as possible to ensure maximum survival. However, during cool weather it may be advantageous to hold the flies 48 hours at 80°F until the males are sexually mature, particularly in newly treated areas. At 60°F more than a week is required for development of sexual maturity and considerable delay would occur before immature released males could compete with mature wild males.

During hot weather flies are released as early in the day as possible to avoid overheating during the loading of aircraft and release. Also, flies released in hot barren areas have little chance for survival during the heat of the day, unless shelter, food, and water are promptly located. Portable air-conditioning units are used to reduce cabin temperatures when loading must be done under high temperatures. During cold weather releases are delayed until air temperatures approach 60°F to allow flight mobility of the flies. If temperatures are expected to drop below freezing on the night following release, releases are also delayed to avoid losses from the cold. Since storage life for the flies is limited and production cannot be geared readily to variable weather conditions, flies ready for release are usually deployed into warmer areas if available in the release zone.

Single-engine Cessna aircraft under contract during the southeast program were modified to provide space for 1200 cartons. Airspeed was maintained at 100 mph. The right front seat was reversed to allow an attendant to fill the dispensing unit, which was timed automatically to dispense the cartons at the required rate. The dispenser protruded through the fuselage of the plane and a conveyor forced the carton beneath rollers which disengaged the top locking flaps. As the carton left the dispenser a hook engaged the front flap to open the carton. An air deflector, attached to the dispenser, directed the cartons downward to prevent impact with the fuselage or tail wheel of the plane.

During the southwest program release efficiency has been increased through the use of a Mooney aircraft modified to hold 1600 cartons delivered at a ground speed of 140 mph. Larger, twin-motored aircraft such as the military C-45 are also being used for added safety in mountainous areas and to increase the operational range. The carton dispenser has been installed entirely within the fuselage of the plane to prevent drag and to allow emergency maintainance without landing the aircraft. Airspeeds up to 150 mph during release have shown no ill effects on the flies. Releases are normally made 1500 feet above the terrain; however, recoveries from releases as high as 10,000 feet have been as high as those from lower altitudes.

In the Southeast screw-worm flies were released along parallel flight lanes 1 mile apart to cover the entire area within a 2-week period. This procedure has been followed in the Southwest and northern Mexico in high population areas. However, tests are being conducted to determine if release costs can be reduced through the use of flight lines 6 to 12 miles apart. In low population areas releases are concentrated on known infested premises and favorable habitats such as watercourses.

G. QUALITY CONTROL

Following irradiation pupae are sampled from each canister to determine viability of the pupae, and sterility and longevity of the adults. Release cartons are returned from each flight to determine if release has been scheduled properly to avoid losses from concussion or predation (if pupae are dispersed) or from weakness or death of the flies if they are subjected to extended storage after emergence. Sexual aggressiveness tests are conducted in the laboratory on males from routine production as well as tests to evaluate the effect of proposed changes in diet or handling. Field tests for competitiveness of the released males in nature are also conducted as required.

H. PLANT SECURITY

Since fertile screw-worms from the plant could threaten success of the eradication program, elaborate precautions are taken to avoid their escape or accidental transport to the outside. Workers change into plant clothing upon entering, then remove it and shower before leaving. Movement of unnecessary items into and out of the plant is restricted. Other items are either fumigated or heat-treated prior to removal unless visual inspection is adequate. Workers, supplies, and equipment must pass through a series of rooms or vestibules which are inspected and kept free of viable screw-worms. The entire plant is checked routinely for openings which may allow escape of adults or larvae, and the entire area is cleaned each 8-hour shift further to reduce the chance of escape. As an added precaution special releases of sterile flies are made in the vicinity of the plant; however, this procedure would have little effect on mated females that might escape.

VIII. NUTRITIONAL REQUIREMENTS

Efforts to develop an improved diet for screw-worms have been hampered by a lack of understanding concerning their nutritional requirements. Testing of substitutes in the diet has been primarily on a trial-and-error basis, evaluating various nutrient sources on the basis of cost reduction without lowering the vigor and competitiveness of the flies produced. Recently Gingrich (1964) completed studies on the qualitative requirements for screw-worm larvae. A synthetic diet was developed that contained casein, yeast extract, cholesterol, inorganic salts, water, and agar. The role of casein in the diet was defined through the substitutions of L-amino acids and that of the yeast extract through substitution of vitamins and ribonucleic acid (RNA). He found that thiamine, riboflavin, calcium pantothenate, niacin, and choline were absolutely necessary for growth and that biotin and folic acid were essential for development to the adult stage. Inositol, B_{12}, carnatine, and pyroxidine and its analogs were not essential to growth. Growth failed if arginine, histidine, isoleucine, leucine, lysine, methionine, phenylalanine, proline, threonine, tryptophan, and valine were absent. Cystine and glycine were required for normal growth. Although ribose, glucose, and maltose inhibited growth, glycogen and starch at 0.5% were acceptable but not required.

In summary, vitamin requirements were similar to other insects in that only the B-complex was required; however, the nonrequirement for B_6 is known for only one other species, *Pseudosarchophaga affinis* (Fallen). In addition to the common amino acids required for insects, proline also was required by screw-worms. Choline was required in large quantities, indicating that screw-worms had lost their ability to synthesize it. The need for RNA represents one of the few known requirements for insects. Various substitutes were tested as replacements for known requirements. This study should aid greatly in future research to develop improved screw-worm rearing media.

REFERENCES

Baumhover, A. H. (1963a). Susceptibility of screw-worm larvae and prepupae to desiccation. *J. Econ. Entomol.* **56**, 473–475.

Baumhover, A. H. (1963b). Influence of aeration during gamma irradiation of screw-worm pupae. *J. Econ. Entomol.* **56**, 628–631.

Baumhover, A. H. (1965). Sexual aggressiveness of male screw-worm flies measured by effect on female mortality. *J. Econ. Entomol.* **58**, 544–548.

Baumhover, A. H., and Spates, G. E. (1965). Artificial selection of adult screw-worms for extended survival without food and water. *J. Econ. Entomol.* **58**, 645–649.

Baumhover, A. H., Graham, A. J., Hopkins, D. E., Dudley, F. H., New, W. D., and Bushland, R. C. (1955). Control of screw-worms through the release of sterilized flies. *J. Econ. Entomol.* **48**, 462–466.

Baumhover, A. H., Husman, C. N., Skipper, C. C., and New, W. D. (1959). Field observations on the effects of releasing sterile screw-worms in Florida. *J. Econ. Entomol.* **52**, 1202–1206.

Bushland, R. C., and Hopkins, D. E. (1951). Experiments with screw-worm flies sterilized by X-rays. *J. Econ. Entomol.* **44**, 725–731.

Bushland, R. C., and Hopkins, D. E. (1953). Sterilization of screw-worm flies with X-rays and Gamma-rays. *J. Econ. Entomol.* **46**, 648–656.

Gingrich, R. E. (1964). Nutritional studies on screw-worm larvae with chemically defined media. *Ann. Entomol. Soc. Am.* **57**, 351–360.

Graham, A. J., and Dudley, F. H. (1959). Culture methods for mass rearing of screw-worm larvae. *J. Econ. Entomol.* **52**, 1006–1008.

Jefferson, M. E. (1960). Irradiated males eliminate screw-worm flies. *Nucleonics* **18**, 74–76.

Knipling, E. F. (1955). Possibilities of insect control or eradication through the use of sexually sterile males. *J. Econ. Entomol.* **48**, 459–462.

Knipling, E. F. (1960). The eradication of the screw-worm fly. *Sci. Am.* **203**, 54–61.

Melvin, R., and Bushland, R. C. (1936). A method of rearing *Cochliomyia americana* C. &. P. on artificial media. *U. S. Dept. Agr., Bur. Entomol. Plant Quarantine, E.T.* **ET 88.**

Melvin, R., and Bushland, R. C. (1940). The nutritional requirements of screw-worm larvae. *J. Econ. Entomol.* **33**, 850–852.

Chapter 38

Tephritid Fruit Flies

LOREN F. STEINER AND SHIZUKO MITCHELL

Entomology Research Division,
Agricultural Research Service,
U. S. Department of Agriculture,
Honolulu, Hawaii

I. INTRODUCTION

In recent years the increasing crop losses caused by certain tephritid species, together with recurrent threats of eventual permanent establishment by destructive species in previously uninfested fruit-growing areas, stimulated interest in research on more efficient methods of control. This created a need for millions of fruit flies of several species and resulted in the expansion of fly production research in many countries. In Hawaii, from 1949–1951, Finney (1956), Maeda *et al.* (1953), and Hagen (1953) developed the first large-scale rearing methods that used artificial media and new adult diets that equaled any the species could find in nature. Their work provided the foundation for most present-day formulas used in mass production laboratories.

Important studies on mass production methods are now underway in fruit fly laboratories in Australia, Costa Rica, Egypt, France, Greece, United States (Hawaii), India, Israel, Mexico, Pakistan, Spain, and Tunisia. At least seven species are being produced.

Prior to 1955 most laboratory-reared tephritids were used to breed parasites or to support research programs that required not more than a few thousand flies per day. Knipling's (1955) concept of eradicating certain well-established pests from isolated areas by over-flooding with irradiated males was based on the premise that effective low-cost mass production methods involving millions of insects could be developed. Preliminary tests of the sterile-insect-release method on subtropical fruit flies (Steiner and Christenson, 1956) indicated that it would be adaptable for control or eradication of tephritid populations.

Intensive efforts to improve mass production methods for three species—the Mediterranean fruit fly, *Ceratitis capitata* (Wiedemann), the Oriental fruit fly, *Dacus dorsalis* Hendel, and the melon fly, *Dacus cucurbitae* Coquillett—had already been initiated at the U. S. Department of Agriculture Hawaii Fruit Fly Investigations Laboratory in 1951. Progress since led to the production of more than 1.4 billion pupae in the period from 1960 to 1965 at rates often exceeding 1.5 million per day (Mitchell *et al.*, 1965). Of these, 257 million *D. cucurbitae* were used in the first successful test of the sterile-fly-release method against a tephritid species. Several hundred million of the other two species were used in other partially successful tests (Steiner *et al.*, 1962, 1965). These and other advances in fruit fly research demonstrated the need for and the usefulness of adequate fly stocks.

Many important results of research on production methods by workers in the countries referred to above are too recent to appear in print. While space does not permit an exhaustive review of information available it is our intention to point out certain pitfalls as well as promising leads, and to provide detailed information on successful rearing methods for three species. For excellent recent reviews pertinent to the subject see Finney and Fisher (1964), Fisher and Finney (1964), Hagen (1964), Bursell (1964a,b), and House (1961, 1963).

II. SOME IMPORTANT BIOLOGICAL AND ECOLOGICAL PARAMETERS IN LABORATORY AND FIELD

A species in its natural habitat often provides important clues to efficient methods of mass production. However, some developmental thresholds can be determined readily under controlled laboratory conditions. Flies from field collections may be produced under various degrees of stress. They could have been survivors of high temperatures or have come from hosts deficient in important nutrients, either naturally or because an excess of larvae produced undersized flies of reduced fecundity and sometimes longevity. One may seriously question whether the F_1 progeny from such flies can be used to reveal the parameters that impose limitations on the species in nature.

A. THE ADULT FRUIT FLY

1. *Adaptation to Laboratory Conditions*

It is often difficult, and may not be desirable, to produce strains fully adjusted to the laboratory environment. In the evolution of tephritid species vast differences developed in their adaptability to natural conditions. For example, some are univoltine, others multivoltine; yet some of the latter, like *C. capitata* and *Dacus oleae* (Gmelin) (the olive fruit fly) survive in mild temperate climates without diapause. *Dacus oleae* with its limited host range has a highly specialized adjustment to olive fruit; its larvae appear to require the extracellular symbiont, *Pseudomonas savastanoi* Smith, which accumulates in the female fly and is transmitted via egg to larvae to aid in the digestion of proteins (Hagen *et al.*, 1963).

Ceratitis capitata can tolerate about the same temperature range as *D. oleae*, but it attacks a large range of hosts. Possibly because its dietary needs in the larval stage are more easily satisfied, the development of mass production procedures is well advanced (Delanoue and Soria, 1958; Feron *et al.*, 1958; Finney *et al.*, 1966; Hafez, 1964; Mitchell *et al.*, 1965; Nadel, 1964).

Collections of *Dacus (Strumeta) tryoni* (Froggatt) from Queensland and Sydney, Australia, near the extremes of the 2000-mile range in latitude covered by the species, showed substantial differences in the effects of temperature on reproductive capacity. The Queensland strain was found by M. A. Bateman to be most productive at 30°C and least at 20°C, while the converse was true of the Sydney strain (Andrewartha and Birch, 1960).

Although wide differences between species may preclude the use of uniform laboratory procedures when more than one is being produced, the large within-species variation that has occurred in nature provides assurance that most species can, by moderate selection, be made more amenable to artificial environments. Selection to strengthen the desirable characteristics and eliminate the undesirable is possible. In Hawaii Mitchell *et al.* (1965) found that collections of wild *D. dorsalis* when reproduced by laboratory methods required about 10 generations to become fully adapted to an efficient dry diet. Greater excitability in the early generations of the new strain appeared partly responsible for its slower development in the laboratory through interference with the response to food.

The adaptation of a strain to efficient laboratory manipulation techniques should be most rapid if large collections of wild flies are used initially. The long time usually required to develop suitable diets can be a limiting factor because both behavioral limitations and minimum nutritional requirements must be identified. Hagen (1953) indicated that, although a diet of solid protein hydrolyzate, solid sucrose, and water, given separately (referred to hereafter as a dry diet) was best for *D. dorsalis* and *D. cucurbitae*, the formula was not effective for *C. capitata*. This species fed best on a liquid combination renewed daily. Adaptation by each strain and use of a nutritionally adequate protein hydrolyzate of proper physical nature enabled Mitchell and associates (1965) to standardize on a dry diet formula for all three species. Such a diet saves labor and allows flies some choice of nutrients that is denied them when offered in solution. Hagen *et al.* (1963) concluded that *D. oleae* adults would not feed effectively on a dry diet. Tzanakakis and Steiner (1964), working on the premise that the species in very dry parts of Greece must utilize comparatively dry food sources for survival and reproduction, offered a moderately hygroscopic commercial protein hydrolyzate powder, sugar cubes, and water separately. At 25°–26°C and 60–70° relative humidity (RH), with a light intensity 90% less than open shade, they obtained as many as 330 eggs from a single female in her first 24 days of life. Of these, 87% hatched. A marked difference was noted in the response of individual females to the protein hydrolyzate and in the elapsed time (1–5 weeks) before oviposition began. Selection of a strain adapted to the dry diet appears possible. Later Tzanakakis and Tsitsipis (1964) obtained evidence that flies reared from olives collected from dry areas in Greece were better adapted to the dry diet than those from moist areas.

There is no evidence that the reproductive qualities of tephritid species under mass culture can be adversely affected by continuous propagation. However, we believe that one should determine the advisability of removing eggs for stock replenishment from among the first eggs produced and compare the progeny with that from eggs taken periodically throughout the holding period and also from near the end. The first period may, for example, select for early sexual maturity and early adaptability to the diet while the last may select for longevity, resistance to disease, delayed sexual maturity, or poor adaptation to the diet. Any changes that develop may thus affect reproductive capacity.

The changes in adaptability to conditions that place stress on the species either in field or laboratory, as cited above, demonstrate the need for the periodic evaluation of laboratory strains. They must be tested for possible losses in field adaptability and compatability with wild flies if they are to be used to study mating and searching ability, natural movement and behavior, or longevity, or for sterilization and release to suppress wild populations.

2. Effects of Temperature, Humidity, and Light

Much research must be done before the optimum meteorological conditions for adult utilization can be established for any one species. When other stages must be reared in the same environment as the adult, a compromise is generally necessary since the optima vary among developmental stages. Recognition of the tolerance limits for each species is important because if approached or exceeded laboratory stocks can be slowed in development or completely destroyed within a few hours. The temperature level not only controls fecundity and longevity but mating and feeding habits as well. The adult requires an ample water supply and many workers have reported rapid mortality when water is withheld. The degree of relative humidity can greatly affect the physical state and palatability of the dry diet. It can also limit or promote important insect diseases.

Light intensity and time of exposure of adults or larvae set the diurnal rhythm in the emergence of *D. tryoni* (Bateman, 1955). Light intensity also affects mating, oviposition, and the response to food.

Keck (1951), using constant temperatures, found that *D. cucurbitae* could not live long enough at 38°C to oviposit and would not lay eggs at temperatures below 13°C. Some labeled γ-irradiated males and females of the same species, released on the subtropical island of Rota, Mariana Islands, in the rainy season, lived more than 4 months in temperatures ranging from 22°–34°C (Steiner *et al.*, 1965).

The best constant temperatures for rearing tephritids probably differ only slightly with the species. Sacantanis (1954) suggested that *D. oleae* rearing should be carried out at 23°–25°C with at least 60% RH in the cages and with a light intensity of 2000 lux (about 190 ft-c) provided. In Israel, Moore (1960) found that the fecundity of *D. oleae* appeared greatest at temperatures of 22°–24°C but was only slightly less at 25°–27°C. For the production of *C. capitata* Feron *et al.* (1958) used a constant temperature of 25°C and relative humidity of 80% to obtain 2000–4000 eggs from 500 females/cage/day between the 6th and 20th day after emergence. Mitchell and associates (1965) maintained adult populations of three species at a constant temperature of 27°C and relative humidity of 80% or less in cages stocked initially with about 22,000–26,000 flies of *D. cucurbitae, D. dorsalis,* or *C. capitata,* and obtained averages of 150–310 eggs per pair during the first 3–4 weeks after emergence.

Pterandrus rosa (Karsch) will not mate at temperatures above 27°C; its optimum range for mating is between 19° and 25°C with a light intensity of 0–10 ft-c, whereas *C. capitata* mates best in the range 22°–30°C under light intensities that exceed 200 ft-c (Myburgh, 1962). Roan *et al.* (1954) found that sexually mature *D. dorsalis* held 25 days at 15°C would not mate during the period; however, copulation began at temperatures above 15.6°C. In tests conducted at temperatures of 24°–30°C a gradual decrease in light intensity by a factor of 2 always induced copulation in sexually mature flies; an abrupt light change did not.

From the results reported for several species good production appears attainable if adults, on an adequate diet, are held at 25°–27°C, at a relative humidity of 60–80% and the light is kept sufficiently subdued to permit normal feeding and oviposition, and with normally spaced real or simulated dusk periods of diminishing light to stimulate mating where needed.

3. *Dietary Requirements*

The most universally used sources of nutrients in modern diets for tephritids are several commercially available, hydrolyzed proteins and sucrose. The former contain the important amino acids, minerals, and vitamins found in honeydew and certain other natural foods of fruit flies. Hagen (1958) identified *C. capitata, D. cucurbitae, D.*

dorsalis, *D. oleae*, *Dacus diversus* Coquillett, and *Epochra canadensis* (Loew) (the currant fruit fly), as species to which honeydew was important as adult food. Craig (1960) cited several reports concerning the amino acid content of honeydew. He noted similarities in the composition of honeydew and that of the host sap as it undergoes seasonal changes. The tephritidae have been reported to feed on plant saps, fruit juices, nectars, yeasts, fungi, bird dung, and several other natural sources of food as well as honeydew, but some species, such as *C. capitata*, *Rhagoletis completa* Cresson (walnut husk fly), *Rhagoletis pomonella* (Walsh) (apple maggot or blueberry maggot), and *Rhagoletis cingulata* (Loew) (cherry maggot or cherry fruit fly), can produce many eggs on diets containing only a carbohydrate and water (Christenson and Foote, 1960). However, Fluke and Allen (1931) and Dean (1938) found that inclusion of unhydrolyzed yeast increased the fecundity of *D. pomonella* and the latter noted a further benefit from feeding proteose peptones. While testing diets for *D. dorsalis*, *D. cucurbitae*, and *C. capitata* in Hawaii, Hagen (1953) and Hagen and Finney (1950) made the important discovery that commercial protein hydrolyzates could provide most of the nutrients (except sucrose) required by those species and could both reduce the preovipositional period and increase the fecundity. Mitchell and associates (1965) compared several of the protein hydrolyzates reported most attractive for bait-spray use by Steiner *et al.* (1958) and found that one, designated type M,[*] gave results in *D. dorsalis*, *D. cucurbitae*, and *C. capitata* diets equal to the best previously used materials. The diet for these species now consists of yeast hydrolyzate (type M), sucrose, and water, offered separately. Both the physical characteristics and nutritional composition account for the successful use of type M in dry diets. The results suggest that other equally effective protein hydrolyzates may be available.

In Israel *C. capitata* is now being reared on a dry diet of type M yeast hydrolyzate mixed with sucrose (Nadel, 1964). In Costa Rica a mixture of two yeast hydrolyzates, sucrose, and orange crystals is used (Morales and Gonzales, 1964). In Mexico Rhode (1957) used a 2:1 mixture of orange crystals and sucrose with a yeast hydrolyzate offered separately to rear *Anastrepha ludens* (Loew) (Mexican fruit fly). For *D. oleae* in Israel, Moore (1962) included brewers' yeast with enzymatic yeast hydrolyzate, sucrose, and water atomized on glass plates. The possibility that this species might be reared on a dry diet was mentioned in Section II,A,1. Excessive humidity causes sugar and most of the protein hydrolyzates to deliquesce. The sticky

[*] Fleischmann's type M yeast hydrolyzate, Standard Brands, Inc., New York, N. Y.

residue entangles flies and may cause high mortality. Liquid diets require more materials and labor because of the daily renewals that are necessary (Mitchell *et al.*, 1965). Additional research is needed under conditions of low humidity to determine if liquid and mixed-solid diets allow flies to properly adjust their intake of carbohydrates and protein hydrolyzate to best fit the needs of maximum productivity. Information is also needed to determine the extent to which the sex and differences in age and egg production have on dietary requirements.

The length of time required to produce complete eggs or viable sperm differs among the species but is regulated by both temperature and diet. The last is particularly important to those species or individuals that do not carry over appropriate nutrients from the larval stage. The adequacy of the diet cannot be reliably measured in the laboratory if environmental factors interfere with the response to food. At a constant 27°C and 60–80% RH *D. dorsalis, D. cucurbitae,* and *C. capitata,* when given the most productive diet available, will begin depositing fertile eggs when 7, 7, and 3 days old, respectively (Mitchell *et al.*, 1965). Feron *et al.* (1958) attributed the short preovipositional period of *C. capitata* to its ability to carry over necessary elements accumulated during its larval period. At a mean temperature of about 25°C and relative humidity of 50% *A. ludens* required at least 9 days for its preovipositional period (Rhode, 1957). *D. oleae* reared from olive fruit at 23°–25°C required 2–3 days of feeding before sexual maturity was reached (Sacantanis, 1954).

In *Drosophila* the age of the ovipositing female significantly affects rate of larval growth, but the assumption that this is a consequence of differences in the food content of the eggs remains to be tested (Sang, 1959). Such an effect of age has not been observed in tephritids but is worthy of study since, if true, compensatory modifications in diets for older flies might be feasible.

4. Disease and Other Contamination

Sometimes disease invades adult cultures if proper sanitary precautions are not maintained. *Nosema* spp. infected adult stocks of *D. cucurbitae* and pupae of *D. dorsalis* and *C. capitata* (Finney *et al.*, 1966). Hagen *et al.* (1963) found that bacteria of one or more unidentified species replaced the symbiont *P. savastanoi* in its usual morphological sites in *D. oleae* reared in the laboratory and prevented oviposition and excretion. Control of the bacteria by inclusion of streptomycin in the adult diet greatly increased fecundity and longevity but, by also eliminating the symbiont, it apparently destroyed the capability of the larvae to survive in olive fruit. Moore (1960) observed that honeydew produced by *Pseudococcus citri* (Risso) breeding on pumpkin was toxic to *D. oleae* unless diluted by a fine water spray. The reason for the toxicity is unknown but if not associated with insecticide residues a possible cause would be an imbalance of ingested nutrients to which the fly's metabolism could not adjust.

In addition to disease, insecticides or toxicants from other sources may reduce adult fecundity and longevity. Laboratory cages utilizing copper or bronze screen, certain woods, or plastics may prove toxic to some insects (Finney and Fisher, 1964).

B. THE EGG

Eggs are normally inserted under the skin of fruits, vegetables, nuts, or fleshy parts of plant stems or flowers where they are protected from desiccation. Some species, if on a nutritious diet, will, in the absence of suitable real or imitation hosts, drop their eggs or insert them in cracks or under objects. Unless continually protected from loss of water, eggs will die quickly. *Ceratitis capitata* eggs can be held in water all or most of the incubation period (Feron *et al.*, 1958; Nadel, 1964). The same is true of *D. dorsalis* and *D. cucurbitae* eggs, but there is enough evidence of an adverse effect on the larvae to justify more investigation (Mitchell *et al.*, 1965). Most workers have preferred to hold tephritid eggs for incubation on wet paper in a moist chamber.

Reports of diseased tephritid eggs are rare. A bacterium tentatively identified as *Serratia marcescens* Bizio prevented *C. capitata* eggs from hatching (Moore and Nadel, 1961).

Messenger and Flitters (1958) reported 33.6°C as the most rapid developmental temperature for the eggs of *D. dorsalis* and *D. cucurbitae* and 32.2°C for *C. capitata*. The upper limit for the first two species was 37.4°C; for *C. capitata*, 35.5°C. The threshold limits ranged from 11.1°–12.8°C.

When variable temperatures representing natural patterns were studied swiftest egg development under the fluctuating temperature conditions occurred at mean temperatures 2.7°–5.5°C below the temperature for most rapid growth under constant conditions (Messenger and Flitters, 1959).

For the most efficient use of larval-medium facilities, eggs will usually have been collected and incubated so that new medium can be reset with hatching larvae on the day that the preceding lot of larvae reached maturity. It is only necessary to egg flies far enough in advance to permit complete incubation in the time required for the temperature that is to be used.

C. THE LARVA

1. *Important Factors Affecting Survival and Rate of Development*

The temperature thresholds that set upper and lower limits of activity can be identified with reasonable accuracy. The developmental-rate parameters for temperature are established by strong interaction with the nutritional and physical characteristics of the substrate. This is evident from the variations reported in the time required to complete larval development at a given temperature. For example: at 25.7°C *D. cucurbitae* required 4, 10–13, and 7–17 days for larval development in papaya, Bartlett pear, and cantaloupe, respectively (Back and Pemberton, 1917). *Ceratitis capitata* at 25°–26°C averaged 18, 16, 12, and 11 days for the combined egg and larval stages in apple, pear, peach, and banana, respectively (Feron and Sacantanis, 1955). At 23°C Moore (1959) found that development of *D. oleae* from egg to adult lasted 28 days in olives but required 38 days in his artificial medium; Moore concluded that the medium required improvement. Indication that time spent in the larval stage might be increased by factors other than temperature and diet was first recorded by Back and Pemberton (1914), who reported *D. cucurbitae* larvae developing in thick-skinned fruits like watermelon and pumpkin, the larvae often remaining in the fruit several days after becoming full-grown before emerging to pupate. During the 1956–1957 Florida Mediterranean-fruit-fly eradication program Steiner *et al.* (1961) noted fully mature *C. capitata* larvae trapped in hard-shelled, off-season and overripe sour oranges and grapefruit with plugged exit holes, and surviving as long as 20 days without pupating. Such behavior by mature larvae in artificial media has not been reported. In well-adapted artificial media under mass production conditions *D. cucurbitae* develop from time of hatch to larval maturity in 5 days at 27°C; most of them will leave the medium at that time, although *C. capitata* and *D. dorsalis* require a sixth day (Mitchell *et al.*, 1965).

A rearing medium and its method of use should permit most larvae to reach maturity and vacate, or be removed from, the medium on the same day and in the shortest time possible for the species, so that facilities will not be encumbered for additional days of waiting for retarded larvae to reach maturity.

When larvae were reared at constant temperatures the upper limit was reported to be approximately 35°C (Shaw and Starr, 1946; Koidzumi, 1934; Keck, 1951). The lethal limit for most insects during short exposure of about an hour was reported to be between 40° and 50°C, with some exceptions. Comparative studies are complicated in some species by the phenomenon of acclimation, which may vary according to the thermal history of the population tested (Bursell, 1964a). Vapor heat treatments have long been used to disinfest fruit. Larvae and eggs of *Anastrepha ludens* will be killed by internal temperatures of 43.3°C held for 6 hours, after an approach period of 8 hours (Baker *et al.*, 1944), or by a quick run-up to 49°C followed by gradual cooling (U. S. Dept. Agr., 1962). Various workers have observed high mortality among larvae inside fruits that were exposed to bright sunlight. Midday temperatures in the center of growing, unshaded, immature cucumbers and nearly ripe tomatoes were found to have increased to as much as 45°C, or 13.5°C above ambient temperatures (Steiner, 1962).

Where substantial aggregations of insects occur, metabolic heating may be an important factor (Bursell, 1964a). The significance of this is not fully realized in fruit fly mass production where, as soon as suitable media are developed, the goal has been to extract maximum numbers of full-size larvae. The result is that part or all of the larvae may be overcrowded enough to cause interference with their natural cooling by evaporation or conduction. When *C. capitata, D. dorsalis,* and *D. cucurbitae* were produced in a thick medium that became moderately dry, high larval concentrations caused temperature increases to 35.5°C, or 8°C above ambient, in the medium during the 24-hour period immediately before larval maturity. The temperature declined to the ambient level as the larvae vacated the medium (Mitchell *et al.*, 1965). A similar rise in temperature in a thick medium of a different formula used to rear *C. capitata* larvae was noted by Nadel (1964). Research is needed to determine if this trapped metabolic heat can have adverse latent effects on the pupae or adult stages of the involved larvae.

In their natural hosts larvae of different species are subject to large variations in moisture but are well protected against water loss. Newly hatched larvae must be protected against desiccation and can remain in water without injury for several hours (Mitchell *et al.*, 1965), or days (Feron *et al.*, 1958). Finney *et al.* (1966) noted that mature larvae of the above species could be made manageable while collecting and measuring if they were immersed in water to stop their jumping. The time-temperature limit for safe holding in water to delay pupation has not been adequately investigated. Normal pupation rates that may follow periods of immersion do not prove absence of injurious effects because the latter may be deferred to later stages.

2. Nutritional Needs as Indicated by Rearing Media

Multiple generations are needed to measure the adequacy of nutrients in larval as well as adult diets. The masking of requirements occurs if nutritional reserves are stored in the immature forms and subsequently mobilized to nourish the adult or are passed from adult via egg to young (House, 1963). This suggests that ability to carry over essential nutrients may help a species maintain a high reproductive rate in its natural environment by changing hosts as needed in successive generations to obtain the deficient nutrients. If true, more than one generation will be required in the laboratory before the optimum succession of diets for adults and larvae can be determined.

As might be expected from the great differences among nutritive content and physical characteristics of their hosts, the development of suitable media for rearing larvae has been neither easy nor rapid. No satisfactory medium that will efficiently produce many successive generations of *D. oleae* is available, but progress is evident in the work of Moore (1959, 1962), Hagen *et al.* (1963), and others. In contrast, the media developed for species such as *D. dorsalis, D. cucurbitae,* and *C. capitata* are now considered simple. With little or slight variation these were subsequently adapted to *A. ludens* and *D. tryoni.* The development of modern artificial larval media took its greatest step forward during the period from 1949–1951 as a result of the work of Finney (1956) and Maeda *et al.* (1953) in Hawaii following the outbreak of *D. dorsalis.* A formula based on fresh carrots was perfected and used for *D. dorsalis* and *C. capitata.* The carrots were shredded and pulverized to a thick, smooth consistency with a mechanical blender. This could be substituted for all the ingredients that had been used in earlier media except brewers' yeast, provided mold and bacterial inhibitors were included. The formula generally used consisted of 800 ml of blended raw carrots, 16 gm powdered brewers' yeast, 15 ml 2 N HCl, and 1.04 gm of Butoben (*n*-butyl *p*-hydroxybenzoate). Pans holding 3200 ml spread 1 inch deep could produce 5000 mature *D. dorsalis* larvae 6 days after hatch of 7000–7500 eggs. The medium was less successful for *C. capitata,* but up to half of the eggs produced full-fed larvae. *Dacus cucurbitae* did not tolerate the chemical preservative and therefore could not be reared in the formula. This species continued to be reared by allowing egg deposition in pumpkin, squash, or cucumber sections, which were then placed on the carrot medium without any mold inhibitor but not without serious mold problems. In the 6 months before termination of the project on July 1, 1951, more than 5 million *D. dorsalis*, 660,000 *C. capitata*, and several hundred thousand *D. cucurbitae* were produced (Finney *et al.*, 1966).

Important improvements in larval media have been made by the U. S. Department of Agriculture since it began its mass production research in Hawaii in 1951. In 1953, after screening available mold inhibitors, sodium benzoate at 0.10–0.15% was substituted for all others. This greatly improved *D. cucurbitae* production (Mitchell *et al.*, 1965). The substitution in 1955 (Christenson *et al.*, 1956) of dehydrated carrot powder for the raw product constituted another major advance in Oriental fruit fly mass production. This yielded better quality larvae at less cost. The substitution also gave improved results with *D. cucurbitae* and *C. capitata*. New egging procedures initiated in 1957 in Hawaii (Tanaka, 1965) provided free *D. cucurbitae* eggs for the first time and obviated the need for prior infestation of chunks of cucumber or squash for placement on the artificial medium. Other important advances by Mitchell and associates (1965) included the substitution of powdered dehydrated squash, after evaluation of many other products, for about 40% of the dehydrated carrot powder in the *D. cucurbitae* medium only, and increases in brewers' yeast from the 2–3% used in *D. dorsalis* or *C. capitata* medium to 4% in the *D. cucurbitae* formula.

Raw or dehydrated carrot media, fortified with brewers' yeast and variously modified with mold inhibitors and pH changes toward acidity, have been used to culture *A. ludens* in Mexico since 1954 and *D. tryoni* in Australia since 1956 (Finney *et al.*, 1966). Delanoue and Soria (1958) in Tunisia successfully utilized diverse fruits for *C. capitata* production until 1957, but then substituted the Hawaii formulas modified by an increase in brewers' yeast to approximately 4% and the use of 2% benzoic acid instead of sodium benzoate. A further benefit was noted when they included ⅓ to ⅔ bran in the total medium. Feron *et al.* (1958), using the same formula for *C. capitata* but without the bran, obtained adults from 80% of the eggs used. Following the experience of Delanoue and Soria with bran, Nadel (1964) developed a low-cost formula for *C. capitata* that is based on wheat bran, sucrose, brewers' yeast and water, with HCl, Nipagin [methyl paraben (Merck)], and Nipasol [propylparaben (Merck)] as preservatives. This formula must be mixed with boiling water and requires special handling after egg setting to prevent desiccation of eggs and caking of the medium surface, but yields 27 pupae per gram of solids used. The simple formula, containing one or more dehydrated vegetable products such as carrot or squash supplemented with brewers' yeast, provides all the nutrients needed by larvae of D. dorsalis, D. cucurbitae, C. capitata, and probably A. ludens and D. tryoni.

Slow or arrested growth and development, diminutive size, high or complete mortality of the immature stages, and little or no reproduction in the adult are familiar symptoms of most nutritional defects (House, 1963).

It appears that the maximum number of larvae or hatchable eggs that can be applied to a medium of particular formula, volume, and depth without adversely affecting size or quality must be determined for each species and condition of use. The utilizable depth will be governed by consistency and by species. Competition from mold or bacterial growth will affect the nutrients available to larvae and can reduce both size and number. More and larger larvae will sometimes be produced by increasing the proportion of brewers' yeast, however, additional mold growth is promoted and the increased concentration of chemical preservative needed to control it may prove toxic to the larvae. Uncontrolled fluctuating temperatures and humidities also disturb the balance established between the volume and quality of nutrients, the xenic conditions in the medium, the additives for control of bacteria, and the number of larvae.

3. Contamination and Disease

Insecticidal residues in the bran used by Nadel (1964) were avoided by selecting only supplies lightly infested by grain pests. For the Hawaii work rigid specifications for the dehydrated vegetable powders were established to minimize the insecticide residue hazard (Mitchell et al., 1965). Disease has not been reported as a serious problem of larvae in laboratories using the dehydrated powder formulas under constant temperature and humidity conditions. Snowball et al. (1962), when using fruit for parasite production in the same laboratory as their larval medium, found that Drosophila sp. was a vector of a nematode Phabditis sp. which multiplied freely along with Drosophila larvae in the medium and sometimes completely stopped D. dorsalis development. In other laboratories Drosophila (Mitchell et al., 1965; Nadel, 1964) and a phorid (Hafez, 1964) have infested the medium. Elimination of these pests was effected by the use of fine-mesh screen on adult and larval medium cages, and by improving sanitary conditions.

D. THE PUPA

Larvae of several species leave the fruit to pupate during the early morning hours. Most penetrate the soil rapidly and pupate under the surface. Puparium formation may require as little as 1 hour and complete pupal formation within the puparium less than 48 hours (Christenson and Foote, 1960). Some larvae, if forced to do so, will pupate in the open air but the pupae may then be subject to desiccation, radiant heat, or mechanical injury. The relationship of temperature to diapause in univoltine species and the role of other physical, biochemical, or genetic factors in stimulating or breaking diapause in fruit flies are in urgent need of critical investigation (Christenson and Foote, 1960). Such species could probably be stockpiled so that large numbers, if needed for seasonal operations, could be accumulated by continuous operation of a small producing facility.

The length of the pupal stage in multivoltine species is regulated largely by temperature, although Sacantanis (1954) reported that in *D. oleae* it was affected by the quality of food available to the larvae. At 23°–25°C he noted a pupal stage of 8–12 days' duration. At 27°C the mean pupal period for *D. dorsalis* and *C. capitata* was 10 days and for *D. cucurbitae* 9 days (Mitchell *et al.*, 1965). These periods are approximately 1 day longer than reported by Koidzumi (1934).

The avoidance of immediate or latent damage from excess metabolic heat was a problem of major importance in the production, manipulation, and shipping of large volumes of pupae for eradication programs in the Western Pacific (Steiner *et al.*, 1962, 1965; Mitchell *et al.*, 1965). Pupae held in bulk, without an insulating substrate or forced ventilation, accumulate metabolic heat that will cause a rapid temperature rise to lethal levels during the 2 or 3 days immediately before emergence. Those pupae that eclose after having been overheated produce weaker, shorter-lived flies.

In mass production most workers usually allow mature larvae to pupate in slightly moistened sand or sawdust. For several years Mitchell *et al.* (1965) used sand but found that mortality sometimes reached 40% if the sand contained too much moisture or excess larvae. Larvae were reluctant to enter wet sand and containers had to be covered to prevent escapes. Tests of several products led to use of a nearly dust-free grade of fine vermiculite. Since the larvae enter and pupate in this quickly box covers are not needed; survival is greater and because of lighter weight, labor is less. Emergence of *D. cucurbitae* from 73 million pupae produced in sand from 1959–1961 averaged 81%. In the 3 years since vermiculite was substituted emergence from 250 million averaged 93%.

When it is necessary to hold naked pupae in bulk, the controlled temperatures and forced ventilation required to avoid overheating may lead to some desiccation. This has been avoided by holding the relative humidity above 85% (Mitchell *et al.*, 1965).

Pupae at 20°C are able to tolerate fumigation with 0.5 ml dichlorvos volatilized in the air of a 900-ft³ room at least 1 day before emergence. There is no latent effect and no toxic residue on the puparia at time of emergence. The treatment was used regularly on irradiated pupae in open, well-ventilated cartons to prevent shipment of living, nonirradiated adults of the same or other species (Steiner *et al.*, 1962, 1965).

The ecdysis rhythm established by normal diurnal light changes was unchanged when pupae of *D. dorsalis* and *D. cucurbitae* were transported overnight 3800 miles west to a 4-hour-later time zone where most emergence occurred near dawn (Steiner *et al.*, 1962).

III. PRACTICAL MASS PRODUCTION PROCEDURES, FORMULAS, AND FACILITIES

Efficient mass production of fruit flies must rely not only on dependable methods, diets, and equipment but on the initiative, ingenuity, interest, and constant vigilance of each worker. Ability to recognize and correct problems before they make inroads on rates of production can be acquired. Other skills will develop with practice so that original productivity may eventually double or triple.

The most efficient facilities will have temperatures and humidities automatically regulated. Provisions for the maintenance of sanitation and the exclusion of contamination are also important. The program will involve frequent, if not daily, checks on the condition of adult fly stocks, their longevity, fecundity, and the fertility of their eggs; the physical condition of the medium whenever a new supply of any component is first used; and the size of the insect produced. Periodic tests will be needed to evaluate field adaptability of the laboratory strain.

This section will review the methods currently in use at the U. S. Department of Agriculture Hawaii Fruit Fly Investigations Laboratory as described by Tanaka (1965) and Mitchell *et al.* (1965). Production of 1.4 billion pupae of three species—*C. capitata, D. cucurbitae,* and *D. dorsalis*—without interruption over a 5-year period demonstrates the effectiveness of the procedures developed.

A. FEEDING AND HOLDING ADULT STOCKS

Adult flies are held in cages made in two parts with the base a shallow aluminum pan 1 inch deep (Fig. 1). Circular openings 3-3/16

FIG. 1. Each stack of 4 egging cages can produce about ⅓ million eggs daily.

inches in diameter, for holding egg receptacles, are evenly spaced in the wood panels on each side. A thin sheet of polyethylene film is placed as a floor covering in each pan before the cage top is lowered. Stacks of 4 cages are set on movable bases. A 52-inch wick of 0.5-inch diameter cotton dental roll is placed in a removable, aluminum, V-shaped channel that extends the entire length of each cage (3 inches below the top) and out 2 inches at each end. A detachable pipe having 4 spigots is positioned above the channels at the front of each stack of cages. These feed fresh water slowly from an overhead gravity system. The surplus water flows out a rear drain. The dental rolls are replaced once or twice as they become soiled. This equipment has provided an ample and very important fresh water supply for the large fly colonies.

The room is lighted with two lines of 80-watt fluorescent lamps positioned 3 feet above the 10 stacks of cages. Lights are operated between 0800 and 1630 hours. In Hawaii length of day (sunrise to sunset) varies from approximately 11 to 13 hours. The natural light entering through lightly painted windows on opposite ends of the room is sufficient to set the diurnal rhythm for ecdysis. The natural change in intensity provides the stimulus for mating. The subdued daylight and uniform artificial lighting in the room reduces the excitability of the flies, gives them more opportunity to feed undisturbed on the dry diet, and avoids piling up in cage corners. The facility is operated 6–7 days per week on a one-shift basis. If on a full 24-hour schedule the stocks would have to be divided among two or more rooms to ensure adequate periods of light and darkness for each cage. The minimum space requirement for each stack of four cages is 30 ft² or approximately 10 ft² per 1 million eggs produced per week. Stacks must be 3 feet apart to permit adequate light for oviposition to reach the lower cages.

Room temperature is held at approximately 27°C and relative humidity to less than 80%. Each cage is initially stocked with about 25,000 *D. dorsalis* or *D. cucurbitae* pupae, or 30,000 *C. capitata* (Fig. 2). Two pounds cube or granulated sugar and 0.5 pound dry yeast hydrolyzate (type M) on separate plates are supplied the first two species; *C. capitata* requires only one-quarter as much. The flies require no additional food or other attention except for watering. *Ceratitis capitata* stocks are held 3 weeks and the other species 4 weeks. Average emergence of pupae approximates 90% and results in initial adult populations of 11,000–13,000 pairs per cage. Egging is initiated on the 4th to 9th day after emergence, depending on the species.

One-third or one-quarter of the cages are restocked each week. The stacks are wheeled to a steam generator, surviving flies are killed with live steam, cage top and pan are separated, flushed with hot water, then steam sterilized. The polyethylene is also cleaned for reuse. Cages need be idle only a few minutes.

This cage design and its feeding and watering systems were copied by Morales and Gonzales (1964) in Costa Rica where they soon attained production levels up to 18 million *C. capitata* eggs per month.

B. COLLECTION, INCUBATION, AND HANDLING OF EGGS

When stocked with *C. capitata* or *D. cucurbitae* the 40 cages had a weekly production capacity of more than 25 million eggs. Stocked with *D. dorsalis* their capacity exceeds 35 million eggs per week. The present receptacle is a yellow polyethylene, 1-qt container perforated with 300 holes of 0.3-mm diameter (Fig. 3). It can be inserted

Fig. 2. Sugar, protein hydrolyzate, and pupae are placed in separate trays. Water on a cotton roll is available in the trough. Flies are calm and well dispersed.

FIG. 3. Eggs are deposited through 0.3 mm holes into egging receptacles moistened with fruit juice. Tubes are capped when in use. When receptacles are removed holes are covered.

snugly in one of the holes along the side of each cage. Its tight cap prevents desiccation of the eggs. When the inner walls are wet with water or dilute lemon juice to stimulate oviposition and prevent desiccation of eggs, *C. capitata* oviposits readily. For *D. dorsalis*, guava juice diluted 2:1 with water is used; for *D. cucurbitae*, a 2 × 6 × 1-inch cellulose sponge is saturated with a 1:1 tomato juice-water solution and placed in the receptacle. During the first week or two of egging, six receptacles per cage are adequate to collect all available eggs within a 20-hour period. Later four or three are ample. Egg production can be increased by daily egging.

FIG. 4. Eggs are measured in units of 40,000 to 50,000 and incubated on moist pad in shallow covered dish.

Eggs are washed into a fine mesh bag and from there to a beaker, where they are held under water for not more than 2 hours. During this period they are divided volumetrically into lots of 40,000 or 50,000 and placed in shallow plastic containers on moist cloth (Fig. 4). These are held at a temperature that will start hatch at a convenient time for medium setting, usually 20°C for *D. dorsalis* (to delay hatch one-half day), and 27°C for *C. capitata*. *Dacus cucurbitae* eggs hatch in 23 hours at 27°C; hence they can be placed on the medium as soon as the quantities are measured. The timing eliminates any need for protection of the medium surface from desiccation. Egg hatch rates are determined frequently. Any necessary adjustment is made in the setting rate for subsequent batches if it deviates significantly from 90%.

Methods of egging *C. capitata* in other laboratories include the use of a perforated polyethylene bottle that has been moistened inside (Morales and Gonzales, 1964), and a poultry egg container of yellow polyethylene sulfide which is perforated and lined with moist muslin (Feron *et al.*, 1958). A simple method was devised by Nadel (1964). Females were induced to oviposit through a heavy silk cloth stretched over the lighted side of the fly cage, angled so that eggs pushed through could drop directly into a pan of water. Banks of 5 cages were so positioned that all eggs drop into the same container.

Dacus oleae deposits single eggs in its own fresh punctures, and Moore (1959) constructed thin, hollow, paraffin domes that induced oviposition by this species.

For egging *A. ludens*, McPhail and Guiza (1956) developed a reusable hollow hemispherical dome made of cheesecloth, paraffin, and petrolatum. This was colored orange and females punctured the dome to lay eggs. The inside was kept moist with wet cotton wool.

C. Production of Larvae

Larvae are produced in an air-conditioned room held at 27°C. Moderate daylight enters windows on one side. Artificial lighting is used during working hours. The larvae require no special lighting to control or reset the ecdysis rhythm, but would if larval production required night work.

TABLE I

STANDARD FORMULAS FOR LARVAL PRODUCTION

	Amount for	
Ingredient	*Ceratitis capitata* and *Dacus dorsalis*	*Dacus cucurbitae*
Sodium benzoate	0.1 kg	0.1 kg
Conc. HCl (CP)	0.5 kg	0.5 kg
Brewers' yeast (powder)	3.2 kg	4.25 kg
Dehydrated squash (powder)	0	4.0 kg
Dehydrated carrot (powder)	12.0 kg	6.4 kg
Water	90.7 liters	91.2 liters
Total weight of medium	106.5 kg	106.5 kg
Volume	100.0 liters	100.0 liters

Larval medium is mixed outside the air-conditioned facility to avoid clogging of air-conditioning filters by the hygroscopic dust. The research on media (see Section II,C,2) led to development of the standard formulas listed in Table I.

The average production by these formulas approximates 28 *D. dorsalis*, 29 *D. cucurbitae*, or 35.5 *C. capitata* per gram of nonwater ingredients. The pupae average larger than those from natural sources. Adjustments in the acid to provide a pH of approximately 4.5 are made as needed. Variations in mean particle size and moisture content of different batches of the vegetable powders affect the water: powder ratio; consequently, adjustments must be made in the quantities of water or powder called for by the formula. These media stiffen soon after mixing. A smooth, thick, but slightly flowable mix is desired (Fig. 5). Hand-mixed media do not attain their thickest consistency in less than 2 hours. Continuous machine mixing will thicken the same formula in about 20 minutes.

Medium for large-scale production is prepared in batches of 180 liters, utilizing a large vat and electric mixer. The vat has a large valve through which 6 liters of medium is dropped quickly into an aluminum pan (12 × 32 × 1½ inch) to a depth of 1 inch. The pan is lined with a sheet of polyethylene plastic that protects it from the acid and facili-

FIG. 5. The larval medium is barely flowable after mixing.

FIG. 6. One pad of eggs is touched down several times on medium to transfer hatching larvae. Trays are stacked in screened cabinets that hold 15 on each side. Larvae mature in 5 to 6 days.

tates subsequent manipulation of larvae and the medium residues. One or two toilet-tissue strips 2 inches wide are placed across the top of each pan in contact with the medium. One cloth patch containing 40,000 or 50,000 eggs that have started to hatch is touched upside down to the top of the tissue strips. The pan is then placed in a double cabinet (6 × 3 × 3 ft) having a screened center partition and 32 × 32 mesh/inch plastic screen doors on opposite sides (Fig. 6). The cabinet is on casters and holds 30 pans spaced about 3 inches apart, 15 on each side. A pan (12 × 33 × 5 inches) containing vermiculite covers the floor on each side and collects early maturing larvae as they drop from the traps. The screened cabinets exclude *Drosphila* but permit the aeration necessary to prevent overheating of maturing larvae.

Ceratitis capitata and *D. dorsalis* larvae mature in 6 days and *D. cucurbitae* in 5 days at 27°C. At the end of this period larvae that have left the medium are redistributed in pupating boxes containing slightly moist (5% water by volume) vermiculite. The remaining larvae, usually 50–90% of the total, are collected by slipping the contents of the pan into a vat of water. After removal of the plastic, the slurry is washed through a sieve that retains only the larvae. The residue can be flushed down the drain. The washed larvae from 15 trays (350,000–450,000) are accumulated in a large pail of water, then poured into a cloth bag for separation from the water, and finally placed in a cement mixer of 4.5 ft³ capacity containing 75 liters of vermiculite. The mixer is driven at a speed of 25 rpm for 5 minutes. The resultant blend is then divided among 12 plastic, stackable, pupating boxes (6 × 12 × 18 inches).

All larval culture pans and cabinets are flushed out and steam-sterilized for reuse. When operated at full capacity the 15 cabinets can produce 13–16 million mature larvae per week. No losses from disease or nematode infestations (introduced by *Drosophilia*) have occurred since live steam was first used for cabinet cleaning.

D. MANIPULATION OF PUPAE

Pupae must be protected from desiccation, overheating, and concussion. The moistened, lightweight vermiculite now used is an almost ideal pupation medium and may be reused many times without sterilization. All larvae are allowed 2 days in the vermiculite at 27°C to complete pupation; then they are programed for appropriate holding periods at 20° or 27°C to advance development of different aged pupae for simultaneous emergence on predetermined dates. Two days at 20°C permits the same development in the three species as 1 day at 27°C.

A mechanical sifter with a soft action was devised to separate pupae quickly from vermiculite without concussion damage. Pupae held at 27°C are not separated until almost ready for shipment or emergence. After the sifting they are spread about 0.4 inch deep in 20 × 20 × 1-inch (inside diameter) screened-bottom trays and held in an air-conditioned room at 20°C at not less than 85% relative humidity. The trays are stacked and so positioned that an electric fan can force air between and through the layers of pupae. Unless this is done during the 3 days before emergence, accumulated heat among the massed, naked pupae may reach lethal levels or reduce longevity in adults that emerge.

Numbers and size of pupae are estimated from slightly compacted samples measured volumetrically shortly before emergence. Numbers per liter approximate 30,000 *D. cucurbitae,* 35,000 *D. dorsalis,* and 55,000 *C. capitata.*

IV. PRODUCTION COSTS

Most equipment for the U. S. Department of Agriculture Hawaii program is highly functional and was constructed by laboratory personnel to fit specific needs. Costs per million pupae for fly food, wicks, larval medium components, and other expendable items approximate $41 for *D. dorsalis* and *C. capitata* and $46 for *D. cucurbitae* (Mitchell *et al.,* 1965). These costs are based on conservative estimates of 2 million eggs/cage/generation and on pupal recovery rates of 65% of the egg set.

Labor requirements with highly skilled workers approximate 5.5 hours per million pupae. This includes 15 minutes for the steam cleaning and sterilization of cages, preparing food, and changing wicks; 40 minutes for all egging operations, including determination of the mean hatch rate; 80 minutes for preparing and setting medium; 115 minutes for collecting and washing larvae from medium, mixing them with vermiculite, placing in boxes, and cleaning plastic sheets; 35 minutes for steam cleaning of medium cabinets and pans; 25 minutes for the sifting and distribution of pupae in holding trays and determining emergence rates; 20 minutes for miscellaneous items, such as cutting wicks, tissue, plastic sheets, and egg pads. The labor estimates are based on full-time utilization of workers.

Where more than one species must be produced concurrently, costs tend to be greater than where techniques that best fit a single species can be used. At the start of a mass production program many unexpected problems can create temporary or permanent cost increases above estimates. When fresh field strains of flies must be used methods that have been found useful elsewhere for the species should not be discarded until tested against several consecutive generations of laboratory-bred flies. When recommended formulas fail to function as expected, the use of food materials that differ from the original in physical or chemical composition could be responsible. Differences in the microflora or the insect species that attack laboratory colonies may require substitution of other preservatives or of new procedures. The over-all production costs will be influenced greatly by the success attained in overcoming unexpected problems.

REFERENCES

Andrewartha, H. G., and Birch, L. C. (1960). Distribution and abundance of insects. *Ann. Rev. Entomol.* **5**, 219–242.

Back, E. A., and Pemberton, C. E. (1914). Life history of the melon fly. *J. Agr. Res.* **3,** 269–274.

Back, E. A., and Pemberton, C. E. (1917). The melon fly in Hawaii. *U. S. Dept. Agr., Tech. Bull.* **491**, 1–64.

Baker, A. C., Stone, W. E., Plummer, C. C., and McPhail, M. (1944). *U. S. Dept. Agr., Misc. Publ.* **531**, 1–155.

Bateman, M. A. (1955). The effect of light and temperature on the rhythm of pupal ecdysis in the Queensland fruit-fly, *Dacus* (*Strumenta*) *tryoni* (Frogg.). *Australian J. Zool.* **3**, 22–33.

Bursell, E. (1964a). Environmental aspects: Temperature. *In* "Physiology of Insecta" (M. Rockstein, ed.), Vol. I, pp. 283–321. Academic Press, New York.

Bursell, E. (1964b). Environmental aspects; Humidity. *In* "Physiology of Insecta" (M. Rockstein, ed.), Vol. I, pp. 323–336. Academic Press, New York.

Christenson, L. D., and Foote, R. H. (1960). Biology of fruit flies. *Ann. Rev. Entomol.* **5**, 171–192.

Christenson, L. D., Maeda, S., and Holloway, J. R. (1956). Substitution of dehydrated for fresh carrots in medium for rearing fruit flies. *J. Econ. Entomol.* **49**, 135.

Craig, R. (1960). The physiology of excretion in the insect. *Ann. Rev. Entomol.* **5**, 53–68.

Dean, R. W. (1938). Experiments on rearing apple maggot adults. *J. Econ. Entomol.* **31**, 241–244.

Delanoue, P., and Soria, F. (1958). Elevage d'insectes en laboratoriere: *Ceratitis capitata* Wied. Rapport sur les travaux de reserches effectues en 1957. *Sta. Entomol. Agr. Serv. Botan. Agron. Tunisia* p. 22.

Feron, M., and Sacantanis, K. B. (1955). L'elevage permanent de *Ceratitis capitata* Wied. au laboratoire. *Ann. Epiphyties* **6**, 201–214.

Feron, M., Delanoue, P., and Soria, F. (1958). L'elevage massif artificiel de *Ceratitis capitata* Wied. *Entomophaga* **3**, 45–53.

Finney, G. L. (1956). A fortified carrot medium for mass-culture of the oriental fruit fly and certain other tephritids. *J. Econ. Entomol.* **49**, 134.

Finney, G. L., and Fisher, T. W. (1964). Culture of entomophagous insects and their hosts. *In* "Biological Control of Insect Pests and Weeds" (P. DeBach, ed.), pp. 328–355. Chapman & Hall, London.

Finney, G. L., Hagen, K. S., and Mitchell, S. (1966). The development of techniques for mass-culture of three species of fruit flies and their principal parasites in Hawaii. Manuscript in preparation.

Fisher, T. W., and Finney, G. L. (1964). Insectary facilities and equipment. *In* "Biological Control of Insect Pests and Weeds" (P. DeBach, ed.), pp. 381–401. Chapman & Hall, London.

Fluke, C. L., and Allen, T. C. (1931). The role of yeast in life history studies of the apple maggot *Rhagoletis pomonella* Walsh. *J. Econ. Entomol.* **24**, 77–80.

Hafez, M. (1964). Unpublished data.

Hagen, K. S. (1953). Influence of adult nutrition upon the reproduction of three fruit fly species. *In* "Third Special Report on the Control of the Oriental Fruit Fly *Dacus dorsalis* in the Hawaiian Islands," pp. 72–76. Senate, State of California, Sacramento, California.

Hagen, K. S. (1958). Honeydew as an adult fruit fly diet affecting reproduction. *Proc. 10th Intern. Congr. Entomol., Montreal, 1956* Vol. 3, pp. 25–30. Intern. Congr. Entomol., Ottawa, Canada.

Hagen, K. S. (1964). Nutrition of entomophagous insects and their hosts. *In* "Biological Control of Insect Pests and Weeds" (P. DeBach, ed.), pp. 356–380. Chapman & Hall, London.

Hagen, K. S., and Finney, G. L. (1950). A food supplement for effectivity increasing the fecundity of certain tephritid species. *J. Econ. Entomol.* **43,** 735.

Hagen, K. S., Santas, L., and Tsecouras, A. (1963). A technique for culturing the olive fly *Dacus oleae* Gmelin on synthetic media under xenic conditions. *Proc. Symp. Radiation Radioisotopes Appl. Insects Agr. Importance, Athens, Greece, 1963,* pp. 333–356. Intern. At. Energy Agency, Vienna.

House, H. L. (1961). Insect nutrition. *Ann. Rev. Entomol.* **6,** 13–26.

House, H. L. (1963). Nutritional diseases. *In* "Insect Pathology" (E. A. Steinhaus, ed.), Vol. I, pp. 133–160. Academic Press, New York.

Keck, C. B. (1951). Effect of temperature on development and activity of the melon fly, *Dacus cucurbitae. J. Econ. Entomol.* **44,** 1001–1002.

Knipling, E. F. (1955). Possibilities of insect control or eradication through the use of sexually sterile males. *J. Econ. Entomol.* **48,** 459–462.

Koidzumi, K. (1934). Experimental studies on the influence of low temperatures upon the development of fruit flies. *J. Soc. Trop. Agr. Taiwan* **6,** 687–696.

McPhail, M., and Guiza, F. E. (1956). An oviposition medium for the Mexican fruit fly (*Anastrepha ludens*). *J. Econ. Entomol.* **49,** 570.

Maeda, S., Hagen, K. S., and Finney, G. L. (1953). The role of micro-organisms in the culture of fruit fly larvae. *In* "Third Special Report of the Control of the Oriental Fruit Fly, *Dacus dorsalis*, in the Hawaiian Islands," pp. 84–86. Senate, State of California, Sacramento, California.

Messenger, P. S., and Flitters, N. E. (1958). Effect of constant temperature environments on the egg stage of 3 species of Hawaiian fruit flies. *Ann. Entomol. Soc. Am.* **51,** 109–119.

Messenger, P. S., and Flitters, N. E. (1959). Effect of variable temperature environment on egg development of three species of fruit flies. *Ann. Entomol. Soc. Am.* **52,** 191–204.

Mitchell, S., Tanaka, N., and Steiner, L. F. (1965). Methods for mass culturing oriental, melon, and Mediterranean fruit flies. *U. S. Dept. Agr.,* ARS **ARS 33–104,** 1–22.

Moore, I. (1959). A method for artificially culturing the olive fly (*Dacus oleae* Gmel.) under asceptic conditions *Ktavim* **9,** 295–296 (English ed.).

Moore, I. (1960). A contribution to the ecology of the olive fly *Dacus oleae* Gmel. *Israel Agr. Res. Sta., Spec. Bull.* **26,** 1–53. (English summary).

Moore, I. (1962). Further investigations on the artificial breeding of the olive fly, *Dacus oleae* Gmel., under asceptic conditions. *Entomophaga* **7,** 53–57 (French summary).

Moore, I., and Nadel, D. (1961). A bacterium present within the eggs of the Mediterranean fruit fly, *Ceratitis capitata* Wied. *Ktavim* **11,** 133.

Morales, E., and Gonzales, T. (1964). Technica de reproduccion artificial de la mosca del Mediterrano. *Organ. Intern. Reg. Sanidad Agropecuar.* **1,** 1–18.

Myburgh, A. C. (1962). Mating habits of the fruit flies, *Ceratitis capitata* Wied. and *Pterandrus rosa* Ksh. *S. African J. Agr. Sci.* **5,** 457–464.

Nadel, D. (1964). Unpublished data.

Rhode, R. H. (1957). A diet for Mexican fruit flies *Anastrepha ludens. J. Econ. Entomol.* **50,** 215.

Roan, C. C., Flitters, N. E., and Davis, C. J. (1954). Light intensity and temperature as factors limiting the mating of the oriental fruit fly. *Ann. Entomol. Soc. Am.* **47,** 493–494.

Sacantanis, K. B. (1954). Methode délevage an laboratoire de la mouche des olives (*Dacus oleae* Gmel.). *Rev. Pathol. Vegetale Entomol. Agr. France* **32,** 247–257.

Sang, J. H. (1959). Circumstances affecting the nutritional requirements of *Drosophila melanogaster. Ann. N. Y. Acad. Sci.* **77,** 352–365.

Shaw, J. G., and Starr, D. F. (1946). Development of the immature stages of *Anastrepha serpentina* in relation to temperature. *J. Agr. Res.* **72,** 265–276.

Snowball, G. J., Wilson, F., and Lukens, R. G. (1962). Culture and consignment techniques used for parasites introduced against Queensland fruit fly, *Strumeta tryoni. Australian J. Agr. Res.* **13,** 233–248.

Steiner, L. F. (1962). Unpublished data.

Steiner, L. F., and Christenson, L. D. (1956). Potential usefulness of the sterile fly release method in fruit fly eradication programs. *Proc. Ann. Meeting Hawaiian Acad. Sci.* **31,** 17–18.

Steiner, L. F., Mitchell, W. C., and Ohinata, K. (1958). Fruit fly control with poisoned bait sprays in Hawaii, *U. S. Dept. Agr., ARS* **ARS 33–3.**

Steiner, L. F., Rohwer, G. G., Ayers, E. L., and Christenson, L. D. (1961). The role of attractants in the recent Mediterranean fruit fly eradication program in Florida. *J. Econ. Entomol.* **54,** 30–35.

Steiner, L. F., Mitchell, W. C., and Baumhover, A. H. (1962). Progress of fruit fly control by irradiation sterilization in Hawaii and the Mariana Islands. *Intern. J. Appl. Radiation Isotopes* **13,** 427–434.

Steiner, L. F., Harris, E. J., Fujimoto, M. S., Mitchell, W. C., and Christenson, L. D. (1965). Melon fly eradication by overflooding with sterile flies. *J. Econ. Entomol.* **58,** 519–522.

Tanaka, N. (1965). Artificial egging receptacles for three species of tephritid flies. *J. Econ. Entomol.* **58,** 177–178.

Tzanakakis, M . E., and Steiner, L. F. (1964). Unpublished data.

Tzanakakis, M. E., and Tsitsipis, J. A. (1964). Unpublished data.

U. S. Dept. Agr., ARS (1962). "Plant Quarantine Treatment Manual." 2nd ed. Section 390–620.

Chapter 39
Yellow Fever Mosquitoes[*]

HARVEY B. MORLAN

Aedes aegypti Eradication Branch,
Communicable Disease Center,
Public Health Service,
U. S. Department of Health, Education and Welfare,
Atlanta, Georgia

I. INTRODUCTION

Laboratory rearing of *Aedes aegypti* (L.) has been a common procedure among entomologists and other scientists for over 50 years. Recent publications with comprehensive references to the literature on this species include Christophers (1960) and Clements (1963). Mosquito culture techniques have been described by Trembley (1955). Modification for special purposes and improvements in methods were reported by McKiel (1957) and Porter *et al.* (1961). Production by these and similar methods has proved adequate for studies using as many as several thousand specimens. However, experiments on dispersal (Morlan and Hayes, 1958) and on control by release of sexually sterile males (McCray *et al.*, 1961; Morlan *et al.*, 1962) require the sustained production of millions

[*] This chapter was written by Harvey B. Morlan in his private capacity and no official support or endorsement by the Public Health Service or the Department of Health, Education, and Welfare is intended, or should be inferred.

of specimens. Following are descriptions of the equipment and procedures developed during 1955 and 1956 for rearing broods of as many as 1.3 million larvae (Morlan *et al.*, 1963) and of subsequent modifications (Fay *et al.*, 1963) to permit mass production of sterile males.

II. PROCEDURES

A. MAINTENANCE OF ADULT COLONIES

Two laboratory rooms, each 10 by 13 by 10 feet; and maintained at about 80°F and 80% relative humidity (RH), were required for the mass production of *A. aegypti*. One room was used for adult colonies, emergence cages, and egg storage. The second room contained the larval rearing trays.

Six mosquito colonies, each with approximately 10,000 adults, were used for egg production. Seedless raisins soaked in water, a cotton pad soaked with a 1 *M* sucrose solution, and water were provided fresh each week as nourishment. A rabbit was available for 4 hours each day to provide a source of blood.

Each colony was maintained in a cage 22 by 22 by 22 inches (Fig. 1). A hinged platform within a screened tunnel through the cage was used to facilitate the feeding of the female mosquitoes (Hayes and Morlan, 1957). A rabbit with clipped back was placed in a metal tray 21 by 6 by 1.5 inches and inserted into the tunnel on the platform, which was then wedged upward to force the animal's back against the 20-mesh screen of the tunnel. A wood block 6 by 5.5 by 1.5 inches was placed beneath the rabbit's abdomen to keep it from withdrawing its back from the screen. The outer end of the tray, 3.5 inches high, served as a barrier to prevent the rabbit's escape. The mosquitoes readily fed on the rabbit through the screen, and the cage design eliminated the loss of mosquitoes that usually occurs while a host animal is being placed in or removed from a colony cage.

To maintain relatively uniform populations, approximately 3000 pupae were added to each colony weekly. To prevent oviposition in the dish (6 inches in diameter and 3 inches high) containing the pupae, it was covered with a screen. The screen was removed briefly each day to permit the escape of the young adults. Each week, colony cages were cleaned and inspected for the presence of spiders or other predators.

A 600-ml beaker, lined with a strip of paper toweling 3 inches wide and about half filled with water, was provided for egg laying.

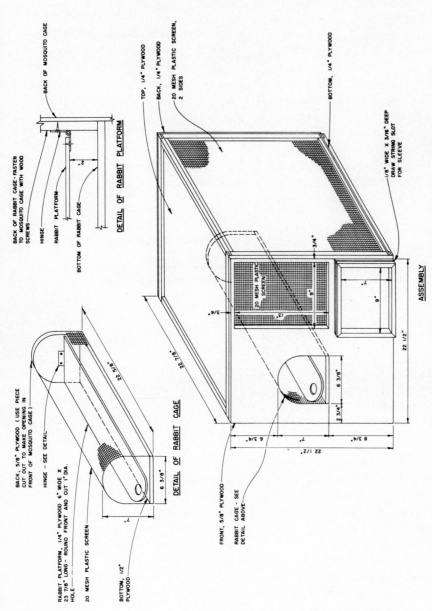

FIG. 1. Mass production of *Aedes aegypti* mosquito colony cage.

The beaker was covered with a paper cap having a centered 1-inch^2 opening. The females entered through this opening and deposited their eggs on the toweling near the water line.

To obtain eggs of known age, each beaker was removed from the adult mosquito colony cage after a 24-hour period, but the water and the toweling containing the eggs were left in the beaker for an additional 24-hour period. The toweling strips were then removed and hung to air-dry for 1 day, then stored in a covered glass container.

Eggs stored up to 10 weeks gave satisfactory hatches of 78 to 92% when immersed in a 24-hour mixture containing 0.1 gm of ground dog chow and 0.1 gm of brewers' yeast to each liter of water. The percentage of eggs hatching during 4-hour periods of submergence decreased as the age of the eggs increased (Table I).

TABLE I

PER CENT OF *Aedes aegypti* HATCH OBSERVED DURING 4-HOUR PERIODS
WITH EGGS OF KNOWN AGES

Age of eggs (weeks)	No. of trials[a]	Hatch (%)	
		Range	Average
1–5	78	84–92	88
6–10	85	78–88	83
11–15	53	46–75	62
16–18	9	22–41	31

[a] Several hundred eggs per trial.

During mass rearing for sterile-male-release studies, colonies were maintained in cages that were designed to minimize the escape of adult mosquitoes (McCray, 1963). The modified colony cage (Fig. 2) has openings in the front panel for (A) a screened observation port (5 × 8 inches); (B) a tray (6 × 3½ × ¾ inches) containing a cellulose sponge to retain liquid food; (C) a tray (22½ × 4 × ¾ inches) for holding pupae; (D) front panel (8½ × 9 inches) of removable frame with screened tunnel for blood-host; (E) oviposition tray (21 × 4 × 1½ inches); (F) oviposition strip of 22-gauge stainless steel (22 × 3 inches), which is inserted through a slot (4 × ½ inches) lined with thin latex flaps. The steel oviposition strip, covered on each side with wet paper toweling, was slid into the tray containing 1¼ inches of water, where it was held in a vertical position by a notched partial cover of the tray and by a sliding metal door (G) on the front panel of the cage. New colonies were stocked with 10,000 male and 10,000 female pupae and supplemented with 5000 female and 1000 male pupae per week. A rabbit was held in the screened tunnel for 3 hours every second day, and the sponge in the food tray was saturated twice weekly with a 1:1 mixture of 40% honey-water:raisin juice. Oviposition strips with eggs less than 24 hours old were removed daily and held for an additional 24 hours in a second tray containing 1 inch of water. The toweling and eggs were air-dried (80% RH) for 1 day and then stored in a plastic box.

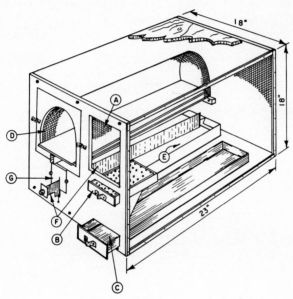

FIG. 2. Mosquito colony cage. A, Observation port; B, food tray; C, tray for pupae; D, blood-host tunnel; E, oviposition tray; F, oviposition strip; G, sliding door.

B. REARING TRAYS

The choice of a larval rearing container was primarily dependent upon the consideration of laboratory space and ease of feeding, draining, and cleaning the container. A galvanized metal tray, 2 by 10 by 72 inches, was designed as the standard rearing container. Each tray had a ¾-inch copper-tube outlet to facilitate draining and was stacked on a metal rack made of ⅛- by ¾- by ¾-inch angle iron. Eight racks held 24 rearing trays each, for a total of 192 trays. Detailed specifications for construction of the trays and racks are given in Figs. 3 and 4.

To prevent any adverse reaction between the galvanized metal and the medium, each tray was coated on the inside with a thin layer of paraffin. This was readily accomplished by applying melted

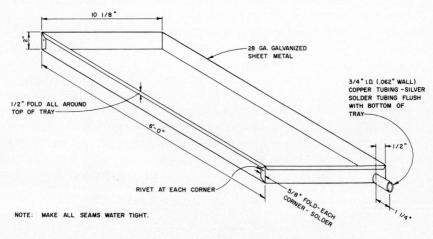

FIG. 3. Mass production of *Aedes aegypti* larval rearing tray.

paraffin to preheated trays. After the tray was lightly coated, the excess wax was poured into the next tray.

C. ESTIMATION OF LARVAL NUMBERS

A total of 7000 larvae were reared in 7 liters of water in each tray. Water loss by evaporation was replenished daily.

To stock each rearing tray accurately and rapidly, egg strips containing an unknown number of eggs were placed in known amounts of the hatching mixture. Two liters of mixture were satisfactory for up to 20,000 larvae. After 4 hours the egg sheets were removed. The larvae were then dispersed evenly with a two-beater food mixer. Twenty 2-ml samples of the mixture were taken, using a graduated bacteriological pipette, and the live larvae in each sample were counted. All samples were taken from approximately the same position in the pan—about equidistant between the rotating beaters and the margin of the pan and at half the depth of the mixture. The average number of larvae per milliliter was then calculated and the proper volume was transferred to a rearing container. The method provided estimates of larval numbers that were accurate to ±5%.

For estimating populations of up to 0.5 million larvae in 50-liter mixtures, an agitator-type washing machine was used to disperse

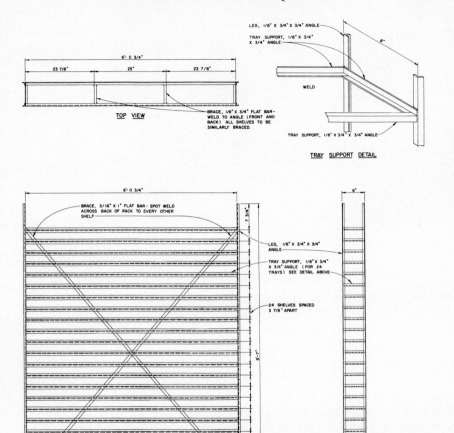

FIG. 4. Racks for larval rearing trays.

the larvae. The machine was modified by cutting out sections of the agitator fins to reduce splashing and by installing a plunger-type valve in the bottom of the tub to provide a free-flowing but controllable gravity drain. To permit uniform agitation of small volumes of fluid, three tapered, finger-like extensions, about 2 inches long and ⅜ inch wide at the base, were attached to the base of the agitator.

After the number of newly hatched larvae dispersed in a known

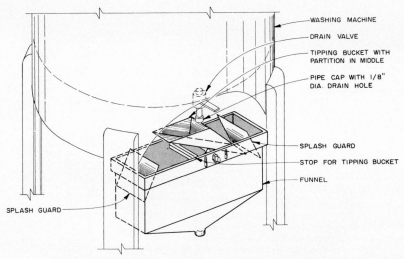

FIG. 5. Mass production of *Aedes aegypti*—automatic dispenser.

volume of water was calculated, water was added to reduce the density of larvae to 7 per ml. One liter of the preparation containing dispersed larvae was then added to 6 liters of water in each rearing tray. Agitation in the machine for periods up to 30 minutes produced no detectable adverse effect on larvae.

Use of single-liter lots of this preparation for stocking trays was satisfactory for mass rearing; but in stocking experimental trays, greater accuracy was desirable for reliable comparative evaluations of culture methods. For this latter purpose, the differences in numbers of larvae per tray were reduced by dispensing serial aliquots of dispersed larvae. If six experimental trays were to be stocked, each received ten 100-ml aliquots collected so that the first tray received aliquots 1, 7, 13, 19, 25, 31, 37, 43, 49, and 55; the second tray received aliquots 2, 8, 14, and so forth.

An automatic dispenser was used to obtain the desired volumes of dispersed mosquito larvae. It was patterned after the tripping-bucket rain gauge used by Blair (1942). Essentially, it is a pan with two compartments mounted below the valve drain at the bottom of the washing machine tub (Fig. 5). As one compartment fills, the weight of the water causes it to tip and empty its contents, and thus the other compartment is presented for filling.

D. LARVAL FEEDING

The larvae were fed dog chow (5% crude fat) ground to pass through a 40-mesh screen. The feeding schedule was 0.2, 0.3, and

0.4 mg of food per larva on days 0 (day of hatching) through 2, respectively, and 0.6 mg per larva on days 3 through 7. Plastic spoons
of appropriate capacity were constructed and used to measure the
scheduled amount of food for the 7000 larvae in each tray.

E. MODIFICATIONS OF LARVAL CULTURE

In developing the method outlined above, numerous modifications were tested and evaluated on the basis of the percentage
of larvae that developed to adults within 11 days.

Decreased adult production resulted from (a) daily addition of
70 gm of sucrose to each larval rearing tray, or (b) addition of 0.7
gm of dog chow to water in rearing trays 12 to 24 hours before adding
newly hatched larvae.

No increase in adult production occurred with (a) sheltering
of larval rearing trays from variable light intensities or air movement, (b) daily addition of 15 gm of sucrose to each larval rearing
tray, (c) autoclaving larval feed (250°F for 15 minutes), (d) transferring larvae from old culture medium to fresh medium on day 3,
or on day 2, and again on day 4.

Limited tests showed an increase in production of adults with the
addition of 1 liter of water containing 0.7 gm of moist yeast cake to
each rearing tray on the third day after hatching of larvae. This supplement and a larval density of 10,000 per tray resulted in increased
female production, both in terms of percentage of larvae and total
numbers. Increasing larval density to 15,000 resulted in increased
total numbers of males but decreased numbers of females, and reduced the percentages of larvae that became adults in 11 days. As
the increased larval density slowed development of females more
than males, it provided a means for partial control of sex ratio in
each brood of mosquitoes.

In the initial production of male pupae for irradiation on a weekly
basis, Fay *et al.* (1963) placed 8000 larvae in each tray with a constant rearing-room temperature of 80°F, but later increased pupal
production by 20% with a temperature schedule of 81, 82, 83, 83, 84,
84, and 85°F on days 1 through 7, respectively.

F. SEPARATION OF PUPAE

To separate large numbers of male pupae, Fay *et al.* (1963) combined larvae from five rearing trays, and about 4 hours before collecting pupae on day 7, killed the slower-developing larvae with
2.8 gm of Paris green. When placed in buckets of water the dead
and moribund larvae sank and the pupae were skimmed from the

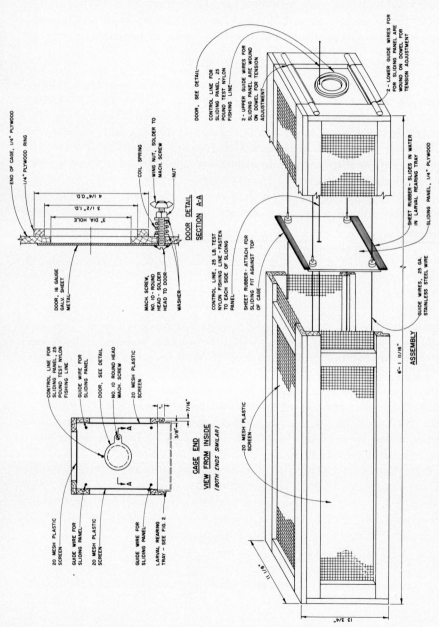

FIG. 6. Mass production of *Aedes aegypti*—adult mosquito emergence cage.

water surface. The pupae were placed on a mechanical separator (McCray, 1961) and washed with a fan-shaped stream of water. Male pupae dropped through louvered slits (1 inch × 0.039 inch) of an inclined aluminum screen which retained the female pupae. The accuracy of separation was checked periodically with an adjustable separator (Fay and Morlan, 1959).

The use of Paris green reduced potential production by restricting collection of pupae to a single day with resultant loss of many mature larvae. Total production was improved by use of a magnetic-iron technique of Bar-Zeev and Galun (1961). Iron oxide dust at 100 ppm was placed in rearing trays on day 2. On day 6, larvae were trapped with an electromagnet. After removal of prepupae and pupae, larvae were released from the magnet and allowed to continue development for another 24 hours, when the process was repeated.

G. ADULT EMERGENCE

On the seventh day after the eggs had hatched, each rearing tray was drained of its contents. The larvae and pupae, which were removed from the medium by straining it through a 20-mesh screen container, were transferred to trays of fresh water, each accommodating the yield from as many as 17 hatching trays. An emergence cage (Fig. 6) was placed over each tray to collect the emerging adults.

Equality of adult production from successive broods was improved by treatment of emptied rearing trays before reuse. To control accidental and unequal introduction of deleterious scum-forming microorganisms, rearing trays were cleaned after each use, filled with water, and treated with 0.1 gm of calcium hypochlorite. After 12 to 24 hours, they were drained and filled with clean untreated water.

The majority of the adults emerged during the following 4-day period. The sliding plywood panel in the emergence cage facilitated their rapid collection by concentrating them at one end of the cage. A canister-type vacuum cleaner with a bypass and adapter assembly (Fig. 7), which produced a vacuum of 2.0 inches manometric water pressure, was used to remove them through the doors at each end of the emergence cage and to dispense concentrations of them without injury into plastic collecting cages with screened bottoms (Fig. 8). Once in a collecting cage, the adult mosquitoes were readily weighed, anesthetized, or transferred to other containers.

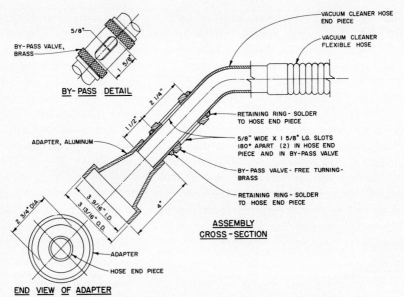

FIG. 7. Mass production of *Aedes aegypti*—vacuum cleaner by-pass and adapter.

H. ADULT COUNTING

Volumetric estimation of adult numbers was too inaccurate for experimental studies, but enumeration by weight proved to be satisfactory. Adults emerging on days 8, 9, 10, and 11 were found to be progressively lighter in weight (Table II). Weight depended upon sex, day of emergence, and larval rearing conditions; hence it was necessary to obtain an average weight determination from random samples of males and females on each emergence day.

TABLE II

WEIGHT[a] OF UNFED *Aedes aegypti* ADULTS EMERGING
8–11 DAYS AFTER EGG HATCH

Emergence day	Males			Females		
	Number	Total weight	Average weight	Number	Total weight	Average weight
8	937	1313.3	1.40	248	710.6	2.86
9	1049	1430.3	1.36	751	2053.4	2.73
10	1160	1466.5	1.26	1240	3226.6	2.60
11	481	568.5	1.18	207	498.9	2.41

[a] In milligrams.

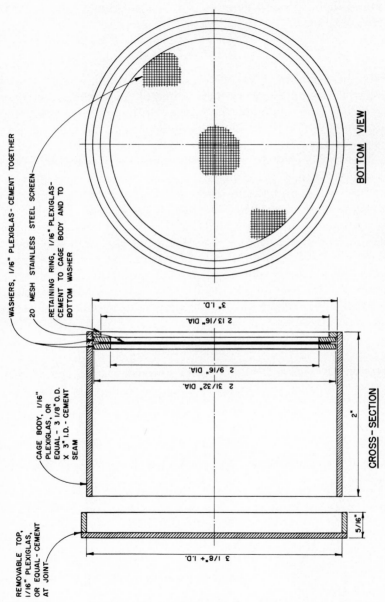

FIG. 8. Mass production of *Aedes aegypti*—adult mosquito collecting cage.

Random samples comprised of approximately 100 males and 100 females were obtained by killing or anesthetizing adults, since it was found that aspirated samples of live adults tended to be biased in favor of males.

III. DISCUSSION

With the equipment and techniques described, it was possible for 2 men to set up 192 trays with a total of 1,344,000 larvae. These men could easily maintain the larvae during their development, concentrate the larvae in the emergence cage trays, remove the adults from the emergence cages, and estimate their numbers. Each brood produced from 0.5 to 0.8 million adults within 11 days of hatching. Further increases in mosquito production could be obtained by making appropriate increases in equipment and personnel.

An average of nearly 250,000 male pupae were produced during each of 16 weeks in 1960 and each of 27 weeks in 1961. Separation, irradiation, and packaging of male pupae for shipment was accomplished by 3 men during a period of 6 hours. The entire operation required a weekly expenditure of about 96 man-hours.

Although the techniques used were dependable and practicable, there is no doubt but that further investigation would result in improved methods.

REFERENCES

Bar-Zeev, M., and Galun, R. (1961). A magnetic method of separating mosquito pupae from larvae. *Mosquito News* 21, 225–228.

Blair, T. A. (1942). "Weather Elements, a Text in Elementary Meteorology." Prentice-Hall, Englewood Cliffs, New Jersey.

Christophers, S. R. (1960). *Aedes aegypti.* "The Yellow Fever Mosquito: Its Life History, Bionomics and Structure," pp. xii and 739. Cambridge Univ. Press, London and New York.

Clements, A. N. (1963). "The Physiology of Mosquitoes," Intern. Ser. Monographs Pure Appl. Biol., Zool. Div., pp. ix and 393. Macmillan, New York.

Fay, R. W., and Morlan, H. B. (1959). A mechanical device for separating the developmental stages, sexes, and species of mosquitoes. *Mosquito News* 19, 144–147.

Fay, R. W., McCray, E. M., Jr., and Kilpatrick, J. W. (1963). Mass production of sterilized male *Aedes aegypti. Mosquito News* 23, 210–214.

Hayes, R. O., and Morlan, H. B. (1957). Notes on *Aedes triseriatus* egg incubation and colonization. *Mosquito News* 17, 33–36.

McCray, E. M., Jr. (1961). A mechanical device for the rapid sexing of *Aedes aegypti* pupae. *J. Econ. Entomol.* 54, 819.

McCray, E. M., Jr. (1963). Escape proof colony cage (*Aedes aegypti*). *Mosquito News* 23, 309–311.

McCray, E. M., Jr., Jensen, J. A., and Schoof, H. F. (1961). Cobalt-60 sterilization studies with *Aedes aegypti* (L.). *Proc. Ann. Meeting New Jersey Mosquito Exterm. Assoc.* **48**, 110–115.

McKiel, J. A. (1957). A simplified method for large-scale laboratory rearing of *Aedes aegypti* (L.). *Mosquito News* **17**, 25–29.

Morlan, H. B., and Hayes, R. O. (1958). Urban dispersal and activity of *Aedes aegypti*. *Mosquito News* **18**, 127–144.

Morlan, H. B., McCray, E. M., Jr., and Kilpatrick, J. W. (1962). Field tests with sexually sterile males for control of *Aedes aegypti*. *Mosquito News* **22**, 295–300.

Morlan, H. B., Hayes, R. O., and Schoof, H. F. (1963). Methods for mass rearing of *Aedes aegypti* (L.). *Public Health Rept.* (*U. S.*) **78**, 711–719.

Porter, J. R., Kozuchi, G., and Kuck, M. J. (1961). Scientific notes. *Mosquito News* **21**, 340–342.

Trembley, H. L. (1955). Mosquito culture techniques and experimental procedures. *Am. Mosquito Control Assoc. Bull.* **3**.

AUTHOR INDEX

Numbers in italics refer to pages on which the complete references are listed.

A

Abalos, J. W., 187, 189, *199*
Abdel-Rahman, H. A., 262, *269*
Abul-Nasr, S., 506, *524*
Adcock, P. H., 215, *224*
Adkins, T. R., Jr., 176, 178, 179, *182*
Adkisson, P. L., 357, 358, *366*, 482, *486*, 507, *524*
Aizawa, K., 504, 505, 510, 519, *524*
Alexander, M. W., 367, 368, *381*
Allen, J., 34, *47*
Allen, L., 243, *255*
Allen, N., 480, 481, 485, *486*
Allen, T. C., 561, *581*
Allison, W. E., 357, 358, *366*, 482, *486*, 507, *524*
Allred, D. M., 37, 44, 57, 59, 67, *68*
Ames, C. T., 187, 189, *199*
Anastos, G., 65, *71*
Anderson, G. B., 434, 436, 439, *443*
Andres, L. A., 462, 464, 468, 474, 475, *478*
Andrewartha, H. G., 558, *581*
Anthony, D. W., 52, 56, 67, *68*, 118, *124*
Appleby, J. E., 147, *151*
Arai, N., 282, 283, 288, 297, *299*
Arant, F. S., 176, 178, 179, *182*, 371, 375, *381, 382*
Arbuthnot, K. D., 335, *338*
Arima, K., 510, 519, *529*
Armstrong, T., 400, 401, *404*
Arthur, D. R., 49, *68*
Asahina, S., 96, 99, 104, *113*
Asano, S., 221, *224*
Atger, P., 505, *529*
Atkins, E. L., Jr., 462, 474, *477*
Auclair, J. L., 275, 277, 282, 283, 288, 297, 299, 432, 433, *442*
Audy, J. R., 25, 26, 38, 39, 40, 41, 42, *44*, 46, 50, *68*
Auer, C., 506, *528*
Averill, A. W., 430, *442*
Ayers, E. L., 564, *583*

B

Back, E. A., 254, *255*, 564, *581*
Backs, R. H., 253, *255*, 288, 297, *300*

Bacot, A. N., 74, 80, 81, *82*
Bailey, A. E., 356, *366*
Bailey, J. B., 342, 346, *353*
Bailey, K. P., 50, 54, *68*
Baker, A. C., 565, *581*
Baker, G. J., 149, *151*
Baker, R. H., 87, 88, *99*
Balashov, Y. S., 60, *68*
Balch, R. E., 502, 506, *524*
Ball, H. J., 367, 378, *381, 383*
Barber, G. W., 213, *224*, 333, *337*
Barbesgaard, P., 221, *224*
Bare, C. O., 265, 266, *269*
Barlow, J. S., 280, *301*
Barnes, M. M., 341, 342, 343, 347, *353*
Barnes, O. L., 312, 319, 320, *321*
Barney, D. L., 246, *256*
Barnhart, C. S., 176, 179, *182*
Barrass, R., 162, *172*
Bartlett, A. C., 247, *255*
Bar-Zeev, M., 106, 112, *113*, 216, *224*, 595, *598*
Bateman, M. A., 559, *581*
Baumhover, A. H., 534, 537, 539, 545, 548, 551, *554*, 556, 569, 570, *583*
Beards, G. W., 425, *427*
Beck, A. J., 28, 33, 36, *44*
Beck, S. D., 274, 276, 277, 278, 288, 289, 291, 292, 294, 296, *299, 300, 303*, 324, 326, 327, 334, 336, *337*
Beckman, H. F., 356, *366*
Becton, A. J., 324, 325, 326, 327, *337*
Bedard, W. D., 309, *310*
Bell, J. F., 30, *44*
Belozorov, V. N., 60, 62, *68*
Benjamin, D. M., 506, *524*
Bennett, G. F., 141, *143*
Bequaert, J. C., 128, 129, 130, *144*
Bergamin, J., 441, *442*
Berger, R. S., 507, 510, 511, *524*
Bergold, G. H., 502, 507, 510, 519, 520, *524*
Bertram, D. S., 35, *44*
Bhattacharji, L. M., 74, *83*
Bigger, J. H., 368, 371, 375, *381*
Bilanova-Zachvatkina, E. M., 33, *44*
Biliotti, F., 506, *525*

600

SUBJECT INDEX